J —

CHILD DEVELOPMENT

Physical and Psychologic
Growth Through the School Years

MARIAN E. BRECKENRIDGE, M.S.

Physical Growth and Nutrition, Merrill-Palmer School

E. LEE VINCENT, Ph.D.

Human Development and Behavior, Chatham College

THIRD EDITION · Illustrated

W. B. SAUNDERS COMPANY

PHILADELPHIA · LONDON

PREFACE

The main reason for studying child development is to improve the lives of children. We hope that this book will contribute to the well-being of children and their families. It is designed for professional students in psychology, teacher training, home economics, medicine, nursing and social work as well as for parents. It is written also in full appreciation of the fact that most college students will become parents and hence will need to understand children.

Although the title leads one to expect discussion of the school age mainly, we have included sketches of growth stages which precede this age since teachers and other workers with children of early elementary school age often encounter immature forms of behavior, which can be dealt with successfully only if the origins and early patterns of the behavior are understood.

Parents, of course, are all important to children's development, not only because they guide the child through the most formative years, but because their influence continues longer than any other in the child's life. Parent-child or teacher-child relationships cannot be understood fully without a knowledge of the interplay of extra-family and extra-school influences on the child's character and attitudes.

Social workers and clinicians are likely to meet children at important crises in their lives, so that whatever they do with children carries the permanency of vividness and dramatic excitement. Even a single visit to the doctor's office or to the dentist may have a lasting effect upon a child's attitudes and feelings—favorable if the doctor or dentist understands the child and approaches him properly, unfavorable if the reverse is true. A year spent in any given school teacher's room is sure to influence not only the child's academic learnings, but his attitudes and feelings about learning, about adult authority, about society's institutions, and about living and working with his peers. It also affects his health. Some teachers give children a fine year physically and academically, setting up a genuine impetus toward good character; others give children a bad year all around, leaving them not appreciably improved academically, fatigued and nervous physically, re-sentful, deceitful, and socially antagonistic. It is our belief that all of these professional workers profit from an understanding of child development.

We have attempted to bring together some of the current findings and viewpoints in the rapidly advancing research field of Child Development. We have quoted some controversial material with a view to helping students overcome a habit of reading a single article and accepting its results as final.

We would like to urge college teachers not to use this book as a text alone, but rather as a focus for vigorous class discussion of experiences and observations made by the students. The Experiences to Vitalize Class Work at the ends of chapters are suggestive of ways in which students may enrich their understanding of children. It will doubtless be impossible in most classes for all students to do all of the visiting outlined. Many teachers, however, have found it a successful plan to send out student committees, each to study a particular aspect of the material and to report to the class for general information and discussion. Every attempt should be made by the teacher to keep discussions constantly referred to scientific and published materials, thus seeing that students gain not only local color and interest but acquire a genuine background of substantial knowledge. References to current literature have been included in order to keep the student abreast of the rapid progress in the field of Child Development. It is also helpful to have the examinations (or at least part of them) take the form of problems assigned in advance and designed to summarize and integrate knowledge previously learned.

Many teachers have found occasional use of sound-track movies a valuable supplementary teaching device. At the end of the book is a list of films which the authors have found to be useful in connection with the subject matter of the book. It is assumed that only a few of those suggested will be used. Each is annotated and running times are indicated in order to assist the teacher in making selections. Most teachers have found that the 10- to 12-minute films can be used frequently, but that the 35- to 50-minute films must be carefully selected if they are to supplement rather than to replace other teaching devices and crowd out valuable factual material.

Films may be purchased or rented from the companies listed. Most of them may be rented from such agencies as The Film Center, University of California, Berkeley, California; The Film Center, Indiana Teachers College, Bloomington, Indiana; The Film Center, University of Illinois, Urbana, Illinois; The Film Center, Pennsylvania College For Women, Pittsburgh, Pa.

At the end of Chapter 1 there is an outline for a case study to be done throughout the course by the student. Many teachers find that such a case study, assigned at the beginning of the course, serves as a focus of orientation for application of the principles and patterns of growth as the course proceeds. It also proves to be a useful device for integration of chapter materials. Students who have done such case studies have found them invaluable as a way of making the course meaningful.

Most teachers find it wise to have some fairly definite framework around which to build the case study. The outline and procedures at the end of Chapter 1 may be suggestive. The teacher may wish to use an outline which is built through class discussion, thereby using the creation of the outline as an additional device for teaching some of the principles of growth. The authors have found it wise to ask that part of the case study be handed in at about the middle of the course as a reminder to the student that it is something he should keep in mind as he proceeds through the course.

Important to the preservation of the college community relationships is preliminary discussion of which child to choose for the subject, how to approach the parents, what questions to ask or not to ask, etc. It has been our experience that most students have no difficulty in choosing a child. In case they do have difficulty, a review of their own childhood proves a satisfactory substitute. It is important that the students be reminded in class, as they are in the outline, that they are not to give advice; nor are they doing a "diagnosis" of the child. They should choose normal children rather than "problem" children as such. They should not concentrate on the problem aspects of growth but rather on the normal, usual patterns of development. Principles for observing children (as outlined in Item 2 of the Experiences to Vitalize Class Work at the end of Chapter 1) should be discussed in class as applying also to the case study.

In order to avoid extensive footnotes, a system of numbers which refer to items in the reference bibliography at the end of the book has been employed. Thus, the continuity of the text has been maintained while at the same time the substantiating and pertinent documentation has been presented. The suggested references at the ends of chapters are meant to give the student further interesting reading on the subject matter of the chapter.

Without the work of the various Child Development Research Centers and of other research personnel this book would not have been possible. We are grateful to the several readers who have carefully criticized the first and second editions and given help in the preparation of this revision. The W. B. Saunders Company has also given invaluable assistance in the preparation of the manuscript.

MARIAN E. BRECKENRIDGE
E. LEE VINCENT

CONTENTS

Chapter 5

INFLUENCES ON GROWTH: HOME, SCHOOL, CHURCH, CAMPS....... 152

Chapter 6

INFLUENCES ON GROWTH: FURTHER COMMUNITY FACTORS....... 183

Chapter 7

GROWTH AND USE OF THE BODY: PHYSICAL GROWTH. 206

Chapter 13

SOCIAL AND PERSONALITY DEVELOPMENT: CONFLICT
AND AGGRESSION; COOPERATION AND FRIENDSHIP.... 365

Chapter 14

SOCIAL AND PERSONALITY DEVELOPMENT: MORAL
JUDGMENT AND PSYCHO-SEXUAL DEVELOPMENT..... 388

Chapter 15

A SUMMARY OF GROWTH ACHIEVEMENTS.............. 423

CHAPTER 1

Some General Principles of Development

Intelligent handling of children requires a knowledge of how children grow, and of how such growth can be influenced favorably. It is based not only upon knowledge of general principles, but also upon an understanding of each child encountered: What has made him what he is? How does he compare with other children? What direction should *his* growth take?

Let us, then, in this introductory chapter, look at some of the general aspects of development.* Later we shall study its stages and patterns more in detail. What does Life demand? What, therefore, must growth accomplish if the child is to meet Life adequately? What are some of the laws which govern growth? Does every child grow "according to the law"? How can we utilize these laws to know what to expect from children and how to promote their well-being? How are people trying to find out what we do not now know about growth?

WHAT GROWTH MUST ACCOMPLISH IF LIFE DEMANDS ARE TO BE MET

Life Requires that One Find and Hold a Job. Society expects every able-bodied adult to earn his way, with all that this means in physical and intellectual skills, and in ability to meet and get along with people. For many women this may not mean a remunerative position in the vocational or professional world, but a job as homemaker and mother, which tests as many abilities and skills in its own way as does competition in the vocational world. Specifically, winning and holding a job require:

1. HEALTH AND PHYSICAL STAMINA. Physical vigor should be such as to permit regular attendance at work rather than frequent absence; it should lend "punch" to one's approach to the task in hand, should aid one to do not only what is required, but also that extra bit which means promotion. Attractive appearance, smooth coordination in posture and movement, neat and appropriate grooming are also definite assets in job-getting and job-holding.

2. EMOTIONAL AND NERVOUS STABILITY. A person must be able at least

---

* The terms development and growth, used synonymously in this text unless otherwise indicated, refer to the emerging and expanding of capacities of the individual to provide progressively greater facility in functioning. The processes involved are growth, maturation and learning.

1

to endure the strains of responsibility, the frustrations and defeats and disappointments which every job offers at some time or other. Personality characteristics which guarantee honesty, dependability, ability to take responsibility, and which make possible initiative, resourcefulness, and imagination are also essential. One of the most important of personality traits required to get on in a job is the ability to work hard when things are not particularly interesting, and especially when they are discouraging. Ability to take orders from supervisors, to get along with peers, and, when necessary, to direct others is also imperative in most types of jobs.

3. SOME SORT OF SALABLE SKILL OR ABILITY. It goes without saying that unless one has some skill or ability worth paying for no employer will hire one.

Personal Happiness and Social Well-Being Require the Ability to Win and Hold Friends. If the adult is to have the greatest happiness and the most effective balance of personality he must win and hold friends. This involves kindness to others, consideration for the wants and moods of others, sympathy, tolerance, and generosity, all of which are based upon an adequate control of one's own whims, desires and moods. This in turn implies the accomplishment of an adequate social development through the growing years, and the accumulation of experience with people without which no person can hope to deal adequately with the wide variety of people he must meet vocationally and socially. The acquisition of social techniques and skills as well as an emotional capacity to understand and appreciate friendship are important parts of this accomplishment. Health is also a requisite here, as everywhere, to the fullest enjoyment of friendships, since one needs enough health to be an asset rather than a liability in social activities, or even in the quiet sharing of a substantial friendship. Appearance helps to win friends, although beyond the first "shoppings-about" of adolescence, other character and personality traits are probably of greater importance. A reasonable background of knowledge of interesting facts and a varied set of interests increase the dynamic quality of personal attractiveness. A sense of humor is invaluable.

The Ability to Select, to Win, and to Hold a Mate, and to Establish a Satisfactory Family. A well-rounded personal life and the living out of one's deepest emotional potentialities hinge upon the adult's ability to select, to win, and to hold a mate, and to take on the responsibilities of parenthood. Wise selection of a mate requires a fairly wide knowledge of members of the opposite sex, their particular traits and reactions, both as these traits are similar to and as they are different from those of one's own sex. It also requires a thorough insight into one's own self, one's own peculiarities of character make-up, both physical and psychologic, a knowledge of one's own tastes, habits, attitudes and moods. Such self-knowledge is also important in all the other life adjustments, but is particularly vital in the intimate adjustments of the marriage relationship. Winning and holding the mate demand all of the social skills and techniques necessary in winning and holding friends, plus a stronger control, a keener insight, a deeper emotional capacity.

A clear knowledge of what it means to be a young man as different from a young woman, of what the role of lover, husband, and father should be in courtship and in family life are all essential if a boy is to participate adequately in marriage. The same awareness of the role of woman, lover, wife and mother is indispensable for the girl. Each must know what may reasonably be expected of the opposite sex, and how to fit one's own needs, desires, and personality traits into the courtship and marriage picture. All of this requires long training, which takes place consciously or unconsciously throughout childhood. The understandings, attitudes, and feelings basic to successful marriage and parenthood are largely acquired from one's own parents and in one's own childhood home. To attain success one needs the fullest physical, psychologic and spiritual maturity.

The Ability to Live Happily with Oneself. Important to one's ability to hold a job, to win and hold friends, to win and hold a mate, and imperative to peace of mind and adequate spiritual growth is the ability to live with oneself without too great loss of emotional energy. As the child grows he must learn to understand his assets and to use them constructively; he must discover his liabilities and, if possible, correct them; or if this is not possible, to accept them and make the best of them. A sense of one's responsibility to others, balanced by a sense of self-protection sufficient to keep one functioning at an efficient level, must be developed.

The ability to accept wise authority, to bend one's will to necessary authority without loss of self-confidence or initiative, requires a well-balanced experience with parental and school authority in early childhood, and with civil and ethical authority in later childhood and adolescence. The ability to live an imaginative and resourceful inner life without withdrawal from the realities of the world must be balanced against the ability to mix happily and successfully with people without continual dependence upon social stimulation. To control emotion without stifling and repressing it; to express emotion and to utilize the driving power which it provides without impetuousness or personal disaster: these are lessons which require continued learning throughout childhood and youth.

A Workable Philosophy of Life. In meeting each of these demands in adult life there occur griefs and failures, loss of loved persons, disappointments—the crises and the tragedies of life. There are also joys and successes, the deep satisfactions and the thrills of life. Great strength of character, fine emotional balance and a mature philosophy of life are required to meet either joy or sorrow well. To succeed without losing one's head, to fail without losing one's faith: these are the final tests of life. Most adolescents build air castles and dream dreams. To have their ideals and theories checked against the facts of adult life is a severe test of balance. To fall in love, to produce children, to lose loved ones demand or of themselves may produce a substantial spiritual philosophy. Somewhere in the process of growth children and young people, if they are to live meaningfully, must acquire a workable philosophy of life. This involves not only ability to withstand failure and grief and a capacity to absorb success satisfactorily; it involves also a vision of humanity as a whole, a sense of responsibility to the total social good, since without this the individual could not live comfortably in a social organization nor could society itself exist. Somehow the people who rear and influence children must make certain that they arrive at adulthood with constructive social attitudes. Only so can delinquency and crime be avoided; only so can careless traffic accidents be curtailed, selfish aggrandizement limited, wars stopped; in other words, only through such attitudes can the "good life" be achieved.

Essentials in Meeting All the Tests of Life.   A review of these tests of life should make us aware of certain essentials in coping with all of them:

1. Vigorous health, or at least maximum efficiency of the body one inherited.

2. Attractive appearance along with an understanding of, and an ability to work successfully and to live happily with other people.

3. Efficient use of the intellect one inherited.

4. A desirable body of usable knowledge, and a capable set of habits and skills.

5. A trustworthy character.

6. An understanding of and an ability to live with oneself.

7. A dependable philosophy of life.

These are minimum for secure and full living, for happiness and success for the individual, and for the continued progress of society.

WHAT ARE SOME OF THE LAWS WHICH GOVERN GROWTH?

Growth Is Both Quantitative and Qualitative.   "Growth"* includes two aspects of change. They are not interchangeable but, nevertheless, are inseparable. It is said that a child "grows" and "grows up." He "grows" in size; he "grows up" or matures in structure and function. In maturing he passes through successive changes, which indicate his progress. These indicators are called maturity indicators. Ultimately, as he has passed through each successive stage of growth he reaches the end point of this process, which is called maturity.**

There are many illustrations of this maturing or "growing up" process which accompanies growth in size. The baby's digestive tract, for example, not only grows in size, but also changes in structure. This permits digestion of more complex foods and increases its efficiency in converting foods into simpler forms which the body can use. The child, therefore, can widen his experiences with foods as he grows, and this will in turn contribute to his physical well-being and his social development. The structure and functional efficiency of many of the internal organs change with development.

Younger children are not only smaller than older ones; they are also

---

* The biologic terms are growth and differentiation. For an extensive discussion of the term growth see Meredith.[655]

** Complete maturity does not arrive full blown at one time. In some aspects of life maturity arrives at a fairly early age; in others, much later.

simpler organisms, both physically and psychologically. The young baby, for example, learns motor controls over his larger muscles first. Only gradually can he master such fine coordinations as are required for reading and writing. Reasoning too, in children of preschool age is, of necessity, relatively simple and uncomplicated. Only later, when his nervous system has developed more complex organization and when accumulated experience exists as a basis, can the child attempt more complex forms of reasoning.

Emotions are simpler, the younger the child. Babies feel things "with all of themselves," being completely joyous or completely miserable about rather simple things. Differentiation of structure and accumulation of experience produce more and more complex emotional reactions to more and more complicated situations. If we permit children to go on expressing "full-blast" emotions about simple, babyish things instead of growing into greater controls and more "civilized" responses to more "grown up" situations, we are not helping them to live up to their growth potentialities.

Some people, failing to understand this double aspect of growth, do not realize that children's intellectual capacity and character traits are essentially different from those of adults. We cannot without disaster expect the motor skills, intellectual complexities or character insights from children that we expect from adults, or from younger children that we expect from older children. They have simply not "grown up," any more than they have "grown."

These aspects of "growing up" are discussed later under the effect of maturation upon learning. We have many experiments to prove that children cannot learn what they are not ready through growth or maturity to learn.

Growth Is a Continuous and Orderly Process. Growth is a continuous process which moves with an urgency supplied from deep inner sources. We may well ask how the relatively helpless, unskilled, uncontrolled infant finally reaches a level of maturity at which he can meet the tests of life just discussed. The answer is that he does it by an orderly sequence of acquisitions. He will grow because of a strong impulse to grow which is inherent in the organism; and his growth will be orderly—the product of his innate gifts of inheritance, enhanced or modified by his experience.

This should comfort us, since we realize that we do not need to make him grow. He will do that anyway. Only severe neglect or abuse will seriously disrupt his growth. Because growth is continuous we must realize that what happens at one stage carries over into and influences the next and ensuing stages.

Even the seemingly sudden spurts in tempo of growth lead into and grow out of quieter, less dramatic periods. It may be possible that in the quieter periods the child is mobilizing his forces for ensuing spurts. Parents rightly celebrate the appearance of baby's first tooth, the first independent step in walking, or the first word spoken, the first evidence of reading ability, or the first "date" with a girl (or boy) in adolescence. Each of these noticeable changes is a sort of graduation from the school of preliminary developments. The first step in walking cannot be taken until a long chain of learnings in

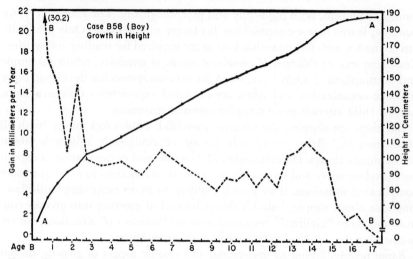

Fig. 1. Growth in height of a boy, expressed in Profile A as height at successive chrono-logic years and in Profile B as growth rate during successive periods, illustrates the changes in tempo of growth. (From Stolz, H. R., and Stolz, L. M.: Somatic Development of Adolescent Boys. New York, The Macmillan Co., 1951.)

bodily control has preceded (see Chapter 8). This is true also of the first word spoken, the first evidence of successful adjustment to other children, or any other conspicuous event in growth. Each of them is a milestone which marks progress in a long process.

Fortunately for students of child development these milestones appear in an orderly sequence. It is not difficult to chart the steps by which growth takes place or to describe the patterns which it follows. No child, for example, learns to walk without having first learned to stand, nor does any child speak clearly before he has passed through the babble stage of syllables in language. As Gesell[348] so delightfully puts it: Each child "sits before he stands; he babbles before he talks; he fabricates before he tells the truth; he draws a circle before he draws a square; he is selfish before he is altruistic; he is dependent on others before he achieves dependence on self." For the great mass of children, these patterns or stages of learning follow each other in so fixed a sequence, and parallel certain birthdays so consistently that standards of what to expect at each age have been set up.

The Tempo of Growth Is Not Even. These sequences of development do not move along in time at a steady pace. Maturity indicators do not appear at regular intervals. There are periods of accelerated growth and periods of decelerated growth. During infancy and the early preschool years growth moves swiftly and the maturity indicators of each of the various aspects of growth appear in rapid succession. During the later preschool and school years the rate of growth slackens. But this does not mean that significant changes are not taking place. Before puberty certain phases of growth become accelerated before they taper off to the adult level. Figure 1 illustrates the change in tempo of growth. It shows the growth profiles of height

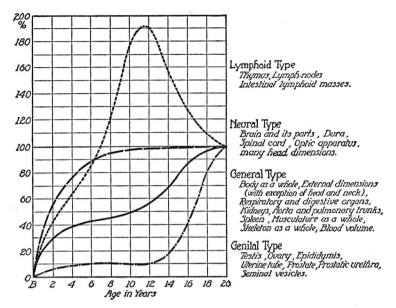

Lymphoid Type
*Thymus, Lymph-nodes
Intestinal lymphoid masses.*

Neural Type
*Brain and its parts, Dura,
Spinal cord, Optic apparatus,
many head dimensions.*

General Type
*Body as a whole, External dimensions
(with exception of head and neck),
Respiratory and digestive organs,
Kidneys, Aorta and pulmonary trunks,
Spleen, Musculature as a whole,
Skeleton as a whole, Blood volume.*

Genital Type
*Testis, Ovary, Epididymis,
Uterine tube, Prostate, Prostatic urethra,
Seminal vesicles.*

Fig. 2. A graph showing the major types of postnatal growth of the various parts and organs of the body. The several curves are drawn to a common scale by computing their values at successive ages in terms of their total postnatal increments (to twenty years). (Scammon in Harris: The Measurement of Man. The University of Minnesota Press, 1930.)

for a boy and demonstrates the rapid growth in infancy, the slower growth during the preschool and school years before pubescence, and the pubescent acceleration followed by the tapering off of growth during adolescence. Profile A shows the general trend of his growth; Profile B shows his growth rate during successive periods. This pattern, with the exception of the pubescent spurt, would be as evident in typical intelligence growth curves.

Different Aspects of Growth Develop at Different Rates. Not all aspects of growth develop at the same rate at the same time; that is, they do not proceed along an even front. For example, parents often worry because children characteristically speak three to five words at twelve months of age, but in the next three or four months they seldom acquire new words and often even forget the ones they knew. Language growth slows up for the time being because the child's physical energy and enthusiasm for learning are thoroughly occupied with the thrills of upright locomotion. Development in general bodily skill spurts ahead at this time, apparently leaving little growth energy (if we may use such a phrase) for language development. Similarly, school work sometimes suffers a slump while children's growth energy is being expended on the rapid increase in height and weight characteristic of pubescence. It is important to know which aspects of growth can be expected to absorb much of the child's capacity for growth at any given time of his life. We do not now in our public schools, for example, make provision for the fact that physical development proceeds rapidly during pubescence. Academic loads are stepped up rather than reduced in junior and senior

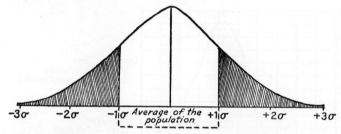

Fig. 3. Normal probability curve. Range within which the great mass of "normal" people lie. Shaded areas represent extremes in either direction.

high school, extracurricular activities, home work, and rapidly increasing social interests frequently replace the extra hours of sleep which rapid physical growth requires. It is slight wonder that we have in this country so high a tuberculosis rate among adolescent children.

Figure 2 shows how some of the different parts of the body develop at different rates at given ages. We have no comparable charts to show tempo of growth in intellect and character. We can see that the nervous system develops rapidly in earlier years. This parallels rapid acquisition of control over the body, and rapid expansion of intellectual capacities. Children probably learn more new things in the first five years of life than in any comparable period during the rest of their lives. On the other hand, we can see that the most rapid development of the genital system occurs during pubescence. Certain definite social interests and emotional capacities increase concurrently or soon afterward.

Both Rate and Pattern of Growth Can Be Modified by Conditions Within and Without the Body.   Although the impulse to grow is strong through innate force and even though patterns are fairly definite for all children, both rate and exact pattern can be changed when the child's environment is not fulfilling the fundamental needs of the child. Nutrition, activity, rest, psychologic challenge, opportunity to learn, security in affection, an adequate and understanding discipline and many other circumstances are of great importance in determining how fast and to what extent the potentialities of the child will be realized.

Around the world there are children who have been so poorly fed during their growing years that they have been unable to achieve healthy growth. Psychologic deprivations are also producing damaged personalities. Physical and psychologic scars incurred by conditions during World War II, such as lack of food, separation of families, loss of parents, destruction of home and communities, have in many cases become permanent when the deprivations were very severe and of long duration. The resilience of the growing mind and body has its limitations if environmental conditions prove to be too unfavorable for growth. In addition to such conditions as those resulting from war or other crises there are also dramatic evidences of modification in the changes in growth produced by such things as lack of iodine in community drinking water, which results in an increase of cretinism

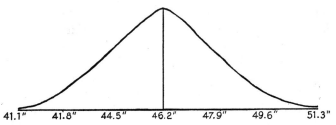

Fig. 4. Normal probability curve of height for six-year-old boys. (Average and standard deviation taken from Simmons, K., and Todd, T. W., "Growth of Well Children: Analysis of Stature and Weight 3 months to 13 years." *Growth, 2. No. 2.*)

(dwarfism due to inadequate thyroid secretion) in the population concerned. This will be discussed in some detail in Chapter 2. The disease called rickets, which results from deficiency in diet or sunshine or both, may leave permanent evidences on the body in the form of flat chests or deformed pelves, and crooked backs, all of which interfere with the efficient functioning of the body. Similarly, deficiencies in affection and security in childhood may leave permanent scars on the personality in the form of explosive tempers, "grudges," fears, and other severe handicaps to the adequate functioning of personality. Poor methods of teaching reading or other primary school subjects may leave a child with a resistance to all academic work.

On the other hand, if a child's inheritance is good, and if he has adequate diet, security in love, good teaching and other favorable circumstances he will flourish in his growth, and will develop in excellent health, with a keen intellect and a well-balanced and likable personality. We cannot, however, set up "ideal" environments, even if we wished to do so. Human nature has its weaknesses; germs exist in abundance; accidents will happen. Fortunately, the body and the personality have great resiliency. They can make up for temporary retardations, provided the disturbing factors are removed in time or the accidental damage is not too devastating. We must, in fact, consciously avoid an attempt to set up a too protected environment, since if the child is reared in early years in an aseptic (germ free) atmosphere he develops no immunity to life's ordinary germs; if he is protected and coddled too much he becomes what is known as a spoiled child; if he struggles for nothing he gains no moral strength.

Each Child Grows in His Own Unique Way.   Some children are tall and some short, some slender, others stocky. Some are physically strong, others are weak; some are intellectually keen, others are dull. There are the energetic and the phlegmatic, the agile and the awkward, the courageous and the fearful, the outgoing and the ingoing in personality. Almost every trait measured by any scale scatters individuals along a distribution known as "the normal probability curve," or "the range of normal probability." Figures 3 and 4 show the idea of normal distribution of traits. We can see from this that there is a midpoint, or theoretical average. It is quite possible that no given person in any group would measure exactly at the theoretic average for his group in any given trait. The great mass of "average" people spread over a certain span of measurement called "the normal range," within which development or growth may be considered desirable. The extremes may or may not be undesirable. In weight measurements, for example, excessive overweight or underweight is considered detrimental to health at any age. On the other hand, on the "mental age" scale people are usually desirous of belonging in the most extreme upper brackets of accomplishment where one is referred to as in the "genius" class. There is some discussion in the literature, however, as to whether even in this trait it is not possible to rank too far from the average of the population to be understood easily by others or happily adjusted to them.

An example of how widely these differences vary within the same age range can be found in Meredith's[654] study of eighteen anthropometric measurements on Iowa City boys between birth and eighteen years in whom he noted wide individual differences. The lightest boy at eighteen years was no heavier than the heaviest boy at eight years. The lightest boy at eight years weighed hardly as much as the heaviest two-year-old. These, of course, represent extremes but are warnings to us in using chronologic age scales too rigidly in classifying children.

While all children pass through the sequence of maturity stages, some may omit some of the intermediate steps. For example, some children walk upright without creeping or crawling, even though most children crawl, creep, walk in sequence. Then again, a sequence may be disturbed because of a structural defect. Such may be the case of deaf children who sometimes learn to read and write before they learn to speak or understand spoken language, this being a reversal of the usual order of development.

Some children also differ in their rate of development, going through the sequential steps as expected but at a slower or faster rate than average children. Thus there are *slow growers* and *fast growers* (see Figures 5 and 6). The period of adolescence initiated by the beginning of pubescent changes illustrates dramatically these differences. For some it begins early; for some it begins late. Stolz and Stolz[899] give a range of at least five and one-half years in the chronologic age at which adolescence began for the boys in the California Adolescent Study and at least four and one-half years at which it ended.

"Thus one boy may be entering adolescence at age ten years while he is in the high fifth grade, while for an age peer classmate childhood may continue until he is fifteen and a half years old and in the low eleventh grade."[899, p. 423]

There are also definite *differences between boys and girls*. Figure 7, representing growth in weight of boys and girls from three months to seventeen years shows that boys generally exceed girls in weight in the early years and after fourteen years of age. In the early school years they are somewhat similar in weight, but between nine and fourteen years girls, because they mature earlier than boys and therefore pass through the pubescent spurt of growth earlier than boys, are temporarily heavier than boys. Within each sex, there is considerable difference in the ages at which children arrive at maturity.

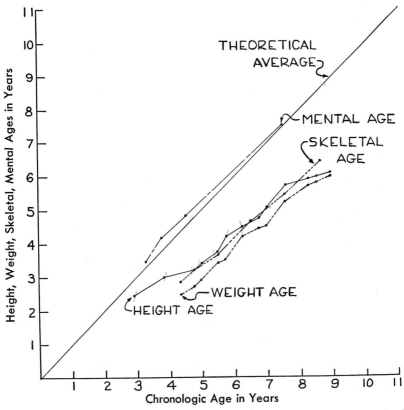

Fig. 5. Growth curves of a physically slow-growing but intellectually average-growing boy.

There seems to be very little difference between boys and girls in general intellectual capacity, but there are certain definite differences in interests and behavior, as we shall see later. Whether these differences in interests and behavior are innate or a product of the way we rear children is not clear, but much depends upon which interest or which trait is under discussion.

Goodenough and Maurer[366] after a comparison of a number of types of tests of preschool children and test performances at later years found that in nearly all instances girls' scores showed a more consistent correlation between early and later tests than boys' scores. Thus girls showed a reliable tendency toward greater stabilization of performance on tests than boys in the early years. They discuss this by saying:

Although it is possible that sex difference represents an earlier stabilization of mental level in females than in males it is probably more reasonable to assume that better coopera-tion and greater docility in the test situations—characteristics in which a number of girls are likely to exceed boys—provide sufficient explanation for the differences found. Never-theless, the other possibility is by no means excluded. Because of the theoretical significance of the problem further investigation is desirable.

We must understand these unique aspects of each individual child's growth if we are to treat children intelligently. A tall, slender child does not

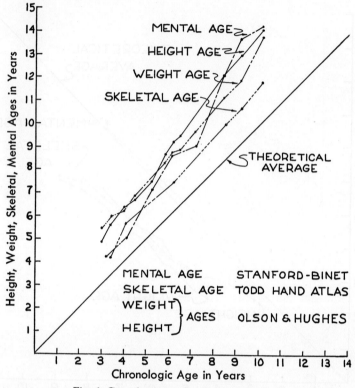

Fig. 6. Growth curves of a fast-growing boy.

put on weight at the same rate, nor does he weigh as much for his height, as does a stocky child. Some parents create unnecessary feeding problems in their attempt to achieve "standard" weight gains. Certain intellectually fast growing children have the physical stamina and social maturity to enter school at five and one-half years of age. Other children of the same chronologic and mental ages will be quite unable physically or socially to stand the competition of other first graders. Some children seem "slow to catch on" in school for several years, yet prove later to be excellent students. Forcing the pace of growth at any stage will not produce good results in the long run, and may incur serious damage along the way. Forcing children into any pattern of growth which is not in harmony with their natural potentialities is likely to result in tragedy both for the child and for the misguided adult. Fathers, for example, should not try to make "go getters" out of sensitive, artistic boys; nor should Susie be compelled to try to make Phi Beta Kappa because her older sister did.

Growth Is Complex. All of Its Aspects Are Closely Interrelated. The many failures in attempting to discover simple causal relationships in development speak for the fact that growth is an extremely complex process, the various aspects of which are intimately interrelated. It is impossible to understand the physical child without understanding him at the same time

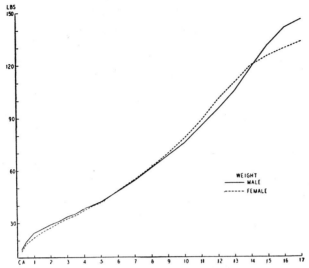

Fig. 7. Curves showing the growth in weight of boys and girls from three months to seventeen years. From Brush Regular Series. (Simmons, K.: The Brush Foundation Study of Child Growth and Development. II. Physical Growth and Development. Monogr. 9 (1). Washington, D.C., Society for Research in Child Development, National Research Council, 1944.)

as a thinking and feeling child. It is likewise impossible to understand his mental development without a real knowledge of his physical body and its needs. There is a close relationship, for example, between his total adjustment to school and his emotions, his physical health and his intellectual adequacy. Such simple things as fatigue or hunger may influence his behavior. An emotional disturbance may contribute to difficulties in eating or sleeping. An illness may be an incubation period for a behavior problem. A physical defect may have been the starting point for certain attitudes and social adjustments. It is important to an adolescent not to be too tall, too short or obese. It makes a difference in the total picture of the child whether he is energetic or phlegmatic. The posture of a child may express his physical well-being or the reverse, and also may reveal something of his attitudes. An understanding of this principle of the interrelatedness of growth is one of the major themes of this book. In order to focus attention upon it we are devoting the following section to a more complete discussion of it.

ALL ASPECTS OF GROWTH ARE INTERRELATED

The Child as a Whole.   Clear understanding of what is meant by the statement that a child reacts as a total being is essential if we are truly to educate or modify any part of him. His intellect is related to his physical well-being; his physical health is sharply affected by his emotions; his emotions are influenced by school success or failure, by his physical health and by his intellectual adequacy. His growth—physical, intellectual and social—is a product of his family history, his personal history, his current satisfactions

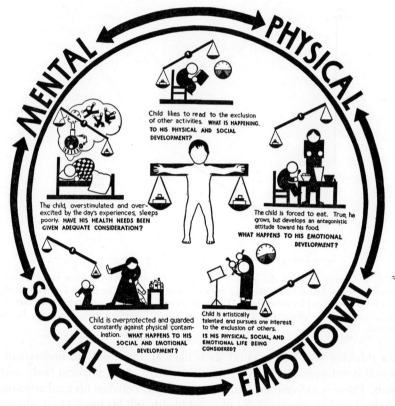

Fig. 8. The interrelatedness of a child's life.

and strains. His daily schedule affects all phases of his growth; and, in turn, the pattern and speed of his growth affect his reaction to his daily schedule. What he accomplishes in school, in play or in any other part of his living, is deeply and continuously affected by his physical health, by his intellectual adequacy, by his interest in his work or play, and by his emotional freedom to attend to it.

If, for example, the school fails to appreciate what has happened to any given child before he got where he is, and if it refuses to take into account the experiences of the child's current out-of-school life, it cannot hope to contribute constructively to his intellectual, much less to his total, growth.

Mental Age Is an Inadequate Basis for Determining School Placement. Taken from another angle, we can see the importance of knowing more about children than their mental ages as an index of school success. Careful studies of school achievement in relation to growth in general have been done by Olson and his co-workers.[706] They have analyzed school progress,* as measured by achievement tests (and computed as achievement age), in

---

* A valuable discussion of the relation of school achievement to general development can be found in Millard,[668] who participated in these studies. He notes that the reading curve will naturally follow the child's maturity curve.

relation to various aspects of growth progress, such as height age, weight age, dental age, carpal age computed from x-rays of the hand and wrist, grip age measured by a dynamometer to test strength of grip, and mental age. They have found that reading age, or arithmetic age, or any subject matter age is not as closely correlated with mental age or any other single growth age as it is with a composite of growth ages. The indication, for example, is that educational achievement sticks more closely to the "center of gravity" of growth or "organismic" age* than it does to the mental age. This is significant to the educator who makes whatever academic adjustments he makes at all in terms of mental age.** Teachers frequently complain that a child is not "working up to capacity," meaning that he is not working up to the limits of his "mental" age. Increasing numbers of schools are realizing that most children work up to their "total" capacity, or as Olson calls it, their "functioning capacity." Few schools, however, are making even reasonably adequate attempts to adapt school programs to individual children in the light of all-round physical and social, as well as mental development.

Behavior Problems Are Often Related to Patterns of Growth.   We must realize that growth itself creates certain situations which lead to behavior problems. Children who have patterns of fast, of slow, or of irregular growth often present school problems. A. S. (see Figure 9) is a case of this kind. At eight years and five months, A. S. was as tall as the average ten year, ten month-old girl, as heavy as the average nine year, eleven month-old[858] and had a mental age of twelve years two months. In one year and three months she had gained $3\frac{1}{4}$ inches and $10\frac{1}{8}$ pounds. Her feet had grown so rapidly that she wore an adult size 6 shoe at the end of the year, in contrast to a size thirteen (children's size) at the beginning. During the year she had complained of being tired and it had been necessary for her to miss about two days of school each month in order to relieve this fatigue. In addition,

* According to the Olson method measurements are converted by the use of norms to ages and plotted against chronologic age. The organismic age is the arithmetic average of as many of the ages (height, weight, dental, carpal or skeletal, grip, mental, reading, etc.) as are available. It is significant only if it includes a substantial number of the physical measurements of which the skeletal age is of considerable importance. It is useful, in other words, only if it is made up of physical measurements as well as mental and achievement measurements. Social and personality "ages" will be an important contribution to these studies as soon as we have learned how to measure them with reasonable accuracy.[706]

Methods of computing these ages and of calculating the average are described in Olson and Hughes.[708] Methods for assessing skeletal maturation of the hand are described in Flory[296] and Todd[949] and more recently Greulich and Pyle.[380]

The degree of precision with which one can use this method is to be considered since (1) there may be some question of the legitimacy of deriving averages from diverse functions and (2) the norms used may not be comparable since they were obtained from different groups of children and by using instruments of widely differing reliability.

Another method of comparing various aspects of growth is by the use of standard scores. This technique is followed at Fels Institute[876] (Composite Sheet) and in the California Adolescent Growth Study.[497]

** Whenever special retarded classes or enrichment classes exist, children are largely classified for them by intelligence tests. Sometimes school achievement tests are a factor in deciding where to place a child in special or enriched classes. Some schools have classes designed to fit special physical defects like classes for blind, deaf and crippled children, or "fresh air" rooms.

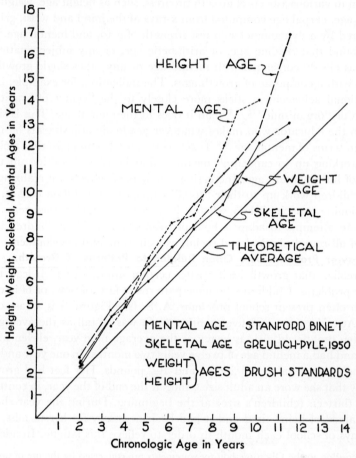

Fig. 9. Growth curves of A. S.

a certain degree of restlessness was indicative of fatigue. This was noticed when she visited the Child Development Laboratory for her yearly measurements of growth. At that time she demonstrated an inability to sit or stand quietly. In school she was reported by her teacher as a disciplinary problem and lacking in initiative. The conflict between teacher and child was alleviated when it was discovered that her seat and desk were not adjusted to her size. It had been necessary for the child to place her feet in the aisle in order to have any degree of comfort. With the adjustment of the chair and desk her behavior improved. Out of school, she generally selected children of her own size as playmates, which meant she was playing with children two to four years older than she was. When the pressure of keeping up with children two years or more older became too great she selected children of her own chronologic age. Thus she had two sets of playmates which she alternated according to her immediate needs, playing with the older children when rested, with the younger ones when tired. In this way, she had solved her own problem of play, but, of course, could not solve her own problem in school.

Such a child illustrates the fact that children use their energy for two purposes: (1) for activity, or the daily program of work and play, and (2) for growth. When energy is being utilized rapidly for growth, there is less for activity, and the child shows signs of fatigue which are relieved only when adequate change is made in his schedule to relieve him temporarily of some of the demands which he is, at other times in his life, able to meet. We see in the case of A. S. also that the inability of elementary school children to sit still for long periods is in part a by-product of rapid growth of the larger muscles, complicated by slowness of learning to inhibit movement.

When growth slows up noticeably emotional disturbances and social maladjustments may appear. Olson reports, in Barker et al.,[57] that such association has been observed clinically. The observation has been confirmed quantitatively by Mecham.[639] Olson reports:

> Research on the association of growth and social and emotional disturbances is not at a point where one can readily ascribe causes or decide with certainty whether faulty growth produces the disturbance in feeling and behavior or whether environmental factors and emotional disturbances produce the faulty growth. Probably neither can be called antecedent or consequent. It is probable that both are interrelated and circular and practical programs of treatment had best be pluralistic in methods of attack.[57]

Another so-called problem of this period of growth is adolescent awkwardness which appears probably in part because of rapid physical growth, in part because of the physiologic instabilities (organic imbalances) of adolescence, and in part because of rapidly developing social self-consciousness. Adults are not always helpful to children at these times, usually because of lack of understanding of what is happening within the child.

Children's Programs Must Be Adjusted to Growth Patterns if Behavior Problems and Growth Retardations Are to Be Avoided. We need to consider ways of adapting school work and social programs to the growth needs and interests of the two sexes as well as to the needs and interests of individual children. Boys arrive at the period of pubescence with its growth spurt and its maturational changes about two years later than girls. Most of these changes occur while they are in junior and senior high school. For example, the year of maximum growth in height comes in the thirteenth year for girls and the fifteenth year for boys.[851] Thus boys and girls of the same age and in the same upper grades will vary considerably in their physical maturity. The school curriculum makes no academic differentiation at this time. The social differentiation may or may not be recognized and utilized in planned activities. Differences in behavior in intellectual and social activities between boys and girls of these ages may be rooted in part in this maturational difference.

An Example of How One Aspect of Growth Is Influenced by Others, and in Turn, Influences Others. Something of the nature of the interrelatedness of aspects of growth may be seen in the case of Child A, a girl thirteen years old, in whom, for the sake of illustration, we have taken

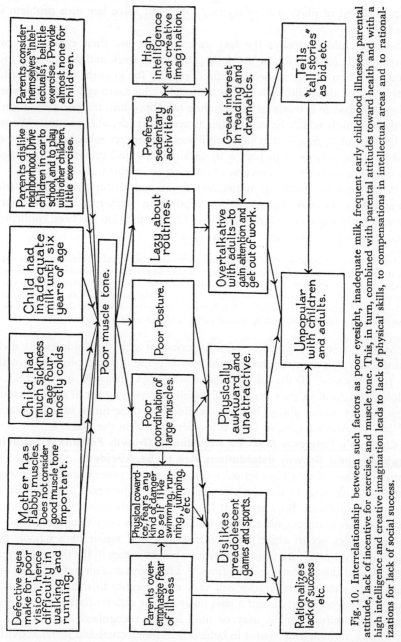

Fig. 10. Interrelationship between such factors as poor eyesight, inadequate milk, frequent early childhood illnesses, parental attitude, lack of incentive for exercise, and muscle tone. This, in turn, combined with parental attitudes toward health and with a high intelligence and creative imagination leads to lack of physical skills, to compensations in intellectual areas and to rationalizations for lack of social success.

a single trait like poor muscle tone and attempted to trace, on the one hand, the factors which may have contributed to the development of poor tone and, on the other hand, the factors which may have grown out of the poor muscle tone. In Figure 10 we see that such factors as poor eyesight, early illness, insufficient milk, which meant for her a suboptimum diet, parental attitudes, and other factors may have all contributed to produce poor muscle tone in this child. In turn, the poor muscle tone, combined with parental emphasis upon fear of illness and with a high intelligence and creative imagination in the child, may have been a contributing factor in a whole chain of events. Her unpopularity with adults and children, for example, was enhanced by her physical awkwardness and unattractiveness, which might be traced to poor posture and poor motor coordination of large muscles. Compensation for this grew out of the high intelligence and general physical laziness, and this child resorted to "tall tales" to impress her contemporaries, and excessive talkativeness as a means of obtaining adult attention. Here, a set of circumstances produced unpopularity with both children and adults. Well-rounded records on any child will, if carefully studied, reveal equally clear patterns of interrelationship among the various aspects of a child's life. Any other focus, such as school success, or reading aptitudes would, for this child, have produced an equally clear set of interrelations among physical traits, physical history, intellectual capacity, parental attitudes, method of spending time outside of school, and so on.

Further illustration of interrelatedness of physical and psychologic factors is illustrated by contrasting Child A cited above with Child B. Both are girls of the same chronologic age. In nursery school both had noticeably poor posture, B's being even poorer than A's. Both had high intelligence quotients (around 130); both came from professional homes in good neighborhoods. Yet, at thirteen years of age, A's posture had failed to improve whereas B's had improved almost to the point of perfection. A, as we have seen above, had no pattern at home for vigorous play; everything conspired to encourage intellectual satisfactions rather than the satisfactions which come from physical activity. Fears discouraged any natural bent she may have had toward active physical play. In contrast to this, B's family greatly enjoyed active physical play, often going on skiing or coasting parties together and sharing enthusiasm about a variety of sports. As early as the age of five, B had been encouraged by her father to roller skate, turn cart wheels, do bar and ring gymnastic "stunts" and was finding keen pleasure in her successes in this field. Her muscle tone and motor skills improved steadily. Because she was so skilled at games she was in great demand socially during the gang years. Success led to continued practice; continued practice led to success. She became the swimming and diving champion of her school and, before leaving the elementary school, won the school posture prize, while A's cycle of development had led to physical awkwardness and social unpopularity, with all the self-conscious interferences with normal school and social functioning which this implies. When B arrived at adolescence, she was well-adjusted and popular. A, on the other hand, struggled self-consciously to acquire passable social techniques and skills. Fortunately, with her high intelligence and the help of the child development center, she eventually succeeded fairly well.

Thus we see two children whose social development during the elementary and junior high school years was quite different. Both hereditary and environmental factors contributed to this. No amount of "counseling" or "teaching" could have changed A into B. Nor could any effort on the part of the school have changed A's family into B's family. However, both school and child development center were able to help A through the difficult years of social maladjustment so that when the social awareness of early adolescent years made her really want to change, she could do so without the handicap of a deep-rooted sense of failure.

Personal and Social Adjustments Reflect the Dynamics of Growth.
What happens to children as they grow and are faced with the cultural pressures of society, especially the expectations of their parents, teachers and peers, is reflected in their social adjustment. Each child has both assets and liabilities. For some the assets predominate; for others the liabilities tend to conceal the assets. The same liability may be a mountain for one child and a mole hill for another. The unimportant at one age may become a subject for concern at another age. A manifest concern may be real or it may be a rationalization or a projection of a deep emotional deprivation which the child cannot express.

It can be said that the growing child is a "biologic slate" on which his experiences are registered. This slate may be insufficient for him to be able to utilize advantageously certain levels of experiences common to children of his given chronologic age. Thus a hazard to a happy life is produced. He may be small in stature, relatively immature in development and give the general appearance of being young for his years. Physical limitations may restrict achievements. Desires and ambitions may far exceed physical capacity. In measuring himself against his peers he may find himself uncomfortably different.

The California Growth Study has demonstrated the social significance to children of physical factors in reports of differences (1) in behavior noticed in early and later maturing boys[501] and (2) in adjustment between two groups of boys who differed in strength.[495] In the former the physically accelerated* were usually accepted and treated by adults and children as more mature. Their behavior indicated that they had relatively little need to strive for status. From this group came the outstanding leaders in senior high school. In contrast the behavior of the late maturers tended to be immature. They had a childish activity pattern with busy activity and boisterousness. Some of these boys seemed to need to counteract their physical disadvantage by greater activity and striving for attention. Others withdrew from the group. Of the boys who differed in strength,** the "strong" rated more favorably in traits of social importance and in personal adjustment than the "weak." Muscular strength is an asset for boys in their contact with their peers.

Strength is one criterion of masculinity which has a high value for boys in this society. The steady and punctual development of the masculine physique in teen-agers is extremely important to a boy, to his peers and to his family.

* Determined by skeletal age (Todd).
** As determined by measure of grip, pull and thrust, using dynamometers.

During the teen years an inadequate masculine physique or distorted concept of what constitutes normal development in pubescence may produce concern and thus influence a boy's behavior. Schonfeld,[814, 815] from a study of boys from 9 years on, reports that generally the boys were disturbed when their pubescent development was slow. Shortness, the size of penis or testes, hair or muscular development, were areas of concern. In other cases the concern centered around physical characteristics which had always been present but had acquired an increased significance because of the boys' age. The expression in behavior of these anxieties differed among the boys. One fourteen-year-old withdrew from ordinary social contacts. Another boy of the same age, because of sexual immaturity, was aggressive, hostile, destructive, domineering at home, a truant from school and a petty thief. Unable to command respect and obedience from other boys, he organized a local gang and barely missed getting into serious difficulties. Not all boys appeared disturbed about their masculinity. It was suggested that this lack or conscious concern might be due to compensatory psychologic mechanism or to a lack of development in certain earlier stages. Parents, teachers, playmates contribute to teenagers' concern about "growing-up" through encouraging boys to take pride in masculine development and frequently imposing tyrannical standards of "normalcy."

That *personal adjustment may be a resultant of a great variety of forces* in a child's life is again demonstrated in the case of John S., one of the boys in the California Adolescent Growth Study.[492] At eleven years John was described as a

. . . rather slim boy with tousled dark hair, a good-natured expression.
    The other boys appeared to like him well enough; however, he was the odd man, without a partner. He was inexpert and a little awkward in games with balls, horseshoes, etc.—like an adult who had not played for a long time. He did not seem to mind this—was a little apologetic and a little amused. As a matter of fact, he was quite at home in the Institute—drawing seems to be one of his special abilities, so he enjoyed himself. He never tried to dominate and yet did not submit to bossiness, resisting interference in a firm, good-natured sort of way. . . .[492]

His classmates rated him average in such traits as happy, leader, masculine, enthusiastic, popular and grown-up. He had the reputation of being inactive in games, afraid to take a chance and avoiding fighting. In no way was he outstanding.

In the next few years John lost status with his group and the stresses and strains became apparent in his behavior until at fifteen years, in the ninth grade, these stresses reached the maximum effect. At this time he was at a low point in popularity, initiative and good-naturedness and at a high point in evidences of anxiety, show-off behavior and affectation. After fifteen years he began to improve so that by the time he had become a high school senior he had made considerable progress toward better personal adjustment and more mature social attitudes.

The next year in college he

. . . was rated by his college advisor as somewhat quiet, shy and unexpressive, but was given markedly favorable ratings in other areas: as having a quick comprehension and strong, well-developed intellectual interests; as being unaffected, independent and showing initiative, and as having a 'pleasing personality.'[492]

Why did John have such ups and downs? There is no simple explanation but one involving the interplay of many factors.

John lacked robust health from his early years and throughout his adolescence. This lack of vitality was a handicap in his relationships with his teachers and even more with his classmates in that he had a limited amount of energy to expend in his work and play. He also was slower in maturing than most of his classmates. Around the ages of fourteen and fifteen years he was smaller in size and more immature than the others. He was a "little boy" among adolescents who had had their growth spurt and greater maturing of physical abilities and social interests. By fifteen years he began his adolescent "spurt" and the accompanying maturing of his body. He caught up with the others in size, in primary and secondary sex characteristics and in the improvement of certain physiologic functions. The delayed maturing could be expected to have some effect on behavior since it can lead to loss of status with others and to anxiety expressed in the question, "Am I normal?"

He had an added handicap in his physique, which varied considerably from that of his more vigorous masculine classmates. No doubt the awareness of this difference made him self-conscious in his relations with his social group. In spite of this, he did not withdraw completely from his peers but, in fact, sought company, although in an extremely awkward way.

The environmental conditions under which John grew up may have in part strengthened the impact of these physical factors. John was a child of the depression. The effect of lack of adequate income was indicated in countless ways—stretching money for food, little margin for clothing, limited opportunities for recreation such as movies or trips that would widen contacts with the community, and increasing home chores and household routines. At the same time John's mother was overprotective and demanding even during his adolescence. So during his adolescence he was having personal troubles both at home and at school.

He did not have the skills* that would lead to popularity, nor was he able to compensate for them with other favorable skills. He had no special gift of intelligence, no special insight into his problem, and little help from parents and teachers in recognizing and solving his personal problems. His response to his lowered status in his group was not to withdraw but to assert himself more strongly. While he took no part in games, he displayed an increased restlessness and became more talkative and attention-seeking. He evidently

---

* Bower[110] found that popularity in the eighth and ninth grades correlated with physical ability and strength but not with intelligence, achievement, home rating (socio-economic status) and height. These relationships are probably due not only to a high premium placed on motor skills but also to the fact that strength and other aspects of physical ability are associated with such favorable traits as activity, aggressiveness and leadership. Some adolescents achieved popularity when low in physical ability but high in some compensating factors, such as exceptional degree of enthusiasm, friendly sociability, or an aggressive enterprise.

was not less friendly, but was immature and inept in his use of social techniques.

John's personal difficulties are the result of many factors. To be sure, his delayed maturity accentuated his problems. It is noted that his lowest point in social relationships was at the time when physical differences were most marked between himself and his associates. John's own reaction depended, however, upon the combination of traits that resulted from the interplay of his heredity and environment. Another boy might react differently.[496]

John's improvement can be attributed, therefore, to changes within himself as he struggled to catch up with the group, and to changes in the group as their values and standards of achievement more nearly approached the aspirations that John has always held important.

The author completes John's story with the following:

> So marked an upturn in John's personal fortunes is evidence not only of the toughness of the human organism but also of the slow, complex ways in which nature and culture may come into adaptation.[492]

What It Means to Be an Early or Late Maturer. In any group of early adolescents there will be those who are late in maturing and others who mature early. Children who are extreme deviates may find this period a very trying one unless understanding adults come to their aid.

For a boy, early maturing may be an asset since with it generally comes the prestige of improved athletic ability and the signs of approaching manhood. However, early maturing may offer a promise of development which is not fulfilled because the superiority over peers proves to be only temporary. It may come at an inappropriate time, as for example during a period of family crisis or of a change in school when adult support is lacking. It may follow an inappropriate pattern so that a boy is unable to achieve a high degree of self acceptance.* How an early maturer will emerge in terms of satisfaction with himself and his life depends upon the interplay of forces within and outside himself.

For the girl, early maturing may create a hazard to her social adjustment.** Menstruation and its problems in the toilet room may disturb her if she associates with girls who are immature and have had no opportunity to learn about it. An early maturing girl is taller and has acquired the figure of a woman. She, therefore, may feel conspicuous, and this feeling may become accentuated if her breasts are especially large. Most boys of her chronologic age will be shorter and will lack the interest in girls that she has in boys. Tallness will create a problem for her at parties when partners pair off for dancing. She can accept this with better grace if she is given some assurance that this condition is temporary. An explanation of her growth pattern will allay her anxiety about whether she will always be so tall in relation to

* See case of Ben in Ch. XVIII in Stolz and Stolz.[899]
** In the California Adolescent Growth Study, it was found that the early maturing girls and the late maturing boys tended to make the poorest social adjustment.[80]

others. Also her attitude toward growing up will influence her feelings. She can be given help to be proud of her body rather than embarrassed and thus she can be encouraged to hold her body in good balance. Some of the poor posture in early adolescence is the result of an attempt to minimize size and conceal developing breasts.

On the other hand, late maturing may create concern for both sexes but especially is this noticed in boys. They find themselves, as did John described earlier, under-developed youngsters in the midst of well-developed classmates. They are short in height and less capable in physical ability and late in acquiring characteristics of masculinity. Their anxiety about their size is intensified because of the realization that some of their peers have completed their growth. Hence they assume that the age when growth ceases is imminent. To them, also, an explanation of their growth pattern, a demonstration that other boys have had a similar experience, and some friendly counseling about ways in which they may hold their own among their contemporaries will help them to adjust to their differences.

It has been said earlier that freedom to grow at one's own pace should be the right of every child. Early maturing children may suffer especially in an environment where an expanding social life and growing independence are restricted. The ensuing conflict between internal desires and environmental restrictions may find an outlet in various ways, either through behavior or some physiologic indication of emotional tension. Bayer reports the case of an early maturing girl who at eighteen years of age weighed 180 pounds and wished to reduce.

She is described as:

. . . a strong, healthy girl with the usual childhood diseases, good appetite, plenty of "pep," normal physiological responses except for mild hypertension.* Laboratory data uncover no metabolic abnormalities. But a sexual evaluation is illuminating. The girl started menstruating at the age of ten, and looks like a Rubens' painting. That is, she is an early maturing, highly differentiated feminine type. One would expect her to be busy with social doings. But, when inquiry is made into her social opportunities, they turn out to be unusually limited. Her father is from Jugoslavia. He thinks a girl should stay at home nights, Sundays, all the time except when she is at work contributing to the family exchequer. While her friends go to shows and parties, this girl stays at home and nibbles in despair. Perhaps her elevated blood pressure is resulting from her suppressed rage. How help her lose weight? By giving her a diet? Of course. But, at the same time, the physician must help her bring the father up to date.[68]

The more "mature" interests which are intensified by biologic development can become troublesome for the early maturing child who is bored by his classmates, as well as for the later maturing child who is left behind and feels strangely out of touch with his peers. A biologically mature girl, reading from childish fifth or sixth grade readers, is not likely to be challenged academically. On the other hand, an underdeveloped child may be bewildered and confused by discussions about marriage and boy-girl relationships, aimed at the mid-point of developmental interest in junior and senior classes in high school.

* High blood pressure.

Obesity Is More Than too Many Calories.   Obese children are almost without exception not the happy-go-lucky individuals that the world tends to associate with overweight.

> Timid and retiring, clumsy and slow, they are not capable of holding a secure place among other children. Over-sensitive and unable to defend themselves, they are helplessly exposed to the jeers and heckling of their more active comrades. Thus they shun healthy play and exercise and become miserable and seclusive.[133]

However, fearfulness and lack of interest precede rather than follow obesity. The obesity is a part of a constellation of traits that portray a child who is immature socially and emotionally, yet is advanced physically, including both bodily size and physical maturation, and has good intelligence.[135] In order to understand him it is necessary to investigate his family, for it is here that we find some valuable clues. The obese child, according to the Bruch studies,[136] typically lives in an overprotective and oversolicitous environment generally with a dominating mother and a weak and submissive father. The oversolicitude and protection of the mother cannot hide her underlying insecurity, possessiveness and often hostility to the child. These inner feelings are reflected in her behavior. The home, therefore, does not fulfill the child's basic needs of being loved and accepted for himself and having opportunities for development along his natural channels. He resorts, therefore, to eating as a substitute gratification.

Spock[886] points out that around the age of seven some children tend to become obese. Such children overeat as a compensation for being unhappy and lonely. This is a period when a child is withdrawing from the close emotional ties of the family. If he is not successful in establishing close friendships with other children he feels alone. Eating, at this time, may give him comfort. He may also resort to it for comfort when he has trouble at school or at home.

Subcutaneous fat for some boys during early adolescence[899] may be disturbing since their body configuration does not conform to their masculine aspirations. A boy may be fearful that he will never become a real man. A wise adult can give needed support to a boy through such a period.

Adults can be of assistance to obese children not only by helping them to regulate their diet* but also by making sure that their home, school and social life are as happy and satisfying as possible. Such children can be guided into activities compatible with their physical health and vigor, and in which they can achieve a definite degree of success and, therefore, satisfaction. Boys around pubescence can be reassured that their obesity will not interfere with their maturing.**

Correlation of Mental and Physical Growth Positive but Not High. Before leaving a discussion of the interrelatedness of growth we need to

---

* Obesity is due to an imbalance of energy intake and output. Too keen an appetite for high caloric foods is a frequent contributing factor.

** Bruch[135] found in a study of more than 200 boys and girls who had become obese before pubescence that they tended to be accelerated in height and bone maturation. Early puberal development was the rule for obese girls and not unusual for obese boys.

survey the evidence of the relationship of mental to physical growth that comes from correlation studies. The type of relationship between physical maturing and mental (or intellectual) maturing is in dispute. The popular idea once was that when people possess physical superiority they are by nature inferior intellectually—"beautiful but dumb"—and that brainy people are weaklings. There is no scientific evidence to support this view of compensation. The evidence, in fact, in spite of some dispute, seems to lean slightly in the direction of correlation rather than of compensation. The inferior child intellectually seems to be slightly inferior all the way around. The superior child intellectually seems to be at least slightly superior also in physical capacity.[941, 554, 451]

It is well known that certain forms of physical dwarfism, such as cretinism, are accompanied by mental defect. Jones,[494] in summarizing the literature on the subject of the relation of physical defects to intelligence level, concluded that there is a small causal relationship between physical defect and slower intellectual development. There seems to be general agreement that minor variations in health and physical conditions have no significant effect upon mental development.[697]

Terman's *Studies of Genius* is widely accepted as evidence of the correlation of physical and personal traits. He studied a thousand children whose I.Q.'s were 140 or over, and reports that gifted children are, as a group, physically superior to the various groups used as a comparison.[933, 936]

There is some evidence that in the wide range of so-called normal children there is a small, but persistent, relationship between socio-economic status, physical and intellectual factors.*

Perhaps some of the confusion in the evidence lies in misunderstanding as to whether we are talking about sheer intelligence, or about the way intelligence functions. That physical condition, short of brain or nerve damage, has little to do with native intelligence is probably true. Promoting physical growth will probably not increase inherent intellectual capacity. In this sense they are not interrelated. However, the manner in which the native intelligence functions, being dependent upon attentiveness, concentration, self-confidence and aggressive attack upon problems, is unquestionably related to physical well-being.[629, 941]

Interrelation Between Emotional Well-Being and Other Areas of Growth Positive and High. In Chapter 3, and in many places throughout the book, convincing evidence will be given to show that the child's physical well-being affects and is affected by his emotional well-being; also that the child's ability to use his intelligence effectively is deeply influenced by the state of his emotional well-being.

APPLICATIONS OF THE CONCEPT OF THE WHOLE CHILD

Applications for Doctors, Nurses, Nutritionists and Dentists. For those who work primarily with children's bodies the chief application of the

* Martin and Stendler[630] give an excellent summary of this.

"whole-child" doctrine would lie in the recognition by these workers that children have personalities as well as bodies. In working with children's physical health the worker should never forget that mental health is of equal importance. Excepting in extreme emergency the doctor, nurse or dentist should be meticulously careful to avoid use of physical force in treatments, since physical force may produce severe psychologic reactions. Antagonism toward doctors, nurses or dentists may, for example, be set up with the result that the patient may thereafter avoid contacts with these professions or, if later contact proves unavoidable, may present so uncooperative an attitude that successful treatment is difficult or impossible.

Under emergency conditions of accident, severe illness, or hospital entrance children are particularly susceptible to emotional conditioning. Recall in this connection the law of learning which states that learning is most permanent when the learning situation is vivid. Attitudes and emotional conditionings set up under emergency or unusual circumstances make a far more permanent impression upon children than would be made under less emotional circumstances. It is, therefore, particularly necessary for workers who treat children in emergency situations to deal wisely with them. For example, the doctor's or nurse's or dentist's lie to the child, "Look out the window and see the bird," followed by the jab of a needle or yanking of a tooth builds deeper distrust of adults than most "emergency" lies by a parent or school teacher. The statement, "This won't hurt at all," immediately followed by pain, leaves an equally unfortunate impression. Children dealt with in this manner can scarcely be expected to believe doctors or nurses or dentists in the future. Few children fail to rise to a quiet statement, "This will hurt, but I'll be careful, and you'll help me by being quiet, and we'll be through in just a minute; . . . there, that's fine. You helped a lot."

Because emotional conditioning is deep and permanent under emergency circumstances, doctors and nurses should learn enough about the psychology of children to know how to reassure them without over-assuring them. Over-assurance leads to the suspicion that there must indeed be something to be afraid of or this grownup wouldn't talk about it so much. Fear is a natural accompaniment of threats to bodily security. Doctors, nurses and dentists must of necessity be associated with pain and terror. It is imperative that these workers learn how to do what must be done in a manner that will minimize fear, distrust and antagonism and that will win from children a maximum of cooperation and trust toward adults in general and toward their professions in particular.

Another aspect of child development is of immediate importance to physical growth workers. Knowledge of child development can afford an understanding of what well children are like both mentally and physically. Doctors who do not know well children are handicapped in the diagnosis and treatment of sick children. More than this, physical growth workers, particularly doctors, are expected to know something of whether a given child is "normal" mentally and emotionally. Unfortunately, the physician or nutritionist, nurse or dentist who has not actually studied the patterns and sequences of normal mental and emotional development may answer parents' questions and make diagnoses and suggestions which are inaccurate and misleading.

A still further reason for knowing something of normal mental and emotional growth and behavior is that physical growth workers are inevitably dealing with habit formation. What good sleep habits, food habits, toilet habits, temper control, obedience and play habits are at one year, at five years, at ten or fifteen years should be part of the basic knowledge and understanding of those who work with children. Not only must these workers know what good habits are; they must also know how to get them established, and they must understand parents, teachers and other child-agency workers well enough to cooperate in the development of good habits. Adolescents are particularly in need of guidance from doctors as well as from teachers and other outside-the-home agents. Their need to understand themselves, and their anxiety about their own physical and physiologic normality lead them to lean heavily upon any understanding adult, particularly upon doctors, nurses and school teachers. The doctor or nurse who knows nothing of adolescent psychology is likely to fail this job completely.

Applications to Social Work and Guidance. Everything that has been said above about emergency situations applies here. The social worker or guidance person also meets children at critical periods, when their homes are being broken up, when illness, death or other dramatic circumstances have entered their lives. The children are frightened, bewildered, or otherwise emotionally disturbed. Wise treatment at such times may make all the difference between a serious emotional disturbance on the one hand and a satisfactory emotional adjustment with accompanying physical well-being on the other. Fortunately, all good schools for training in social work now place great emphasis upon the understanding of and ability to deal with psychologic reactions.

It is necessary, however, to emphasize the importance to social workers and guidance people of a knowledge of children's physical growth and well-being. No steps in psychologic diagnosis or treatment should be taken without clear knowledge of a child's physical condition—past and present. Many attitudes and reactions of children, particularly when they are faced with an emergency or crisis situation, are reflections of current or past physical conditions. The psychologist or social worker who presumes to account for psychologic reactions solely on the basis of current and past psychologic situations may miss the point badly. Just as it is important for physical growth workers to understand basic principles of psychologic development and reaction, so, too, it is imperative that the psychologic worker understand at least the elements of physical development and reaction if intelligent work with children is to be done.

Another analogy with the physical growth worker's situation holds here. Just as the physician needs to know well children, so, too, the psychologist or social worker needs to know healthy, normal children and families. Too often the psychologist or social worker knows only the abnormal or pathologic aspects of children and of families. They cannot deal intelligently with pathology unless they know what normal growth and sound family life are. Too often behavior problems which are aspects of perfectly normal growth, e.g., the negativism of two-to-three-year old children, the aggressive boisterousness of eight-to-ten-year-olds, the "stealing" of the six- to ten-year-old, are picked up by psychologists or social workers as abnormal or problem behavior. Unless such workers are trained to detect the difference between negativism or aggressiveness or stealing which is "normal" and that which is truly problem behavior they run the risk of frightening parents and children unnecessarily. Not infrequently such normal behavior, dealt with as problem behavior, does become a problem. Social workers and psychologists should be trained to correct—not to create—problems in child growth and in family life.

Applications for Schools and Teachers.   Although we have probably always recognized that body, mind and personality are closely interrelated in growth and functioning, and although we have clear evidence from recent studies of the continuousness of each aspect of growth, we still are lagging behind in adjusting our school programs to these facts. The doctrine of the "whole child," emphasized continuously in teacher training and now well taught by means of many texts* used in teacher training institutions is slow to bear adequate fruit in actual school administration and school teaching.

The better school systems have made good beginnings, especially in the nursery, kindergarten and primary areas. However, even in these school systems continuity of growths is frequently lost sight of. Nursery school education, wherever it exists, is typically a thing apart from the kindergarten and primary. The kindergarten is often completely unrelated to the primary. June is the month which ends the freedom of the kindergarten for all children whose birthdays fall between November of the previous year and November of the coming year. September is the beginning of the more restricted activities of the traditional first grader. Children are "promoted" annually in most school systems, semi-annually in others. If the maturing of each child is "ready" on an extremely rough average for the next grade, he passes; if not, he repeats a whole year, or half year. A few progressive school systems are doing away with grade designations, and in so doing are adapting the work much better to the growth tempo of individual children.[107] However, nearly all schools make a transition from kindergarten to primary, from primary to upper elementary, from there to junior high school, and thence to senior high school which is abrupt and which is effected on a rough average-maturity basis with little or no consideration for the continuousness of growth or for individual variations in growth. The slower grower fails to "pass." The faster grower may "skip" grades, or stay with the average growers. The uneven or disharmonious grower fits nowhere in particular, moving along roughly in time with his mental age, but frequently grossly out of tune with his physical age and his personality age.

A number of progressive educators have attempted to meet this difficulty of group classification for individual children. Some have coached children academically to help them carry on with children of their own advanced

* See Strang,[905] Robbins,[785] Baxter,[67] Butterworth,[153] Wiles.[992]

physical and social maturity. Others have offered academic "enrichment" to keep children of advanced mental age happy and intellectually awake in groups which fit their average or retarded physical and social maturity. Some administrators have broken up the day's schedule to permit children to exercise and play with physical and social peers, while doing academics with intellectual peers. Some have even broken up the academic day to permit children to do social studies with peers, but to read or write or do arithmetic (tool subjects) at the reading or writing or arithmetic level of their present capability. These devices to adjust school programs to the growth needs of individual children have worked with varying success, depending upon the insight into and real knowledge of the child's growth levels and other vital factors.

HOW WE CAN UTILIZE THE PRINCIPLES OF GROWTH

It Helps to Know What to Expect and When to Expect It. If we do not know something of stages of growth and of growth patterns we may find ourselves in trouble with our children because we expect too much of them. For example, many parents are distressed at the rough-and-tumble, boisterous behavior of children in the gang age. The parents fail to understand the child's need to stand up against the blunt, egocentric behavior of other children, and to work out for himself a social adjustment to peers who love him less and hence who make fewer adjustments to him than his family does. Failing to understand that this adjustment takes time and comes through a sometimes crude trial and error process, the parents expect adult smoothness in personal relationships.

On the other hand, we may not expect enough of growing children and hence make too little provision for the development of whatever capacities they have. One pair of parents had done nothing to investigate the mental well-being of their child, who at twelve months had made no attempts to sit up. This baby ate and slept well and gained length and weight at a satisfactory rate. The parents had so little understanding of the nonphysical factors of growth that they assumed all was well. Much could have been done to stimulate this baby's activity without forcing him had the parents known that he was a slow-mental-grower and, therefore, that he needed special encouragement and special practice.

Still another set of parents were thrilled that their two-and-one-half-year-old daughter could recite 150 nursery rhymes. They lost sight of the fact that many children of this age can be coached into such a stunt and, therefore, that its accomplishment did not necessarily indicate the genius they thought it did. They also failed to read the signs of high nervous tension which should have indicated to them that they were pushing their own little girl beyond the natural limits of her mental growth, and that they were purchasing a short-lived ego satisfaction for themselves at a serious cost to physical well-being and nervous stability for the child.

Some understanding of what can generally be expected from children at any given age is useful as a background, if one can somehow learn to use

1. Many parents and teachers can, solve many of their problems and anxieties if they can

these standards as guides in judging the natural pace of one's own child. They are disastrous if used as whips with which to drive any given child beyond his own natural pace; yet they can be helpful in locating retardations of natural pace which might be corrected. Knowledge of standards should help us, in other words, to judge the pace of growth for any given child, and should, therefore, keep us from forcing growth. Thus this knowledge can help us to keep growth flowing at its own maximum natural speed.

Parents and teachers are sometimes greatly troubled because they fail to recognize a "passing phase" of growth which, though troublesome, evidences a desirable basic growth. One pair of parents when their son was sixteen years old were ready to place him in a boarding school because, "if he keeps on being as increasingly hard to manage as he has been for the past six months we cannot handle him." They had no insight at all into the fact that the early adolescent stage of development for most children is one of the most trying of all growth periods for the parents. As we shall see later, this period is one in which most children reach out rapidly for independence and, therefore, resist the authority of parents; they are also still lacking some of the knowledge and experience needed to guide their actions, yet they refuse help from their parents. The parents of this particular boy did not understand this as a normal and a temporary period of growth. They could see only the complicated behavior situation which had arisen, and could only suppose that the crescendo of difficulty in managing the boy would soon reach the stage where he would be completely out of hand. When they gained some insight into his needs and how to provide for them they were able to restore at least a modicum of peace in their relationships with him and once more experienced the joy in his development which is natural to parents who are not at loggerheads with their children.

Such misunderstanding of the processes of growth and the needs of the grower often produces disharmony and strain between parents and children, or between the teacher and the child. *Many children are regarded as behavior problems when they are only passing through quite natural phases of desirable growth.* The behavior problem situation arises because the adult in control does not understand what is happening and, therefore, handles the situation badly.

Understanding of Growth Should Help Us to Know How to Make the Most of Each Growth Stage. If we know something of the sequences of growth we should be able to provide experiences which help children to make the best of each phase and to prepare best for each ensuing phase. This means providing materials, companions, incentives and opportunities for expression, appropriate to each stage of development. It means also giving the child encouragement through praise which recognizes a really good performance *for him, at his stage of growth*, but which avoids the discouragement of insistence upon a standard of performance which is beyond him or the smugness resulting from praise too easily given for a mediocre effort and mediocre performance. The same holds true of the corrections which guide learning by pointing out errors of performance. Blaming a child for what he cannot help is discouraging to effort and best learning. Yet pointing out

Fig. 11. A student learns about children while working with them in the craft room at camp.

areas in which performance can be improved, especially if accompanied by suggestions on how to accomplish the improvement, can be most constructive if it leads the child in the direction of a desirable next step in growth.

Although children, if given a reasonably rich environment and a reasonably free opportunity to learn, will make their own next needs apparent* and will take their own next steps in growth, it is helpful for the adult to know what these needs and steps are, not only in order to understand them but also to help provide for them. In adolescence, for example, parents who have known since the child was a baby that eventually he must make his own decisions and carry his own responsibility, will gradually remove the control of their authority. This requires a nice understanding of physical and mental growth steps in order to remove control fast enough, yet not too fast. Removed too slowly the child must fight for independence and, unless completely cowed, will do so. Removed too rapidly, the child is left making decisions and taking responsibility for which he is not ready. In this case the consequences of bad decisions may frighten him away from responsibility on the one hand; or on the other hand may produce the drunken sense of knowing more than he actually does which leads him into brash decisions and real tragedy or at best into smugness of personality. Knowledge of "when is

* Olson[706] uses the term "seeking behavior" to express the child's demonstration of his readiness for new experiences.

enough" of any opportunity or of any experience is basic to intelligent guidance of children at every stage of their growth.

HOW PEOPLE FIND OUT ABOUT THE GROWTH OF CHILDREN

Child Study Is Not New.   Every primitive tribe has its own code for rearing the coming generation. The Chinese and Hindus have patterns for child training which have endured through many centuries. As long as society remains stable, family life proceeds in fairly constant patterns, little change being needed from one generation to the next since each generation of adults meets few new or unprepared-for situations. The extremely rapid changes in manner of living and working which resulted after the Industrial Revolution, however, have necessitated new adjustments with each generation of adults. Scientific research has added tremendously to our knowledge of people as well as of things. Not only has our economic world changed; our social world has changed as radically. This places rigorous demands upon both physical and psychologic stamina. Adjustments have been so rapid that old, socially inherited patterns of family life and child rearing have not always worked. There is current need to learn as much as we can about how to preserve the best values of family life, and how to insure optimal development of all potentialities possessed by everyone.

There are now many important centers for the study of family life and of child development. A number of outstanding colleges and universities offer advanced degrees in child development, family life and human relationships. Many communities have developed child health clinics, child guidance clinics, and family consultation centers. As students who wish to deal intelligently with children and with family life, we should know at least a little of how this science proceeds.

Accurate Observation Is as Important Here as in the Physical Sciences. Much can be learned about children through observation by a person who has acquired the skill of observing. Through his appearance and behavior the child reveals much to a trained observer. However, observation alone is not enough in judging intelligence or in evaluating most behavior or in diagnosing most physical conditions. The color of the skin cannot be relied upon for detecting mild anemias. Looking at a child gives us very little clue to the amount of weight he has gained in a given time or to his increase in height. Rather, the eye and ear must be trained in acuteness and guided in their direction of observation. In addition, precision instruments are selected to measure growth in size, change in structure and in efficiency of function. Scales, measuring boards, calipers and tape measures are devices used to detect changes in size. The observation of bone development is made possible by the use of the x-ray. Biochemical tests and various instruments are used to determine the status of body functions. Performance tests measure motor achievement. Batteries of intelligence tests form the basis for evaluating intelligence. Projective techniques, including the Rorschach and the Murray

Thematic Apperception Test, are used to study emotional characteristics and adjustment. Sociometric techniques are used to study social development and behavior.

There Are Two Ways of Studying Growth: Cross Sectional and Longitudinal. There are two methods of studying growth, the cross sectional and longitudinal. The cross sectional method involves the measuring or testing of different groups of children at different ages or stages of development. In such studies the same child is not represented at different levels. Many of the norms now used were collected in this way. Such norms as the mental abilities at various age levels, vocabulary norms, interests of the six-year-old, and the Children's Bureau Standards of height and weight are examples. By the use of such norms, general trends can be determined. It thus becomes possible to determine what is generally expected and how great will be the difference among individuals. However, individuality is lost sight of in such studies.

On the other hand, the longitudinal method involves the measuring or testing and study of the same children through a number of years and, therefore, through each successive stage of growth. To collect norms in this way requires more time but is more reliable for determining growth trends.*

In addition to serving as another method of establishing norms, the longitudinal method can be used also to study individual patterns of growth as the cross sectional method cannot. When a battery of tests and observations are repeated regularly much can be learned about the dynamics of growth.

Many research centers studying child development** have used the longitudinal method, following the same children through periods of years. In doing this these centers have usually studied the growth of an individual child (1) by comparing his growth at any given moment with that of representative groups of children—that is, comparing him with appropriate norms—and (2) by following his individual progress through successive stages. The first way gives the status of the child at one point in his life; the second way reveals from whence he has come, in what direction and at what speed he is going. A judicious combination of status and progress evaluation is thus obtained.

Standards Must Be Used Wisely. One must remember, in using these norms, that such figures are only averages. It must be understood that approximately one-half of six-year-olds examined do better than, or are taller than, the figure given for "mental age" or for "height age"; correspondingly, the same proportion do worse, or are shorter. Such standards, or average

---

* Shuttleworth[852] found that for the purpose of determining growth trends of height of homogeneous groups repeated measurements on the average population of only 248 cases represented the equivalent of approximately 270,000 cross sectional measurements.

** Brush Foundation, Western Reserve University; Child Research Center, University of Illinois; Child Research Council, University of Colorado School of Medicine; Division of Maternal and Child Care, Harvard School of Public Health, Boston; Experimental School, University of Michigan; Fels Research Institute, Antioch College; Merrill-Palmer School, Detroit; Institutes of Child Welfare, University of California, University of Iowa, University of Minnesota.

figures, have often been used unwisely.* There is a tendency among some workers and parents to check all children against a fixed figure regardless of individual differences and in complete disregard of a "normal range" of variation in growth.

It is important, too, in considering standards not only to consider the "normal range" of the population at large, but also to think of the "normal range" of the specific group in which the child finds himself growing up. We know, for example, that size of children has increased in the last few decades.** Therefore, when norms for height and weight are used it is desirable to see that they are as recent norms as are available.

Children also will differ in size according to their socio-economic status and their ethnic group.† Thus a false sense of security or needless anxiety about the growth of a child might result from lack of consideration of these factors. We know, too, that boys and girls differ in height and weight and that girls are ahead of boys in bone maturation (see Chapter 7). Since the expected optimum of development differs from hereditary group to hereditary group and from one environmental circumstance to another, *one should always use standard figures in the light of full knowledge of their relevance to any given group of children or to any given child in that group.*

In the same way "mental age" standards are useless in dealing with children whose opportunity to learn differs from the average opportunity or whose emotional conflicts keep their intelligence from full functioning, unless full account is taken of these circumstances. A child, handicapped in vision or other sense, or crippled in body, cannot be measured by scales standardized on normal children. Social development scales and standards also must be utilized only with a clear understanding of the group experiences available to the child or children being measured, to the ethics or moral standards of the families and neighborhoods in which the children live, and to other important factors which inevitably determine the stage and the pattern of growth possible for any given child at any given age. The "normal range" of any group in any measurement will differ according to hereditary and cultural background and for each environmental opportunity.

Further illustration may serve to clarify the need for care in interpreting any given child's standing in relation to standard tests and measurements. For example, acceleration on a language scale may not mean at all a special gift in language; it may mean only that the given child has been especially coached in language accomplishment, or has been continuously exposed to

---

* Thompson reminds us, "Norms are not criteria for optimal development. They are statistics for basic comparisons."[942]

** Yale University freshmen in 1952 were 2.5 inches taller and 18 pounds heavier than those in 1853.[829] Seven-year-olds at the University of Iowa Elementary School were 1.1 inches taller and 4.5 pounds heavier in the period of 1940–47 than in the period of 1920–27.[649]

† Combining studies done in Canada and in U.S.A., seven-to ten-year-old boys representing professional and managerial groups average 1 inch taller and 3 pounds heavier than those in the unskilled and semi-skilled groups. Similar differences were found in boys attending public schools in the best and poorest districts.[653] Average Norwegians are 5 inches taller than average Japanese.[829]

an environment especially rich in language usage. Usually, in a case of this kind, the rich language environment would be provided by a pair of parents themselves especially endowed in language. A child of such parents may or may not have inherited the special ability. If he has, he will naturally benefit markedly from the superior language environment, and will move forward in language more rapidly than most children. If he has not inherited the ability he will benefit less from his rich language environment. However, one must be alert to the occasional child of only average native language ability who, because it is the thing to do in his family or because accomplishment in this field wins him special attention, concentrates unusually hard, learns more rapidly than he would without such incentives, and gives greater early promise than he can later fulfill. A precocious vocabulary in young children has often led parents or teachers to predict and to expect great things in writing which the child as an adult could not produce. Vocabulary is often a reflection of a special environment, rather than a natural literary gift.

On the other hand, retardations in "vocabulary age" have often been misunderstood as indicating lack of intellectual or at least verbal capacity, whereas in many public school children they may only mean that another language is being spoken at home and that the child has not had a "normal" opportunity to learn English. A child, lacking such opportunity, may at age six have an English vocabulary equal only to that of the average four-year-old. This would not at all mean that this child, now only two-thirds "developed" in vocabulary, would remain proportionately retarded throughout his growth period, having only an eight-year-old vocabulary at twelve, and so on. Having had restricted opportunity, such a child will, at six, have made only a beginning in the learning of English. What one needs to watch in such children is the increment of progress, or increase in rate of growth. *It is how fast the child learns, or grows, rather than where he is at the moment, that counts.* Even this child of four-year-old vocabulary at age six may grow in vocabulary eighteen months in the next twelve, so that at age seven he will measure five and one-half in vocabulary age. Being still a year and one-half "retarded" in vocabulary, he will, nevertheless, have indicated accelerated growth, and will probably shortly "catch up" with his chronologic age. In fact he may eventually prove to be "gifted" in language.

In the Use of Standards, Each Child's Unique Pattern Must Be Considered. The practice in the past simply of examining the child at the moment and matching him in a Procrustean fashion with the norms is losing some ground. The emphasis on fitting the child to the expected mold is being replaced slowly by that of letting the potentialities of the child unfold in an environment rich enough to meet his needs. Therefore, *where he is in his growth at the moment means little unless it is set in the framework of where he has been and in what direction he is going.* For example, a child might compare favorably with standards at the moment, yet actually be a superior child who has lost his impetus, so that he is lagging in what should be *his* rate of growth. The fact that he has lost impetus may be of tremendous significance, and it is this fact with which we must deal, rather than with the fact that he is average for his age at the moment of measurement. Or again, a given six-year-old boy may be only as tall as the average standard of the five-year-olds of his ethnic and socio-economic group, yet he may be at the time making a perfectly satisfactory height gain. Mature height for him, measured in terms of that of his two parents, may be below the average of mature adults of his group. In other words, he is now and will continue to be a short person, and his present "retardation" in growth is not a retardation at all, but optimal development for him.

Since children differ widely both in their pattern and pace of growth our understanding of a so-called "normality" must widen. As described in Rand *et al.** we can see development traveling in channels. These authors discuss the application of the channel system to social growth with the successive steps or maturity stages of each channel having their own characteristics. In this way a child is measured by his progress along his own channel or pathway of growth.**

It is important, then, that school and other agencies dealing with children should develop devices for studying the wider background of children and for keeping cumulative records, so that studies of any given child at any given time may have the perspective lent by a knowledge of his background as well as of previous and present trends in his growth.

BOB, A NORMAL SEVEN-YEAR-OLD BOY

In order to get a clearer picture of how an understanding of growth principles may be utilized in helping a child to adjust to the demands made upon him, let us look at Bob, aged seven years and one month and in the first grade at school. In February he began showing signs of fatigue.

Since Christmas he had been absent several times, two or three days at a time, with colds. His disposition, ordinarily cheerful and cooperative, had been somewhat "prickly." He found it hard to concentrate, was "fidgety," and had been biting his nails. All these signs were particularly evident from eleven o'clock on in the morning, and lasted until the noon recess. Again, fatigue was apparent from two-thirty on in the afternoon. He had been tardy frequently in the mornings, although this was not new. It probably indicated a lack of sense of responsibility about getting himself off in the morning, or bad management on the part of his mother, or late bed hours. If due to late bed hours it might be related to his present fatigue. Mentally alert, he had learned to read quite well, but his attention shifted, and he seemed unable to hold himself to definite goals. Although he was not failing in school he definitely needed help.

What should one look for in order to understand his situation and to be able to help him? In the first place, his colds, his fatigue at the end of the school sessions, and his nervousness mean that we should know more about him physically. Is he suffering from some infection or other physical drain? What is his daily routine? What are the demands upon his energy, and what is being done to replace the energy used up? The school nurse, called in by the teacher to discuss his case, suggested a thorough physical examination and the teacher decided to visit the home in order to learn more of his routine as well as to talk with his parents about the desirability of a physical examina-

* For further discussion of the channel concept see Rand, Sweeny, and Vincent,[756] Chapter I.
** The channel idea is clearly demonstrated by the Wetzel Grid,[550, 980, 982, 983]—a device for evaluating children's growth in height and weight. It is described later in Chapter 7.

tion. In many school systems this home call would be the business of the school nurse, who would supposedly have a specialized training in home contacts. The teacher actually knows far more about each individual child, however, and if she will take the time she can give the parents a much clearer picture of the child's school situation. At the same time she can learn much from the parents which will help to explain the child to her and upon which she can build a good school program for him.

Bob's home was a brick bungalow, containing seven rooms and a recreation basement. It was situated on a quiet residential street in an above-average neighborhood where there were trees, wide lawns and several vacant, wooded lots. It was quite evident that there was ample play space, and the vigorous whoopings of a nearby game of "cops and robbers" indicated that Bob had plenty of available playmates. His mother, already informed of the visit by a note from the teacher, was at home, and proved thoroughly cooperative since she understood that both she and the teacher had a common goal, namely, Bob's welfare. Boyish as Bob was, he ran in from play when he caught sight of his teacher. Eagerly he showed off his home, of which he seemed proud. Special points of interest were his room, shared with his nine-year-old brother, the well-equipped play room in the basement, and his bicycle stall in the garage. Twin beds, carefully allotted closet and drawer space, and duplicate stalls all indicated care to give each boy a feeling of his own place in the household. There was a two-year-old brother who still occupied a nursery room. There was no evidence from Bob's relationship with either brother or with his mother that he suffered from being a middle child.

The teacher had noted that Bob's face was flushed and perspiring as he ran in from what appeared to be a strenuous game. She sensed that Bob's fatigue in school might be related to a too vigorous effort to keep up with his older brother. She, therefore, asked who his playmates were, how old they were and what games they most often played. As she suspected, they proved on the whole to be his older brother's gang, a group of strenuous boys averaging nearly two years older than Bob. He was "put to it" to keep up with them, but had enough motor ability to be accepted by them. His parents faced a difficult decision in the matter since there was no other desirable group of boys with whom he could play. Unless he suffered more physically than was apparent, it was their feeling that he should be permitted to play with this gang rather than with no one at all. Some other way of reducing his fatigue seemed preferable, if any such way could be found.

Bob was sent off to play while the teacher settled down for a chat with his mother. She explained that Bob was showing fine promise in school, was succeeding well with his reading and other academic work, but that toward the end of each morning and afternoon session he became irritable, distractible and restless. She added that his absence for so many days in the past two months because of colds and his frequent tardiness made her wonder if he were getting enough rest and if he should not have a thorough physical examination in order to check his general physical condition and any possible source of infection. The teacher suggested, too, a check on his eyes, for, although he had given no evident signs of eye strain, and could read well for his age, he seemed particularly restless during the reading period. She added that many eye defects go unnoticed until the strain of reading proves too severe a test for what seems otherwise a fairly adequate visual equipment.

Bob's mother replied to this that she was glad of the teacher's check on her own recent observation that Bob appeared overtired upon return from school each day. He had been fussy about eating lunch, and, although he dashed out eagerly to join the gang in the afternoon, he seemed drowsy and too tired to eat at dinner. She had of late tried to urge him into bed earlier but he stoutly refused to go before his older brother.

"Anything which might be interpreted as babyishness is anathema to him," said his mother.

Further analysis of the strains and demands of his day indicated that he was very hard to rouse in the morning, seemed heavy and "yawny" until after breakfast, when the prospect of school "pepped" him up. The school is six blocks distant; he frequently had to run to make it, and, as we have seen, rather often failed to arrive on time even then. An inquiry about the amount of time allowed for the important morning bowel movement revealed that his mother did not know if or when he had his daily movement. She is not to be condemned for this, since in many homes the beginning of school represents a period of increasing self-care for children who at that time take over for themselves whatever they have not already acquired of the dressing, bathing, tooth washing and bowel movement routines. With two boys to get off to school and a husband to get off to work every morning, the mother had slipped on her checking of the toilet routine. Bob's noon hour was hurried. With six blocks to walk (or run) each way, lunch to eat, and the natural urge for some out-of-door play driving him still further to hurry, the hour and a half from eleven-thirty to one o'clock was crowded. Bob's older brother, being in the third grade, did not get out until twelve o'clock. Lunch was served at twelve-fifteen. Teacher and mother agreed that there was no reason for so much rushing on Bob's part, and that, if he came straight home from school without playing he could rest fifteen to twenty minutes before eating. He should also go to bed half an hour earlier at night. This would require some "sales talk" to Bob, and the teacher agreed to undertake the task of convincing him that rest was not "sissy," but was sensible, especially for him. Just how much he was eating his mother, again, could not say, having three boys to take care of at noon, and four (including her husband) at breakfast and dinner. She was sure, however, that it was not enough, and recalled nagging him lately about eating his vegetables and drinking his milk. She promised to keep an exact record of what he ate for two or three days and to take this with her to the doctor for his guidance.

Questions about Bob's father showed a happy relationship. He was an automobile salesman and did a great deal of night and Sunday work. They lived forty-five minutes by car from his place of work. He seldom saw his children excepting at mealtime morning and night, on occasional Sundays, and in the summertime when they took a family vacation for two weeks. However, he was much interested in all of them, followed their "daily doings" closely through the mother's reports at night when he did finally get home. They minded him well, but without fear. Although his work consumed most of his time, he was not under any special strain, being reasonably sure of his job and more than average in his success in it. Their income ranged from $1800 in their worst year since marriage to $7500 at present.

Meanwhile, the teacher observed that Bob's mother allowed him to take the initiative in showing her about the house and yard. Although he was rather boisterous, and a bit "smarty," he nevertheless obeyed when spoken to. The mother seemed a little high strung, but her voice was not sharp, nor did she nag any of the children. Aside from the clear knowledge that Bob was playing too hard with a too strenuous group, that he needed more rest, and that a physical examination was desirable, the teacher felt that all was well, especially in his personal emotional life. She felt that there was nothing she could do in school hours to increase his rest without singling him out from the others. So she decided upon a quiet talk with Bob about the effect of too great fatigue upon his school work. She decided also to report to him his mother's decision and hers that he needed rest at noon and an earlier bed hour. She knew children well enough to know that he would cooperate if she could convince him that the truly manly thing to do was to face the fact that he was two years younger than his brother and, therefore, needed more sleep, especially if he wished to keep the pace of his gang in play.

Following the teacher's interview Bob's mother had a talk with his father, and together they agreed upon the wisdom of a physical examination. She took along the two days' dietary to show just what Bob had actually eaten, and she was also ready, after special observation of his routines, to answer the questions which the doctor asked about them.

The doctor asked especially about the following points, and received these answers:

What time did Bob get up in the morning? Seven o'clock.

Did he have to be wakened? Yes.

Was he rested or tired? He seemed tired.

How long did he take to get dressed? Nearly half an hour.

How long was he at the breakfast table? Twenty minutes.

What did he eat? Orange juice, toast, milk, and, if he would take it, an egg.

Did he have a bowel movement before leaving for school? In the past two days he had had one on the first day. On the second day he was late and refused to take time.

What quantity and of what character were his bowel movements? The mother did not know.

How far away was school? Six blocks.

How much time was allowed for him to make this distance? Certainly not enough. He often ran, and was not infrequently late to school.

How frequently was he absent from school? Eight days in the past two months.

What caused his absences? Mostly colds.

What grade was he in? Second half of the first grade.

Was he doing well? What was his report card like? Very satisfactory. Here the mother explained about the teacher's visit and Bob's evident fatigue in school.

Did he like school? Yes.

How much time did he have at noon? One hour and a half.

What did he do with it? Played, ate hurriedly, raced back to school. Here the mother explained the suggestions for change which she and the teacher had discussed.

What did he usually eat for lunch? What, e.g., had he eaten yesterday? Soup, a peanut butter sandwich, milk, an apple.

When was school dismissed in the afternoon? At three-thirty.

What did he do after school? Grabbed some candy or a cookie and ran out to play. (The mother described the strenuousness of his play. The doctor agreed that he could not be asked to stop playing with this gang, but urged that he be called half an hour before dinner and told to rest. He proposed as a compromise to Bob that he follow one or two of the better children's dinner hour radio or TV programs at this time.)

What did he have for dinner last night? Lamb stew, mashed potatoes, lettuce salad, bread and butter, milk, cup custard. However, Bob did not eat much of any of this, since he seemed too tired.

What time did he go to bed as a rule? Here the mother explained the situation with the older brother, and added that she and the teacher had agreed upon an earlier hour. The teacher had already talked with Bob about it, and he seemed cooperative with the new plan. At least, he had gone to bed at eight o'clock for the past two nights. As yet he apparently had not caught up with needed rest since he was still hard to waken in the morning.

The doctor's examination showed the following:

Height 50 inches and weight 53 pounds, which classified him according to the Stuart percentiles[915] as a fairly tall, slender boy. During the past year he had gained 2 inches and 2 of the approximately 5½ pounds he might have been expected to gain. When his measurements for the last three years were plotted on the Wetzel Grid the curves indicated that he had lost physique and slowed up in growth.

Eyes and ears—normal

Tonsils—normal

Heart—normal

Lungs—normal
Teeth—2 cavities
Muscle tone—fair
Posture—forward shoulders, prominent abdomen, slumped upper back—a fatigue
   posture.

As the result of the examination and the questioning, the doctor proposed the
following:

1. Seven-thirty bed hour; rest at noon. Doctor pointed out the connection between
   fatigue and lack of appetite, poor muscle tone and poor posture.
2. Increase the amount of breakfast. Explained that Bob's intake of energy was not
   equal to the outgo. Energy intake must exceed energy burned up if weight is
   to be gained and growth to occur. Bob therefore needs more food.
3. Improve quality of food as well as quantity. Add foods rich in vitamins and
   minerals. The family food is adequate but Bob needs to extend his food likes.
   Have a sandwich or some fruit ready for him in the afternoon instead of the
   candy or cookies. Too many sweets may have contributed to the carious teeth.
4. Don't discourage play with the older boys. Play with his brother and his friends
   is strenuous, but the doctor sees no reason for interfering with this play provided Bob comes in early before supper so that he will have rest before the
   meal. This rest should help to improve his appetite. He explained the situation
   to Bob, trying to make clear the connection between rest, food, and elimination on the one hand and growth and physical strength on the other.

We see in Bob a boy who, when compared to the standard for children as a whole,
is at or above the average for his birthday age in intellectual capacity, motor skills,
and social interests. Some, at least, of his accomplishments in the latter two were
achieved because of the drive to keep up with his older brother and the only play group
available to him. It is evident that he is pushing himself. The strain is evidenced in
his physical picture, since his progress in growth has not been satisfactory. His school
work as evidenced by his academic marks has not suffered as yet, but, thanks to the
alertness of his teacher, his growing inability to make the best of the school situation
has been detected and followed up.

Bob illustrates the need for everyone dealing with children to remain alert to signs
of trouble in general development. Both his mother and his teacher were aware that
all was not well; yet it took cooperation between them to set the wheels in action for
doing anything about the situation. Bob also illustrates the fact that, although his
physical measurements, his intellectual capacity, his bodily and social skills all measured "favorable" on standardized scales, only a comparison of these measurements
with his own past record revealed the fact that his growth was not progressing favorably.

EXPERIENCES TO VITALIZE CLASSWORK

1. Discuss possible sources in your community for obtaining information about children
   a. How much will it be possible to visit public schools in your community:
      To visit classes, playground and other activities?
      To talk to teachers of given children?
      To gain access to school records of a particular child?
   b. How much will it be possible to visit settlement houses, community centers,
      Sunday School classes, organized group activities such as Scouts, 4-H Clubs, etc.?
   c. How possible will it be to visit hospital clinics?
      To see the children who are being served?
      To get medical and psychologic information?
      To get home information from parents either through interviews at the clinic or
      through home visits?
   d. How possible will it be to take care of children of various ages in their homes
      and thus have an opportunity to observe children in their home setting?

2. Discuss how to get this type of information without making children or their parents self-conscious. Discuss in class how a satisfactory approach may be made to parents in order to win their good will and cooperation. Study the following rules which should govern your observations:

    a. An observation should be a fact-finding expedition only. It should never be regarded as an occasion for diagnosis of behavior.

    b. A student, while learning, is never in a position to give advice to parents, teachers or clinicians.

    c. Since the student is learning rather than serving, great care should be taken not to disturb situations or routines for children, parents, teachers or clinicians.*

    d. Before taking anyone's time (including the student's) for an observation, a careful plan should be worked out so that the student knows exactly what he is looking for.

    e. No public agency should be contacted except after official arrangement has been made by the instructor.

    f. It is imperative to maintain a professional attitude toward all facts learned about children and their families. Breach of confidence or a "gossipy" treatment of materials is highly unprofessional.

    Discuss other rules which should be followed.

3. Observe two children of the same chronologic age in junior or senior high school, one of whom is large for his age and the other of whom is small for his age—in the classroom, on the playground, and in the lunch room (if there is one).

    a. Are there physical differences other than size, e.g., do they differ in physical skills?

    b. What are the differences in ability to accomplish work?

    c. What are the differences in their behavior with other children?

    d. What are the differences in the selection of food and the amount they eat?

    e. As nearly as you can judge what are the differences in the way they feel about themselves?

    f. To what extent can these differences be attributed to sheer physical factors?

    g. Find out if you can what their twenty-four hour schedules are. Do they fit the physical and psychologic needs of each? Suggest any desirable changes.

4. Build a chart, like Fig. 10, using a keen intelligence as the central factor, in place of muscle tone. Chart possible contributing factors, as well as resultant factors.

5. Survey the Child Development literature of the past five years for case studies illustrating any of the principles of growth.

SELECTED READINGS

Gesell, A., and F. L. Ilg: The Child from Five to Ten. New York, Harper & Bros., 1946, Chs. 1 and 2.

Gray, G. W.: Human Growth. The complete physical, physiological and psychological histories of 160 boys and girls recorded by the Denver Child Research Council are yielding a clear picture of how a normal individual grows up. Scientific American, 189: 65–76, 1953.

Millard, C. V.: Child Growth and Development. Boston, D. C. Heath & Co., 1951, Part I.

Olson, W. C.: Child Development. Boston, D. C. Heath & Co., 1949.

Overstreet, H. A.: The Mature Mind. New York, W. W. Norton & Co., 1949.

Rand, W., et al.: Growth and Development of the Young Child. 5th ed., revised by M. E. Breckenridge and M. N. Murphy. Philadelphia, W. B. Saunders Co., 1953, Ch. 1.

Stolz, H. R., and L. M. Stolz: Somatic Development of Adolescent Boys. New York, The Macmillan Co., 1951, Chs. 1 and 18.

Thompson, G. C.: Child Psychology: Growth Trends and Adjustments. Boston, Houghton Mifflin Co., 1952, Ch. 1.

Zachry, C.: Emotion and Conduct in Adolescence. New York, D. Appleton-Century Co. 1940, Ch. 2.

* Bailey says: "The more carefully you study your information concerning this (or any other) youth, the more unwilling you will find yourself to 'prescribe' for him. You will feel that those who know him by daily association, perhaps from his birth, are so much better informed than you that any suggestion from you would be an impertinence."[47]

CASE STUDY OUTLINE

(To be used as a focus for your course work. To be handed in in final form near the end of the semester)

One of the best ways to make the materials of this course meaningful is to write a case study of some child you know well enough to get the necessary data. This child may be a younger brother or sister, some neighbor's child in your home town or some child you have come to know in your college town. It is best to have a child of four or five years or older, although if you are baby-sitting for a family and are able to see a younger child (one year or older) at very frequent intervals you can get much relevant material. Important are the consent of the parents and their willing cooperation in the project.

You may wish to do a case study of yourself; if so it is necessary to be as objective as possible. If you choose yourself or a sibling or a child in your home town, it is vital that you make a very careful plan for the study so that you can get the many details of information during the one or two vacations during which you will be at home.

If you choose a young child you will, of course, emphasize the details of early growth, as well as the growth which occurs between now and the end of the semester. This will require fairly frequent observations. For a younger child your main use of the case study outline in the later age levels will be by way of prediction—a "look into the future."

If you choose an older child you will carry through details into the later ages in the outline, with less detail on the earlier levels.

In such a case study as this one you are *not* a psychiatrist looking for "complexes" or "repressed" and hidden materials. Nor are you equipped to give parents advice about how to handle their children. You are, rather, a beginning student who is seeking information which will help you better to understand certain principles of child growth and development.

The parents are doing you a favor to give you any information at all and it is extremely important *not* to ask "leading" or personal questions, e.g., "Do you and your husband get along well?" "What is your family income?" "Do you go to church regularly," etc. You should not ask direct or leading questions except in such areas of developmental history as "When did he walk?" "When did he talk in sentences?" "How does he get along in school?" The best interview with a parent is one in which he takes the lead, telling what he sees as significant material. Some parents will "tell all," but you should leave blank spaces in your case write-up rather than embarrass or antagonize the parents. The same general principles hold for any interview you have with the child, a teacher, or anyone else concerned.

Begin your work on your case study immediately so that you can be gathering relevant data (in your mind and on your detailed outline) in order that each possible interview or observation can be fruitful.

The following outline is suggestive only. You may be able, either as an individual or in a class project, to build an outline which more closely follows your course progress. The principles sketched above in 2 of Experiences to Vitalize Class Work are important in your case study as well as in observation of children anywhere.

SUGGESTED OUTLINE FOR CASE STUDY

Course name and number_____

Age of child_____Sex_____

A. Family Background.

    1. What do the parents consider to be the strengths (and, if they are willing to talk about them, the weaknesses) of the child's physical and psychologic inheritance?

    2. Occupation of father_____of mother_____

       Your best guess at income level_____

    3. Body type of father_____

Body type of mother_____

Health and vitality of father_____

Health and vitality of mother_____

4. General personality of father_____

    General personality of mother_____

5. Other people living in the home_____

6. Whatever you can observe or they are willing to tell you about:
    a. Their relationships to each other.
    b. Their relationships to the child under study.
    c. His relationships to each of them.

7. What dreams (or ambitions) does the father have for the child? Does the mother have? Do they adjust these dreams to the child's actual capacities and accomplishments as these become evident?

8. If the child is an adolescent, what dreams does he have for himself? How do these fit (a) his capacities, (b) his parents' dreams?

B. The Home.

1. Is it the same one he was born into? If not, how many moves have there been and of what kind?

2. Is the space adequate for convenience and for the daily routines of eating, sleeping, bathroom activities; for being quiet or noisy, for study, play, hobbies for each member of the family? Space for outdoor play?

3. What is the general psychologic atmosphere?
    a. Happy, relaxed, perhaps untidy? Orderly, yet not comfortable and "lived-in"? Tidy to the point of discomfort?
    b. Father-centered? Mother-centered? Child-centered? Family-centered?
    c. Father-dominated? Mother-dominated? Child-dominated? Shared domination?
    d. Is the discipline strict? Permissive? Well-balanced? Kinds of occasions requiring punishment? What kind of punishment?
    e. How is the child being helped to make decisions? What kind of decisions? Are they appropriate to his age and stage of development?
    f. How is the child being helped to grow up in responsibility? Give specific instances. Are the jobs assigned fitted to his age and stage of development? How does he respond?
    g. How is the child being helped to understand the value of money? To be able to handle it?
    h. How is the child being helped to achieve self-control? How does he respond to this help?
    i. How is he being helped to learn consideration of others? How does he respond to this help?
    j. How is he being helped to learn honesty and integrity?
    k. How is he being helped to develop self-confidence? A well-balanced humility? A sound acceptance of his own strengths and limitations?
    l. Other influences on emotional and personality development.

4. What is the child's daily routine? Get details.
    a. How well does it contribute to his physical well-being? Food, elimination rest, exercise, etc.
    b. What satisfactions and fulfillments does it provide for him?
    c. What tensions and strains exist for the child in the routine?
    d. Does he appear to be well adjusted to his routine? Poorly adjusted? What makes you think so?

C. The Neighborhood.

1. Is it homogeneous or heterogeneous in race, national and religious background? What are the advantages and/or disadvantages of this to the child?

2. What is the attitude of the close neighbors to the child? What, if any, effect does this have on the child?
3. What is the space for play and for relaxed outdoor living in the near neighborhood? How much does the child (and his family) use this? What is the effect on the child's growth?
4. Kind and availability of schools, churches, shopping area? Effect of these on family and child?
5. What is the attitude of the family toward the school? Their opinion of its adequacy? Attitude toward the church (or their church) and its effect on them?
6. Your opinion of the adequacy of health protection and general health environment of the neighborhood?
7. Other neighborhood children—ages and sexes, especially of those your child sees most?

D. Circumstances of Child's Birth.
1. Have the mother tell you anything she chooses to about this; as far as her feelings and attitudes go (*do not ask questions here*), she will probably tell you.
   a. Length of pregnancy.
   b. Length of labor.
   c. Birth weight and length of child.
   d. His general appearance, how he nursed.

E. Development from Birth through Five Years.
1. Pattern of his physical growth. History of childhood diseases and effect, if any, on his growth and development.
2. Early feeding history, including attitudes toward food; sleep history; history of learning control of elimination.
3. Learning body control; head, trunk, sitting, creeping or crawling, standing, walking, more advanced body controls. Use of hands and finer motor skills. Body balance.
4. Learning language.
5. Learning sense perceptions and judgments.
6. Development of emotions; reactions and controls.
7. Development of social awarenesses and skills.
8. Development of sense of right and wrong.
9. Religious training.
10. How well (did) (has) your child accomplish(ed) his "developmental tasks" for this age period? Be specific.

F. Development from Age 6 to Pubescence.
1. Pattern of his physical growth and body balance.
2. Health history.
3. Twenty-four hour schedule including activities, meals, snacks, sleep.
4. Food habits and attitudes: Kind and approximate amounts of food, preferences and prejudices, emotional and social significance of food. Attitudes of parents toward child's eating. What role does the school play?
5. What is he learning about his physical self at home and at school (information and attitudes)?
6. Continuation of growth in areas 3 to 9 of E above.
7. Adjustment to school.
   a. If possible visit the school. Get school records, or the teacher's opinion of the adequacy of the child's academic success, his social and personal adjustments to school.
   b. What is the school like? Does it provide for all of child's needs?
   c. What is the teacher like? What do you judge to be her relationship to the child? His to her?

8. How well do you feel the child accomplished (is accomplishing) the "developmental tasks" of this period? Be specific.

G. Pubescence and Adolescence.

1. When did pubescent development begin?
2. What was the sequence and age of occurrence of bodily changes including growth in height, in weight, in genitalia and in secondary sex characteristics such as pubic hair, axillary hair, facial hair (boys); growth of breasts, age of menarche in girl; year of greatest spurt in growth, change in voice?
3. When did growth cease?
4. Was the developmental pattern appropriate according to the standards of society? If not in what way did it deviate?
5. How adequate was the child in motor strength and skills? Was he awkward? When?
6. Did he have acne? Did it bother him?
7. What was his health history during this period?
8. What were his food habits? Kinds of foods, amounts? The social and emotional significance of food for him.
9. What were his sleep habits; his daily schedule, his activities?
10. Tired easily or abounding energy?
11. How did the child feel about his physical self? Satisfied? Dissatisfied?
12. If he is (was) an early or late maturer, what effect does this seem to have (had) on his school work? Social development? Reactions to parents and teachers? Feelings about himself?
13. How does he seem to be accepting his new status as an adolescent?
    a. Is he clinging to childhood? If so, how?
    b. Is he reaching out for adulthood? If so, how?
14. Discuss his growth and adjustments in areas 3 through 9 of item E.
15. Is he accomplishing the "developmental tasks" of pubescence and adolescence? Be specific.

H. Summarize this child with your own evaluation of his general situation, his equipment for dealing with life, his reaction to life, and your idea of his probable future.

CHAPTER 2

Influences on Growth—*(PHYSICAL)*

The knowledge of growth would be meaningless without some understanding of the substances which go to make up the individual and the forces, within and without, which set the direction and pace for growth. Through knowing the factors which affect growth, adults can open the way to optimal development for children by providing satisfactory environment and guidance. In the following five chapters, therefore, we shall discuss the various influences upon growth. We shall begin with those within the child himself and proceed to those which operate through his environment. Thus, we shall discuss some of the physical factors within the child, the emotions, and such typical environmental factors as nutrition, home, school and community influences. We shall begin with heredity.

HEREDITY

The moment of conception when the parent cells fuse and when, therefore, a unique biologic pattern is fixed, is the most important moment in the life of a child. At that time a pattern for future growth and development of the individual is set. To what extent and in what direction a child's potentialities will be realized will depend upon his environment. Certain potentials may be partially or entirely repressed. A potential genius may become a moron because of a birth injury. Early rheumatic fever may injure the heart of one who otherwise would have been an outstanding athlete. Thus, these two influences of heredity and environment are so closely interlocked that one cannot be considered separately from the other.

The dynamic relationship between these two factors may be seen by the influence which a child's genetic endowment may have upon his use of the environment. For example, a musical environment may be very stimulating to a child whose pitch and time discrimination are sensitive and who is emotionally able to respond to music. On the other hand, the same environment may leave another child untouched because he lacks these qualities. Given the same environment and all other factors being constant, a child with a higher intellectual endowment will tend to exploit his environment more completely than one with smaller potential. Thus a very bright child may learn more from a meager environment than a less gifted child may learn from richer surroundings.

In view of observed facts, there is no doubt that some individuals with certain genetic combinations are more liable to certain diseases, such as tuberculosis and diabetes or certain mental diseases. An individual who springs from a family in which there is a history of tuberculosis, diabetes or certain mental diseases is not necessarily doomed to have the disease. Tuberculosis is not an hereditary disease. Rather, it is caused by the tubercle bacillus. Whether an individual acquires the disease depends upon (1) exposure to the bacillus, (2) his genetic makeup, and (3) his health and nutrition. Some people inherit a high resistance; others inherit so little resistance that they cannot be protected by the best of environments; most people fall between. Diabetes, also, is not inherited as such but a predisposition to it can be transmitted. Whether diabetes develops depends partly upon diet and partly upon the physical conditions of life.* Certain types of mental illness develop because of the impact of certain kinds of environment upon a constitutionally weak nervous system. This was indicated during World War II when the stresses and strains of warfare were too much for some of the boys and they became mentally ill. It must be remembered that, on the other hand, there are certain types of exposure to nervous strain which will eventually break down the best psychologic constitution. For example, the strains of combat flying in the war eventually produced nervous symptoms in even the best selected of the boys.

Environment includes habits of living, such as sleeping, eating, activity and adjustment to one's circumstances and to people. These factors need to be more carefully controlled for children with a family tendency toward a disease than for children from a healthy background. Children with constitutional weaknesses need particular help in recognizing their own needs and in assuming responsibility for living the kind of life compatible with their constitutions. They need also, of course, to be protected from undue fear of, or anxiety about, the disease.

How Heredity Operates. In the nucleus of the fertilized egg are found 48 units which comprise the heredity of the individual and in which lie his potentialities for development. These are the 48 chromosomes. These chromosomes are arranged in pairs, with twenty-four different kinds as to shape, size, etc. In each of these chromosomes there are a number of small substances, called genes, the bearers of heredity, which are arranged in a systematic way like beads on a string. Each gene has its own place in this chain; and each has its distinct function in inheritance.

Genes do not act independently; they cooperate one with another and with the environment to affect development. Each body characteristic, as for example, body build, requires the action of many genes. These genes affect one another, and in turn, are affected by the medium in which they exist. Genes are believed to operate in much the same fashion as enzymes in the digestive tract, namely, through influencing chemical processes. A chemical reaction is dependent not only upon the reactive substances, but

---

* Some cases of diabetes are not caused by defective genes; some are due to disease or injury of the pancreas.

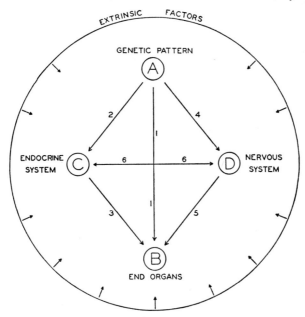

Fig. 12. Pathways through which genetic factors may influence the growth, development or "constitutional pattern" of an individual. Diagram illustrates the fact that genetic factors may influence the growth and development of the body directly (A-B) or may cause constitutional differences in the endocrine (A-C-B) or nervous system (A-D-B). Extrinsic factors, such as nutritional deficiencies or disease, may exert an influence at any time during prenatal or postnatal life. (Wilkins, L.: The Diagnosis and Treatment of Endocrine Disorders in Childhood and Adolescence. Charles C Thomas, Publisher.)

also upon the solution in which they are placed. So it is with genes. They operate by interacting (1) one with another, (2) with the cytoplasm of the cell, (3) with the chemical products of gene activity and (4) with materials obtained from the environment outside the organism. In this complex organization the alteration of one gene may so disturb the reactions within the cell that the course of development of a particular trait may be changed. Modification or defectiveness of a part of the body may be due to modification or imperfection of the genes cooperating to produce that part.* In influencing the development or constitutional pattern of an individual, genes, interacting with extrinsic factors, may have a direct effect or one through their effect upon endocrine glands or the nervous system. See Figure 12.

Environment in the Uterus May Change the Course of Development Set by the Genes. It has been stated above that the immediate environment within the body influences the action of these hereditary units. The normal course of development as set by the genes can be altered by changes in the environment of the child in the uterus.** Inadequacies in the

---

* The need for brevity here leaves much unsaid. Scheinfeld[811] is recommended as collateral reading since he discusses heredity from a practical point of view in a manner easily understood.
** See Montagu, M. F. A.[675]

maternal diet may alter the course of development. Also, a child whose mother has had German measles during the first six to ten weeks of pregnancy is likely to have congenital defects.* The virus evidently affects the young developing tissues of the brain, eyes, ear or heart. Such malformations, however, are rare.

Yet another example is that of the result of an incompatibility of an inherited factor in the blood of the mother and child called the Rh factors.** Some people inherit Rh factors from both parents; some from one parent and some inherit none. If a mother who has no Rh factor (Rh negative) has a baby who has the Rh factors (Rh positive), the substance from the baby stimulates the formation of a substance in the mother which in time may act upon the blood cells of the baby and prevent them from distributing oxygen as they should.† The child is, therefore, deprived of sufficient oxygen and thus development may be altered. Since the brain is especially sensitive to the lack of oxygen, mental deficiency might result if this should happen when the brain is in a critical stage of development.‡[675]

A discussion of how the genes and their immediate environment in the cells interact, however, is beyond the scope of this book.§ We merely call attention to the fact that environment affects development even in the earliest stages of growth.

How the Child Receives His Inheritance. The child receives from his parents a uniquely new combination of parental genes, a combination of the genes which the parents themselves received when they were conceived (see Fig. 13). These genes are not changed by alterations in the body cells of the parents. The fact that a father has several college degrees in itself does not affect the inherited mental capacity of his children. A mother who has been crippled by infantile paralysis will not necessarily produce crippled children. Becoming proficient in playing a musical instrument will not assure a parent that he will have a child with exceptional ability in music. One does not pass on an acquired appreciation of the beauties of nature or art through the germ cells.

Figure 13 shows that the child receives forty-eight chromosomes, half from each of his parents. The particular twenty-four chromosomes which he receives from either parent may come from either or both grandparents on that side of the family. The child, therefore, may have certain traits in common with one or both of his parents; in others he may resemble one of his

* For references to studies see Toverud, Stearns and Macy.[954]

** Rh factors are substances in the blood so named because they were first discovered in the blood of a rhesus monkey. Later they were found to be present in the blood of 85 per cent of tested white people.[743]

† This seldom happens to a first child. Even though about one in every twelve pregnancies involves an Rh-negative mother and an Rh-positive baby the Rh disease (erythroblastosis fetalis) has been found to appear in no more than about one in every 150 to 200 full-term deliveries.[811] With present knowledge and safeguards which can be taken an Rh-negative woman and an Rh-positive man need not hesitate to marry and have children.

‡ Two recent studies of infants recovering without motor nerve damage from erythroblastosis fetalis[224, 343] indicate that impairment of intelligence is slight. In one study the I.Q. was 11.8 and the other 6.13 lower than their unaffected siblings.

§ Students are referred to a discussion of the action of genes by Stern.[895]

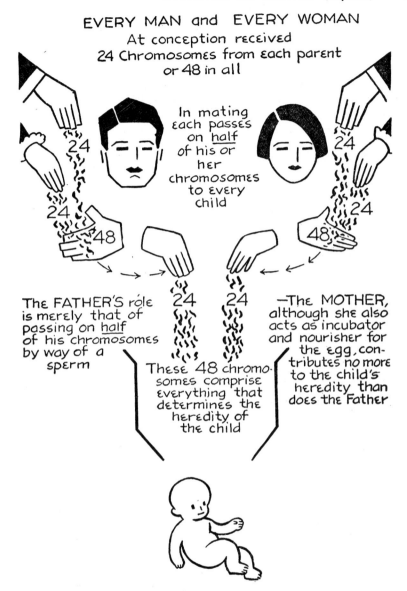

EVERY MAN and EVERY WOMAN
At conception received
24 Chromosomes from each parent
or 48 in all

In mating
each passes
on half
of his or
her
chromosomes
to every
child

24
24
48
24
24
48

24   24

The FATHER'S role
is merely that of
passing on half
of his chromosomes
by way of a
sperm

These 48 chromosomes comprise
everything that
determines the
heredity of
the child

—The MOTHER,
although she also
acts as incubator
and nourisher for
the egg, contributes no more
to the child's
heredity than
does the Father

Fig. 13. The heredity process. (Scheinfeld: The New You and Heredity. Philadelphia, J. B. Lippincott Co., 1950, p. 10.)

grandparents or he may be different from his immediate family. What he is like depends upon the particular assortment of chromosomes he receives. Because of the numerous possibilities of chromosome combinations it is not surprising that children of the same family are different, that one sister may be dark while another is blonde; that a brother may have curly hair while his sister's hair is straight. Only in the case of identical twins do children have the same genetic constitution and are therefore genetically alike.

The matched chromosomes contain a series of genes. Each gene in one of a pair of chromosomes is paired with a gene in the other chromosome. These genes perform the same function either in a similar or dissimilar manner. If the genes in a pair are similar in their performance the characteristic influenced by them will appear, provided no other pair of genes interferes. If they are dissimilar the different influences of the two genes may blend to produce an intermediate characteristic or one gene may conceal the effect of the other. A stronger gene, which produces a characteristic in the presence of another gene, is said to be dominant; the concealed one, recessive. This recessive factor remains intact and may be passed on to a child in the next generation. If in the succeeding generation this recessive is paired with a like recessive, its influence will become evident.*

The particular combination of genes which a child receives is merely a matter of chance. There is no high degree of certainty, therefore, in predicting the characteristics of a child from knowledge of the family type. There is more certainty in predicting defects provided the nature of the transmission of the particular defect is known and a careful study of the family history is made.** The hereditary basis of many human characteristics† is known and new knowledge is being added rapidly. The type of inheritance discussed above is called Mendelian after Mendel, who discovered it.

Some characteristics are associated with the sex of an individual, namely the sex-linked, sex-controlled, and sex-limited characters. Sex-linked characters—for example, color blindness and hemophilia—are produced by genes carried by the chromosomes responsible for determining sex. Such characters appear more often in men than in women.‡ They rarely appear in both father and son. They are transmitted from a man through his daughter to some of her sons. According to the law of averages there is a fifty-fifty chance that a grandson (daughter's son) of a man having hemophilia or color blindness would have this characteristic, but none of his sons' sons would have it. In a large number of cases this ratio would be true, but it does not necessarily hold in a single family. For example, if a color-blind man has two grandsons (daughter's sons), the grandsons may be (1) both color-

* The probability of the appearance of a dominant or recessive trait in a family that carries that trait can be determined mathematically. See Stern,[895] Snyder.[873]

** Services for analyzing pedigrees are available in many places. Individuals can be given information regarding the possibility and probability of the appearance of certain undesirable traits in their children. For a discussion of techniques used in analyzing hereditary characters in man see Stern,[895] Snyder.[873] Scheinfeld[811] gives "forecast" tables for transmitting defects, diseases or abnormalities to a child.

† Genes may influence development directly or indirectly, as stated before. A characteristic may be produced by the presence or absence of one or more genes, as we have pointed out. On the other hand genes may affect development indirectly by influencing the pattern of endocrine balance or by influencing metabolic processes. There is a recent concept of a partial genetic block which involves an inherited trait characterized by a reduction in the ability of an organism to carry out specific steps in metabolism. This condition may increase the body's need for some nutritional factor or factors and may explain to a considerable degree why each individual possesses a characteristic and distinctive metabolic pattern.[995]

‡ Color blindness, for example, occurs in about 5 to 9 per cent in males and is about twenty times as rare in females. Hemophilia is practically unknown in women.[895]

blind, (2) both normal or (3) one color-blind and one normal. Sex-controlled characters are those which represent different expressions of the same genes in the two sexes. Examples can be cited such as the differences in voice changes in boys and girls at adolescence, which are mediated through the sex hormones, and baldness with its higher frequency in males. Sex-limited characteristics are those capable of expression in one sex but not in the other. Among these might be listed the secondary sex characteristics which are controlled by the secretion of endocrine glands.

Characteristics Influenced by Heredity.   As has been said before, heredity and environment cannot be separated. However, there are gradations in the relative influence of the two factors. Certain characteristics can be attributed to heredity almost exclusively. In others there is a strong environmental component. Yet again, others can be attributed primarily to heredity in one set of circumstances and to environment in another.

Sex of the child is basically determined by the genes of a special pair of chromosomes. In the female the two chromosomes are alike (XX); in the male they are different (XY). Every ovum that is ready to be fertilized contains one X. Some sperms contain X; some sperms contain Y. If an X-bearing sperm fertilizes the ovum, the new organism will be a girl. If a Y-bearing sperm fertilizes the ovum, the new organism will be a boy. It is, therefore, the father who unknowingly determines whether his child will be a girl or a boy. Sex determination is a matter of balance between these sex genes carried in the X chromosome and sex-influencing genes that are distributed among the other chromosomes. The genes outside the sex chromosomes are slanted in the direction of maleness; the genes in the X chromosome are slanted in the direction of femaleness. In the case of the fertilized ovum with only one X chromosome the pull is toward the development of a male; in the case of the fertilized ovum with two X chromosomes, the pull is toward the development of a female. (See Figure 14.) Sometimes this sex balance is upset by defective, weakened or injured genes in which case defective sexing results.

The characteristics which are accepted as due almost exclusively to heredity are color of eyes and hair, blood types, form of features, structure of body and many physical peculiarities. Differences in health and vigor, mentality, behavior, susceptibility and immunity to various diseases including dental caries, color of skin, stoutness or slenderness are considered to be due either to a goodly portion of both or a relatively small dose of heredity and a large dose of environment. They have been found to be the traits more readily affected by their surroundings than those enumerated as due almost exclusively to heredity. While we never inherit criminality as a full-fledged behavior pattern, life patterns are set by heredity that help to determine whether behavior will be "social" or "anti-social." Some people become criminals not because of a particularly bad environment, but because of internal instabilities that prevent a person from making a satisfactory adjustment to the requirements of life. Most criminality, however, is thought to be environmentally determined. Most diseases, like tuberculosis, have a genetic component of susceptibility, and a large nongenetic component in-

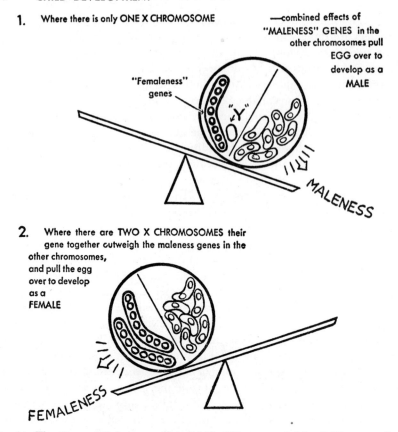

1. Where there is only ONE X CHROMOSOME

—combined effects of "MALENESS" GENES in the other chromosomes pull EGG over to develop as a MALE

"Femaleness" genes

MALENESS

2. Where there are TWO X CHROMOSOMES their gene together outweigh the maleness genes in the other chromosomes, and pull the egg over to develop as a FEMALE

FEMALENESS

Fig. 14. The "sex-gene" balance. (Scheinfeld, "Women and Men," Harcourt, Brace and Co.)

volving environmental factors. The fact that a child can be immune to diphtheria because he is born that way, as some children are, or because he has been immunized by toxoid, illustrates the fact that the same characteristic in different people may be due to genetic or to environmental force. Another example is feeble-mindedness, which can be inherited, or result from a birth injury or early childhood disease.

Effect of Heredity upon Intelligence. There have been many studies of the effect of heredity and of environment upon the development of intelligence and personality. Studies[700,863] of pairs of identical twins reared separately, and of identical twins reared together, as contrasted to pairs of fraternal (nonidentical) twins reared together have led to the conclusion that environment does modify those characteristics described as intelligence, as personality, and as educational achievement.

In summarizing the studies on intelligence, Jersild[475] says (p. 555): "It appears that resemblance between 'identical' twins who have been reared apart is likely to be higher than that between ordinary brothers and sisters reared in the same home." This indicates that the factor of inheritance in intelligence is of considerable importance. Studies of the correlation between the intelligence of foster parents and adopted children indicate that a good home environment can help a child to make the best of whatever intelligence potential he has. One important study[863] confirms the long-accepted clinical opinion that emotional warmth and security are of great importance in developing the best of the intellectual potential in own as well as in adopted children.

Environment probably cannot, however, change this potential by more than a certain amount in either a good or a bad direction.[363, 695a, 722, 863] It appears that as far as intelligence is concerned heredity seems to set the stage for the major level of intelligence.* An idiot cannot be made normal, although his functioning level can be improved. A low normal child cannot be trained into a genius. The greatest I.Q. gains recorded in any study are in the neighborhood of 20 to 30 points. This amount is of great significance since, it can mean all the difference between successful functioning in life and failure. But if one sets these changes in terms of 100 I.Q. as average, even a change of 30 points still leaves 70 points which heredity claims for its own.

Effect of Heredity upon Personality and Behavior. The extent to which personality and behavior are determined by inheritance as contrasted to environment has been the subject of extended debate and research. It becomes evident that both are important; the basic differences of opinion center around which is the more important.

Heredity has been proved to be of significant importance in many studies. It seems evident that heredity may influence personality and behavior through its effect upon the metabolic processes of the body since the genes can be thought of as potent physicochemical activators. Williams,[994] a biochemist, states that man inherits a distinct "metabolic personality" which can affect almost every aspect of behavior and social relationships.

The personality of an individual can be viewed as the resultant of the interaction of this "metabolic personality" with the psychologic, social and cultural forces about him. That environmental forces are potent in the formation of personality is evident in a number of studies. For example, studies of the inheritance of mental disease[895, 873] reveal a situation very much like that in physical disease. A potential vulnerability to given mental illnesses may be inherited, but whether or not any given offspring will develop the disease will depend upon the type of his life experiences.

Studies of identical twins[700, 841] are generally interpreted as indicating that hereditary-constitutional factors are of considerable, if not of predominant importance in determining the general direction or core of personality pattern. There is not such clear agreement about the development of specific personality traits. The tendency on the part of the growing child to show himself as a certain kind of person and then, in spite of rather marked environmental changes, to be true to this pattern as time goes on has been corroborated in several types of studies. In summarizing these studies, Jersild[475] notes that this persistence of personality characteristics is an important fact whether

* See Gates,[340] Penrose.[722]

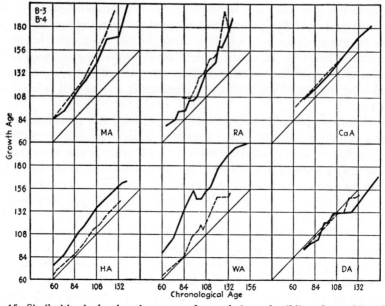

Fig. 15. Similarities in level and pattern of growth in male siblings born thirty-three months apart.

MA..Mental Age   HA..Height Age   RA..Reading Age
WA..Weight Age   CaA..Carpal Age   DA..Dental Age

(From Olson, W. C., and B. O. Hughes: Growth of the Child as a Whole in Barker, R. G., J. S. Kounin and H. F. Wright: Child Behavior and Development. McGraw-Hill Book Co., Inc., New York, 1943, p. 207.)

it is attributable to gene-heredity or stems from environmental factors which affect the child in very early life.

Martin and Stendler[630] have also called attention to this persistence of personality trend and have discussed it as a possible constitutional difference in emotionality. Their conclusion, after careful review of the literature agrees with that of many writers, namely, that:[630, p. 108] "It is not really the physical characteristic alone that determines that the child shall be dominant or assertive or easy-going. It is the significance and value which his society places upon that physical characteristic which become the crucial determinant." This social-cultural influence upon personality development has been emphasized by many other writers[222, 631] in recent years.

Thus we see in the nature-nurture discussions differences in emphasis but general agreement that gene inheritance, the early family environment, and the social-cultural impact all have a part to play in determining the pattern and direction in which personality develops.

Implications for Child Development. Earlier we discussed the importance of recognizing individual differences in children in planning for them as individuals and in groups. In this chapter we have seen that the interplay of heredity and environment produces these differences. A look at heredity offers us one explanation for children's selective response to their environment. All children have certain needs for growth. All children do

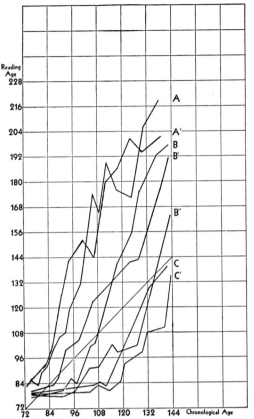

Fig. 16. Growth curves showing familial resemblance in Reading Age for children of three families. Compare A with A′, B, B′ and B″, and C with C′. (From Olson, W. C., and B. O. Hughes: Concepts of Growth—Their Significance to Teachers. Child. Educ., Oct., 1944, p. 8.)

not meet these needs in the same way. Children will differ in the kinds and amounts of food they need for optimal growth. They will differ in sleep and activity requirements and in sensitivity to emotional stimuli. There can, therefore, be no program which is standardized in detail for all children in the home or school. It is to be remembered that children in the same family do not generally have exactly the same genetic makeup, so their response to the home environment will differ. Also the environment for each child in the family will be somewhat different, either because of time and the changes which come with it, or because of differences in relationships.

If the parent has knowledge of the family background with its assets and liabilities, this knowledge may allay unnecessary fears on the one hand, and give a realistic approach to possible difficulties on the other. Knowledge of possible potentialities will help parents to plan intelligently for their children.

Checking on the hereditary ledger should not result in a laissez-faire policy. It should give one a basis on which to operate. Environment is a strong

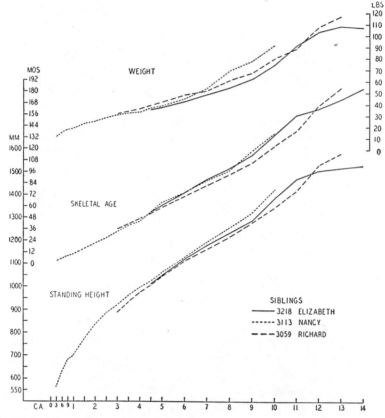

Fig. 17. Standing height, weight and skeletal age of three siblings, No. 3218, No. 3113, and No. 3059. (Simmons and Greulich: Jour. of Pediatrics Vol. 22, 1943.)

factor to be remembered. As Todd once said, "The adult physical pattern is the outcome of growth along lines determined by heredity but enhanced, dwarfed, warped, or mutilated in its expression by the influence of environment in the adventure of life."[948] The same can be said for psychologic growth.

Growth Patterns in Families Reflect the Interaction of Heredity and Environment. Various longitudinal growth studies* provide evidence that children of the same family tend to show a notable similarity in their patterns of growth. Figure 15 shows the similarities in the levels and growth pattern in mental age, reading age, carpal age, height age, weight age and dental age of two brothers born thirty-three months apart. The authors call attention to the striking dip in weight near eight years of age for both boys.

Olson and Hughes[707] have studied the growth curves in reading for forty-six pairs of siblings. The growth curves in Figure 16 are samples of sibling curves which represent high, intermediate and low achievement. A and A'

* Studies at the University of Michigan, Fels Institute for Research, and Brush Foundation.

are brothers born twenty-five months apart. B, B' and B" are three brothers born at intervals of twenty-seven and twenty-five months and C and C' are brothers born at an interval of thirty-six months apart. Their reading ages are plotted against their chronologic ages. The rate and level of achievement for A and A' and C and C' are strikingly similar. B and B' cling together but B" drops behind for several years. However, he is approaching them toward the end of the record.

In physical growth there also is evidence of similarities in families. Similar growth patterns in height,[103] in bone development[773] and in tooth decay,[535] and similar speed of maturing[368, 926, 469] have been seen in families. There are slow-maturing and fast-maturing families. Simmons and Greulich[859] contrast two sets of brothers and sisters, one illustrating an early-maturing pattern and one a late-maturing pattern. An early-maturing pattern* is reproduced here in Figure 17.

Knowing the father and mother of a child may help in the interpretation of his health status and growth. There are some children who, in spite of the best environments, are underweight, perhaps have poor muscular tone or are just "not robust." When such a child is seen with his parents he may be recognized as a "chip off the old block."**

Members of a family may have different as well as similar patterns of growth. Such differences are not evidence against the force of heredity but rather in favor of the differences in the genetic backgrounds of the parent.

MATURATION

Behavior is possible only because a child has a body with its bony framework, its muscles, its vital organs, its nervous system. Only as these organs and systems develop and become increasingly mature in structure and function can higher and higher levels of behavior become possible. The relationship of maturation of the nervous system to learning is particularly close. Hidden deep in the nervous system, yet vital for capacity to learn, is the growth and maturing of the nervous system itself. Its effect upon learning has occupied much space in the literature.

There are also within the child powerful inner forces which preserve the balance of the total growth pattern and which regulate the direction of the growth trend. These are forces which produce the so-called "readiness" to learn and to act.

Learning Easier When Children Are "Ready." There are many studies which indicate that most forms of learning cannot take place until children are "ready" both in general bodily development of muscles, nerves, and physical proportions, and in interest and willingness to learn. Many of these studies in the child development field† are in motor learnings, although

* Evidence of early maturation: E menstruated at ten years, five months; R had his prepuberal spurt of growth before twelve years; N had marked increase in rate of growth before ten years of age.

** For further discussion see Reynolds and Sontag.[778]

† For an excellent discussion of maturation in behavior see McGraw,[615, 616] Olson,[706] Thompson,[941] Rand et al.[756]

some concern the learning of language, of academic skills and of social skills.

In general the evidence from these studies indicates that until a child has the neural readiness to learn, training in any particular activity is useless and may even establish negative feelings toward the activity which will retard later learning. When he is "ready" in the neural sense, he usually becomes psychologically ready and displays this fact by showing an interest in the activity for which he is ready. At this point he will benefit greatly from practice and teaching in the activity; he will, in fact, be eager to learn and will often practice the newly developing skill assiduously.

Environmental Opportunity Also Important. Deprivations of opportunity to learn what the child may, by maturation, be ready to learn, require further consideration. It is one thing to force a child beyond his natural capacity. We have seen that, in certain areas, this can be done, but without very lasting results and without any marked superiority over the skills other children can achieve with much less effort a short time later. We must not come to the conclusion, however, that children will learn without teaching whenever they are ready. Sterile environments and restrictions upon normal learning experiences may prove detrimental to learning. William James insisted as early as 1890 that, unless one strikes in education "when the iron is hot," the urge to learn any given skill may cool, with the result that extra effort and training will be necessary later. There are a number of experiments in the field of child development to corroborate or to refute this.*

Dennis[232] offers a study of seven months of restricted environment for a pair of infants. These babies, in spite of the lack of specific opportunity to learn, seemed to develop in most motor capacities according to the normal standards. This seemed true of the social development as well, since, in spite of a "dead pan" approach by the attendants, these babies laughed and cooed and made "social" advances. Dennis concludes that the impulse to grow is strong, that behavior mechanisms mature, and that these children, in spite of lack of encouragement, found means of exercising their abilities.

Benezet[85] tried postponing many of the formal operations in arithmetic until the sixth or seventh grades, far beyond the grade in which they are now usually taught. These fundamentals were readily mastered when presented at the later age level. This recalls to mind the position which educators such as Dewey took early in the century, when they maintained that, if one waited for maturational development to occur, learning could be done with far less waste of effort. Several educational groups tried keeping children out of the formal school room until they were ten or twelve years old, then found that the basic fundamentals of the tool subjects (reading, writing, arithmetic) could be learned in two or three years instead of the usual eight grades. Meanwhile, it was maintained, the children had the extra five or six years for

* Thompson[941] has a particularly fine summary of this in his chapter on Maturation: a Basic Process in Psychological Development.

physical development and free social learnings. Many of the maturation studies would lead us to review this idea favorably again, since they seem to indicate that learning can be accomplished with less effort if somewhat delayed.

A number of factors, however, need to be considered. One of the reasons for the failure of the early educational experiments, which kept children from school work until ten or twelve, was that most children in our culture do go to school at five or six. Children of eight or ten who cannot read or write or add at all develop feelings of inferiority in the face of the mass of children who can. Unless we can keep all children from reading until a later age, or unless we can keep the children who cannot read isolated from those who can, the ones who cannot seem to feel different and less adequate. This sometimes leads to emotional blockings which prevent learning at the desired speed, once the child is given lessons.

It might be possible to consider the idea of subjecting no child to academic learnings until he is ten or twelve. This has been seriously considered earlier in our United States educational history. However, in modern living, with little opportunity for constructive work available as it once was in normal family activities, children would, without school activities, be too long delaying one of life's most valuable lessons, namely, learning how to work. Particularly in cities, where constructive play opportunities are likely to be limited, children might, as they enter the gang age and find an urgent need for group activities, develop delinquent behavior. It seems better to have them spending an appreciable amount of their waking time under some sort of supervision. This seems best offered through school programs in the winter and camp or playground opportunities in the summer. Only time can tell whether further controlled studies will suggest a universal change in early elementary school programs.

ENDOCRINES AND THEIR RELATION TO GROWTH

Do Glands Affect Growth and Personality?   Knowledge of the effect of the endocrines upon health and development is increasing rapidly. With this increase in knowledge it is possible to differentiate more clearly between fact and fallacy, to know that one is not entirely the victim of his glands except in rare cases and that education or training of character and personality is not futile. While the endocrine glands do have a definite effect upon the development of a child physically, mentally and emotionally, the effect is one which not only leaves room for training, but also is subject to some degree of medical control. People who expect to work with children will profit by some knowledge of the effects of these glands

What the Glands Are and How They Function in General.   The endocrine, or ductless, glands are widely distributed throughout the body and differ from each other in their structure and in the nature of their secretions. The glands and organs which are known to have endocrine function are the pituitary, thyroid, parathyroids, adrenals, pancreas, stomach and intes-

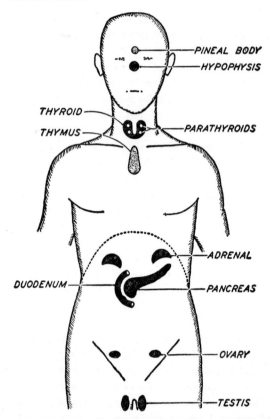

PINEAL BODY
HYPOPHYSIS
THYROID
THYMUS
PARATHYROIDS
ADRENAL
DUODENUM
PANCREAS
OVARY
TESTIS

Fig. 18. Locations of the glands of internal secretion. It is uncertain whether the pineal body or thymus are endocrine glands. The liver (perhaps a gland of internal secretion) and the stomach (which secretes gastrin into the blood) are not shown. (Carlson-Johnson: The Machinery of the Body, The University of Chicago Press.)

tines,* ovaries and testes. At present there is no final proof that the thymus and the pineal body have endocrine functions.[444]

The endocrine glands affect health and development through the secretion of complicated chemical substances, called hormones, which are liberated directly into the blood stream (hence the term "ductless") and are carried to all parts of the body where they have special functions of initiating, regulating and controlling some of the activities of organs and tissues. Although the amount of the secretions of these glands may be almost inconceivably small, they have incredible potency.**

The functions of these hormones are widely diversified. They range anywhere from influencing the rate and pattern of growth and maturation to regulating the amount of water excreted by the kidneys. They even regulate one another. The activity of one gland is affected by the secretion of another,

* Hormones of the gastro-intestinal tract will not be discussed since their effects are localized in the digestive tract.
** Normally the body uses about one-fourth to one-third of a milligram of thyroxin per day although its influence is great.[444]

and thus the performance of one gland reflects the activity of another. This is nicely demonstrated, as will be shown later, in the relationship between the activity of the pituitary gland and the adrenals and gonads.

Differences in the amount of hormone secreted and differences in the response to these substances produce diverse patterns of bodily function and development. An individual may have too little, too much, or a normal amount of a particular hormone. Thus, there is a possibility of three functional patterns being produced by each hormone. In the case of the pituitary, too little growth hormone may produce dwarfism; too much may result in gigantism; a normal level of secretion will make for normal growth. Just how far the differences in growth within the range of normality can be attributed to differences in endocrine function cannot be determined at present.

Thyroid. The thyroid gland, consisting of two lobes connected by a narrow strip, is situated in the front of the neck and secretes a hormone which regulates the rate of oxidation in the body and, therefore, is related to cellular activity. The activity of the thyroid influences the rate of growth, the development of the bones, the nervous system, circulation, muscles and, in conjunction with pituitary and gonads, the functioning of the reproductive organs. It also affects the rate at which food stuffs are utilized for body maintenance and growth.

A decrease in the thyroid function, called *hypo*thyroidism, results in a decrease of tissue activity. When the thyroid deficiency existed before birth it is called cretinism.* In this condition growth is retarded and bodily proportions remain infantile. Bone development is retarded. Dentition is delayed. Sexual maturation is delayed or does not take place at all. The muscles of cretins are flaccid and the maladjustments of the neuromuscular system are evidenced by marked apathy, defective speech, clumsy gait and incontinence. The skin is thick and dry; the hair is sparse; the nails are thin and brittle. The tongue is large and protruding. The cretin is pale and anemic, has a low basal metabolic rate and a lowered body temperature. In most cases intelligence is seriously retarded and attention is dulled. Movements are slow and awkward. The general impression is that of one with radically retarded intellectual ability.

If the administration of thyroxin is begun early in infancy and continued uninterruptedly, the chances for approximately normal physical growth and development are good. Mental development, however, is not so satisfactory. It usually will remain somewhat retarded probably because of congenital brain defect or damage done to the brain during embryonic life and early infancy due to hormonal deficiency.**

When the deficiency in thyroid hormone is less severe, naturally the signs will also be less severe in degree. Age at the beginning of the deficiency and its degree and duration will influence the manner in which it is manifested.

Johnston[484] states that some degree of hypothyroidism is fairly common

---

* Cretinism is not to be confused with mongolism, which is not of endocrine origin.
** For follow-up studies of congenital hypothyroids see Radwin et al.[754] and Topper.[951]

around the onset of sexual maturity.* The symptoms which he has noted have been delay in growth and development, mental retardation, fatigue and menstrual disorders. Many of his patients with hypothyroidism have been referred to him because of unsatisfactory progress in school. After treatment an increased attention span has been noted. It would be wise to check the functioning of the thyroid gland in adolescents of the so-called lazy group.

An excess in thyroid function called *hyper*thyroidism is characterized by excessive movement and emotional instability, trembling, increased activity of the circulatory system and stary eyes. It is rarely found in childhood but more likely to appear at the onset of pubescence.**

Simple, endemic goiter, an enlargement of the gland, occurs in childhood and adolescence. Usually there is no evidence of disturbed thyroid function but occasionally a child with a goiter will have mild hypothyroidism.[993] This type is a deficiency disease generally recognized as being caused by a lack of iodine. Its incidence is relatively high in certain regions of the world. In North America such regions are found in the basin of the St. Lawrence River and the Great Lakes, in the Pacific Northwest and the great plains. In these areas the iodine content of the water and soil is so low that some source of iodine other than food and water has to be found to satisfy the body's need for this substance. Michigan, which is one of the states in such a region, at one time had a high percentage of school children with goiters. A survey of school children in four counties in Michigan in 1924 showed that 47.2 per cent had enlarged thyroids. Iodized salt was introduced throughout the state accompanied by an educational program. A resurvey in 1951 indicated the success of such a program by showing that the incidence of enlarged thyroids had been reduced to 1.4 per cent.[14]

The Council on Foods of the American Medical Association states that the prevention of goiter is a nutritional problem and that table salt containing not more than 1 part iodides per 5000 parts of salt may be considered as prophylactic. It maintains that iodine deficiency and the prevention of goiter are an educational problem while cure is a medical one.

Parathyroids. The parathyroids, four in number, are small glands adjacent to the thyroid gland. Their secretion acts as a homeostatic mechanism for maintaining levels of calcium and phosphorus in the blood which are necessary for regular tissue activity.[926] Indirectly through its effect upon calcium metabolism this hormone plays a role in the maintenance of the integrity of the structure of bone, regulation of neuromuscular activity, in the conduction of heart impulses, in the coagulation of blood and in the permeability of cellular membranes. Through its regulatory effect upon the availability of phosphorus it can influence body tissues, many enzyme systems and the regulation of acid-base balance in the body. The parathyroid secretion ebbs and flows according to physiologic needs. When hormonal production is out of keeping with physiologic needs, which rarely occurs in

* The high incidence may be due in part to the fact that the observations were made in Michigan, an endemic goiter area.
** For a complete discussion of thyroid disorders see Wilkins.[993]

children, certain symptoms are noted. Underactivity may result in tetany, an abnormally increased reactivity of the nervous system to stimuli. Overactivity leads to decreased neuromuscular irritability so that the muscles of the body are less responsive to stimuli. Demineralization of bone may occur, resulting in spontaneous fractures because of bone fragility.

Pancreas.   The pancreas is a gland of both external and internal secretion. It is a part of the digestive tract in that it secretes and pours through a duct into the intestine a substance necessary for the digestion of foods. In addition, scattered throughout the gland, are clusters of cells (known as the islets of Langerhans) producing a secretion which is poured directly into the blood and which regulates the use of sugar by the body. The hormone produced is called insulin. When inadequate amounts of insulin are produced, carbohydrate metabolism is disturbed. There is a rise in blood sugar, sugar appears in the urine, and the condition known as diabetes mellitus results. This condition can be treated by regulated doses of insulin.

Adrenal Glands.   The adrenals are paired organs located on top of the kidneys. They consist of two parts: the cortex (outer portion) and the medulla (inner portion), which differ in their embryonic origin and in their functions. The cortex is formed from the same embryonic tissue as the reproductive organs. The medulla has its origin in common with that of the sympathetic nervous system.

The cortex secretes a number of hormones which can be separated into three types, namely, those which (1) influence the metabolism of salts and water, (2) influence sugar, fat and protein metabolism, and (3) induce pubic and axillary hair and acne.[926] These hormones, therefore, affect development, play an essential role in the body's homeostatic mechanisms and in muscle fatigue, and also aid in the body's adaptation to stress and strain.*

The androgens of the adrenals, which induce the development of sexual hair, unlike the other adrenal hormones, do not generally begin to be secreted in significant amounts before the eighth or tenth year.[926] Thereafter their secretion increases steadily. In both boys and girls these hormones are responsible for the accelerated growth and muscular development which occur in adolescence.[993] Without a sufficient amount of these androgens girls fail to develop pubic and axillary hair and acne. In boys the androgens in the testes can substitute for adrenal androgens in producing these developmental changes. Disturbances of an adrenal cortex origin are relatively uncommon in children.**

The secretion of the medulla, called epinephrine, plays a role in aiding the body to adapt to sudden stress. On the one hand it causes the release of ACTH from the pituitary gland which in turn stimulates the secretion of hormones of the cortex.[993] It also reinforces the sympathetic nervous system by releasing sugar from the glycogen stored in the liver, thus preventing fatigue of heart and skeletal muscles, dilating air passages in the lungs so

* See Selye.[833, 834]
** See Talbot et al.[926] and Wilkins[993] for greater detail regarding the effects of adrenal androgens upon development and various adrenal disorders.

that more oxygen may be available, and increasing blood supply to the muscles. Thus the body is made ready for vigorous physical action under fear, anger and other emotions. (See Chapter 3.)

Sex Glands or Gonads. The sex glands consist of the testes in the male and the ovaries in the female. These glands produce the germ cells plus internal secretions, and thus play a dual role in influencing the growth and development of the individual. The male sex hormones* and the female sex hormones are responsible for bringing about changes characteristic of pubescence. The male hormones stimulate the growth and development of the male genital organs and the secondary sex characteristics, including growth of the beard and deepening of the voice. Secretion of the male hormone has no cyclic variations. The ovarian hormones, in the girl, stimulate the growth of the breasts, the uterus, fallopian tubes, the vagina, are responsible for menstruation, and provide an environment suitable for growth of fertilized ova. Unlike the male, the female hormones are secreted in a periodic cycle, commonly termed the menstrual cycle.**

With the development of the gonads and the accompanying increased liberation of the sex hormones into the blood stream, changes in the quality and amount of sex behavior may be expected. † The many physiologic changes in boys and girls due to gonadal development have many accompanying psychologic changes, which will be discussed later.

The presence of a sufficient quantity of these sex hormones is necessary to stop growth in height at the proper time. If the testes and ovaries mature early and produce their secretions too soon, growth is prematurely arrested, and the child is abnormally short at maturity. ‡ Excessive secretion in early childhood produces precocious puberty. If, however, adequate production of the sex hormones is unduly delayed, growth, especially that of the arms and legs, continues longer than would be expected, and the individual becomes quite tall with disproportionately long arms and legs. The development of the sex organs and the appearance of the secondary sex characteristics are also delayed.

Studies of the excretion§ of sex hormones have indicated that boys and girls have both estrogen and androgens in their bodies and that the absolute and relative amounts vary with age. §§ Small, about equal amounts of estrogen are found in the urine of both sexes until around ten years of age when the estrogen increases rapidly in girls but remains much the same as formerly

---

* Male sex hormones are called androgens; female sex hormones are estrogen and progesterone.

** For a discussion of the function of hormones in producing the periodic changes including menstruation see Talbot et al.[926]

† It would seem that any relationship between the level of gonadal secretions and the pattern of sexual behavior of preadolescents and adolescents is not simple and direct.[529] Sexual behavior is a resultant of a number of factors, physiologic, psychologic and sociologic, among which learning and experience in a particular culture are important.

‡ Shortness is not always due to an endocrine disturbance.

§ Excretion of these hormones in the urine was studied because of the difficulty in devising methods to ascertain the small amount in the blood.

§§ Probably these hormones come from the adrenals instead of the sex glands during preadolescence.[993]

in boys.[687] Similar amounts of androgens are also found in boys and girls until later, in the middle teens when they begin to increase more markedly for boys than girls.[251] Thus during pubescence and later adolescence a marked sex difference in these secretions becomes apparent. This is interesting in relation to the widening differences noted between boys and girls during pubescence. What this might mean in terms of these sex differences is not known at the present time.

Pituitary Gland. The pituitary gland is a small gland about the size of a large pea and weighs about one fifth as much as a five cent piece. It is attached to the base of the brain and consists of two parts, the glandular anterior portion and the posterior neural portion. This gland influences almost every organ in the body either directly or indirectly by way of other endocrine glands. It therefore influences growth and maturation.

The anterior lobe produces several hormones. The growth-promoting hormone regulates body growth. If there is an excess of this hormone during the growing years, an individual may become a giant, attaining a height of as much as 8 or 9 feet. Excessive tallness is due to the excessive growth of the long bones. Ordinarily, growth in these bones ceases during adolescence but, in giants, these bones continue to grow for a longer time. If the excessive secretion occurs after the growing years (about twenty-five years) the bones cannot grow longer but become coarser and heavier. This is especially true of the bones of the jaw, hands and feet. The condition is called acromegaly.

A deficiency in the secretion of this growth hormone suppresses growth. The extreme of such a condition is one type of dwarfism.* Such an individual has body proportions normal for his chronologic age; the features are immature; the skeleton is delicately formed and retarded in maturation; sexual maturation usually fails; mental development is usually normal.[310]

Other pituitary hormones stimulate the growth and function of other endocrine glands. They affect the thyroid (thyrotropic), adrenal cortex (adrenocorticotropic, ACTH) and the gonads (gonadotropic). Ham[394] calls the pituitary gland the "chairman of the endocrine society." All the different members report to it regularly about their activity and the pituitary, in turn, by its hormones, has a controlling influence on the structure and function of the various members. The anterior pituitary is not the master organ, however. It appears that it in turn is controlled by the hypothalamus of the central nervous system,[926] and is affected by hormones of the other glands.

Normal growth and development depends upon the reciprocal and properly timed action of the various hormones. The developmental changes during adolescence** arise from the interaction of the anterior pituitary, adrenal cortex and gonads. Apparently the hypothalamus stimulates the pituitary gland to secrete the hormones which stimulate the immature gonads to develop into mature ovaries and testes.[926] At the same time the

* For discussion of dwarfism of various origins including endocrine and hereditary see Wilkins,[993] Chapter VIII.
** As defined by Talbot et al.[926] adolescence is the whole period of childhood during which sexual differentiation occurs. It terminates when full capacity to reproduce and full bodily growth and maturation have been attained.

adrenal cortex increases its secretion of androgens. Increasing amounts of sex hormones and adrenal androgens are produced which stimulate the development of the reproductive organs and secondary sex characteristics. With the maturing of the sex glands and their hormonal activity, growth ceases either through the direct action of these hormones upon the developing long bones or their inhibiting action on the pituitary growth hormone.[993] Thus the interaction of these hormones is responsible for the pubescent changes and the subsequent cessation of growth. Differences in the timing of this activity and receptivity of the gonads and adrenal cortex may account for individual differences in the pattern of adolescent development.[993]

The gonad-stimulating hormone continues to be important since it is necessary for the regular functioning of the sex organs including the cyclic changes involved in menstruation throughout the individual's reproductive life.

In addition the anterior pituitary plays a role in the body's adaptation to stress through the effect of its hormone, ACTH, upon the adrenal cortex activity. There is also a hormone which stimulates and provides for the continuation of lactation.

The posterior lobe influences water metabolism, increases the concentration of urine and causes contraction of all involuntary muscles, including those of the blood vessels, intestines and uterus.

The Relationship of Endocrines to Behavior. The principle of the interrelatedness of the many facets of an individual as expressed in Chapter 1 applies to the relationship of endocrines and behavior. Physiologic and psychologic processes are mutually dependent variables. Endocrines play a role in the physiologic processes and, through these in behavior and personality. They influence strongly the speed and violence with which an individual breaks into emotional behavior, and, in important ways, the pattern of moods he develops. Differences in the functioning of the thyroid gland, as indicated earlier, produce differences in available energy. This in turn determines to a great extent the amount and kind of activities an individual chooses, and the tempo and endurance with which he pursues them. The on- or off-schedule of sexual maturation, which depends in part on the gonads, may create ease or difficulty for an adolescent in fitting into society. The gonads play a role in establishing differences in size, body configurations, muscular strength, and endurance between the sexes and these differences may be directly responsible for differential reactions to the environment. Individual responses to stresses both physical and psychologic seem to be tied up with an endocrine chain reaction.[341,735,833] These are some examples of possible relationships of endocrine functions to behavior.

There is also another factor which is always present, namely, the feelings of satisfaction or concern about oneself and one's relationship to parents, siblings, friends and the larger social group. Personal adjustment of children who have noticeable physical deviations due to endocrine dysfunction, may be facilitated or hindered because of attitudes of parents and teachers, and by the training and help the children get in adjusting to the defect.

Much research has been and is being done on this problem of the relation of endocrines and behavior.* At present it can be said that endocrines in contributing to good or poor physical health, growth and functioning, contribute to wholesomeness and balance in personality or to malfunction in the personality as well as in the physical area.

PREMATURITY

Because of the immaturity of the infant and abnormalities which may be present, the premature** has a more difficult adjustment to make to life after birth than a full term infant. Particular care in the early months of life is demanded in order to protect the organism and provide for its development. The greater the prematurity the greater the mortality and the more difficult will be the adjustment for those who survive. One of the greatest hazards of being born prematurely is that of intracranial hemorrhages which may interfere with the development of the central nervous system. The structure of the eye seems to be particularly vulnerable so that blindness occurs in some; visual defects appear to be found more frequently in prematures than would be expected.†

After adjustment to extra-uterine life the healthy premature has as good chances to develop into a normal child and adult as other infants. Follow-up studies of prematures to six years of age, through the school years and into adulthood indicate that in the absence of abnormalities the premature catches up with other children in height and weight before entering school, and even the very small at birth have an excellent chance of growing as large as comparable full term children.[545] They learn to walk and talk in a reasonable time.[545] Prematurity seems to have neither beneficial nor harmful long range effects upon intelligence except in cases of brain damage.[445, 424] However, damage done to the brain by intracranial hemorrhage may be reflected in the higher incidence of mental retardation among prematures than among full term infants.[760] The histories of 445 prematures ranging from less than one year to twenty-eight years, who weighed 1250 grams (2¾ pounds) or less at birth[423] reveal that 83 per cent were known to be living; of the living, 85 per cent were average or above in physical development, 90 per cent were average or above in mental development, 14 were married and 10 had given birth to 12 living children.

In personality traits prematurely born children compared with full terms are more frequently dependent on their mothers, less self-reliant and somewhat less adequate in their early social responses.[424] One follow up study‡

* See Beach[81] and Cleghorn.[187]

** Term premature applies to all infants of birth weight less than 2500 grams (5½ pounds).

† Retrolental fibroplasia, a major cause of blindness in children today, is found in small prematures. One survey[10] has indicated a frequency of 10 per cent in infants weighing less than 4 pounds at birth. The incidence appears to increase inversely with birth weight. Vision, defective enough to make correction by glasses necessary, was found in 11 of 22 prematures at the age of 8 years or later.[445]

‡ 22 children whose ages ranged from 8 to 18 years when examined.

of prematures of birth weight up to 1820 grams (4 pounds),[445] found through the use of personality tests and interviews that one half had made unsatisfactory or below average personal adjustment. Some were of the submissive, passive type while others showed unusual aggressive tendencies. Several of the children had difficulty in utilizing their abilities. The authors offer as contributing factors: prematurity, over-protection by parents, poor physical endowment and perhaps rigid postnatal care. Thus prematurity offers a hazard which many children overcome satisfactorily.*

INFLUENCE OF ILLNESS ON THE PATTERN OF GROWTH

Acute Disease Affects Physical Growth. Acute illness may change the course of physical growth temporarily. A temporary depression in weight and sometimes a deceleration in growth in height may occur. The degree to which an illness affects growth undoubtedly is dependent upon its nature, severity and duration. Some studies[396, 715, 284] give evidence for these statements in indicating no significant differences in the growth in size of children who had had frequent illness and those who had been relatively free from illness. Thus the ordinary illnesses of children probably have, in general, no permanently measurable effect upon growth in size during the school years.

However, severe illnesses may produce metabolic disturbances which can be registered in children's bodies. Transverse lines may appear on certain long bones indicating that normal growth has been interrupted.[273, 380, 403, 551] Some children after a severe illness will show bone scars; others of comparable age and with an illness of the same severity will show none. The reasons for these different physiologic responses are still unknown. The absence of scars does not necessarily mean that a recent illness has not had an adverse effect upon a child. However, the presence of such scars would indicate that it is highly probable that it had done so.

Illness may affect muscles, since during illness they lose some of their tone and tend to become flabby. If the muscles are not given an opportunity to regain firmness, fatigue and its accompanying poor posture may result. This effect upon posture may be temporary or may lead to habitually poor body balance.

Long and even permanent effect upon posture may result from diseases which affect bones or muscles, as for example rickets and infantile paralysis. The deformities due to rickets are well known, such as weak feet, knock knees, bow legs, exaggerated spinal curves, scoliosis (lateral curvature of the spine) and deformities of the ribs.** Infantile paralysis, both mild and severe, may affect posture because certain muscle groups are weakened or lose their function entirely. Such conditions as foot weakness or scoliosis may result from this muscular weakness.

* See Dunham.[260]
** In a study of Dunham and Thoms[261] nine of ten children with severe rickets in early childhood were found to have skeletal deformities when examined between fifteen and nineteen years of age. Eight had retarded growth of the legs; five had abnormal pelves.

An illness may produce some degree of anemia. Some of the fatigue noted after a child has been sick may be due in part to a lowered hemoglobin count. A study of seasonal variation[740] in hemoglobin of young children showed that the low point for hemoglobin values came in the winter, especially in the month of February, the time also of the highest incidence of upper respiratory tract infection, as for example, colds and influenza. Genuine recovery from illness, therefore, means not only the disappearance of the symptoms of the particular disease but also a return to the usual state of positive health. Hence a gradual, rather than a sudden, return to normal activities is desirable. Often a child returns to school before his bones, blood and muscles have recovered. If a teacher or parent is not aware of the fact that the child after illness is not up to par physically, that he lacks his usual reserve of energy and, therefore, tires more easily, too much may be demanded in attempting to help the child to catch up with his class in school.

Certain diseases may leave characteristic after-effects (sequelae): rheumatic fever, for example, leaving a damaged heart; scarlet fever leaving damaged kidneys or deafness; infantile paralysis leaving a paralysis; and encephalitis leaving damage to the brain. Little can be done to modify these handicaps other than to help the child adjust himself to them. The real effort of society, however, should be placed on prevention of these diseases and on early and adequate treatment whenever they occur.

Emotional Significance of Illness to Children. Illness may have many meanings to children. These meanings may differ from child to child and for the same child at different developmental levels. For children who must be hospitalized the additional strain of absence from home and family, and the strangeness of the hospital and persons giving care may create additional anxieties and fears. An illness is strange and often poorly understood by a child. He may not only be physically uncomfortable but confused. He may be anxious and fearful. He may conceive of this happening as punishment, especially if parents have related the illness to some shortcoming of the child. He may revert to earlier social and emotional behavior; he may react rebelliously; he may enjoy being sick because of the attention he receives. On the other hand, a child may grow in emotional maturity because of the experience. Such a constructive response is dependent upon the child's emotional stability and his relationship with his parents. The meaning of illness to an individual child will surely depend upon his inner resources, the understanding and resourcefulness of adults and the kind of care he receives.*

Illness May Affect Behavior Later. Many children do not "bounce back" emotionally and behaviorally promptly after an illness. A child may have a so-called emotional, as well as physical, convalescence. He may expect more adult attention and solicitude than formerly. This expectation coupled with a tendency to fatigue more easily may result in occasional temper

---

* See Langford,[563] Prugh et al.,[750] Freud,[324] Josselyn[508] for emotional reactions of children to illness. See Schwentker et al.[820] for a home play and occupational program for the bedfast child.

tantrums, in being easily discouraged, or in overaggressiveness. Parents and teachers who appreciate the origin of such behavior can help the child to grow out of it. In cases of long illness teachers have the added responsibility of helping the child to adjust to school after a long absence and possible loss of work, accumulating school retardation and accumulating loss of confidence. There should be no pressure to make up back work until the child is obviously physically able to do so. Teachers also can smooth the way for the child returning to school by preparing other children for his return.

A food problem may emerge from a period of illness. Lack of appetite creates a temporary disinterest in food, and parental concern may lead to urging, cajoling, and even forcing the child to eat. After recovery there may be a lag in the return of appetite, and the return to normal eating habits is likely to be slow. The time required for recovery of appetite depends to a great extent upon the attitude of the parents during the child's illness as well as upon the speed of convalescence.

Certain Behavior Symptoms May Indicate the Onset of an Illness. Not only is it important to protect a child after illness, it is also important to recognize the onset of illness in order to protect the sick child, as well as to avoid exposing other children in the group to any infection. The onset of illness can generally be detected early by careful observers. A sudden lack of interest in work or play, disinterest in food, fussiness and increased irritability and restless sleep all point to possible imminent sickness.

Chronic Disease Influences Growth. Certain chronic infectious diseases can affect growth. Children may suffer from chronic disease, especially in the nose, throat, mouth and ears. Chronically infected tonsils and adenoids may and sometimes do affect growth. Chronic infection with parasites as, for example, hookworm, may affect health and growth. The child with congenital syphilis is known to be undersized and chronically ill with a number of symptoms. Rheumatic heart disease and diabetes are two of the chronic diseases which present real problems to the school-aged child and adolescent.

RHEUMATIC FEVER. Rheumatic fever, the onset of which is most common between five and fifteen years and has a high chance of recurrence,[*] interferes with the normal life of a child because of damage done to the heart and the care which needs to be taken to prevent recurrences. The authors know of a number of children in whom recurrent attacks have been prevented, who have grown satisfactorily, have had no heart damage and live a normal life with certain minor restrictions as preventive measures against infections. On the other hand, many children acquire a chronic heart disability which may or may not interfere with growth[**] but definitely limits physical activities. Because of this disability these children have to live a life of certain restrictions.

DIABETES. Studies show that essentially normal growth and maturation

---

[*] There is a 60 to 70 per cent chance of recurrence during the first ten years following the initial attack.[97]

[**] See Wetzel, N.C.[984]

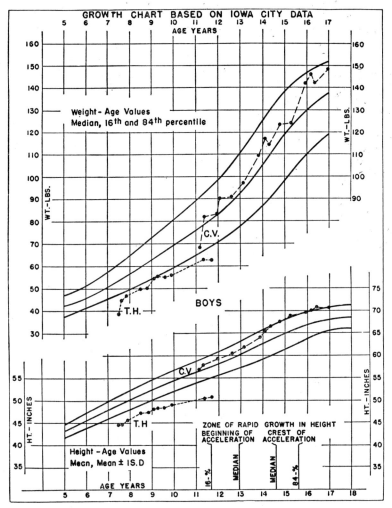

Fig. 19. The growth curve of C. V. was selected to demonstrate the satisfactory growth in height and weight of a boy with moderately severe diabetes kept under excellent control. The growth chart of T. H. illustrates the unsatisfactory growth in height of a child with moderately severe disease kept under poor diabetic control. (Jackson and Kelly: Journal of Pediatrics, Vol. 29, 1946.)

may be anticipated if the diabetes is well controlled.* Children in whom the disease is well controlled tend to grow better, and girls begin to menstruate normally; children in whom the disease is not well controlled grow more slowly, and girls begin to menstruate later. Figure 19 shows the growth curves of two boys, both with severe diabetes but one with good control and the other with poor control. The one with good control has a curve above the average in height and weight. The boy with poor control has retarded growth in both height and weight. Degenerative changes in eyes and blood

* For reference on growth and maturation of diabetic children see [111, 131, 467, 468, 926, 971].

vessels frequently accompany long standing diabetes.[926] One author[468] states that the level of control as well as the duration of the disease is an important factor influencing degenerative changes and that good control will delay and possibly prevent such changes. Thus careful medical supervision and dietary control are extremely important for the diabetic child.

Avoiding retardation both of growth and maturation whenever possible is important from a psychologic as well as a physical point of view. One study[613] reports that many of the children studied were more disturbed over their shortness than their diabetes. Such a child had a tendency to become exclusive or compensated by being a show-off or boaster and exaggerator.*

A study[130] of mental and personality comparisons between diabetics and their healthy siblings revealed a normal distribution of intelligence, with 43 per cent of the diabetics having an I.Q. between 90 and 110.** The group compared well with their siblings and showed an even and regular mental development. There was no relationship between the duration or severity of the disease and intelligence. Ratings on the Woodworth-Cady Psycho-Neurotic Inventory indicated no differences between the diabetics and their siblings. In observing behavior during the tests, testers noted that the diabetics were frequently careful, meticulous, earnest and conscientious. This, coupled with good school reports, was attributed by the author to the habit-training forced upon the diabetic child by the strict regimen made necessary by the disease. School reports indicated a predominance of desirable traits, and few instances of feelings of inferiority and attention-seeking devices. The parents reported that the personality of these children had changed little since the onset of the disease. Excitability and irritability were the only traits that had increased considerably. There was some indication that these children had become somewhat more cautious and stubborn. These changes would be expected in children with chronic diseases. The author concluded by saying:

> It is important for the sake of the personality of the diabetic child that not too much attention or sympathy be bestowed on him by parents, teachers, or friends, in case he thus may come to feel different from other children and to expect privileges on account of his illness. He should be given the responsibility for his own welfare (testing his urine and giving his own insulin) as early as possible, and he should be made to feel that success depends upon himself in the matter of his total well-being.[130]

Emotional Implications of Chronic Diseases. Chronic diseases such as rheumatic fever with its recurrent nature, diabetes and disabilities arising from infantile paralysis may interfere with the steady progress of personality development and emotional stability.† Restrictions may hamper growth of independence and the transfer of emotional attachment from parents to peers. Being different from others either in abilities, limited activities or habits of eating is difficult for many children to accept. Boys with rheumatic hearts may have difficulty in accepting themselves in the masculine role since masculinity represents physical ability to deal aggressively with others;

---

* Such compensation for shortness has been noted elsewhere.
** Children studied by Wagner et al.[971] had intelligence quotients ranging from 65 to 130.
† See references [66, 116, 320, 507, 830].

this is restricted for them. Children may continue to carry with them fears and anxieties about their present and future health. They may have acquired the habit of overdependence and oversolicitude about themselves resulting in overcautiousness or perhaps capitalizing on their disability, thus "trading on weakness." On the other hand, they may refuse to follow the prescribed regimen and become "whistlers in the dark."

Different children respond to similar disabilities in different ways. Some are able to accept life at a slower tempo, to select comfortably their activities among those which are compatible with their physical abilities, to capitalize on their assets and to relate themselves well to their peers and adults. The response of a particular child will be influenced by his emotional stability and that of his parents, and his relationships with his parents prior to his disability. It will also be influenced by his parents' and teachers' acceptance of him and the support they can give him in his life at home and in school. Parents and teachers, therefore, need to be understanding, accepting, supportive and realistically encouraging.

Programs to Aid in Personal Adjustment.   As far as possible it is believed to be wise not to segregate children with physical disabilities but rather to assist them to fit into the general stream of life by sharing school and recreational activities with other children. However, there are times when groups of children with the same disability can profit by being together. In 1951, fifteen camps for diabetics were reported.[894] These camps provided a pleasurable vacation along with careful supervision for the children and at the same time released the parents for a time from the tension, worry and fatigue of caring constantly for a diabetic child. A summer camp has also been reported for children with heart disease.[797] In this camp the tempo of life was adjusted to individual needs. The program was similar to that at other camps except for the exclusion of competitive games. It afforded an opportunity for these children to learn how much they were like other children, to learn limits and acceptance of them.

Some camps take a few physically handicapped children along with the "normal" ones. The Girl Scouts of Cincinnati experimented with including a small group of diabetic girls in their camp for two-week periods and found it successful.[699] Such an experience gives a diabetic an opportunity to live and compete on an equal basis with nondiabetic children. In this camp, diabetic children took part in every type of camping activity, including overnight hikes and cookouts. The author warns that a camp to serve diabetics must be well conducted and must have a carefully balanced program and adequate health supervision which includes a medical examination prior to admission; it must have a graduate nurse, a physician in residence or on call, and a good dietetic department.

Hidden Valley Camp, one of the New York Herald Tribune Fresh Air Fund's activities, also mixed physically handicapped with able-bodied children successfully.* Thirty-five handicapped and sixty-five able-bodied children attended this camp for two-week periods. Disabilities ranged from weak-

* New York Herald Tribune, August 17, 1952.

ened hearts to motor paralysis. That children are fundamentally the same except for physical limitations was the basic assumption upon which the camp operated. It was found to be a healthful experience for both groups.

Clubs for diabetic adolescents have been initiated. The Rhode Island Hospital[465] in Providence, by integrating medicine, group work and case work, organized a club for diabetic adolescents. Some of the adolescents attending the clinic were losing social contacts because of embarrassment and feelings of inferiority. Harriet, for example, an eighteen-year-old, seldom mingled with girls in school because she was afraid of being asked to go to a drugstore for an ice cream soda, which was taboo. Edward, also eighteen, working in a National Youth Administration resident center, was so afraid of other boys knowing about his diabetes that he arose every morning at 4:30 to take his insulin. Another boy had been so sheltered by his parents that he had never gone hiking or picnicking with other children.

The Y.W.C.A. and the Y.M.C.A. managed the program of this diabetic club. The social worker of the clinic explained the program to the adolescents and their parents. Beginning with a Christmas party, "The Friday Nighters" held weekly meetings, planned by themselves. Some meetings were educational. They learned about the disease they had, what it was and how they could live with it. Some meetings were devoted to active games and dancing. Sports and active games became an important part of the program, since physical activity aids proper utilization of sugar. The boys and girls moved out into other groups and became a part of a group in which they were not known as diabetics. In the summer they had two weeks at a camp where they lived with normal children, ate in the same dining room but at a separate table, had the same food except for necessary substitutions and took part in all the camp activities. From these experiences these children learned (1) that development, self-control, and good sportsmanship help in adjustment to a chronic disease, and (2) that diabetes need not be a barrier to a normal, happy life.

A program of group therapy with parents of physically disabled children has been reported.[671] In a group situation these parents were able to express their problems, to learn that others had similar problems, to discuss ways and means of meeting these problems and to gain a better understanding of their children and their needs.

Thus we know that programs not only can be but are being developed for the purpose of promoting a better life for physically disabled children and their parents.

PHYSICAL DEFECTS

Physical defects may be the result of disease—for example, the diseases discussed above—of faulty development or of accident. Whatever their origin, they may have little or no effect upon a child's development or they may affect development a great deal.* Much will depend upon the nature of the

---

* Children with physical limitations, whether they are due to disease or to some defect, are like other children in their basic needs and in many aspects of their lives. Similarities to other children should not be lost sight of in concern for the disability.

defect, its severity and the attitude of the child himself, his parents and his peers. Each defect places a specific limitation upon the child. That limitation may be severe enough to interfere profoundly with his activity, as for example, cerebral palsy. It may influence his social development by preventing him from developing useful skills, by setting up a barrier between himself and other children because he is different physically, and also by preventing him from becoming independent. Emotionally he may be unable to satisfy his needs for security, affection, and success and thus be driven to compensate for the lack of these either by withdrawing or showing aggressive behavior. A defect may also interfere with his achievement at school.

Some parents and teachers may try to ignore the child's difference and expect him to carry on without privileges. Others may overprotect the child and by so doing create in him a feeling of self-pity and prevent him from growing in desirable personality traits. Some, however, are able to encourage and assist the child to utilize all of his abilities.* They can also see that psychologic needs are satisfied and thus help these children to become successful and happy members of society.

Effect of Visual Defect upon Development. A visual defect may range from defective vision which can be corrected by glasses, through partial sight to total blindness. The relationship between a serious sensory defect and retarded intellectual development is well known. Blind children are slow to acquire gross motor control, must develop Braille skills in order to learn to read and in infancy may be mistaken for feebleminded babies. There are few reports on the intelligence of pupils in sight-saving classes and the blind. Baker[50] in surveying studies of the intelligence of blind children says that blind children test slightly lower at all mental levels than seeing children, with fewer gifted and more mentally subnormal in the blind group. However, he says that blind children, given adequate opportunity to learn, do not differ very significantly from the seeing in intelligence. He especially calls attention to the many outstanding artists and characters in history who are or were blind. Any serious defect in vision proves a serious handicap to learning unless special conditions for learning and suitable methods are provided.**

Studies of the social behavior and personality of the visually handicapped are limited and sometimes misleading because tests used for those with normal vision are not always entirely applicable to those with partial or no vision. A survey of studies[58] concludes that: (1) the blind more frequently have scores on personality inventories in the maladjusted range (possibly, however, this is an artifact of standardization procedures); (2) social maturity of the blind child is retarded when measured on a scale designed for seeing children; (3) mild visual impairments are probably not crucial; (4) severe disability is not necessarily accompanied by severe personality disturbance; (5) different people respond in different ways to the same degree of defective

---

* It is said that handicapped children succeed, not in spite of their disabilities, but because of their abilities.
** See Hathaway.[410]

vision. Children with unrecognized visual defects may demonstrate behavior patterns which, if properly understood, would tell us that the eyesight is defective.*

Effect of Deafness. The terms "deaf" and "hard of hearing" are generally defined in terms of functional auditory capacity. A Conference of Executives of American Schools for the Deaf in 1937 adopted the following definitions:

> The deaf: Those in whom the sense of hearing is non-functional for the ordinary purpose of life. This general group is made up of two distinct classes based entirely on the time of the loss of hearing: a) the congenitally deaf, namely, those who were born deaf; b) the adventitiously deaf, namely, those who were born with normal hearing, but in whom the sense of hearing is non-functional later through illness or accident.
>
> The hard of hearing: Those in whom the sense of hearing, although defective, is functional with or without a hearing aid.[947]

The deaf or hard of hearing child is often a misunderstood child. His defect is not always recognized and, therefore, his behavior is misinterpreted. He may be mistaken for a child with poor mental ability. He may then be neglected and become withdrawn. Because he does not attend, he may be marked as indifferent, stubborn, careless and impolite. Characteristics commonly attributed to the deaf, such as mental sluggishness, inattention, suspicion and melancholy, are not true, according to teachers of deaf children.[887] The very nature of the deafness may in some cases make adults unduly critical of the child. A child may hear better at one time than another. Some voices may be more distinct than others. It can be easy for any other than a keenly observant and well-informed person to lay such a child's variable response to deficiencies in character. Deaf children can be misunderstood, also, because they may misinterpret situations. Because they fail to hear all the facts, their conclusions and hence their behavior may seem strange to those who, because they can hear, can base their judgment on all the facts. Such children are often considered "dumb" or "queer."

It becomes important, then, to be able to detect the signs of deafness. Baker[50] describes deaf children as follows:

> As a group the deaf are inattentive, imperfect in speech, bewildered and baffled in expression, sensitive and aloof because of deafness. They frequently complain of earache, have discharging ears, are mouth-breathers and hold their heads in peculiar postures so as to hear all they can from meager sounds which fall upon their ears. Theirs is a world of isolation. Although the channels of communication may be kept open by great effort, it is always easy to let them become closed. They become blocked through lack of constant use like the faint trail in a blinding snow storm on a country road.

Studies of personality and adjustment, social maturity and fears of deaf children and children who can hear have been summarized by Barker et al.[58] In comparison with children who can hear, deaf children tend to be more fearful,[141] to be more poorly adjusted and more unstable emotionally,

---

* For signs of eye trouble in children see Signs of Eye Trouble in Children, Publ. 351, Nat'l Soc. for the Prevention of Blindness, New York, 1948.

less socially mature and more inflexible[584] if they attended residential schools[*][141, 146, 888] but similar if they attended day schools.[388] Habbe[888] concludes that a child can solve problems associated with his hearing if his general adjustment to life is good. It must be remembered that deaf children have much in common in their inner impulses and development with children who can hear. Unless they are sent away from home, they also live in individual families where many personality patterns are firmly set, and could, therefore, be expected to develop a variety of diverse personality patterns.[**]

Effect of Orthopedic Handicap upon Personality and General Adjustment. Children with an orthopedic handicap are those who have impaired use of body, legs, arms. Among these are varying degrees of crippling defect from such diverse causes as disturbances in development before birth, accidents, and diseases, such as infantile paralysis, tuberculosis of the bone and many more.

Crippled children, as they are generally called, are more obvious to the public, and hence receive fairly adequate care when contrasted to other "special" children. Medical care is available to a substantial proportion of them through state funds administered in such a way as to provide operative and hospital care, occupational as well as physical therapy and, in many school systems, special educational facilities. Parents and educators have not, however, been helped so universally to understand the psychology of the crippled child. These children, conspicuously different from other children, prevented by their bodies from satisfying childish urges to activity and to social participation in the games which interest their contemporaries, must find basic satisfactions elsewhere. They may resort to playing up their defect for sympathy and attention from adults, although they seldom do so with other children who are not moved for long by such bids and soon prove unresponsive. They may use the defect as an excuse for not accomplishing as much as they could accomplish if they really wanted to. Being unable to defend themselves or to run from danger, they often develop fears, both those based upon real danger and those which are symbolic of other psychologic factors. With proper adult guidance, however, most crippled children can face their defect courageously, and can learn to utilize effectively their abilities. Franklin D. Roosevelt was a splendid example of a fine compensation for defect and was an inspiration to crippled children everywhere.

Because of the differences in crippled children in terms of severity of the disability and its origin it is not surprising that an over-all statement about the intelligence of crippled children cannot be made. In some cases intelligence is affected; in others it is not. A study of children having spinal curvatures or the bone disease osteomyelitis[511] revealed no difference in intelligence from that of physically normal children. However, studies of children with cerebral palsy[147, 669] indicate that such children may be bright, average or dull but that a disproportionate number are mentally defective. One study

---

* Children with more difficult hearing problems generally attend these schools. There may also be the factor of some emotional disturbances due to separation from the family.
** A number of excellent case studies about deaf children can be found in Fiedler.[289]

of identical twins, one of each having had cerebral palsy from birth[532] showed that the one with cerebral palsy in each pair had a lower I.Q. than the normal child. In a summary of studies on intelligence of crippled children Baker[50] reports that, when all children with orthopedic defect are considered as a group, they fall in an intelligence level slightly below average. Any watchful observer of crippled children, however, will find many keenly intelligent children among them.

Crippling in itself apparently has no unique influence on children's behavior. Crippled children tend to be about as well adjusted as noncripples with a slight trend in the direction of maladjustment.[511, 208] Adolescent boys* may indicate difficulty in fitting into the masculine role assigned by our culture. Social adjustment can easily be dependent upon the individual's attitude toward his physical disability.

Baker[50] in summarizing work on personality in crippled children says that physical handicap does not in itself appear to produce personality or social maladjustment unless there are other contributing factors. He notes that the appearance of physical deformity, the need of surgical treatment, and the tendency to rejection by other children tend to set up strong emotional attitudes in both child and parent. Strother[911] stresses in the development of personality of crippled children the importance of complete emotional acceptance of the child by his parents so that the child can develop a feeling of self-respect and self-confidence, as well as a constructive philosophy of life. Personal and social relationships in the home and school tend, as we see, then, to have more effect upon the child than the crippling itself.

Epilepsy. Epilepsy, meaning "seizure," may imply and include everything from emotional outbursts to grand mal convulsions.[723] It is a metabolic disorder of unknown origin toward which there is an inherited tendency.**[574] There also may be brain damage incurred during prenatal life, at birth or later. Children with brain damage are likely to have a more serious disability. The occurrence of seizures bears a close relationship to certain emotional and mental stresses. Therefore, good mental health for an epileptic is an aid in reducing the frequency of seizures.

The effect of this disease upon emotions and behavior of a child will depend upon its severity, medical supervision and the attitudes and behavior of those at home, at school and in the community. The outlook for most epileptics is more hopeful now than in the past. With competent medical treatment a great majority of these children can be protected from or substantially relieved of seizures.[575] Unfortunately, there is still need to remove

---

* Two reports[292,293] indicate that adolescent boys show less freedom in the expression of externally directed feelings of aggression and dependency than do girls or non-disabled adolescents. This may be due to the fact that the adolescent boy is unable to fulfill his masculine role as aggressive and independent while the girl does not have such a conflict.

** The genetic factor is attributed to inherited brain wave patterns[576] which can be studied through the use of the electroencephalogram. It is reported that approximately four-fifths of the children subject to epileptic seizures show abnormalities of brain waves. The types of brain waves vary with the various types of disturbance.[575]

misconceptions from the minds of the public and to guide them into understanding and acceptance of these children.

The intelligence of these children is not determined by seizures *per se* but rather by endowment and presence or absence of brain damage. Of 200 patients under 15 years of age Lennox[575] found the average I.Q. on the Stanford-Binet test to be 109. A 5-year study of epileptics by Zimmerman et al.[1019] showed that the children with petit mal, with its transitory lapses of consciousness, had the high I.Q. levels in the group and least amount of personality deviation. As the type of seizures became more severe the I.Q. became lower and personality deviations became more marked. Lennox points out that the great majority of epileptic children in the community are in general as normal in intelligence as other children. However, social rejection often retards educational progress.

A child subjected to epileptic seizures is likely to develop fear, anxiety and frustration. Both child and adolescent face the cross currents of overprotection at home and of rejection outside. The uncertainty of seizures and the handling of such situations when they occur are barriers to the child or adolescent in leading a normal life with his peers. Such children need understanding adults to support and guide them and bridge the gap between them and their peers. Children who are unable to make satisfactory adjustments may react either by withdrawing or by overcompensation.

Schools Must Make Adjustment to Children Suffering from Long-Term Defects. Among those suffering from long-term handicaps *feeble-minded children* are perhaps the best known to teachers as school problems since their defect, while it has a physical basis, is within the realm of mental age, and the relation between mental age and school adjustment is better known than the relation between other types of defect and school performance. This is discussed in somewhat more detail in Chapter 9. *Epileptics* are also often understood as requiring either rejection from school, or some special arrangement for their education. As a group, the epileptics have probably in the past received less adequate attention from regular school authorities than have other special groups because of the traditional attitude that they will deteriorate mentally. It is now known that this is not necessarily true. With present medical practice it is inexcusable for any school system to refuse some sort of educational opportunity to its epileptic children. Although there is some difference of opinion, Lennox advocates regular rather than special schools for all epileptics whose intelligence and behavior are adequate and whose seizures are reasonably controlled by drug therapy. This is not, of course, to be interpreted as meaning that children whose seizures are not reasonably controlled should be placed in regular school grades with other children. The shock of seeing a severe epileptic attack is too great to other children to warrant any such step.

It is now believed that physically handicapped children, as far as they are able, should attend regular schools with specific arrangements made to facilitate learning. Schools that are alert to the needs of handicapped children are providing experiences both with groups of non-handicapped and with those like themselves. When the experience is with non-handicapped children the handicapped lose the sense of segregation and are helped to become integrated into society. When it is with others like themselves, they learn that they are not unique and at the same time have opportunity for special learning experiences which they need. In such schools screening of children for defects is provided, as well as conditions that will protect the health of each individual child. These schools need teachers who know and are sensitive to the specific needs of their individual children and who can provide for them in the school situation, teachers who by their attitudes and behavior can help the handicapped fit into the group and assist the other children in understanding and accepting them. In such schools counseling of the handicapped can provide assistance in choosing appropriate professions. This is the ideal situation. Unfortunately many schools do not provide these facilities and are failing to help the many children who are partially defective.*

Every school system, however, owes to all of its children the opportunity to utilize whatever capacity they have and to make it possible for them to benefit as much as they can from a standard curriculum. If the curriculum and method cannot be adapted to the individual child, at least the school can guard against damaging the general development of given children by attempts to force them in a standard pattern at a standard rate.**

Some Less Evident Physical Conditions.   Also important to school progress and adjustment are the less evident physical conditions. Children with allergies are fairly common today. An allergic child, who is sensitive to a food or substance in his environment such as dust, feathers or pollen, will have hay fever, if the reaction to the offending substance occurs in the nose. If the reaction centers in the bronchial tract he is an asthmatic. Another individual may have a sensitive gastro-intestinal tract and have digestive disturbances. If the reaction affects the skin, he has eczema. Allergic children may have short attention spans and show behavior fluctuations. MacFarlane† commented that she found many more tantrums among children suffering from skin irritations, such as eczema, hives, etc., than among children not affected.

Knowing that a child is allergic helps a teacher or parent to understand and interpret his behavior. The adult can help the child who must eliminate a particular food or foods from his diet to accept this difference naturally and not become oversensitive or use his allergy as an excuse for more attention or for further fussiness about foods. Adults need to differentiate between real physiologic allergies and "psychologic allergies" used as devices to evade unpleasant experiences.

In adolescence such difficulties as *acne* and *malocclusion* (poor alignment of

---

* See Statistics of Special Schools and Classes for Exceptional Children, 1947–1948, in Biennial Survey of Education in United States, 1946–1948. Education Office, Federal Security Agency, 1950.

** Excellent discussions of handicapped children appear in Teagarden,[931] Miles,[667] Doll,[248] Baker.[50]

† MacFarlane, J. W. Lecture at Merrill-Palmer School, 1939.

teeth) may produce acute self-consciousness and interfere with a child's adjustment in the social group. Attractive appearance is an opening wedge in a group, especially for girls. A blotchy complexion, protruding teeth, or a receding jaw removes that moral support which satisfaction in one's appearance gives to youth.

Another physical condition, obesity, has been discussed in Chapter 1. The effect of nutrition upon school progress will be discussed in Chapter 4.

EXPERIENCES TO VITALIZE CLASS WORK

1. Discuss the practical difference that it might make to know about heredity in evaluating a particular child.

2. Find out if there is a children's hospital or an endocrine clinic in your community, or if there is an endocrinologic service in your public school. If possible visit one of them and report for class discussion some of the cases which you saw.

3. As you write your case study think carefully about which of the child's (or your own) traits and characteristics you consider as having been influenced mainly by heredity. By environment.

4. Recall any instance in your own development when you were pushed to learn beyond your "readiness." What effect did this have upon you?

5. Find what you can in the current literature (since 1948) about the effect of illnesses upon development.

6. What can you find in the current literature (since 1948) about the effect of special sensory defects upon growth and development?

7. Locate a child who is handicapped physically (eyes, ears, crippled, etc.). How does his defect affect his learning, his attitudes and his behavior?

SELECTED READINGS

Baker, H. J.: Introduction to Exceptional Children. New York, The Macmillan Co., 1953.

Emotional Problems Associated with Handicapping Conditions in Children. Children's Bureau Publ. 336. Washington, D.C., Federal Security Agency, 1952.

Fiedler, M. F.: Deaf Children in a Hearing World. Their Education and Adjustment. New York, Ronald Press, 1952.

Heck, A. O.: The Education of Exceptional Children. New York, McGraw-Hill Book Co., 1953.

Josselyn, I. M.: Emotional Problems of Illness. Better Living Booklet. Chicago, Science Research Association, Inc., 1953.

Kingsley, H. L.: The Nature and Conditions of Learning. New York, Prentice-Hall, Inc., 1946, Ch. 10.

McGraw, M. B.: The Neuromuscular Maturation of the Human Infant. New York, Columbia University Press, 1943.

Scheinfeld, A.: The New You and Heredity. Philadelphia. J. B. Lippincott Co., 1950.

Teagarden, F.: Psychology for Professional Workers. Revised ed. New York, Prentice-Hall, Inc., 1946, Chs. 15, 16.

CHAPTER 3

Influences on Growth—(EMOTIONAL)

Psychologic Potential for Growth Varies.   Just as the well-being of the child physically is a primary factor in the quality of his physical growth, so is his well-being emotionally a primary factor in his mental and personality development. As we have already seen, however, the relationship is not only one of physical factors upon physical growth and of emotional factors upon psychologic growth. There is also a cross relationship: physical factors influence psychologic growth, and emotional factors influence physical growth. The child inherits not only his body, with its peculiar type of framework and muscle, of glands and nervous system, and other parts of the structural organism which we may, for convenience, call his physical constitution. He inherits also a certain psychologic structure of mental and emotional potentiality which we may call his psychologic constitution.

The child, because of his unique psychologic constitution, responds individually to emotional as well as to physical factors. Two children in the same family do not respond alike to what on the surface may appear to be the same physical environment, as we have seen. Neither do two children in the same family respond in the same way to what may appear on the surface to be the same emotional environment. The unique physical constitution which the child inherits determines how well he will grow in a given environment and how long he will resist physical illness or breakdown in the face of strain or exposure to disease. In the same way, the unique psychologic constitution which he inherits will determine how well he will grow mentally and emotionally and how long he will resist illness or breakdown in the face of strain or exposure to factors which produce psychologic illness. Just as some people break physically under little physical strain or exposure, whereas others can take almost unbelievable amounts of both, so do some people break psychologically under little psychologic strain, whereas others have tremendous resistance.* The basic psychologic potential, then, varies, as does the basic physical potential for growth and development.

Psychologic Environments Vary.   Just as physical environments for growth vary, so do psychologic environments. Good psychologic environ-

---

* There are some physical situations of continued malnutrition and exposure to disease which no physical constitution can take without breakdown; there are also psychologic situations of continued frustration or strain which no psychologic constitution can take without breakdown.

ment is not highly correlated with good physical environment, nor poor psychologic environment with poverty. Some homes provide a healthful physical environment comparatively free of disease, with adequate food, rest and play and other physical growth-promoting environment, but may provide a very poor emotional environment. For example, in homes which afford the best physical surroundings, conflict of personalities, or overambition, or overprotection or other psychologic factors may exist which seriously interfere with adequate psychologic development. Conversely, happiness and love, fine and well-balanced ideals, may produce so flourishing an emotional climate in a home that even submarginal physical living may fail to damage growth. Happiness makes one benefit to the maximum from what food is available; love can make even a sordid tenement into a home where children can grow well.

Physical and Emotional Factors Interrelated. In the same way that the physical environment of climate, food, rest, exercise, exposure to strain and fatigue, and to disease determine the rate and the pattern of the child's physical growth, so the emotional climate, love or the lack of it, good or poor discipline, adequate or inadequate intellectual growth experiences, psychologic strains or satisfactions, and other psychologic factors will determine the rate and pattern of his intellectual and personality growth. In addition to this, the rate and pattern of his physical growth will influence the rate and pattern of his psychologic growth and vice versa. In general, then, all of the physical and psychologic factors which influence either type of growth will influence both.

How Emotions Affect the Body. We have discussed at some length the effect of physical well-being or defect upon intellectual functioning and successful emotional adjustment for children. There is equally impressive evidence that the converse is true, namely, that emotional state, the adequacy or inadequacy of life adjustment, and the attitudes and feelings which result from such adjustment or lack of it, affect physical well-being.* Emotional strain of any kind is likely to be reflected in physical functioning, just as physical defect or physical disturbance is likely to be reflected in intellectual functioning and personality adjustment.

To understand this we need only to know how, under emotional stress, the autonomic nervous system acts to speed pulse and respiration, to retard digestion, to tense smooth muscles throughout the body, and to impede clear thinking.[161] Severe fear, anger, or even love, too exciting thrills, too discouraging depression all set off secretion of epinephrine, popularly called adrenalin, by action in the autonomic or vegetative nervous system. This inhibits the flow of the digestive juices, redistributes the blood, races the pulse, speeds breathing, and—although the body is thus made ready for vigorous physical action—inhibits clear thinking and fine motor coordina-

---

* One of the best summaries of the evidence in this direction appears in Dunbar.[258] Good discussions of the relation of emotional strain to physical well-being and to educational adjustment can be found in Thompson,[941] Harsh and Schrickel.[406] A good discussion of the school's obligation to recognize and adjust to mental health factors can be found in Skinner et al.[862]

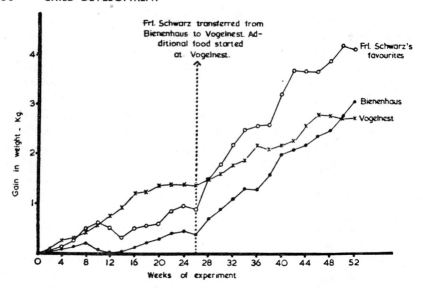

Fig. 20. Emotional climate influences physical growth. Of two orphanages on rations, one, Vogelnest, had its rations increased after six months; the other, Bienenhaus, had no additional food while at the same time a transfer of house mothers meant that a harsh, inconsistent house mother, with favorites who moved with her, moved from Bienenhaus to Vogelnest. From Widdowson, E. M.: Mental Contentment and Physical Growth, Lancet 1:1316–1318, 1951.

tion. Knowing this, we can understand why we have no appetite when intensely worried, why we cannot think clearly when nervous and tense, and why any form of tense emotion is exhausting. Strains or conflicts in the life of a child either at home or at school can interfere with his physical functions and his physical growth as well as with his ability to think clearly and hence to learn.

A good demonstration of this was noted in the growth in weight and height of children in two German orphanages.[990] During the first six months of observations the children were living on the regular rations. For the following six months one orphanage, V, had its ration increased while B had no additional food. At the beginning of the second period the house mothers changed so that the one formerly at B moved to V. She was a stern, forbidding, inconsistent person whom both the staff and children feared. Mealtimes were likely to be extremely unpleasant. She also had favorites who could do no wrong and whom she took along with her when she changed from one orphanage to the other. On the other hand, the women in charge of V for the first period and of B for the second were bright, happy persons, who were genuinely fond of children and whom the children liked. Fig. 20, showing the curves of average growth in weight during the twelve months indicate that these children grew better when happy and contented. It can be seen that on restricted rations growth in weight (and similar but small differences were noted in height) was best for the children in V, in a pleasant atmosphere, and tapered off under the severe housemother, even though the amount of food was increased. When additional food was given the favorites as they moved into V with the severe housemother they made the best progress of any of the children. Those at B, under pleasant supervision with no additional food grew faster than they had previously under the less happy atmosphere, and the children in V with more food but a poor emotional climate did not make the expected gains. Observations on a group of Canadian children and a group of American children living in an institution[90, 327] provide further evidence of the importance of contentment for good physical growth.

Satisfactions and Strains Important. Any set of conditions which drives a child beyond his natural functioning level inevitably produces a strain. So also will any set of conditions which continually frustrates basic needs and drives. This will be discussed later. One of the most important considerations in evaluating any given child's growth and functioning is the consideration of the satisfactions and of the strains he experiences. Satisfactions tend to release tension and to promote growth. Strains tend to produce tension and to impede growth and functioning. Is the child, for example, in the proper grade for his mental ability, his physical strength and his social development? If not, he will be subject to dissatisfactions and strains every day he is in school. Again, regardless of his ability, is his performance meeting the expectations of parents and teachers? If their expectations are soundly grounded upon his real physical, intellectual and social abilities, then he can and probably should be urged along. If, however, their expectations are beyond his natural capacities, he suffers strain not only at school but also at home.

Anxiety over one's place in the gang, or over some real or fancied difficulty with civil or school authorities, may occupy a child's attention so that he cannot concentrate at school. It may also, particularly in less aggressive, less "out-going" children, tie up appetite and interfere with sleep by making the child restless and by producing bad dreams. With more aggressive, "out-going" children, the strain will probably show in irritability, explosiveness and difficult behavior. Any worry over parents, siblings, or over any other thing which is real to the child, reflects in school work and general behavior as well as in general physical well-being.

Adjustment to School Often an Emotional Strain. Kindergarten and first grade children frequently suffer from lack of appetite, sleep disturbances and loss of weight as a consequence of the tension of adjusting to the new requirements of school. In such instances, it is probably not the school which must adjust to the child but rather the child who must make the adjustment to the school, his reaction being an indication that he is ill-prepared to make an adjustment required of all but the most exceptional children. Much can be gained for both child and parent, however, if the teacher "understands" and, through patience and some temporary adjustment at school, helps "wean" the child into the required adjustment on his part.

Part of the critical aspect of school adaptation is the readjustment required by separation of the child from his mother and from the familiar routines of the home. England's experience with evacuation of children during the Second World War[326] showed that separation from home and the "sanctions of the home" produced more neuroses than were produced by actual bombings. Although school does not represent as vital a separation as does evacuation in wartime, it does represent for many children a sufficiently vital separation to be reflected in rest, appetite and excretory incontinence.

Attitudes of Adults Important to Child's Emotional Balance. Every teacher, parent or guardian, to do the job of dealing with children even reasonably well, must learn the emotion-tension stage of each child. We must know how to arouse enthusiasm which does not spill over into tense excitement or neurotic fear of falling short of the mark; we must know how to stimulate interest without too much fatigue. And we must never be unfair enough to treat children in such a way as further to block thinking which is already blocked, or further to disturb motor behavior which is already imperfect. In other words, a quick sympathy with the child who cannot mobilize his thinking in speed drills, or who finds it impossible to read aloud before the large group, may possibly relax him enough to accomplish the end; whereas sarcasm or ridicule can only intensify the original cause of such trouble.

Some teachers say, as the child enters school, "He must adjust eventually— why not now?" and refuse to make any concession to the child. Such teachers tend to be harsh with the child, thinking to hasten his adjustment. These teachers, however, often place such a child in so difficult a situation that his adjustment is greatly delayed. It is not at all unusual to find children relapsing in toilet habits upon entrance to school or upon encountering a "tough" teacher even after a year or so of school.

Dull children, whose thinking and emotions need stimulating, especially those whose physical reactions are slow, can benefit from an enthusiastic teacher who "whoops up" their interest. But superior children whose tempo of emotional responsiveness is high are often overstimulated by a "whoop-up" teacher and are thrown into the type of emotional tenseness which sets off the autonomic nervous system with all of its consequences.

Sarcasm or ridicule on the part of either teachers or parents belongs to the type of discipline which, along with physical violence, throws nearly all children into so emotional a state that the autonomic nervous system is set into action. The simplest understanding of the action of the autonomic nervous system should forever clear our schoolrooms of sarcasm, ridicule and physical violence. No child, roused to emotion by these, or any other emotion-rousing methods, can possibly think clearly or speak or write adequately, since the autonomatic by-products of the tense emotion are a blocking of thought and a disturbance of the motor controls, of which speaking and writing are two of the most delicate. *No proof*

A further application of this principle is that intelligent discussion cannot progress when one or the other party to the discussion is blocked by emotion. Children who are terrified cannot think; therefore, they cannot explain themselves by stating a reasonable defense, nor can they absorb a lecture on behavior. Quiet friendliness between adult and child or between child and child opens the channel for intelligent discussion of the situation before them and provides the best possibility that the child will remember later what was said. A too severe atmosphere in the principal's office, a too glowering expression on the teacher's or parent's face may set off the child's autonomic nervous system so that he can neither think nor speak intelligently. Judgment is required on the part of the adult, of course. Some children, even when mischievous enough to get into trouble, require gentleness of approach for a really effective contact; others need considerable firmness. Any child who seems to need genuine harshness should have an investigation to reveal what is wrong at home or in his neighborhood or with his previous handling in school.

Moods. Moods are pleasant or unpleasant experiences which are less intense and which last longer than emotional experiences. They are often a "hang-over" of emotional experiences, although they may be the background for an exaggerated emotional response because they sensitize individuals to emotional stimuli. For example, a mood of depression may result from an emotional experience of defeat or grief.* On the other hand, a mood of depression may make one cry over things that would ordinarily leave one almost unmoved; an irritable mood may make one explode into anger over comparatively trivial incidents.

Important factors in stabilizing moods are physical health and a fairly stabilized routine of living, especially for growing children. A well child is normally a happy child, although certain moods of explosiveness and negativism are considered "normal" at certain stages of growth, as we shall see later. Zest and interest are important to the mental and personality development of children; but overstimulation and an unstable, overexcitable or explosive emotional environment are likely to produce unpredictable and undesirable emotional behavior in children. The cultivation of a calm frame of mind, the habit of retaining a long range perspective in the face of immediately disturbing circumstances, an ability to analyze one's own moods and to trace them to the emotion or experience which set them off, and good physical habits can all help an individual to understand and hence to be less victimized by his moods. Care in cultivating this frame of mind should be exercised, however, lest the child be subjected to the type of suppression of emotions which leads to explosion or to escape forms of behavior. An emotional environment which is too even or smooth can be dull and boresome, or repressive and therefore dangerous to the development of initiative and to one's zest for living, and hence to mental health.

Basic Psychologic Needs. Human behavior is "set off" or motivated by certain basic drives or needs or urges.** It is now generally recognized that the motivation behind human behavior is always partly a matter of inherent, inborn drives and partly a matter of social and cultural experience and learn-

---

* Moods are, of course, often associated with over-fatigue, illness or other purely physical causes. In adolescent girls and mature women a mood of depression or of restlessness frequently accompanies certain aspects of the menstrual cycle.

** Depending upon the school of psychology to which the student has been exposed, he will recognize these terms as what are referred to by the general public as instincts.

ing.* It is known that the quality and force of the drive behind any specific piece of behavior is colored by emotion which has been built up by previous experiences.

Most introductory courses in psychology will have given the student of child development a list of inherited drives, or instincts considered common to the whole human race. It will have been pointed out that any consideration of human behavior must take into account the fact that, whether we like it or not, the human animal will go after food when hungry, fall asleep when tired, will seek companionship with his fellows, will fight back when crossed or thwarted, and so on. As teachers or parents, we must, then, recognize these drives and must adjust children's programs to provide for them. Otherwise our effort at guidance or education will be futile or even destructive to the child's growth. At the same time, modern studies in child development and in psychiatry emphasize the fact that the force which motivates any given person at any given moment will be made up not only of the basic drives common to all humanity, but also of a lot of emotional conditionings and forces which are unique with that particular person because they are the product of his own individual experiences.

For example, take two five-year-old children who are hungry and who are kept waiting for dinner. Both have a basic instinctive drive toward food which keeps them restless and irritable. But one child may cry, fret and nag until he is fed; the other may manage to control himself and cooperate in setting the table. Thus one child's accumulated experience has provided few curbs upon his inborn drives; the other has developed additional drives which motivate him to find satisfaction in his mother's approval of self-control and cooperation on his part. The second child has accumulated emotional drives which color or influence the basic, universal or primary reaction in a direction of constructive emotional growth.

Understanding how this can happen, we can, perhaps, begin to understand how genuine control or guidance must take into account not only universal drives but also the specific conditioning or "experience accumulation" of the individual child to be dealt with. When we do clearly comprehend the importance of this, we can see why no teacher should attempt to spend a year with any child until she has made it her business to understand everything possible about his previous experiences and emotional accumulations. If we are to recognize the teacher's business as the guiding of emotion and personality as well as the imparting of factual or academic information, then we *must* clearly conceive of some system of records which will present something of the child's significant preschool history, and which will pass on with the child at least the highlights of his behavior patterns and typical emotional reactions, both inside and outside of school. We must also see that each teacher learns to find out how to use such information effectively in her daily dealings with her pupils.**

* Erikson,[282] Harsh and Schrickel,[406] Honigmann,[434] Thompson.[941]

** Very significant recommendations for teacher education which include training in such understanding and skill were made by an International Seminar on Education and the Problems of Everyday Living called by the National Ministry of Education of France and held at the International Center for Pedagogical Studies in Sévres, France, in July 1954.

More Specific Psychologic Needs.   There is general agreement that, in addition to the need for food, clothing and shelter, rest and companionship, there are other needs which must be filled if children are to grow physically, psychologically and spiritually as they should. All children *need to feel affectionally secure*, to be wanted and loved as individuals. There is ample evidence* that without such love and security, particularly in infancy and early childhood, children not only fail to flourish physically, but will develop certain personality flaws which impede adequate psychologic and spiritual development. This need is best filled in the child's life by his parents, both father and mother, whether they are own or adopted parents, and in the setting of normal family life.

Children *need* also *a sense of belonging*, at first (and all through life) to the parents and to the family, later to peer groups, still later to organized groups. Each child needs to know that there is a place for him, and that no other child can quite fill that place. This feeling must be so soundly grounded that the appearance of another child in his family leaves him all of *his* very own kind of love, while at the same time he accepts the fact that the baby sister is loved for her own particular self. So in the schoolroom, each child must feel a sense of worthwhileness and acceptance by the teacher in such a way that he is not jealous of the "teacher's pet" or driven to bad behavior in order to be noticed. This sense of belongingness involves a basic orientation to all of life; it gives that feeling which most people would understand in the phrase "having roots" or "being anchored to life."

The need for status, or for the feeling of success, is, like the need for belongingness or security, widely recognized by writers as a fundamental human need. There is no pattern for filling this need. The mother of twelve children, with a drunken husband, may feel a high type of this kind of success because she is needed, she is important to someone, life would be poorer were she to die. A lonely orphan, burdensome to the State and to his boarding parents, may find this status or "being-neededness" if he is permitted to have a dog whose devotion is clear and whose life, without its master, would be less complete.

It is in order to build a secure sense of being needed and useful, of earning one's way, so to speak, that children should learn to work. Our recent emphasis upon protecting children from child labor,** our urgent planning to fill children's time with happiness and play, our progressive education emphasis upon making learning quick and easy through projects and easily motivated activities—all this has resulted in depriving children of the opportunity to learn to work for the sheer sake of fulfilling necessary obligations or responsibilities. Plant's[738] emphasis upon the fact that the soundest way to insure the fulfillment of the child's need for status is to teach him to take responsibility and to develop skills which will insure his being needed is timely, indeed. Educators, who understand the laws of learning (especially

---

* Deutsch,[241] Freud and Burlingham,[325] Horney,[440] Ribble,[781] Silverberg,[857] Slavson,[864] Spitz,[884] Thompson.[941]

** An emphasis which must, of course, go on, since "child labor," as represented by the children who must earn their living too young and at too demanding work, must stop.

the law of effect), and who appreciate the principles of emotional conditioning, can perhaps safely be trusted to teach children how to work without damaging them or their attitudes toward work.*

Similar to the need to belong and the need for status is the need *to be like other people*, to feel nearly enough like one's immediate group or circle of friends that one feels part of them and accepted by them—not queer or different. This need seems exaggerated during adolescence, when the young person considers it a major tragedy to be different from his group in clothing or behavior. However, there is, at the same time, a need to preserve the advantage of belongingness for one's own sake. Therefore, the young person manages to vary the general effect by individualized detail. Shirts, sweaters, loafers, provide general effect for the high school or college girl in the 1950's, yet each girl manages a specific color or type of sweater, or some other variation which marks her individuality within the pattern of general identity. There is a need to fit into the group, yet at the same time to remain an individual. So basic is this desire to be in general like one's group that the psychiatrist takes a careful look at the person who, at adolescence, exaggerates marked differences or idiosyncrasies, playing away from rather than into the group pattern. It is the fine balance between socialization and individualization that we must help young people to achieve.

Children *need to learn how to adjust to other people* outside of the family as well as within the family. This means that, although they need to be loved and to feel secure in affection, they need also to learn how to adjust their own desires and activities to the needs and rights of others. Important as it is to provide happiness and emotional security for children, it is equally important to provide discipline. Adults must adjust their demands upon children in such a way as to promote sound growth for each individual child. Each child, in turn, must learn how to adjust his own inner drives and needs so that he can live happily and smoothly with other people and with life situations as they arise. This means that he must be helped to adapt his inner impulses, his feelings and his actions so that he may fit reasonably well into the pattern of the culture or society in which he lives. This adjustment must, of course, be a gradual one, adapted to the child's developmental level, and to his own particular capacities. It is an adjustment in which parents and teachers release responsibility and independence to children by progressive steps throughout the childhood years, so that, by adulthood young people will be self-controlled, responsible and adequate members of society. At the same time the growing child must learn self-confidence, freedom to express and use his best talents and interests, joy of living and sound emotional adjustments. Throughout childhood, then, we see that he needs to be deeply loved while at the same time he is soundly disciplined.

Progressive educators have long preached and practised the imperative

---

* Further discussion of such specific needs as that of accepting one's own sex (e.g. if the child is a boy he should learn to like being a boy and to accept the masculine role; similarly for a girl) and the need for recognizing and adjusting to good authority can be found n Rand, W. R., et al.[756]

necessity for adopting teaching programs to fit at least the most outstanding of the "basic needs" of childhood. They have long taught that our work with children proves exceedingly wasteful unless we adapt our demands and our programs to the *individual* needs of *individual* children. Progressive educators have helped greatly to adapt schoolroom teaching and teaching by parents at home to the "basic needs" of children. They have not always remembered, however, the other aspect of genuinely successful education, namely, that the child must be trained to adapt his instinctive drives to the pattern of society. This requires a nice balance between "understanding" or "moulding the environment to fit the child" on the one hand, and "discipline" or "training in self-control and consideration of others" on the other hand.

It is comparatively easy to "discipline" a child into passive obedience to adult commands. It is more difficult by far to provide the kind of discipline which fosters self-directed conduct and which helps the child to mature into the kind of adult who can carry the responsibility of orderly socialized living. Totalitarian governments produce a passive-obedience kind of "disciplined" behavior through rigid discipline and coercive domination. Democratic governments need responsible adults who can act as independent beings in cooperation with other self-directed adults.

Old-fashioned parents and formal educators, motivated by the "children-should-be-seen-and-not-heard" philosophy, leaned much too far in the direction of forcing adult patterns upon children, ignoring many of their basic needs and building up antagonisms or neuroticism as a result. Then the pendulum swung too far in the other direction in a few ultra-progressive schools or homes, with the result that children received no discipline, their whims were catered to and their "individualities" were permitted to flourish uncurbed. It soon became evident that uncurbed drives are no better than completely suppressed ones. No child who has failed to learn how to control his drives in order to live smoothly with other people can be called an educated child.

We now see the necessity for a smooth balance between the two extreme philosophies. We now know that children cannot learn unless the lessons are tempered to their capacities; that they cannot develop initiative, a sense of responsibility, sound physical health, a proper sense of self-adequacy unless their daily experiences fit harmoniously into their need to grow and develop at their own rate, and unless these experiences produce satisfactions which fulfill their basic inner drives. We know also, however, that society will make certain clearly predictable demands upon children, some as primitive as the demand not to excrete urine or feces except under certain conditions, some as complex as the demand that normal adults earn a living and contribute constructively to the progress of society. Parents and teachers must learn how to educate children in full recognition of the value of both of these philosophies. *

The need to express and develop internal resources is part of the need to balance adjustment to the outside world against the need to live happily with oneself. Therefore, the child needs to learn how to be extrovertive or out-going in

* For an excellent discussion of discipline see Wolf.[1008]

much of his behavior, and needs to learn how to be out-going in a manner which adapts successfully to the world as it is; but he also needs to develop the skills and interests which make a full inner life possible. For some years there was an unfortunate reaction to the psychologist's emphasis upon extroversion, with the result that children's schedules became crowded with group activities.* Parents and teachers became anxious lest children fail to develop enough social skills, enough extrovertive interests. The result was that many modern children had little or no time to play freely, to develop initiative in planning of time or activities, but especially time just to read or dream. Granted that the child who only reads or dreams is failing to develop muscles or social skills, we have erred in permitting too little free initiative and in providing too little time for quiet, restful, unplanned activities for most modern children. The American Camping Association[17] is appreciating this need, and is definitely tending away from the highly scheduled, activity-type of camp to the freer, rest-and-play type of camp. "Children," Plant[738] says, "need time alone, time to just sit under a tree—ripening, so to speak. They need to develop inner resources, and a strong life philosophy, so that if and when their outer world goes to pieces around them, they can still live with themselves."

The Concept of Developmental Tasks. The problem of how to adjust the child's inner physical and emotional drives and needs to the necessity of learning how to live successfully and happily in the society in which he finds himself has been greatly simplified for parents and teachers by the idea of the developmental tasks which each child must accomplish as he grows. This idea is the outgrowth of coordinated work among a group of psychologists and educators, and has been summarized by Havighurst.[412] He defines a *developmental task* (p. 2) as "*a task which arises at or about a certain period in the life of an individual, successful achievement of which leads to his happiness and to success with later tasks, while failure leads to unhappiness in the individual, disapproval by society, and difficulty with later tasks.*"

Some tasks, Havighurst says, arise mainly from physical maturation; others arise primarily from the cultural pressure of society upon the individual. An example of the former is learning to walk when maturation of bones, muscles and nerves has reached the point where the child, unless actively inhibited from it, learns to walk. Learning to behave acceptably with the opposite sex

---

* Typical schedule for a city girl of twelve years:
   School from 8:30 to 11:45 and from 1:00 to 3:00 daily.
   Monday: Recreation club (half-hour by bus from home) 4:00 through dinner to 8:00 P.M.
   Tuesday: Once monthly, children's theatre 7:30 to 9:30 P.M. Three times monthly, neighborhood club 4:00 to 5:30 P.M.
   Wednesday: Music lesson 3:30 P.M. Scouts 7:00 to 9:00 P.M.
   Thursday: Family night at parents' club. Dinner, dancing and games 7:30 to 9:30 P.M.
   Saturday: Dancing school; children's concerts.
   Sunday: Sunday school 10:00 A.M. Church 11:00 A.M. Family drvie 2:00 to 5:00 or 8:00 P.M.
   See Dimock[245] for further discussion of sample schedules for pre-adolescent and adolescent children.

at adolescence is another example of learnings which occur primarily because of maturation, although, once the young person feels the interest drive toward the opposite sex, society steps in with a definition of what the word "acceptably" means. An example of a developmental task which arises primarily because of the cultural pressure of society is the task of learning to read.

Havighurst speaks of a third source of developmental tasks, namely, the personal values and aspirations of the individual which are part of his personality or self. He points out that even by age three or four the child's self is effective in defining and accomplishing his developmental tasks. Examples of tasks arising from this source are choosing and preparing for an occupation, or achieving a scale of values and a philosophy of life.* Erikson[282] has discussed certain emotional problems which must be solved if personality is to develop normally. These are analyzed in Chapter 15.

What Happens When Emotion Is Aroused.   When basic human drives or impulses are aroused the individual may (1) behave in a primitive, undisciplined manner, expressing the instinct directly, without control or consideration of others; (2) repress the behavior entirely, for the moment at least; (3) express some sort of modified, socialized behavior which satisfies the need or expresses the emotion in some socialized form.

Our culture, or civilization, permits inherent drives little, if any, unrestrained expression. One does not wolf food when hungry, eliminate without inhibition, strike or scream when angry, run terror-stricken when afraid. Growing up, or becoming civilized, requires that one learn to eat "with manners," to eliminate only at a given place and under certain circumstances, to express anger not at all or only in order to correct the source of difficulty, to develop courage in the face of fear. Such learning is one of the important parts of the educative process.

According to an old school of teaching, the task of parent or educator was to kill or repress instinctive behavior as the instrument of the devil; "discipline" of the regressive, brute-force type was considered necessary in order to curb the "original sin" in every child. This forceful suppression of original impulses and desires in children led to many cases of neuroticism and insanity and to the type of ineffectual, colorless personality which could

* Examples of developmental tasks which should be accomplished at different age levels are as follows:

Infancy and Very Early Childhood: learning to nurse; to walk; to take solid foods; to talk; to control elimination; to relate oneself to others.

Early Childhood: learning a basic attitude of trust; a sense of autonomy; initiative; baics conscience.

Middle Childhood: learning adjustment to school; to read, write, etc.; building wholesome attitudes toward oneself as a growing organism; learning to get along with age-mates; learning an appropriate masculine or feminine role; developing conscience, morality and a scale of values; achieving personal independence; developing attitudes toward social groups and institutions.

Adolescence: achieving new and more mature relations with age-mates of both sexes; achieving a masculine or feminine social role; accepting one's physique and using the body effectively; achieving assurance of economic independence; preparing for marriage and family life; developing intellectual skills and concepts necessary for civic competence; desiring and achieving socially responsible behavior; acquiring a set of values and an ethical system as a guide to behavior.

express neither good nor bad impulses. Explosions of repressed emotional energy occurred; various forms of psychologic escape (explained later in the chapter) resulted in confused and confusing behavior which neither the individual himself nor his companions could account for. From study of the action of emotions and instincts when completely repressed[250, 323, 440, 680] it was learned that the type of discipline which blocks behavior without redirecting it to other useful channels results in maladjustments of behavior. Only when the curbing or redirecting of instinctive behavior is skillfully done, do we get happy, civilized behavior which is adapted or adjusted to the world about us.

Let us see in a little more detail how this comes about. Whenever a child or an adult finds one of the basic needs aroused within him two things may happen to it: (1) Circumstances may permit its fulfillment. If so, the need will be satisfied and the inner tension, roused as the need was wakened, is released. Inner peace and a sense of fulfillment result. (2) Circumstances may not permit the fulfillment, and a mounting tension or drive is felt by the individual. The individual instinctively tends to seek means of releasing this tension, and may make such an attack upon his environment that he eventually finds a means of fulfillment. Or, if he continues to be unsuccessful in finding release and fulfillment, explosion may result. The basic resistance within the innate psychologic constitution, the background of immediate mood, the long-term accumulation of controls, and of means of finding substitute releases and satisfactions will determine whether the individual will explode childishly or will eventually find satisfactory substitute releases.

If, however, the situation does not permit explosion or if the discipline of the child has blocked even substitute releases, the emotion may continue to exist in an unreleased visceral tension, or it may tend to find disguised ways of expressing itself.

The Role of Inner Emotional Conflict in the Life of the Child. It was pointed out earlier that direct expressions of certain impulses cannot find an acceptable place in our "civilized" society, and that, therefore, the child must learn to control such expressions. It was also pointed out that certain kinds of attempts to control these expressions might take the form of an attempt at complete suppression of the impulses themselves and that the damage to the child which results from such an attempt may perhaps prove serious in his psychologic development. Better as an objective for discipline or control than repression of the impulse is a redirection of the impulse so that it can be sublimated or expressed in socially acceptable ways.

This checking and redirection of native impulses usually occurs because the child finds that his own desires or drives to behavior come into conflict either with his physical surroundings, or with his social surroundings. For example, the very young child may be impelled to try to handle a lovely, bright candle flame, only to find that it burns; or he may try to drive his tricycle through an opening in the hedge which he soons finds is too narrow to permit him to go through. Thus he is checked by his physical environment.

He also soon discovers that many of his desires cannot be fulfilled without running counter to the desires of others. He cannot (or should not) be allowed to keep others waiting upon him when his attendants have other duties or obligations to fulfill. Some families "love" the child too much to submit his whims or impulses to any discipline, and he grows into a "spoiled child" who is unable to conceive of the need to modify his impulses so that they fit the needs and desires of others. Children who have never come into conflict with the rights of others or with the need to obey certain routines in daily life, children who, for example, eat when and what they wish, who go to bed only when they like, who have learned nothing about concentration upon work—such children are utterly unprepared to enter school. Although the family may never have permitted the child to come into conflict with the needs of his own physical routines or with the rights and desires of others, it is inevitable that he will meet such conflict when he enters school. He cannot, in other words, avoid the fact that what *he* wishes to do does not always fit into the machinery of a school day or into what other people want to do. Conflict of the right sort, properly guided and expressed, is not only inevitable[129] but healthy.*

The natural causes of conflict for children are listed by Brown[129] as follows:

1. Change of environment or widening of the range of activities; as when the child moves from one neighborhood to another, or as when he enters school or goes off to college, or otherwise naturally widens the range of his contacts with other people. There are inevitable minor or major conflicts between home and school, home and church, school and church, home or school or church and gang, etc. (See Figure 21 for a diagram of these influences.) In these conflicts the child may feel himself soundly grounded and secure, being convinced of the value of home or church or of school ideas, and yet open-minded toward new things. In this case, he can reach a compromise with the new things fairly smoothly. Or he may be "smug" and unwilling to adjust to the new values. Or he may be insecure, swayed too easily and completely by the new values, yet feeling the tug of earlier loyalties and beliefs.

2. The second cause of conflict for children, pointed out by Brown, is the conflict between the child's own undivided impulses or desires (apart from the training of home or school or church) and the approval or disapproval of his group. He cries, for example, and is called "crybaby"; or he must wait his turn at a game, or submit to rules whether he likes it or not.

3. There is the conflict which rises within him as he encounters the intolerances and prejudices of his surroundings.

4. The conflict between Youth, struggling for freedom and recognition, and Age, which imposes restrictions and forbids opportunity. Youth, here, finds Age hidebound and old-fashioned: Age brands Youth as rash and inexperienced.

* "The child, struggling from infancy to win affection and esteem from each member of the family, is living in a world of conflict. This is healthy. This is splendid. The normal child should earn his way by acts and attitudes which are pleasing to good parents, and bring rewards of approval, success and love. It is conflict which makes life interesting. But it should not be unequal, nor should demands be harsh or evil or beyond the powers of the child."[129] See also Ribble[781] and Davis and Havighurst.[222]

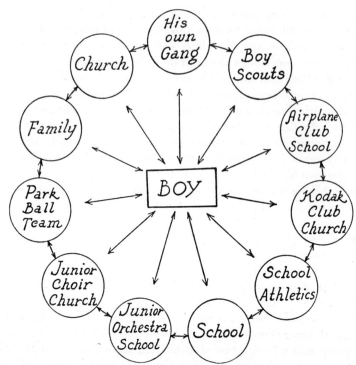

Fig. 21. Conflicting group loyalties of a thirteen-year-old boy. (Brown: The Sociology of Childhood, Prentice-Hall, Inc.)

In addition to this list, there are important conflicts between the child's natural drives and the routines imposed by home and school. Erikson,[282] Bossard[109] and other sociologists bring to our attention the impact of our cultural demands upon children, especially children of school age attending school in the average community. We demand of them (1) attendance at school regardless of how well they fit the available types of school; (2) punctuality; (3) discipline which shows proper, quiet attention and respect for the authorities; (4) "passing" grades; (5) acceptance of the school program, passing hour by hour through the school schedule; (6) acceptance of the prescribed subjects and courses; (7) cooperation with extracurricular activities; (8) cooperation with community programs such as safety programs, thrift programs, and many other such requirements. This is a rather formidable list of demands. Many children find themselves unable to live up to them. Conflict occurs which, when unsuccessfully resolved, results in lethargy, "laziness," bad behavior, or a deep sense of failure.

The wrong kind of conflict, as is so clearly and insistently pointed out by psychiatrists and child psychologists,[54, 266, 272, 406, 864, 941, 1010] not only is unhealthy, but dangerous. Repression and wrong conflict lead to neuroses and delinquency. However, as we have said, the right kind of conflict can prove valuable, since it compels evaluation and judgment, provides training in decision-making, and gives the child experience in making adjustments.

Lrown[129] outlines the values of conflict as follows:

1. Through conflict children learn the necessity of respecting the rights of others; find bases for comparison with standards.

2. Through conflict groups are stimulated to put forth their best effort and to struggle to achieve.

He points out, however, that continued, fruitless conflict, repeated over and over, rouses hatred, fighting and destructive use of energy. Only under proper supervision can we be sure that conflict between children or between a given child and his situation will result in the constructive outcome of learning compromise, fair play, tolerance and achievement in the face of difficulty.

Whatever children learn of standards of behavior at home, they inevitably encounter different standards as they are exposed to the outside world. Young children naturally regard their parents as all-wise and perfect. Parents are tempted to encourage this feeling. Unless prepared for the fact that other people may have other standards, the child entering school may find his security and his trust in fixed standards somewhat disturbed. Adolescents, particularly, as they are exposed to varying standards of behavior, or as their own methods of behaving come into conflict with those of their peer group, may find their goals, ambitions and values badly confused.

In Spite of Many Conflicts Cooperativeness Grows Steadily.　As conflict between children or groups decreases, the amount of cooperation should increase and the type should tend toward higher levels as we shall see in Chapter 13. Unless the child learns some principles of cooperation in his own home, he has difficulty learning them elsewhere. In the family, the constant sharing of the same rooms and the same facilities develops an awakening consciousness of the singleness of the family group, namely, a "we" feeling for the family circle; a "they" feeling for other people. Parents can help to increase this "we" feeling by sharing the activities of the children, but in such a way as not to stultify the growing independence of the child.

Teachers can do much to improve the level of cooperation at which children behave. Yet, teachers cannot do this unless they understand the bases of behavior, namely, emotion and its action, causes and kinds of conflict, methods for changing destructive emotions into constructive ones and poor solutions for conflicts into good ones.

How the Child Learns Control and Redirection of Emotion.　At birth and for a short time thereafter the child has little, if any, mental apparatus which is not identical with his bodily organization.[623] He has certain basic needs, as we have seen, such as hunger, the need to eliminate bodily waste, the need for protection and care. When he is hungry, for example, the inner distress and tension accumulates to the point that it results in an automatic outburst of crying, which does not release the hunger tension but does summon help. It is because the human infant, in contrast to many animal young, is unable to obtain food and to care for his physical needs that he is absolutely dependent upon the nursing care of his mother.

As the nervous system matures the child becomes capable of more differentiated reaction to his environment, of more physical coordination and hence of greater possibility of meeting his own basic physical needs. How adequately he learns these greater differentiations and how well he eventually comes to control his environment are dependent upon how well the adults about him, particularly his parents, help him to develop the necessary awareness, to acquire the necessary skills and to control his inner impulses.* As the infant, and later the child, learns to control his drives he releases energy for constructive development of his personality.** Uninhibited expression of emotion and fulfillment of needs would, in most situations in life, lead to behavior which may cost the individual a tremendous price.

> The young child wants what he wants when he wants it, irrespective of whether his behavior is useful in the long run or dangerous, or whether or not it is at the expense of his own interest or that of other persons or things. (Mahler, *loc. cit.*)

The adolescent who has failed to learn reasonable control over his emotions in general, and who has failed to develop varied satisfactory socialized releases for instinctual drives, will be unable to control his newly emphasized sex drive. He may thus prove not only a social menace to others but a constant source of trouble and danger to his own best welfare.

Fortunately for the child and for Society the child not only develops increasing ability to differentiate factors in his environment, but he also soon learns to value the approval of his parents and of other people. With the development of widening social horizons from three to five or six years of age† he develops the desire to win social acceptance from his parents and older brothers and sisters and later, from his teachers and his playmates. In the normally growing child this desire becomes a major drive which is powerful in controlling impulsive behavior. Davis and Havighurst[222] in discussing this desire for approval say (p. 38), "This drive is really a form of adaptive anxiety. It makes him [the child] anxious, first, to avoid punishment, and, second, to win that approval which leads to social reward."

Disguised Expression. Sometimes the individual hits upon a good form of disguised expression. For example, the child whose urge to physical

---

* Mahler[623] expresses this as follows (p. 45): "The differentiation to higher somatic and psychic organization depends largely upon the successful interpolation of inhibitory controlling agents between perception and action."

** Again, Mahler phrases this (*loc. cit.*): "Whereas the newborn and young infant has nothing but affectomotor paroxysms at his command to release tension and summon help, later on the infant will follow his mother with his eyes in a coordinated way. He will not only cry but wait patiently, because he has learned through repeated experience that his mother is going to feed him at certain times. The difference in behavior between the newborn infant and the three months old, for instance, demonstrates that the controlled drive, like controlled water power, becomes useful energy for ego formation; and indeed, in the entire growing-up process we can see that the controlled impulse is the mechanism which furnishes strength to the ego. In other words, the ego develops into the inhibiting and controlling organization that watches over the instincts which are unruly and blind, and which, if not controlled, would seek release even at the expense of the person's most elementary safety."

† See Chapter 13.

activity is blocked because of illness or a crippled body, may find outlet for his energy as well as status both in his family and among his peers by learning to draw, or to detect an unusual number of bird species, or to play a musical instrument. On the other hand, he may hit upon a poor substitute for finding the satisfaction he seeks. He may, for example, play up his weakness, trying to find in sympathy the attention from adults and peers which he cannot find in approval of accomplishment. Or he may escape into unproductive daydreaming* and tend to live more and more in the world of unreality, and, therefore, less and less in the world of productive action. This is a favorite way of running away from disagreeable situations. Harsh treatment of children who daydream will only force them to retreat still further and hence to daydream still more. Most children can be coaxed back into the world of reality by gradually increasing interest in things in which they can find success. The object with such children is to find something in which they can succeed and with which they can win love and attention, then gradually to widen the areas in which they can find constructive satisfactions.

Another form of disguised emotional behavior may be the development of physical complaints. When an individual cannot find satisfaction in successful action he sometimes tries to solve the problem by developing bodily inadequacies which offer a reason for the failure or which can be used as an excuse for not meeting a situation. One child, for example, developed a sick stomach every morning about half an hour before school time. In most cases a quiet insistence that the child face the necessary situation will provide the necessary help to him and he will eventually overcome his need to escape. This is possible, of course, only when the school situation can be made to provide him with genuine satisfaction. To the degree that the school situation continues to be painful and frustrating to him, he may return physically, but he will be sure to find other means of escape, as, perhaps, daydreaming in school.

One should, however, be careful about forcing children to face situations from which they seek escape. Sometimes children, especially in the first year or in the early years of school, have been so poorly prepared for school entrance that they are emotionally unable to take the impact. Forcing such a child to face the situation may develop in him so deep an emotional association with fear and uneasiness that he may never learn to enjoy school and, therefore, to utilize his full intellectual potentialities in the situation. Such a child should be accompanied to school by a parent or older child, and should receive some special attention from the teacher until such time as his home in cooperation with the school, can help him grow up enough so that he can take school on his own. There is a difference between coddling a weak child into further weakness, and giving him a helping hand over a truly difficult situation. Parent and teacher should both learn the latter art, and should also develop the ability to detect a situation which requires a gentle, but firm insistence upon facing a difficulty. Force, like throwing a frightened

---

* Some forms of daydreaming lead to action, serve as sources of inspiration, or the solution of practical problems. These are productive daydreams.

child into the water to teach him to swim, will only result in a deeply associated fear of water for years to come, perhaps for life.

Another form of escape from frustration or failure is to make excuses which are not the real reasons for one's behavior. For example, the child who fails a fair examination because of lack of adequate study may claim that the examination was unfair, or that he could not study because he had lost his glasses. If he finds it difficult to recite in class he may convince himself that people who recite are "show-offs," or that silence displays more sense than to risk possible wrong answers. He may blame the broken desk or the torn book on someone else, or insist that the desk was broken before he occupied it. One should not jump to the conclusion that any child who appears to be offering excuses or "alibis" is lying or rationalizing. Sometimes the desk *was* broken when he occupied it, or someone else *did* tear the book. Few things upset a child or lose the parent or teacher real influence with a child or with the rest of the children in the room more than a false accusation of lying when the child is really telling the truth. On the other hand, children who habitually escape into rationalization should be given the help of a gentle but firm facing of facts. Some children can be helped by an appeal to the prestige and "manliness" of telling the truth and making adequate restitution for mistakes.

Some children follow the false pattern, which is frequently set for them by adults, of attempting to build up their own prestige by attacking the prestige of others. Tattling, petty gossip, constant unfavorable criticism of others are almost a sure sign that the individual who does these things is insecure within himself and has resorted to a false means of building his own sense of superiority. The idea seems to be that if other people can be made to appear stupid or vicious, then I am automatically better than they are. This is an unprofitable way of building prestige and usually results in the loss of friends, either actual or possible, which, if won would give the sense of belongingness and prestige or status which the individual feels he lacks. Children who use such false means of finding inner comfort should be helped to develop constructive means of winning and holding friends, and to learn constructive accomplishments which will give the status they crave.

Discipline of Children Must Guide Rather than Suppress.   We have seen what happens when emotion is suppressed rather than redirected. It is important that discipline should not be of the unduly severe type which sets off the autonomic nervous system or which forces the child to suppress or to cover up his emotion. It should, rather, be of the type which helps the child to understand himself as well as the world about him, which teaches him gradually increasing control and socialized expression. The object is not to avoid emotion, but, rather, to utilize and guide it. Some vigorous emotion is desirable, since emotion is at the root of all purposeful motivation and provides the energy, not only for inner personality development as we have seen, but also for all really uphill work. Constructive emotions need to be preserved. It is the destructive emotions which most need redirection and control. Parents and teachers alike have great influence upon the pattern and speed of the child's emotional development. Methods which stimulate rivalry, jealousy, material greed, fear, or revenge should be scrupulously avoided. Courage, desire for approval (if not overdone), sympathy (if not maudlin), love of fellows, joy in a hard job well done, and other such constructive emotions should be cultivated.

Emotion Is Contagious.   Emotion is, of course, contagious in the sense that it spreads from person to person. A cross teacher soon has a room full of cross children; a fearful child may learn calmness from being near a calm child. Conversely, of course, a cross teacher may feel herself "healed" and quieted by the joy of being with her children so that she ceases to be cross before she has set them off; and a calm child may learn fear from a fearful child. The strength or valence of the emotion determines whether it will dominate another emotion or be dominated by it. Adults of normal emotional strength in dealings with children are, on the whole, stronger in emotional valence than are children, and can, therefore, set the tone of a group. Adults with weak character, of course, lose the control of even young children.

This should not be confused with the fact stated elsewhere that children imitate or are influenced by the opinions of other children so that they "stray" from the ideas set by parents. In the long run, the parental pattern dominates the totality of the child's behavior unless the parent is weak or loses the child by trying to use force on an arbitrary basis. In any given situation, the adult can more easily set the tone of gaiety or severity, of nervous tenseness or of calm than can a child. Teachers can develop an "atmosphere" in a schoolroom, even when the major trend of the atmosphere is contrary to the previous experience of the children. For example, a group of good workers can be made lazy by a slovenly teacher, or a disorderly group can become reasonably orderly, calm and busy; a fearful, evasive teacher will set an atmosphere quite different from that established by a courageous, direct personality.

Further aspects of the influence upon the child of his family, which is his most insistent immediate environment, will be discussed later.

DEVELOPMENT OF THE EMOTIONS

What constitutes emotional maturity is important for the understanding of emotional stability. Many forms of emotional behavior now called unstable by teacher and parents might better be described as immature forms of reaction. A systematic account of the pattern of normal development of emotional behavior still requires more research than has yet been done. However, much has been learned to date. Some of the observations about patterns of emotional development follow.*

As emotions develop there are changes both in the nature of the stimulus which proves effective in rousing emotion, and in the manner of the ex-

* For a helpful discussion of the meaning of maturity in emotion and personality see Overstreet.[712,713]

pression. Young children* are roused to emotion by tangible events which impinge directly upon their senses. As the child grows older and as his capacity to perceive, to remember, and to anticipate events develops, we have seen above that he becomes emotionally responsive to signs and symbols which promise furtherance and guidance of his welfare and his wishes. He thus becomes increasingly able to control his impulses. As children grow older they will, if given adequate help by adults and if their lives are satisfying emotionally at each level of development, tend to outgrow certain infantile fears, angers, jealousies, joys and pleasures. They will not cease to be afraid or angry, or glad; but they will learn to be stimulated to fear by different, or more "grown up" situations. Their joy will be aroused by less childish things and will be expressed in less childish ways. Expression will be less gross and explosive and will become more subtle and indirect; emotional states will be less transitory and more prolonged and even.[475, 660, 668, 941]

The reduction of number and kind of emotional outbursts does not depend solely upon change of form of the expression of the emotion. Another aspect of the development of emotion lies in the nature of the emotion itself, as well as in the type of the stimulus which sets off the emotion. Fear, for example, may change to apprehension or uneasiness; anger may change to resentment; the "jump-up-and-down" kind of joy may change to pleasant anticipation.

Progress in Crying.   A number of studies of crying reveal a pattern of growth that one may readily observe in normally growing children. In infancy the child cries with vigorous, total bodily expression and largely for causes such as hunger and other internal discomforts. Even by six months of age the vigor and the total amount of crying are greatly reduced, being replaced by the milder expressions of fussing or vocalization. As the child grows through the preschool years he cries less and less; when he does cry it is usually for reasons of physical pain or because he is thwarted by the environment or by playmates or family. In the school years the pressure of the peer group (or gang) helps him to outgrow the "baby" habit of crying. Ultimately, crying in mature adolescents and adults becomes limited in our culture to quiet crying in private only and for reasons of grief or other intense emotion.** Loud crying because of pain or annoyance is socially unacceptable in most cultures, as are outbursts of rage or overt expressions of fear.

Development of Anger.   Goodenough[362] and Gesell[347] both found infants responding with anger to minor physical discomforts, interference with physical activity, removal of attention, or with situations which arose in connection with routine care such as dressing, bathing and the like. Gesell found tantrums at eighteen months caused by resistant objects, as well as by transitions from one activity to another, such as those imposed by necessary routines. At twenty-one months the cause of anger was often a failure to make the rudimentary language then at the command of the child

---

* For an excellent discussion of the development of emotions in infancy and young childhood see Rand[756] and Read;[759] in adolescence, see Cole,[191] Hurlock,[450] Kuhlen,[554] and Malm and Jamison.[624]

** In some cultures loud wailing in public to express grief is expected.

understood by others. Goodenough found a large percentage of anger responses at two years of age arising in connection with establishment of physical habits, with conflicts over authority, or with problems of social relationship particularly with playmates. Responses to minor physical discomfort and restriction of bodily movement were reduced by two years of age. Gesell, however, found anger responses at two and a half years still due chiefly to interference with physical activity or with possessions, with a noticeable reduction of anger for these causes appearing only at about three years of age. Difficulties with playmates as a source of anger reached a maximum between three and four years of age, though other social relationships continued to provide frequent reason for anger after four years.

Goodenough[362] reports that infants and young children respond in anger in a direct and primitive manner, but that as they develop the responses become less violent and more symbolic. Gesell[347] found children of fifteen months expressing anger by throwing objects. At eighteen months they throw themselves down, hit, kick or struggle as expression of anger; they are often rough with children or animals, stamp or step on them, poke, pull, or push them. At two years they may hit, poke, or bite other children, and at two and a half years they often attack other children aggressively with conscious intent to hurt them. At three or four years language begins to take the place of physical aggressiveness as an anger response, the child often calling names, bragging or boasting, making angry, sarcastic, cutting or sullen retorts, swearing, tattling, or using irony or insinuations.[347, 475]

In groups of preschool children who have been together long enough to form a social group, one popular form of showing resentment against another child is to exclude him from the group. Among children who have not been together as a group in the preschool years, this type of anger outlet may take place for the first time during the early elementary years. In any case it remains a frequent means of discipline of one child by another even into adolescent years. Gesell finds a period of less aggressive expression of anger at age five, but a renewal of violent methods of expression at six, with hitting and kicking as typical behavior. At seven, however, less anger aggressiveness seems characteristic; although kicking and throwing stones was observed. The child may now remove himself from groups, rather than try to force the withdrawal of others. By eight and nine years the "hurt feelings" expression of anger appears; in the normally growing child physical aggressiveness is almost at an end, being replaced increasingly from five years on by arguing, alibis, calling names or the making of disagreeable remarks. We see, then, that as children grow older in the early school years, anger reactions become more directed toward a single person and take the form of attempts to hurt the feelings rather than to injure the body of the offender. After-reactions, such as sulking and resentment, increase into the school years.

Socialization, or group play, increases steadily in the preschool years, reaching a peak of development in the early elementary school years, as we shall see elsewhere. *Quarrels increase as group play increases*, since children, playing by themselves, are crossed in the fulfillment of their ideas or are interfered with less than when other children are present, especially when the other children are sharing an idea or equipment in well-organized group play. An important part of the gang-age education lies in learning to maintain such close personal contacts without quarreling. With group contacts at a height, but with skill in social contacts only in the making, it seems evident that quarreling will be frequent and not too skillfully conducted in the late preschool and early elementary school years.

We have far less definite studies of the development of aggressiveness or anger in children of elementary and secondary school ages than we have in preschool children. However, there are many clinical analyses, especially those of the psychoanalysts which help us to build a fair picture of what the successive sequences of development toward "maturity" in anger are. In general we know that children pass through an early elementary school period of loudness and boasting, of gruffness and sauciness toward adults and toward each other. To a close observer this often appears to be whistling to keep up one's courage. Faced with adjustments to school, competition on school playgrounds (much larger and much more crowded than neighborhood lots or home yards), beyond reach of a quick run to mother—all this puts a good deal of strain on most children. They "woof," "boast," and bluster at each other, often finding that the louder the bluster the greater the success among their peers. They sound tough, trying to convince themselves as well as others that they *are* tough. The habit easily fixes itself, and comes stalking into home or schoolroom. More than that, the child seems to feel that what intimidates peers might possibly have the same effect on adults— one can only try it and find out. This disturbs adults, and gets children into trouble.

In dealing with anger in children it should be remembered that many outbursts of anger, especially in young children, are caused largely by the child's lack of skill in handling situations. Explosions of anger diminish in frequency and intensity as children gain skills in the performance of difficult tasks.[452,964] As we shall see later, many behavior problems occur at given stages of growth, being simply by-products of the lack of skill. Such behavior problems are best handled by quietly waiting for growth with its increase in skills and understanding. During the preschool and early school years when much of the anger displayed by normal children is due to the child's inability to handle a given situation, or to the pressure which adults put upon children for learning, adults should be as serene and tolerant as possible in dealing with children.

If discipline for anger behavior is too severe, children may too soon repress these forms of behavior with resulting accumulations of emotional tension and conflict. Control must, however, be developed by gradual, steady stages if the child is to outgrow childish behavior. It is interesting to note that children may submerge overt responses while they are still childish enough emotionally to feel angry over situations to which they have learned not to express anger in open behavior. Studies of the children's play[61,406,522,680,732] show that even young children release certain aggressions or hostilities in play which they cannot release in the direct situation which roused the feelings. Many situations rouse anger or aggression in children,[250] but fortunately any healthy person, whether child or adult, can withstand a considerable amount of frustration without becoming chronically hostile.[440]

A great deal of understanding is necessary if one is to discipline children wisely. For example, children may appear to be very immature in anger reaction when, in reality, they are being pushed beyond reason. A task which is easy for one child may prove an intolerable burden to another, less able child, or to a child who has not had a background of learning in emotional control. Again, it is easier to achieve control when circumstances are favorable, as in the case of a child living in a small, well-regulated, peaceful and well-balanced family. The child who lives with a large family all of whom feel free to boss him, or several of whom are immature and overdemanding or otherwise emotionally unstable will find himself constantly interfered with and frustrated. Control of anger for the latter child is a far more difficult problem than it is for the former child. Children who are physically not up to par also have a more difficult problem of emotional control. Discipline should be adjusted to meet such situations. Parents should evaluate the home situation and the personal background of each child. Teachers should understand the home background and the individual situation of each child if they are to be of the greatest possible help in emotional development.

The Development of Fear. As in anger, both the stimulus to fear and the response develop. In infancy physical and immediate stimuli are the typical source of fear. Such stimuli are sudden noise; strange objects, situation or persons; situations, persons or objects associated with pain; sudden removal of support.[377,479] In general, anything unexpected seems to arouse the startle reaction in infants.[242] Such stimuli rouse not only the startle reaction but also fear reactions in most children up to two years of age. From two years to five, children are roused to fear increasingly by animals; the prospect of being left alone or abandoned by loved persons; dangers associated with the dark or imaginary situations; possible injury through fire, automobiles, etc.[347,475] The increase in such fears indicates the impact of our culture as a factor in determining emotional responses, since these are the things preschool children are typically warned against, or, in the wrong forms of discipline, threatened with as penalties for undesirable behavior.*

As the child passes from the preschool to the elementary school age he becomes more apprehensive about failure and humiliation. In other words as he develops courage and skill, he learns to fear less the threats to his physical body; but as his awareness of and reaction to social situations develops, he learns to fear threats to his prestige and to his ego.

Gesell[347] found that children of six years show fear of the supernatural such as ghosts and witches, and of the elements such as thunder, rain, wind and fire. Some children also showed fear that the mother would die, or that something would happen to her. There was also fear of being late to school,

* For excellent material see in Childhood Education Magazine series of articles on "Dealing with Fear and Tension," 1951–52.

which in the experience of the authors, is proportionate to the pressure exerted by the school for promptness and the penalties exacted for tardiness. By seven years Gesell's children were showing deeper, more worrisome fears such as fear of war, spies, burglars, people hiding under the bed. However they were beginning to resolve the fears by such methods as using a flashlight or getting someone to precede them into feared places. Such social worries as not being liked by parents, teachers or playmates appeared, the fear of being late to school persisted and fear of not finishing school work was added. Fears stimulated by reading, radio, and movies also appeared. By eight years Gesell found less fear of the elements, though fear of fighting, of failure, and of not being liked may still persist. By nine years he found his children worrying mostly about school failure, though some were worried about other competitive situations, as well as about trouble at home. Self-judgment is at this age so well developed that some children also worried about their own mistakes. Zeligs[1017] in a study of sixth graders found that they were most frequently worried about matters of health, bodily injury or pain, school marks and grade promotion.

In adolescence the chief source of fears and anxieties shifts to sexual inadequacies such as physical inadequacies or other reasons to fear that one may fail in boy-girl relations.[107, 628, 1016]

In both the elementary and the high school ages, the child's worry may be, and often is quite disproportionate to the likelihood of the actual happening.[479] On the other hand, when actual disaster strikes, as in the severe bombings of World War II, children show an amazing capacity "to take it."[106, 355, 481] How children "took it" depended far more upon the courage and morale of the adults near them than it did upon the actual physical experiences to which the children were subjected.[6, 481]

Associated or Conditioned Fears.   Many fears of persons at all ages are not actual fear of the many situations which seem to arouse the feeling of fear, but are, rather, associated fears. Once frightened by an object or situation, the individual tends to feel fear of people, objects or situations associated with the original fear situation. For example, children who have been badly handled or who have had extremely severe pain in a doctor's office may thereafter display panic at all persons in white coats. Having been frightened by a dog at a given corner of the street, the child may become uneasy whenever near that particular corner. Having been embarrassed by a real or fancied awkward situation on a first or one of the early dates, an adolescent may thereafter avoid dating because of the uneasy feeling he gets whenever he contemplates a date.

Individuals differ markedly in their susceptibility to such nebulous or generalized fears. It has been observed that people who have a past history of many fears and of general emotional instability tend to react with more severe fright to a given situation and to generalize the reaction to more associated fears.[481] Also, there seems to be a "halo" effect following any severe fright; an individual who has, for example, recently been through a severe automobile accident is almost inevitably "jumpy" about situations which would normally leave him quite undisturbed. A child who has recently seen his drunken father beat his mother or threaten the children in the family will probably be distractable and nervous for a time. Children who are severely disciplined for trifles at home are usually less courageous and self-confident about everything they face than are children who have less reason to fear the consequences of their behavior.

Parental Fear Affects Children.   Children are also responsive to the fears of their parents, either the fears parents have for themselves, or the fears the parents have for their children. These parental fears not only suggest danger to the child but, because the parent is fearful himself, parental fears undermine the child's confidence in the protection which his parent affords him.

Some Reasons for Fears.   Behind the fear of many children as well as grownups are feelings of guilt about some real or fancied offense against the authority of the parents, or, as the conscience develops, against the authority of their own consciences. As we have seen, children as early as eight years of age can worry about their own mistakes. In the fifth and sixth grades children report worrying about such items as "making your parents sad," being scolded, telling lies, doing wrong, etc.[736] Psychoanalysts[241, 323, 440, 864] call attention to fears which are rooted in a sense of guilt, especially those associated with impulses and conflicts related to sex.

People who have been ill frequently seem to exhibit more fears than other people who have been free from serious illnesses. This may be because children who are often ill lack physical strength, with the result that they feel less equal to emergencies. It may also be that children who are often ill sometimes feel the anxiety of their parents that they may die, and hence tend to carry a vague uneasiness which healthy children do not experience. Such submerged fear of death is frequent in children suffering from severe diabetes since they actually live in danger of death. It is also true of children who suffer heart ailments, although many of the cases of anxiety among rheumatic fever cases are due to misunderstanding and overanxiety of parents whose children are not actually in immediate danger of death. Deaf and blind children, being less able to hear or to see and hence to react to danger, typically suffer more fears than do normal children.

Occasionally anxiety in a child is rooted in an overprotective attitude on the part of the mother. Protection, according to Levy[585]

. . . refers to the usual maternal protection of the child against physical danger, illness exposure to bad influence, and the like. "Overprotection," in its specific meaning, consists largely of the mother's refusal to take ordinary risks for her child. She may not let him play with other children for fear, she says, of contagious diseases or of learning bad habits. She may allow the child to play with other children but only in her presence. . . . The indulgent mothers yielded to the demands of their children, allowing them to raise havoc with the rules of the household, rules relating to the discipline of time and speech and food and possessions. The indulged children were undisciplined in all these respects.

When the child is surrounded with protection from possible danger, both physical and psychologic, he comes to feel that life is somehow a dangerous business. The result is likely to be vague uneasiness, timidity about many real and fancied situations, or outright fears. The solution to such fears is, of course, in part a change in the feelings and attitudes of the mother on the one hand, and in part an education of the child. Fundamental treatment of such a mother should probably not be undertaken by anyone less well trained in understanding of the basic personality drives than a psychiatrist. Environmental treatment of the child consisting of visits away from the mother, such as trips to summer camps or to relatives, and a development of the relationships with other children usually produces good results. Some demonstration to the mother of how to handle temper tantrums and disobedience, some broadening of her interests and increasing of her social contacts may help.

How Fears Are Overcome. Many fears appear and disappear in the course of normal growth. As the child develops fears about the dark, about traffic dangers, about being abandoned or left alone in the preschool period, the normal course of growth which gives him greater understanding and greater competence tends to dissipate the fears. If he develops apprehension about failure in school he may find that success is reasonably certain with good effort; or he may develop compensations for continued failure if his experience requires this. Much of what happens to him here depends upon the attitude of his family. If he fears social humiliation or sexual inadequacy in adolescence the achievement of social skills and success will remove the reason for his fear; or, if failure overweighs success, he may develop compensatory interests and activities. Difficulty arises when failure to achieve success, coupled with continued adult pressure, prevents the development of adequate compensations. The result in such cases is continued apprehension and emotional conflict.

Fears of unfamiliar things tend to yield to wider acquaintance with the environment and the growing awareness that new things may more often prove to be fun than dangerous. The experience of familiarity with new places and new situations which prove not to be dangerous removes the initial sense of apprehension with which many children react to the new and unfamiliar.

Many fears which arise in connection with some frightening event will normally fade through forgetting if there is no renewal of associations either by a repeated event or by continued reminders of the event by adults or other children. Frequently fear due to an unfortunate contact such as with an injudicious stranger will fade if not repeated, but will give way to happier experiences with strangers if such experiences are provided. Fear of dogs may, for example, yield to the love of one's own puppy if a puppy is given the child to care for.

There is much that an understanding adult can do to help children overcome fears. A thorough check of physical difficulties and a reasonable program of physical hygiene may restore a child to the level of physical vigor at which he can feel equal to the demands of life. The acquisition of physical and mental skills increases the child's equipment for meeting life and tends to increase self-assurance. A check on the demands being made upon the child by adults or peers may reveal a source of anxiety lest the child fail in meeting his own or someone else's idea of success. An atmosphere of under- standing and sympathetic appreciation along with the security of a fairly regular regimen does much to reassure timid children. Children who fear the unfamiliar may be made more courageous by a program of meeting new things and situations under the auspices of a friendly adult or older child. Explanation and preparation help a little, especially if not overdone to the point where the child becomes suspicious that overpreparation for a situation implies danger. Explanation, however, is not nearly as effective as exposure to the situation under conditions in which the child feels secure and can develop familiarity plus a feeling of protection or security, or in which the situation proves so pleasant that the positive emotion comes to replace the negative. This process of "reconditioning" the child to a given situation may or may not be successful, since unless skillfully used there is a chance that the child may react to the situation so negatively that the actual negative emo- tion outweighs the planned positive emotion.

Poor methods of trying to overcome fear are ignoring it (although this is better than making too much of it); temporarily removing the cause; forcing the child to face the situation without providing him the security of a trusted adult or other child (such as thrusting him into a dark room "to show him there is nothing to be afraid of"); verbal pressure of ridicule. Any of these methods may intensify the fear.

The play interview technique in which a friendly adult helps the child to express hidden fears and to reorient his feelings toward feared situations is helpful.[407, 680] Play techniques will be discussed later in this chapter. Learning to live with fear is important to ultimate mental health because the inroads of fear upon peace of mind and efficiency of living are great. Longtime or acute anxieties force one into a psychologic position in which excessive amounts of psychic energy are absorbed or in which destructive defenses and compen- sations are built up.

The Development of Other Emotions. The development of emotions of love and sympathy will be traced in some detail later (Chapter 14). It is more difficult to trace the development of emotions other than fear, love, and anger since much less work has been done on them. Several studies of jealousy show what happens in behavior when the child is jealous, rather than how the emotion of jealousy develops. These studies[586, 795, 358, 866] show that when children are jealous of a younger sibling they may revert to infantile habits, such as wetting, demands to be fed or dressed, even when they can care for themselves. Or they may take out the suppressed hostility felt toward the baby by scolding or punishing a doll, or in other ways give vent to feelings which they may not express openly. Occasionally the behavior takes the form of unwonted displays of affection toward the baby as a cover-up; or the child may bid excessively for adult attention by excessive affection or helpfulness, or by tattling or lying. Sometimes the behavior is varied and unpredictable, the child, being troubled, trying any and every means of meeting his prob- lem. In fact, none of the studies reveal any behavior which is typical of jealousy alone; all show behavior which could exist in a child troubled by any type of troubling situation.[475]

Studies of laughter and humor[117, 348] show evidence of laughter in the early months of life which resulted as a rule from a gay approach or from nursery tricks on the part of an adult. Gesell[347] notes that at two years the child may himself initiate humor, and may carry on such a game as peek-a-boo even without adult support. At two and one-half, the child may be handled by humor, such as an answer of "yes, yes" to his "no, no"; by seven years this ability to be handled by humor has disappeared. In the preschool years laughter is associated largely with bodily activity and social play,[113, 347] and with feelings of well-being (running, romping, chasing), exciting physical contacts such as tossing and tickling, opportunities to be self-assertive, and other such physical or ego-satisfying occasions. Gesell[347] reports humor at three and one-half years which is involved in imaginary play; at four years humor is likely to be silly and boisterous, wild laughter sometimes accompanying play; at five the child enjoys slapstick humor, which he initiates. One study[555] showed humor at the preschool level in response to inferiority in others, and one[98] showed laughter in nursery school children when a conflict which had lasted or kept the child on "the horns of a dilemma" had been resolved.

One study[555] of children from seven to eighteen years of age concluded that the development of the sense of humor parallels the development of both intellect and other emotions than humor. This study, which was done on English children, showed that the most frequent sources of humor in children of seven to ten years of age was deviation from the normal; at eleven to thirteen years, discomfiture of other people and deviations from the normal. From fourteen to eighteen years there was increased appreciation of verbal humor. Other studies[140, 421] corroborate this in part, in showing that incongruities and distortions of pictures create laughter in young children.

Gesell[347] shows a development of humor which corroborates one's own observations of children of elementary school age, namely, that they are not only reactive to the type of incongruity, frailties, inferiorities and failures of others as shown by the above studies, but that they are also reactive to less negative aspects of life. He found, for example, that although children of eight years enjoy the type of humor in stories in which one person is fooled by another, thus making someone uncomfortable, by nine years they enjoy the element of surprise in stories and even begin to enjoy jokes on themselves. General observation of children of the upper elementary school years shows how much these children enjoy broad puns and other plays upon words. Already they are capable of enjoying many of the radio humorists put on the air largely for adult consumption. If the child's sense of humor is growing as it should, it should give way to the development of the sense of sympathy for others, and the inclination to laugh at the discomfort of inferiority of others should wane. Most emotionally "mature" adolescents have learned not to laugh at such situations, and even to feel discomfited themselves when others do so.

The possibility of being amused at jokes which concern bodily elimination and sex develops as the child develops repressions about either one, or as he is led to think that such jokes show grown-up humor. Such jokes are particularly likely to be exchanged among boys in the later gang age and adolescence. Young people whose sex education is sound, and whose appreciations and interests are widened into varied and wholesome channels, soon grow beyond the desire to spend time on such types of humor.

Behavior Problems. Space will not permit a long discussion of behavior problems. It is important, however, to point out that many so-called behavior problems are merely aspects of normal growth. As we have seen above, explosive expression of emotion is characteristic of very young children. Crying is normal at the early levels of development; anger at physical restriction or thwarting of immediate desires is charactertistic of early preschool levels; fears are usual and numerous throughout the childhood period. In the process of development from childish ways of expressing emotion there are many stages at which behavior is explosive, resistant, or fearful. Parents and teachers who understand children will know when such behavior is a phase of growth and when it is a symptom of something wrong in development.

True behavior problems are those forms of behavior which indicate that something is wrong with the child himself or with the environment in which he lives. For example, perseverance of an early form of emotional behavior into later ages, such as crying over minor physical hurts at six or eight years of age, or bursting into anger over simple frustration at five or six years of age would indicate that the child is not developing in these categories since he is behaving as a much younger child would. This may be an indication of a basic retardation in general growth, as would be true of a feeble-minded child who, even with expert treatment, lags behind the normal rate in all areas of physical and psychologic control. Or it is far more often an indication of wrong treatment of a potentially normal or superior child by the adults who have charge of him. We shall refer throughout the book to the types of behavior which, though troublesome, are merely aspects of growth as it occurs within the framework and under the pressures of our particular social culture. When behavior cannot be understood in terms of a passing stage of growth, or a fairly normal attempt on the part of the child to orient himself to the reasonable frustrations and pressures of life, then the reason for the retardation or the deviation should be sought. If the behavior is excessively immature, excessively explosive, or excessively withdrawn the services of a skilled guidance person (preferably a child psychiatrist if one is available) should be obtained.

Projective Methods of Studying and Treating Behavior. As was said above, children move forward in emotional growth from more overt and obvious forms of expression of emotion to more subtle and socially acceptable forms. As they do this it becomes less possible to judge what their inner feelings and reactions are. If one is to understand and to help children it is important to know what motivations and feelings are potent in determining their behavior. The fact that children sometimes reveal feelings and motives in make-believe settings or in play situations has led to the use of projective methods for discovering inner feelings and to the projective or play technique for helping children to straighten out inner conflicts which lead to difficult behavior.[61, 318, 407, 680]

The projective, or play technique analyzes children's attitudes and feelings through studying their play, their drawings and paintings, their stories, or any other creative activity.* It is also used as a means of helping children to overcome inner conflicts and tensions by making it possible for them to express through play or in the special circumstances set up by the therapist, the ideas and feelings which their environment will not permit them to express otherwise. The basic assumption behind the use of this technique is that children express their inner emotional needs through their work or play if they are permitted to do so. Particularly in free, creative work does the child utilize his clay, or paint, or blocks, as a means of expressing inner wishes and inner conflicts. He does so, too, in free play, utilizing games, or dolls, or imaginative situations to say what he dare not or cannot say directly. Intelligent and understanding study of the creative work and free play of individual children reveals much of their inner emotional life. Properly interpreted, such "projections" of the child's self into his work or play can help teachers to understand and to guide individual children who may need special help. Through the use of the projective technique with children, teachers, if properly trained to do so, are urged not only to interpret children's work and play, but also to provide special opportunity for creative work and free play which can be utilized by children for expression and, therefore, relief of inner conflicts. Properly directed, such "corrective" work or play can be used as a means of correcting emotional difficulties.

There is a natural temptation for amateurs or novices, people who have just discovered, for example, that "a stormy picture" may, on occasion, mean "a stormy inner life," to "interpret" everything children do. This is a great mistake, since accurate interpretation of the meaning of "projected" emotions requires expert training. Far more harm than good results from false interpretations; so that, unless the teacher is especially trained, she should not attempt to interpret seriously, or to correct the deeper-lying emotional conflicts of individual children. As soon as possible, however, every teacher who presumes to do even a reasonably adequate job of personal guidance with her children should become familiar with the potentialities of projective techniques as a means of understanding and helping personality growth in her pupils.

EXPERIENCES TO VITALIZE CLASS WORK

1. Visit some children at play. Select the child who seems best adapted to his group, and the child who seems most poorly adapted. If you are doing a case study, get the following information on your special child:

* A particularly comprehensive bibliography on projective techniques can be found in Sargent.[808] Further items may be found in the bibliography.[237, 238, 318, 680]

a. How does each of these children handle his own emotions? What emotions does he display? (Watch closely for the less obvious emotions.)
b. How does each of these children handle or respond to the emotions of others, both adults and children? What conflict situations do you see?
c. Which of the basic needs are being fulfilled for each of these children? Which frustrated and repressed? How do you see this reflected in their behavior?
d. What strains and what satisfactions is each of these children experiencing in the current week of his life?
e. Do the physical condition and the daily routine of these children reflect in their emotional behavior?
f. Is there anything you could or should do about them if you were their teacher?

2. Trace your own emotional history, or that of someone you know well. Which of his emotions are functioning on a mature level for his age? Which on an immature level? What circumstances produced the maturity, or prevented it? How strong do you think his psychologic constitution is?

3. Keep a diary for several days of your own feelings of anger. What caused them? What did you do in each instance? What should you have done?

4. Do the same for feelings of fear and anxiety. Can you trace the reasons for these fears and anxieties?

5. Look up the current literature (from 1950 on) for further development of projective techniques, or other methods of studying and treating behavior of children.

6. Look up current literature (from 1950 on) for studies of the development of constructive emotions such as joy, sympathy, and love.

SELECTED READINGS

Bakwin, H. and R. M.: The Clinical Management of Behavior Disorders in Children. Philadelphia, W. B. Saunders Co., 1953, Ch. 36.

Despert, J. L.: Play Analysis in Research and Therapy. A chapter in Lewis, N. et al.: Modern Trends in Child Psychiatry. New York, International Universities Press, 1945, pp. 219–256.

Jersild, A. T.: Child Psychology. Revised ed. New York, Prentice-Hall, Inc., 1954, Chs. 9, 10, 11.

Mahler, M.: Child Analysis. A chapter in Lewis, N. et al.: Modern Trends in Child Psychiatry. New York, International Universities Press, 1945, pp. 265–290.

Millard, C. V.: Child Growth and Development in the Elementary School Years. Boston, D. C. Heath & Co., 1951, Ch. 11.

Rand, W., et al.: Growth and Development in the Young Child. Revised ed. Philadelphia, W. B. Saunders Co., 1953, Ch. 10.

Thompson, G. G.: Child Psychology. Boston, Houghton Mifflin Co., 1952, Ch. 5.

Thorpe, L. P.: Child Psychology and Development. New York, Ronald Press, 1946, Ch. 9.

CHAPTER 4

Influences on Growth—*(NUTRITION AND ROUTINES)*

The potentialities for growth, as determined by heredity, cannot be realized without adequate food and conditions favorable to the physiologic processes which convert food into body tissues. Even the life processes of the first cell, or the beginning of life, depend upon specific chemical substances which are present in the cell itself. As the cell multiplies and differentiation takes place, different types of cells acquire different structures and, therefore, have specific needs. Bone, for example, must have calcium and phosphorus in relatively large quantities for its growth. Muscles demand proteins and certain inorganic salts while nerves require, among other things, a fairly large supply of fat-like substances, called lipids.

Going hand in hand with the structure of these tissues are their functions. These functions depend upon the constitution of the tissues plus the materials which are brought to them by the fluids in which they are bathed. Thus the normal beating of the heart depends upon the concentration of the calcium salts, and the quantitative relationship of calcium to sodium and potassium in the fluid which bathes the heart muscle. Nerve irritability, also, is dependent upon these minerals. The secretions of the digestive tract, and of the endocrine glands require supplies of specific substances, as will be shown later.

Food, the source of these necessary materials, becomes all important for the mother during the prenatal period and for the child after birth in providing the body with its needs for growth and activity.

IMPORTANT CONCEPTS

As a basis for understanding the role of nutrition in the development of an individual certain fundamental concepts need to be kept in mind. By so doing the student is able to view with perspective the significance of food and its use in the body during the growing years.

Wholeness. The concept of wholeness, as discussed in Chapter 1, applies in the area of nutrition. What people eat and how that food is utilized by the body in promoting growth and well-being affects and is affected by not only the physical but also the emotional, social and cultural aspects of life. It is important to be aware of the multidisciplinary nature of the child and his relationship to his environment when appraising the influence of nutrition upon development. It has been seen in Chapter 3 how emotions can affect a child's acceptance and use of food. An individual's food can also contribute to his emotional stability. Social prestige and religious practices play important roles in the acceptability of foods. Since man satisfies his nutritional needs according to the food resources of his environment a disturbance of these food resources, such as those which can occur in times of devastation of war or draught or in times of change from diversified farming to the raising of a single money crop,* will affect the nutrition of the people.

The concept of wholeness applies also in nutrition in the reliance upon natural foods rather than purified food stuffs in satisfying nutritional needs and in providing a satisfactory balance of nutrients. In order to build new protein for bodily tissue all of the essential amino acids must be provided at approximately the same time.[12] Too few calories may interfere with the retention of nitrogen[621] which is necessary for the building of protein. The lack or overabundance of one nutrient may affect the body's use of another as, for instance, the need for vitamin D in the laying down of calcium in bone. Thus it is better to think in terms of a well balanced diet rather than focus attention upon one nutrient while at the same time minimizing the importance of others. Natural foods are important because they contain more of the essential nutrients than refined foods and may also provide nutrients the value of which is not known at present.

Flexibility. The body has an important degree of flexibility in its nutritional processes. Studies** with "tagged" atoms demonstrate that nutrient materials are distributed promptly and widely to the different organs and tissues of the body where they may be used in the replacement and renewal of cells and molecules as well as in the building of new tissue. To say that the body is like an engine is not wholly true since the parts of an engine do not change, while those of the body are in a constant state of activity or flux. Even tissues such as fat, bone, and tendon which at one time had been thought not to change after once formed, are now known to be changing constantly.† Thus tissues may be called upon to provide nutrient materials as well as to receive them. *Body is constantly changing.*

Flexibility is also demonstrated by the body's ability to adapt itself within limits to different nutritional levels. Thus when food is limited the body can still function by reducing the amount of energy it expends through lessened activity, loss of weight and a slowing down of the basal metabolic rate or the amount of energy necessary for bodily functions.

Individual Differences. The concept of individual differences also discussed in Chapter 1 applies in the area of nutrition. Different children varying in size and rate of growth will likewise differ in the quantity of energy and nutrients needed for that growth. Also children are different in their ability

---

* de Castro[228] gives several dramatic examples, one of which is that of the Bantu in Africa. Before the arrival of the European settlers the Bantu, who lived by raising cattle, growing corn and hunting, were strong and healthy. With the disorganization of native economy the diet became almost exclusively corn. Pellagra, a deficiency disease unknown forty years ago, became endemic.

** Schoenheimer.[813]

† For a discussion of these metabolic processes see Gerard.[342]

to utilize foods so that some will need more to fulfill their needs than will others. Studies have shown that children eating the same food and living under the same conditions will require different amounts of a substance, as for example, calcium.[449] This means that allowances must be made for this variability when providing food for children. A liberal rather than a minimal intake, according to nutritional knowledge today, is advisable whenever possible since it is impossible to determine the metabolic efficiency of each child in order to ascertain his particular requirements for maintenance and growth.

FOOD AFFECTS HEALTH AND GROWTH

Studies of the dietary habits of groups and their growth, observations of deprivations in war-torn countries and under experimental conditions, and observations of the effect of supplements to the diet upon health and growth indicate the important effect food has upon the physical well-being and growth of individuals.

Dietary Habits and Physical Status. A study of the relationship between man's natural diet and his physical status has been presented by Orr and Gilks.[710] Two African tribes, the Masai and the Akikuyu, live side by side but have very different dietary customs. The Masai live largely on meat, milk and blood. Various roots and barks are used for "teas." The pregnant women are sent into the bush to eat berries. This diet is rich in growth-promoting substances. The Akikuyu diet consists chiefly of cereals, tubers, plants, legumes and green leaves. This diet is limited in growth-promoting substances, especially calcium. The men eat chiefly corn, sweet potatoes or other cereals and tubers. The young children, up to five years of age, are given edible earths from salt licks and ashes of certain swamp plants. One of these earths is especially high in calcium. The girls continue to use these sources of minerals and also have a monopoly of some kinds of green leaves rich in calcium. Even with the supplements for children the Akikuyu diet is not adequate for the best growth.

Comparing the adults, the mature Masai male is, on the average, five inches taller and twenty-three pounds heavier than the mature Akikuyu, and his muscular strength is 50 per cent greater. Deformities of the bones, decayed teeth, spongy gums, anemia, pulmonary diseases, tropical ulcer and other diseases fostered by poor nutrition, are more prevalent among the Akikuyu than among the Masai with a better diet. A study of the children up to eight years of age showed that more than 60 per cent of the Masai boys and girls were rated very good in general physical condition, while only 7 per cent of the Akikuyu boys and 29 per cent of the girls were so rated.

The value of a better diet is shown not only in the comparison of the two tribes but also in the difference between the boys and girls of the Akikuyu tribe. Further evidence of the inadequacy of the diet for promoting growth is shown in the comparison of the growth of the Akikuyu infants with that of English babies. It is found that during the first month the Akikuyu infants are about half a pound heavier than English babies. For ten months the rate of growth of both is similar. After ten months the rate of the Akikuyu infants is slower and at thirty months they are about 8 pounds lighter than the English. This is one of many examples cited in the literature on nutrition which indicate that differences in dietary habits among groups of people contribute to differences in physical status.

Such observations of the dietary habits and growth and health of a people suggest that differences in growth patterns in families and groups of families may have some dietary as well as hereditary basis. It seems probable that family food patterns carried over from one generation to another may be contributing to the differences in the growth of children. Generally speaking, children of today are taller and heavier than children of former generations[649, 829] and are maturing earlier.[368, 663] Nutrition is thought to be one of the factors associated with this increase.

In this period when children have been growing better, there have been shifts in the relative importance of various foods which have been consumed in the United States.[726] There has been increased consumption of dairy products other than butter, citrus fruits, green leafy and yellow vegetables, on the credit side, and refined sugar, on the debit side. These trends, except for the sugar, have enriched diets from the nutritional point of view, and indicate that people are eating more of foods which are important in promoting health. The enrichment of wheat flour[991] and corn meal,[570] with thiamine, riboflavin, niacin, and iron in both and additional calcium in the latter, of converted rice,[526] the fortification of margarine with vitamin A and the fortification of some milk with vitamin D have also contributed to improving the quality of the American diet.*

There are vast differences in the food eaten in families. Income, availability of foods, family size, management and food habits are factors contributing to these differences.[726] Many families still have inadequate food** even though, according to Stiebling[896] in 1949 the food available in the United States, if shared in accordance with need and used with discrimination, was sufficient to give everyone an adequate diet. Studies of differential growth in the different socio-economic levels point to nutrition as a contributing factor. More information regarding the long-term effects of diet upon human beings is needed.

Effect of Nutritional Deprivations during Wartime. Growth of children in weight and to a lesser degree in height has been shown to be affected during wartime by restrictions in food intake caused by scarcity of food.† The extent of the growth deficit is related to the severity of the undernu-

---

* Sebrell[828] reports that the average American in 1945, compared with the period before enrichment was introduced, received in his food 27 per cent more thiamine, 19 per cent more niacin, 17 per cent more riboflavin, and 17 per cent more iron. The greatest increase occurred in the low income groups.

** An example of this condition is given in a survey of families living in rural areas in 1945 (a peak year of supply). In a county of Georgia the food of one third of the white families and two thirds of the Negro families provided less than two thirds of the dietary allowances for one or more nutrients as recommended by the National Research Council.[726]

† For a summary of evidence accumulated during World War I and World War II see Keys, A., et al.[525] Vol. II, Ch. 45.

trition* or mulnutrition. Older children tend to be affected more than the very young, perhaps because the younger children in the family may receive a relatively larger share of the available food than the older ones.

Evidence comes from observations during World War II in France,[956] Belgium,[278] Greece,[965] and Holland.[505] In Holland in 1945, for example, most children over one year of age lost weight, and toward the end of the famine period they ceased growing in height. In Greece 55 per cent of the three- to eight-year-olds were underweight for height in 1942 and 1943 and 64 per cent in 1944. In a French study[956] of children from six to twenty years of age the thirteen-year-old girls were the most vulnerable. Following World War II observations of French children[956] and those of Dutch children liberated from Java and sent to Australia for rehabilitation[230] indicate that children can recover from periods of deprivation, if they have not lasted too long, and will catch up in growth in height and weight. Keys[525] states that from past experiences it can be safely assumed that the food crises of the 1940's in many parts of the world, *if they were not of too long duration*, will probably have no permanent harmful effect on the generation of growing children. However, children who continue to grow up with inadequate food will not have the opportunity for rehabilitation and thereby will be unable to achieve their potential for growth.

Minnesota Study of Human Starvation. The war studies cited above refer to the effect of underfeeding upon height and weight. Information of the effect of undernutrition upon the physiologic processes of such children is lacking except indirectly by the manifestations of such characteristics as chronic fatigue, lack of vigor, listlessness and inactivity as noted, for example, by Stuart[913] during World War II in a group of French children between twelve and eighteen years of age. It seems pertinent, therefore, to cite briefly some of the results of the Minnesota Study of Human Starvation,[525] which demonstrated the effect of severe underfeeding and later restoration of adequate food on a group of young men.**

It was found that all parts of the body underwent change during semi-starvation. Much of the fat disappeared, active tissues—especially muscles—decreased, more water was held in the tissues, while the bones changed relatively little. The men's physiques changed because of the loss of sub-cutaneous fat and muscle. Bodily processes slowed down, including circulation; basal metabolism was lowered; and blood sugar decreased. The skin was cold to touch and the men complained of feeling cold. Sexual functions were reduced; sperm were less mobile and lived a shorter time. Moderate

---

* Undernutrition is a condition due to inadequate food in which the deficiency is quantitative rather than qualitative, i.e., a deficiency of calories with the nutrients fairly well balanced. Such was the condition in much of Europe during and directly following World War II, described in Studies of Undernutrition, Wuppertal, 1946–1949.[645] In malnutrition, on the other hand, there is a deficiency of specific nutrients, e.g., the deficiency of vitamin B complex found in the Japanese prison camps.[869]

** Thirty-two mentally and physically healthy young men, living under carefully controlled conditions, were observed and tested during three successive periods: 12 weeks of adequate diet, 24 weeks of semi-starvation diet, 12 weeks of increased food intake.

anemia developed. Strength and endurance decreased markedly. The men complained of feeling weak. Slowing down of voluntary movements was observed. Coordination deteriorated whenever steadiness of the whole body was involved. On the other hand, no change was observed in accurate movements of small muscles nor were sensory mechanisms disturbed. Capacity for work, both in long, steady and in strenuous activity, decreased. This was shown both in the work done and the lowered efficiency of circulatory and respiratory mechanisms. These physical changes were accompanied by changes in behavior which will be discussed in the following section.

When the food was increased the men improved, although the response was not prompt nor synchronized for all structures and functions. After thirty-three weeks of rehabilitation the men were substantially back to normal. During that time water in the tissues decreased. Fat increased more rapidly than muscle. Muscle regained slowly. Likewise, muscular strength and endurance were slow to return. The extremely slow recovery of strength was reflected in a delayed return to the men's former capacity for work. After twenty weeks of rehabilitation the endurance of the men was still far below that at the beginning of the experiment. Functioning of heart and lungs and energy metabolism gradually improved. The anemia gradually disappeared. Sexual functions, as measured by mobility and longevity of sperm, also gradually improved and returned to normal generally about the time of renewal of sex interests and desires. This experiment has demonstrated that the body does not respond immediately to improving the food needs of men after a period of starvation, but rather that the process of recovery is gradual and tends to be slow. While the result of this experiment cannot be applied directly to children it seems reasonable to assume that functional changes occur in children as well as young adults under conditions of severe underfeeding.

Limited Calories Affect Growth of Healthy Children. That too few calories can be a limiting factor in growth has been demonstrated in healthy children living under satisfactory conditions. Macy et al.[621] in a study of children living in an excellent institutional environment found that too few calories may not only interfere with satisfactory weight gains but also may reduce the amount of nitrogen available for the building of body tissues. One boy who was losing weight and nitrogen gained weight and retained nitrogen when 10 calories for every kilogram (2.2 pounds) of his weight* were added to his diet daily.

Supplementing the Diet. Studies have shown that improvement of inadequate diets can improve the health and growth of children. Spies and his co-workers[878, 254] have demonstrated that milk added as a supplement to poor diets of malnourished children will improve their growth. Children of four to fifteen years of age during a twenty-month period of supplementa-

* A total of little more than 200 calories, equivalent to about a glass of milk and a slice of bread with butter.

tion* averaged an increased monthly gain of 3.6 per cent in height and 29 per cent in weight. When the milk was withdrawn for the following twelve months the improvement ceased. These children gained an average of 1.23 cm. (.48 in.) and 1.35 kg. (3 lb.) more than another group of ethnically and nutritionally comparable children. But even with the supplement very few of the children completely reduced their growth lag. This was thought to be due, separately or in various combinations, to too little additional food, too little time on the experimental diet imbalances in the diet, and irreversible changes produced by long-term undernutrition.

A second study[883] was made of the skeletal maturation of 82 children, half of whom received a dietary supplement of dried milk equivalent in protein value to three quarts of milk per week for forty months after which the supplement was increased to twelve quarts of milk per week for six months. The other half of the children served as controls. During the forty months little difference in progress in bone maturation was found between the two groups. However, when 19 of the experimental group were given twelve quarts of milk a week they increased their rate of bone maturation by 80 per cent over that of the former period and far surpassed the other children who had no milk or only three quarts. Whole milk and skimmed milk were equally effective. Apparently the three quarts of milk per week did not supply sufficient bone-forming nutrients to produce a change. The quantity as well as the quality of a supplement is important.

Supplementation of a diet with a specific nutrient may correct a chronic deficiency. A survey in a community in Vermont[127] revealed signs (conditions of the eye, the gums and the tongue of school children) indicating possible deficiencies in vitamin A, vitamin C and niacin. Half of the children showing these signs were given vitamin A, vitamin C or niacin, depending upon the specific signs and the other half given placebos. The difference between the two groups in improvement was significantly in favor of those receiving the supplement. This study and the former ones cited indicate that improvement of an inadequate diet according to the nutritional needs for an individual child may very appreciably affect his health and growth.

NUTRITION AFFECTS BEHAVIOR AND MENTAL PERFORMANCE

Behavior. Nutrition can affect behavior and emotional adjustment.** However, to demonstrate a clear-cut relationship between nutrition on the one hand and behavior and emotional adjustment on the other is extremely difficult since nutrition is only one of a number of factors affecting the expression of interaction of the individual and his environment. Nevertheless the effects of undernutrition or malnutrition can be discernible in situations which are complicated by poor physical environment and emotional stresses

---

* Six quarts of milk per week were added to a diet deficient in calories and in several of the essential nutrients. The milk was given as reconstituted milk solids equivalent in protein value to that contained in six quarts of cow's milk. Some children received whole milk; some received skimmed or non-fat milk.

** See Keys, A.,[525] Vol. II, Chs. 36–42.

and strains. Periods of severe underfeeding provide evidence. Spies et al.[879] describe a child whom they had observed from 5 to 12 years of age. He was a white boy, the fourth child in a family of ten that had lived on a diet consisting chiefly of cornbread, biscuits, fat pork, sugar, occasionally turnip greens, corn, tomatoes and berries in season. Rarely did this child have any milk, eggs, meat, fish or cheese. At 5 years of age he was retarded in growth and showed clinical evidence of deficiencies in thiamine, riboflavin and niacin. His mother reported that he had had "cracks"* at the corner of his mouth most of his life and frequently his tongue was red and sore.** During the following three years his mother complained that he was "fractious," and his teacher stated that he did not concentrate on his school work, had poor grades and was quarrelsome. At eight years and nine months he was given a skimmed milk supplement which increased his intake of protein, calcium, thiamine, riboflavin and niacin. No other changes were made in his life. During the first year there was little change in his lip and tongue condition, his disposition and his school grades. Following that year gradual improvement in lip and tongue symptoms were noted. His mother reported great improvement in his disposition. His teachers said that he could concentrate better on his studies, his school grades had improved and his behavior was excellent. This relatively small improvement in his diet had contributed slowly to somewhat better living for this child even though it was insufficient to improve his growth rate in height and weight.

The behavior in school of children in Trier, Germany, during World War I is another example.[96] After three years of undernutrition the children showed a decrease in physical and nervous energy and an increase in nervous disorders. The teachers reported that the children grew tired more easily than in the prewar days, were unable to concentrate, slower in comprehension, poorer in memory, inattentive and restless. Discipline was hard to maintain. One teacher reported that she could keep the attention of her class for only five minutes in contrast to thirty minutes formerly. The standard of school work was lowered. The number of children who failed to pass about doubled; the number of children doing superior work was not compatible with their mental capacity since the children apparently had not lost any of their mental capacity as measured by the usual mental tests. They lacked the staying qualities found in a well-nourished child.†

Observations during starvation in real life situations have been corroborated by the changes in behavior of the subjects of the Minnesota Study on starvation. The progressive anatomic and biochemical changes which produced sensations, drives and limitations to physical functions rendered the men increasingly ineffective in their daily life. During the period of semistarvation men who had been energetic, even-tempered, humorous, patient, tolerant, enthusiastic, ambitious and emotionally stable became tired, apa-

---

* Symptom of riboflavin deficiency.
** Symptom of niacin deficiency.
† It should be noted that lack of food was also accompanied by unfavorable conditions at home and school due to the war.

thetic, irritable, lacking in self-discipline and self-control. They lost much of their ambition and former self-initiated spontaneous physical and mental activity. They moved cautiously, climbed stairs one step at a time, and tended to be awkward, tripping over curbstones and bumping into objects. They lost interest in their appearance. They dressed carelessly and often neglected to shave, brush teeth and comb their hair. They became more concerned with themselves and less with others. It required too much effort to be social. Their interests narrowed. The educational program which was to prepare them for foreign rehabilitation work collapsed. Humor and high spirits were replaced by soberness and seriousness. Any residual humor was of a sarcastic nature. They had periods of depression and became discouraged, in part because of their inability to sustain mental and physical effort. They were frustrated because of the difference between what they wished to do and what they could do. They found themselves buying things which were not useful at the time. They stopped having "dates." All sex feelings and expression virtually disappeared. All the time they were being distracted by hunger sensations and showing great concern about and interest in food.

When their food was increased during the rehabilitation period their psychologic recovery was somewhat faster than their physical improvement, although many months of unlimited diet passed before recovery was complete. Emotional stability and sociability were regained more rapidly than strength, endurance and sexual drive.

The sudden feeling of improvement, however, was temporary. Morale became low because many anticipated quick, complete recovery. As energy increased, they no longer were willing to accept conditions unquestioningly and showed annoyance at restrictions. Many grew argumentative and negativistic.* Humor, enthusiasm and sociability reappeared; irritability and nervousness diminished. The feeling of well-being increased the range o interest. The sense of group identity which had become strong during the semi-starvation period was dissipated as men began looking forward to making plans for their futures. An interest in activity and sex increased, their concern about food decreased after a period of insatiable appetite when they were first permitted to eat all they desired.

These were general trends in behavior changes, but considerable individual differences were noticed in the men's ability to withstand the stresses and strains of the experience, which appeared to bring out their innate strengths and weaknesses.**

Intelligence. It has been shown that undernutrition or malnutrition can affect mental activities or the way an individual uses his mental abilities. However, whether nutrition affects the mental capacity of children is a moot

---

* In a study in Scotland of the effect of milk consumption on the growth of school children[573] the teachers were asked to give their general impressions of the effect of the milk supplement upon the children. One teacher remarked, "In the playground buoyancy and pugnacity are developing to an alarming extent." No doubt these children had more available energy to expend.

** Some of these behavior changes were reflections of personality changes measurable by psychologic tests.[525]

question. Mental capacity seems to withstand deprivations which will affect mental activity. The children in Trier, Germany, in spite of their poor school performance had still the same mental capacity as measured by tests. In the Minnesota Study, according to both clinical judgment and quantitative tests the men's mental capacity did not change appreciably during either semi-starvation or rehabilitation. The subjective estimates of loss of intellectual ability may be attributed to physical disability and emotional factors. Whether similar resistance exists at earlier ages when the nervous system is immature has yet to be demonstrated. *

The original promise that glutamic acid fed to mentally defective individuals might improve their level of intelligence has not been fulfilled. The conflicting results, due probably to differences in procedures and interpretation, and the mounting negative evidence seem to indicate that glutamic acid is not a "brain food." **

There have been some investigations of a relationship between some of the B-complex vitamins (i.e., riboflavin, thiamine and niacin) and intelligence. A well controlled experiment[383] with men, planned to test deprivation of these vitamins and subsequent supplementation of thiamine, has been reported but no comparable experiments have yet been done with children. Young men were partially and then severely deprived of thiamine, riboflavin and niacin, after which thiamine was restored. A minimal drop in two out of six tests, in which speed appeared to be the essential factor, occurred during the period of deprivation. There was no evidence of an impaired rate of learning. However, there is little doubt that definite, prolonged vitamin deficiencies, especially of thiamine and niacin, will eventually result in mental retardation. †

Studies of the effect of thiamine supplements upon learning ability have given no assurance that adding thiamine to the diet of school-aged children will be followed by increased ability to learn. ‡ Harrell's[401, 402] reported positive effects were not confirmed when Robertson et al.,[788] using identical twins and thus controlling the genetic factor, fed thiamine supplements to one of each of the twins, all of whom lived at home.

At the present time we have no means of ascertaining the effects of inadequate diets fed to children throughout their growing years. When the mental abilities of children thus deprived have been followed throughout their growth period there will be better evidence to ascertain to what degree nutrition affects the development of intelligence.

Evidence has been cited that underfeeding has a real effect upon the well-being of an individual and is reflected in his behavior. It would be wise, therefore, to keep in mind the nutritional needs of children and to meet them

---

* An experiment[87] with rats deprived of vitamin B showed a varying response at different ages. During the 6th to 12th weeks such deprivation resulted in no difference in water-maze learning from that of a control group, but the rats deprived during their nursing period showed considerable retardation in learning.

** For specific references and summary of results see[360] and[269].

† See Spies, T. D., et al.[880]

‡ For discussion of studies see [268, 647, 939].

wherever possible. When lack of spontaneous activity, undue fatigue and irritability are apparent it would be profitable to investigate nutrition along with many other factors.

NUTRITIONAL NEEDS OF CHILDREN

There are two fundamentally different kinds of food needs, termed *energy requirements* and *structural requirements*. The body requires energy for many activities, such as beating of the heart, breathing, digestion of food and voluntary muscular activity. Energy is also needed for growth. This energy requirement, expressed in calories (total calories or calories per pound of body weight), is obtained chiefly from carbohydrates and fats.

The Energy Requirement. The amount needed varies from individual to individual and is dependent upon a number of variables, none of which can be considered independently but rather as a part of a constellation of variables. It differs with *size*. A large child requires more energy-producing food than a small child. It differs with the *rate of activity of the body processes while at rest*, that is, with the basal metabolic rate. The faster the rate of basal metabolism, meaning the faster the heart beat, respiration, etc., the greater the number of calories used in a given time; and, conversely, the lower the rate, the lower the number of calories needed.

The energy requirement differs, too, with the *amount of voluntary activity*. A very active child requires more calories per day than a quiet one. The same child will need more calories during a day of vigorous activities than during one of quiet activities.* It differs also in accordance with the *efficiency of the body in using foods*. Some bodies are more economical in the use of foods than others. In some cases food is more easily digested and absorbed than in others. In all individuals some food value is lost in bowel movements, but the amount varies considerably from child to child. Finally, the need for calories depends on the *rate of growth*. The fast-growing child will need more calories than the slow-growing child. During the periods of his life when the impetus to grow is most intense, infancy and pubescence, the amount of energy required for growth will be greatest.** It is not surprising that the baby eagerly demands food and that parents of pubescent children complain that their boys and girls cannot be filled up. In order to permit growth there must be a surplus of energy over the actual energy expended by the body.

In proportion to their weight, children's food needs are greater than those of adults, because of children's relatively greater basal metabolism, their tremendous activity and their growth. Figure 22 indicates how energy needs of children will outstrip those of their parents during early adolescence, when children are both active and growing rapidly. Boys generally catch

* In a series of studies[927, 928, 929] nine- to eleven-year-old boys increased their energy output over their basal metabolism 202 per cent for dressing and undressing, 44 per cent for sitting and listening to a recorded story, 54 per cent for sitting and singing, 63 per cent for quiet play and 219 per cent for cycling. In the first three activities, girls exerted less energy than boys.

** Johnston[484] shows that the caloric requirement of the adolescent girl parallels her rate of growth.

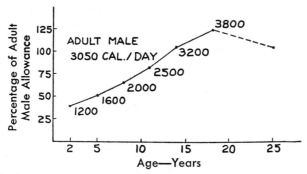

Fig. 22. Calorie needs of boys expressed as per cent of adult needs. (Calorie needs represented by N.R.C. allowances using as male adult needs a value midway between the 25 and 45 year male allowances.)

up with their fathers in need for calories between thirteen and fourteen years and exceed them by 25 per cent at eighteen. Girls generally equal their mothers in their energy needs sometime between eight and eleven years, exceed them at fourteen by 13 per cent, after which their caloric needs gradually drop to the adult level.*

If sufficient food is available and the child is well and has a good appetite, he will meet his energy needs. A well rounded diet, with emphasis on the "protective" foods, as discussed later, will include sufficient calories.

The Structural Requirement. The structural requirement covers the needs for materials which go to make up tissues and to regulate the functions of those tissues. The child does not require in a ready made form all the chemical substances which he uses for building tissues; he can make some of them himself if given the necessary materials from foods. The necessary food elements, or nutrients, are something like 40 in number, including some of the amino acids from proteins, at least one digestive product of carbohydrates, namely glucose, some unsaturated fatty acid or acids, derived from the digestion of fats, minerals and vitamins. The body needs all of these in adequate amounts for the building and repair of its tissues and for these tissues' daily activities. Since all foods do not contain all of these nutrients, a balanced diet of "protective" foods, that is, foods rich in the essential nutrients, is necessary.

Some Ways in Which Minerals Function. Minerals serve as *constituents of tissues*. Calcium and phosphorus are responsible for the rigidity of the bones and teeth. The softer bones of children contain less minerals than the firmer bones of adults, and the process of hardening, called ossification, demands calcium and phosphorus in generous quantities. An inadequate amount of these minerals may result in poor teeth and poorly formed bones. Poor teeth are a barrier to good health and attractiveness. Poorly formed bones detract from the attractiveness of an individual and limit his physical efficiency. These minerals, together with others, are also a part of the soft tissues of the

* Calculated from N.R.C. allowances,[688] using a figure midway between the twenty-five and forty-five year allowance.

body, such as muscle, nerve and blood cells. Phosphorus and iron are necessary components of every living cell, in both the nucleus and cytoplasm. Phosphorus is an important element in muscle, glandular and nervous tissues. Iron is a part of hemoglobin, that substance in the red blood cells which makes it possible for oxygen to be carried from the lungs to the various parts of the body and for carbon dioxide to be removed, thus serving in the function of respiration and contributing to the life activities of all the tissues. Iron cannot be available for this function unless copper is present.

Minerals serve as *regulators of body processes*. The part played by minerals in the beating of the heart and in the activity of the nerves has been mentioned. For coagulation of the blood the body needs calcium. Too little calcium in the blood at the time of an accident may result in excessive bleeding and perhaps death. Phosphorus takes part in the chain of events in muscle activity and in the transfer of energy. The digestive juices, such as salivary, gastric and intestinal juices, depend upon minerals for their acidity or alkalinity. Digestion depends upon a condition of acidity in the stomach and alkalinity in the intestine. Minerals regulate the flow of liquids in the body by which substances are absorbed, passed to and from body cells and excreted through kidneys or intestines. Iodine is a part of thyroxin, the hormone of the thyroid gland. Without iodine the proper functioning of this gland, normal growth and the maintenance of health are impossible.* These minerals play many and varied roles in the body. Their importance cannot always be gauged by absolute amounts. Relative amounts or the balance between these minerals must be considered as well.

Some Ways in Which Vitamins Function. The vitamins, as regulators of body processes, have a vital role to play in keeping children well and furthering their development. The vitamins now recognized as contributing to the health and growth of children and youth are vitamins A, D, C, K, thiamine, riboflavin, niacin, B_6, folic acid and B_{12}. There are also vitamins of undetermined significance, such as others in the B complex group and vitamin E. The value of the latter to man has not been definitely established, although in animals it has been demonstrated to be necessary for reproduction and for the health of muscles and nerves. It is also believed to protect some substances, such as vitamin A, from oxidation. Vitamin K aids in the formation of prothrombin which is associated with the mechanism of blood clotting. Sufficient amounts of K to meet human needs are produced by bacteria in the intestines except shortly after birth, before the intestinal flora has been established, and possibly during prolonged treatment with sulfa drugs.

Vitamin A, itself, or carotene, its precursor, which can be converted by the liver into vitamin A, is a necessary part of the visual process and thus is associated with the ability to see in dim light. A lessened ability to see after the intensity of the light has been changed (night blindness) may occur because of a vitamin A deficiency.

* See the discussion of the thyroid gland in Chapter 2.

Vitamin A is also necessary for maintaining the health of epithelial tissue, namely, the tissue of skin, covering of the eye, the lining of the respiratory, alimentary and genito-urinary tracts. A deficiency of vitamin A structurally impairs what the Journal of the American Medical Association called "the body's first line of defense." With the change in epithelial tissue local infections occur and bacteria may penetrate through the walls of the injured membrane which is no longer able to resist their invasion.

In addition it is necessary for the orderly development of bones and teeth. It seems to direct the activity of the two types of cells involved in the process of bone formation.[642] It is also essential for the formation of enamel of the teeth. Given the other necessary elements—calcium, phosphorus, vitamin D—but a deficiency of vitamin A, the cells responsible for the laying down of enamel will not be able to perform their function satisfactorily and defective teeth result.

Vitamin D is essential for the normal growth and mineralization of the bones and the teeth. The body cannot make proper use of the calcium and phosphorus supplied by food unless vitamin D is present. Rickets in infancy, and occasionally in adolescence, dramatically demonstrates failure in calcification. In addition to preventing the condition of rickets, a liberal amount of vitamin D tends to promote growth, provided there is sufficient calcium and phosphorus to meet the needs of growth of soft tissues and bones. According to some infant studies,[471,865,891] there appears to be an optimum of vitamin D for promoting growth beyond which increasing the D has a depressing rather than a stimulating effect upon growth in length. This effect of D on the rate of growth of bones in infancy would point to the need for sufficient vitamin D throughout the growth period. The need for vitamin D in older children has also been demonstrated.[485] This need for D in promoting growth is one reason for prescribing cod liver oil or some other fish liver oil for infants and children.

Together with other factors, vitamin D is of importance in the formation of normal teeth. The fact that calcium and phosphorus constitute a large percentage of tooth structure is indicative of the importance of vitamin D in its formation.

Thiamine is one of the vitamins in the B complex. Others now known to be associated with human nutrition are riboflavin, niacin, folic acid, B_6 and B_{12}.* Thiamine is essential for the maintenance and normal function of the nervous system. It has been known for some time that beriberi, a disturbance of nerves, can be prevented by including sufficient thiamine in the diet. In studying the function of thiamine in the body it has been found that it is necessary in carrying carbohydrate metabolism through an essential step. With a deficiency of thiamine certain acids, particularly pyruvic acid, accumulate in the tissues and this accumulation is apparently responsible for many clinical symptoms. A deficiency in thiamine lowers efficiency in

---

* Other factors in the B complex will not be included in this discussion since their roles in human nutrition have not been established definitely.

physical work,[960, 961, 1000]* mental activity[525] and in morale.[132] The experiments referred to here were done with adults as subjects. As yet only clinical observations have been made on children.

This vitamin also has some contribution in promoting growth. Experimentation with animals and demonstration with infants and older children have shown the importance of this vitamin in promoting growth.[679, 796, 918] This vitamin is necessary, also, for maintaining a normal appetite** and the normal motility of the digestive tract. Undoubtedly, decrease of appetite and a disturbance in digestion resulting from a lack of thiamine are factors contributing to its effect upon growth.

Riboflavin plays an important role in the internal environment in which the body cells live, where it is involved in the life processes of active cells. Riboflavin is, therefore, essential to growth and to normal nutrition at all ages. A deficiency produces characteristic changes in the lips, tongue and skin. Deficiencies in riboflavin in children have been noted. A study[881] of Alabama children, four months to fourteen years of age, who had been living on diets deficient in riboflavin demonstrated that they were usually underweight and underdeveloped. Many were apathetic, indifferent and were making poor progress in school. Frequently they complained of a sore mouth and itching and burning of their eyes. These symptoms waxed and waned with the season and the changes in the quality of the diet. Increased exercise and infection precipitated borderline cases. Upon treatment with riboflavin the symptoms disappeared.

Niacin, like riboflavin, is involved in the life processes of the cells. It prevents pellagra,† with its characteristic skin lesions, digestive and nervous disturbances, provided all other essentials are included in the diet. The deficiencies found in a pellagrin's diet are generally multiple. Children, who have pellagra,[882] are usually underweight and underdeveloped. They appear to be undernourished, are irritable, easily frightened, "fretful," listless, tired, apprehensive. Those who are in school make poor progress, and have difficulty in concentrating. They do not have the normal interests of children. They are too tired to play but cannot rest.

Niacin and the amino acid tryptophane are interrelated. When tryptophane is low, as in a predominantly corn diet, more niacin is needed. The value of milk, on the other hand, in the prevention or treatment of pellagra appears to depend on the sum of its niacin and tryptophane contents as well as the other B vitamins.

* It takes considerable time for the physiologic response to work to be affected by a thiamine deficiency and similarly for recovery to take place. Individuals differ in their response.

** Schultz and Knott[818] found that the appetites of children between four and eleven years were improved and food consumption was increased when thiamine, in the form of wheat germ or crystalline thiamine, was added to the diet. Thiamine is only one of many factors contributing to poor appetite. Appetite responds to additional thiamine only when thiamine intake has been inadequate. Many appetite problems are caused by factors other than thiamine.

† For a discussion of pellagra and other nutritional deficiencies see Duncan, G. G.[259]

B_6 is a member of the enzyme system associated with protein metabolism. Recently in a study of two infants[874] arrested growth followed deprivation of B_6.

Folic acid has been found to play an important part in the body's blood-forming activities. It is effective in the treatment of certain types of anemia.

Vitamin B_{12}, the most recently discovered vitamin, is essential for the prevention or treatment of pernicious anemia, a disturbance of red blood cell formation. Since it has also been demonstrated to affect the growth of animals, it is natural that an interest in its possible effect upon children's growth should arise. A number of studies* on school-aged children with differing results have been reported.** At the present time, to what degree vitamin B_{12} may affect the growth of school-aged children cannot be stated categorically. It would seem that B_{12} may be a limiting factor in the growth of some children and not in that of others, as is true of other essential nutrients.

Vitamin C, or ascorbic acid, is essential to the health of intercellular material which acts as a cementing substance in holding the cells of a tissue in their precise positions. Many of the effects of insufficient vitamin C in the body can be traced to this function, such as fragile bones, poor development of the teeth, and weakness. The disease, scurvy, is the result of a severe deficiency. While scurvy occurs with relative infrequency, children who habitually take too little vitamin C may show a loss of energy and fleeting pains in the joints and limbs usually mistaken for rheumatism. Hess[422] repeatedly pointed out that children may be irritable, lacking in stamina and more or less retarded in growth because of a lack of vitamin C, even though they show no distinct scurvy symptoms. By increasing vitality vitamin C also plays a part in the body's mechanism for combating infection.

Functions of Proteins. Proteins make up a part of all body cells and, therefore, are necessary for growth. Through digestion they are broken down into amino acids which are used by the body in building its tissues: bone, muscle, nerves, skin, blood, etc. Eight of these amino acids cannot be manufactured in the body and so must be supplied in the diet.[794] Deficiencies in particular amino acids may lead to specific types of injury. For example, when arginine is deficient there is a decrease in the number of sperm and their motility.[432] All proteins do not contain all of these essential amino acids, so the kind of protein must be considered as well as the amount. Animal proteins are richer sources of these amino acids than vegetable proteins. Proteins are necessary for the manufacture of enzymes used in digestion. They play a role in regulating the flow of fluid in and out of cells. They are also a source of the amino acids which are a part of the hormones of the endocrine glands such as thyroxin of the thyroid gland, epinephrine of the adrenals and insulin of the pancreas. Proteins also function as antibodies to resist infection. A depletion of protein contributes to lowering the body's resistance

* See[183, 490, 824, 985, 986].

** Further studies with more children under well controlled conditions are needed. For a brief review of the studies to date see[919, 969].

to infection.[160]* In addition to fulfilling these structural and functional needs, proteins may be used as a source of energy. However, this is an expensive source of energy and, in childhood, the protein should not be diverted from its function of tissue building to satisfy energy needs.

Function of Carbohydrates and Fats. Carbohydrates and fats, as the chief sources of energy, are necessary for growth, in that they furnish energy for the growth process. Inadequate energy-yielding substances will slow down the rate of growth (see p. 121) and if severe will affect body composition and function.**

The body tries to compensate when there is a shortage of food energy, as happens in famine or wartime. Stuart[912] reports that one of the common symptoms of the underfed children in France in 1942 to 1943 was a pronounced lethargy, which doubtless meant (in addition to other factors, perhaps) an attempt to bring the energy output as near as possible to the level of intake.

Fats and carbohydrates also furnish the body with adipose tissue which serves as a protection against the loss of heat, acts as a cushion to the abdominal organs, and is a potential source of body energy. Fat-like substances are essential parts of body cells, as has been mentioned before. These substances are found in relatively large amounts in nerve tissue and are necessary in the formation of natural vitamin D and of sex and adrenal cortex hormones. Certain fats perform another important function in that they are carriers of vitamins A and D. Glucose, a digestive product of carbohydrates, is a constant constituent of the blood. Galactose, another sugar, is apparently used in the construction of nerve cells.

Role of Water. The human being lives in water, even though it is not an aquatic species.

> ... separating us from the air which surrounds us is a layer of horny scales, the scurf of the skin. Inside this lifeless covering are the parts of us that are alive. Whenever we look inside the body we find fluid (blood or lymph) bathing the masses and meshes of cells which constitute the living tissues. Indeed, we reside in a sort of fluid matrix, composed mainly of salty water.[162]

Water is a part of every tissue in the body, even of the proverbially dry bone.† Mature bone contains nearly half its weight in water. About 75 per cent of muscle and at least 80 per cent of the gray matter of the brain are water. No cell can carry on its activities when it is absolutely dry and most cells must be constantly bathed with fluid in order to do their work. These cells have their food brought to them and their waste products removed by the "water route," the blood. Many of these waste products are eliminated through the urine. The digestive juices, saliva in the mouth, the gastric and

---

* A study[626] in France during World War II indicated that a deficiency of animal protein was a determining factor in the incidence of tuberculosis.

** See Keys.[525]

† In children, the percentage of water in tissues is higher than in adulthood.

intestinal juices require large quantities of daily water.* Water serves as a regulator of body temperature. Evaporation from the skin, perspiration, provides one of the most important methods of removing surplus heat from the body. Water protects internal organs. The central nervous system is bathed by the cerebrospinal fluid. Fluid also lubricates joints, thereby making movements at joints easy. Water is, therefore, tremendously important in life. Rubner[800] estimated that a man could lose most of his stores of glycogen and of fat and even half of his protein without serious danger to life, but a loss of 10 per cent of body water is a serious matter and a loss of 20 per cent is scarcely to be endured.

In childhood, the need for water is even more urgent than in maturity. In addition to the demands for water, the body loses water more easily since the mechanism for maintaining constant conditions in the fluids of the body is still immature.[163] Precautions should be taken, therefore, to insure an adequate and regular intake.

MEETING THE NUTRITIONAL NEEDS OF CHILDREN

Nutritional Allowances. A child's food should provide him with energy and nutrients necessary for achieving a state of health and growth in accordance with his potentialities. Just as health means more than absence of disease, so the state of good nutrition means more than an absence of a gross deficiency. It is not enough to prevent a child from having rickets, scurvy or tetany. It is important that his body be ready to do what the will commands and to do it without undue conscious effort. That means calcium-rich rather than calcium-poor bones and teeth, tissues that are well supplied with the vitamins, and a bountiful supply of red blood cells well stocked with hemoglobin. Many children today live in that twilight zone between the absence of actual disease and the level of buoyant health which liberates the body and makes enjoyment of life possible. These children are victims of a "hidden hunger" almost as devastating as "hollow hunger." Such subclinical handicaps "cripple confidence, initiative and efficiency, impair daily achievement and satisfaction, shatter ambition and cast a gray veil of uneasiness over what should be the very joy of life."[950] This does not mean great quantities of food but rather quantity and quality in keeping with the current knowledge of nutritional needs for development and daily living. It is possible to have too much as well as too little of something, as, for example, in the case of calories and possibly vitamin D.

Recommended dietary allowances have been established in several countries.[122, 159, 301, 688] In the United States the Food and Nutrition Committee of the National Research Council has formulated recommended daily allowances for specific nutrients for children and adults (see table) based on all available experimental evidence of human nutritional needs and the careful

---

* The adult secretes daily about three quarts of gastric juice, two and one-quarter pints of saliva, one and one-half pints of bile, one and one-quarter pints of pancreatic juice and one-half pint of intestinal juice. (Source: Cleveland Health Museum.)

Food and Nutrition Board, National Research Council—Recommended Daily Dietary Allowances,[1] Revised 1953

Designed for the Maintenance of Good Nutrition of Healthy Persons in the U.S.A.

(Allowances are considered to apply to persons normally vigorous and living in temperate climate.)

	AGE YEARS	WEIGHT KG. (LB.)	HEIGHT CM. (IN.)	CALORIES	PROTEIN GM.	CALCIUM GM.	IRON MG.	VITAMIN A I.U.	THIAMINE MG.	RIBO-FLAVIN MG.	NIA-CIN MG.	ASCORBIC ACID MG.	VITAMIN D I.U.
Men......	25	65 (143)	170 (67)	3200[2]	65	0.8	12	5000	1.6	1.6	16	75	
	45	65 (143)	170 (67)	2900	65	0.8	12	5000	1.5	1.6	15	75	
	65	65 (143)	170 (67)	2600	65	0.8	12	5000	1.3	1.6	13	75	
Women....	25	55 (121)	157 (62)	2300[2]	55	0.8	12	5000	1.2	1.4	12	70	
	45	55 (121)	157 (62)	2100	55	0.8	12	5000	1.1	1.4	11	70	
	65	55 (121)	157 (62)	1800	55	0.8	12	5000	1.0	1.4	10	70	
	Pregnant (3rd trimester)			Add 400	80	1.5	15	6000	1.5	2.0	15	100	400
	Lactating (850 ml. daily)			Add 1000	100	2.0	15	8000	1.5	2.5	15	150	400
Infants[3]....	0–1/12[4]	6 (13)	60 (24)	kg. x 120	kg. x 3.5[3]	0.6	6	1500	0.3	0.4	3	30	400
	1/12–3/12	9 (20)	70 (28)	kg. x 110	kg. x 3.5[3]	0.8	6	1500	0.4	0.7	4	30	400
	4/12–9/12	10 (22)	75 (30)	kg. x 100	kg. x 3.5[3]	1.0	6	1500	0.5	0.9	5	30	400
	10/12–1												
Children...	1–3	12 (27)	87 (34)	1200	40	1.0	7	2000	0.6	1.0	6	35	400
	4–6	18 (40)	109 (43)	1600	50	1.0	8	2500	0.8	1.2	8	50	400
	7–9	27 (59)	129 (51)	2000	60	1.0	10	3500	1.0	1.5	10	60	400
Boys......	10–12	35 (78)	144 (57)	2500	70	1.2	12	4500	1.3	1.8	13	75	400
	13–15	49 (108)	163 (64)	3200	85	1.4	15	5000	1.6	2.1	16	90	400
	16–20	63 (139)	175 (69)	3800	100	1.4	15	5000	1.9	2.5	19	100	400
Girls......	10–12	36 (79)	144 (57)	2300	70	1.2	12	4500	1.2	1.8	12	75	400
	13–15	49 (108)	160 (63)	2500	80	1.3	15	5000	1.3	2.0	13	80	400
	16–20	54 (120)	162 (64)	2400	75	1.3	15	5000	1.2	1.9	12	80	400

1 In planning practical dietaries, the recommended allowances can be attained with a variety of common foods which will also provide other nutrient requirements less well known;† the allowance levels are considered to cover individual variations among normal persons as they live in the United States subjected to ordinary environmental stresses. . . .

2 These calorie recommendations apply to the degree of activity for the reference man and woman described on page 3 of the text. For the urban "white-collar" worker they are probably excessive. In any case, the calorie allowance must be adjusted to the actual needs of the individual as required to achieve and maintain his desirable weight.

3 The recommendations for infants pertain to nutrients derived primarily from cow's milk. If the milk from which the protein is derived is human milk or has been treated to render it more digestible, the allowance may be in the range of 2–3 gms. per kg. There should be no question that human milk is a desirable source of nutrients for infants even though it may not provide the levels recommended for certain nutrients. (See discussion in text.)

4 During the first month of life, desirable allowances for many nutrients are dependent upon maturation of excretory and endocrine functions. Therefore no specific recommendations are given.

† It will be noticed that phosphorus and iodine are not included in this table. It has been found that satisfactory amounts of phosphorus will be provided when the needs for protein and calcium are met. Meeting the need for iodine is not a practical nutritional problem except in certain geographic areas where iodine is lacking in the water and soil. The use of iodized salt meets this need.

judgment of recognized authorities in nutrition. The quantities recommended are allowances, not requirements, and allow for a margin of safety in meeting the needs of individuals. These allowances are revised from time to time in order that the latest scientific knowledge may be utilized. The table represents the fourth revision.*

Foods to Meet These Allowances. Nutrients are not taken as such but are consumed in foods which are mixtures of protein, carbohydrate, fat, vitamins and salts, together with more or less residue which has no food value. All foods are not equally good sources of these nutrients. Some foods, sugar for example, provide only one nutrient. On the other hand, a small orange contains as many calories as a tablespoonful of sugar but, in addition, contains vitamins and minerals. In terms of its contribution to the growth needs of children, an orange is more economical than a tablespoonful of sugar. Some foods owe their right to priority at the table to the fact that they are particularly rich sources of some nutrient, and, unless they are included in the diet, the amount of that particular nutrient is likely to be inadequate. Such is the role of citrus fruits and tomatoes as invaluable sources of vitamin C. Milk is outstanding in its contributions to the diet and holds its place in a child's dietary because of its diversity of constituents as well as richness in one particular element. Milk contributes protein of high quality, calcium, phosphorus, some iron, vitamin A, thiamine, and riboflavin. Its calcium value is of particular importance. There is approximately as much calcium in a cup of milk as in 5 cups of orange juice, 133 tablespoonfuls of butter or about 3 cups of carrots.

Because of the particular nutritional value of certain foods, it is possible to formulate

* For the present knowledge of the effect of different climatic conditions upon nutritive requirements see Mitchell and Edman.[673]

a basic or fundamental diet, containing foods which should be included daily, whether the individual be a preschool child, a child going to school, an adolescent or an adult. Differences at these various ages will be differences in amount and perhaps in methods of preparation. Foods which are good for the younger ages are all good for adults. Unfortunately, food eaten by adults is not always good for children.

The following foods provide a basic daily diet:*

> Milk
> Egg
> Meat, fowl, fish or cheese
> Green or yellow vegetable (cooked)
> Raw green or yellow vegetable
> Fruit, including a citrus fruit or tomato
> Whole grain or enriched cereal or bread
> Butter or margarine fortified with vitamin A
> Some source of vitamin D
> Iodized salt for seasoning in endemic goiter regions

The value of milk has already been given. Eggs are important because they furnish proteins of excellent quality, iron, riboflavin, thiamine, vitamin A, and are one of the relatively few foods that contain some vitamin D. However, the amount of vitamin D is small, for it takes 12 egg yolks (all the vitamin D is found in the yolk) to give the same amount found in 1 teaspoonful of cod-liver oil. Meat, fowl, fish and cheese furnish additional high quality protein. Milk, egg, and meat or its substitutes will assure older children and adolescents the amount of protein they need, which exceeds that of their parents. Meat has the added advantage of good flavor. It adds zest to a meal. Of all meats, the glandular organs have the highest nutritional value. Thus liver and kidney are especially good foods for children. Serving one of these weekly is an excellent practice. The green or yellow vegetable furnishes minerals, with special emphasis on iron, vitamins and roughage which aids in intestinal elimination. The whole grain or enriched cereals give additional protein and calories, are good sources of minerals and excellent sources of thiamine. Whole grain cereals are better than refined or milled cereals because much of the mineral and vitamin value of the grain is lost in the milling process. Enriched white bread and flour, introduced in 1941, as stated before, has thiamine, riboflavin, niacin, and iron added to it in sufficient quantity to make up for the loss of those elements in the milling process. Enriched wheat or corn bread may be substituted in part for the whole grain breads; however, it should not replace whole cereal products entirely, for there may be additional unknown nutritional factors in whole grains which are necessary for human nutrition.

The citrus fruit or tomato is included to insure sufficient vitamin C. Citrus fruits include oranges, grapefruit and lemons. If tomato juice is used,

* These are basic foods for children in the United States. Each area of the world needs to plan its own basic diet in accordance with the prevailing conditions, which include the food resources, the economy, and the meanings of various foods to the people.

a larger amount is required. At least twice as much tomato juice is needed to give the vitamin C value equivalent to orange juice.

After these foods have been included, others which are added will depend upon the family pocket book, background and habits.

Nature evidently expected man to obtain his vitamin D from the action of sunshine on the skin, for there are relatively few foods that contain vitamin D. In some sections of the country it is possible to obtain enough ultraviolet light from the sun, but in many parts of the country during the winter months the amount of available ultraviolet light is inadequate. In the north, the low altitude of the sun in the winter is a factor in limiting the ultraviolet light. The smoke and dust of city communities reduce it even more. Clothing further prevents the rays which are available from reaching the body. It is, therefore, necessary to supply the child and adolescent with vitamin D through cod liver oil, some of the many concentrates, vitamin D milks, or sun lamps. The pediatrician or family physician should determine how much vitamin D the individual child will need and in what form it shall be given.

Distribution of Food during the Day.   Not only the kind and amount of daily food but also its distribution throughout the day has a bearing on the well-being of an individual. Hutchinson,[454] in reviewing the literature on meal habits and their effects on performance, concluded that small meals at short intervals have an advantage for the individual over large meals at long intervals. Such a regimen tends to maximum efficiency by eliminating the drowsiness and disinclination for mental and physical work following a large meal, and the irritability, restlessness, diminished concentration and feelings of weakness and emptiness attending long periods between meals. Most of the studies reported used adult subjects but one could assume that a regimen of fairly even distribution of food at reasonable intervals would benefit school-aged children as well.

Research on protein metabolism* (as mentioned before) indicates that all amino acids need to be taken at approximately the same time for them to be available for the synthesis of protein. Thus, assurance that all the amino acids are supplied in a meal, either through the use of good quality proteins such as animal proteins or adequate supplementation of proteins of less adequate quality such as those found in some of the cereals, is important.

Studies indicate that breakfast is a very important meal, nutritionally speaking.** Such studies have significance for parents and workers with older

---

* See Almquist.[12]

** In one study, young adults[213, 959] had decreased maximum output of work and increased muscular tremor during a morning after no breakfast, or only coffee. In another study,[709] blood-sugar levels dropped below fasting levels and some of the subjects reported hunger, weakness, headache and lassitude following no breakfast except coffee. A breakfast containing a protein food, such as milk or eggs, was followed by a slower drop in the blood-sugar level. A sense of well-being was consistently reported after breakfasts that provided large quantities of protein-rich food. The breakfast meal influenced blood-sugar levels even in the afternoon. In another study,[5] the minimum amount of protein appeared to be 15 grams, which was supplied by an egg and a glass of milk as the protein foods or 2/3 c. cereal, 2 T. peanut butter and 2 slices of bread as the chief protein sources. In yet another study,[582] the same amount of protein during the day was used more efficiently when some was eaten at breakfast. Protein at breakfast appeared to be more important than protein at lunch, according to another study.[583]

children and adolescents, especially since surveys[853, 892] have shown that many children in different parts of the country go to school without an adequate breakfast. This is true of both elementary and high school years. High school boys tend to have better breakfasts than girls;[892] college men likewise have better breakfasts than college women.[100]

FOOD HABITS—UPON WHICH THE MEETING OF FOOD REQUIREMENTS DEPENDS

A child's food habits reflect his nutritional needs, the degree of maturity of his body, the food habits and attitudes of his parents, his personal satisfactions and dissatisfactions and the impact of the economic and social world upon him. The acquisition of good food habits is to be considered one phase of growing up. Good food habits can be said to include: (1) a good appetite to insure eating enough food, (2) the experience of eating and enjoying the foods which furnish a well balanced diet, and (3) an interest in and willingness to eat a widening variety of foods so that the child is guaranteed an adequate diet, is adding to his store of knowledge and is establishing a flexibility toward food. Flexibility, here as elsewhere, is a mark of maturity.

Hunger and Appetite. Hunger and appetite are distinct physiologic manifestations, but they operate together as determinants of the food intake of an individual. Appetite is the foundation on which food habits are built, and hunger is closely allied with appetite. Hunger is that urge to eat which impels one to seek food and to eat until that urge is inhibited or satisfied. Appetite is the factor that determines the acceptance of specific foods. The mechanism of the hunger drive and behavior associated with it are still poorly understood. However, experimentation with animals and man suggests that the central origin of hunger lies in a subcortical center of the brain, the hypothalamus.* It is believed that from this area come the initiation and direction of the motor responses that constitute this drive. Further, Mayer suggests[634a] that the regulation of food intake in this area is due to the available glucose and is therefore related to the intricacies of carbohydrate metabolism.

The sensation of hunger is characterized by successive phases of restlessness, sensations of tightness in the back of the mouth, feelings of emptiness and acute unpleasant aching, gnawing sensations, "hunger pangs."[890] These sensations are associated with rhythmic contractions of the stomach which appear in the newborn at birth and recur after feedings as the stomach empties. These contractions are augmented by bodily activity. They are diminished by eating, by the sight of food which produces a flow of gastric juice, by fatigue, by strong emotions, by pressure on the abdomen, by smoking and by fever. Normally, everyday hunger sensations are stopped by eating. This is a natural sequence of events. Since fatigue, emotional disturbances and fever interfere with the natural "ebb and flow" of food intake, prevention of these factors is advisable whenever possible.

The hunger drive begins to function at birth. Almost immediately it

* See Keeton,[516] Mayer.[634a]

becomes integrated, through other hypothalamic mechanisms, with emotional reactions. Recognizing this, it is important to see that babies are fed under conditions which provide affection and security. Thus the hunger of the stomach is relieved and the emotions are given basic gratification at the same time.

In the development of hunger and feeding behavior, both of which are basic to physical survival, there grow up many conditioned* feelings and emotions which affect the vigor of the hunger drive, the willingness to try new foods, the rejection of certain once-accepted foods, and many things related to food and hunger which do not appear on the surface. As the child grows and widens his social contacts the emotional satisfactions from food or frustrations in the feeding area become extended to objects and relationships which are not always apparent to the observer. Food, generally and specifically, acquires different meanings to different people and to the same person at different times. Thus, human relationships play a profound role in maintaining a sound hunger drive and thereby influencing food habits.

Appetite is defined by Keeton[516] as resulting from modification of the behavior of the hypothalamic hunger drive by cerebral activity. It is usually a pleasant sensation based on previous experience of taste, smell and other pleasant associations with the food. It motivates one to eat the food in order to experience the sensation of well-being that will follow its ingestion or to enjoy the pleasant sensory experience of eating it.

Thus, the practice of self-regulation in which the time for eating is set not by the clock but by the natural rhythm of the child and at the same time providing him with emotional gratifications as a part of eating is in accordance with this concept of the hunger-appetite mechanism. A young infant soon settles into a rhythmic pattern of eating with a gradual reduction in the number of feedings a day.** Gradual adjustment to the feeding habits of his cultural group should develop so that he progressively fits his meals into the pattern of the family. In most children this will have taken place naturally so that long before the child enters school his pattern and that of the family have become synchronized. A physically and psychologically healthy regimen in which the maturing child fits smoothly into the life of the home, school and community in accordance with his degree of maturity will aid in maintaining this mechanism in a healthy state.

Hunger and Appetite Can Be a Gauge of the Amount of Food to Eat. Hunger and appetite are adequate in determining the amount of food children need. This mechanism is adequate in serving as a gauge of the amount of food necessary for health and growth of a child when it is normal and healthy, and not diminished or perverted by physiologic or psychologic factors. When hunger and appetite fail to operate at an optimal level, the body lacks sufficient materials for efficient performance and growth. At the other extreme, occasionally, when the satisfaction from eating is substituted

---

* Closely associated responses which grow up through being repeated over and over in immediate connection with the feeding situation.

** See Rand, Sweeny, Vincent,[756] pp. 232–233.

for another satisfaction lacking in the child's life,[134, 644, 753] the desire for food may go beyond physiologic needs. Occasionally, a child overeats in compensation for lack of affection, insecurity, lack of status in his work, etc. This condition, however, should not be confused with the ravenous appetite of the growing, active pubescent child.

Since children generally can decide for themselves the amount of food they need, they may have a share in determining how much food will be served to them. Often adults overestimate a child's capacity for food. It is well to remember that appetites vary from meal to meal, and from day to day, and it is a wise parent who recognizes and accepts these variations.

Appetite an Unreliable Guide in Food Selection. That man has a physiologic mechanism which will guide him involuntarily in food selections to meet his specific nutritional needs has not yet been demonstrated. If such a mechanism does exist, it is obscured by the multiplicity of economic, social and cultural forces which influence food selection. The process of self-selection as indicated by animal experimentations[821] and the experiment of Davis[217] with newly weaned infants seems to be that of learning and thus is subject to the laws of learning.* Davis demonstrated that a group of infants, with no former experience with food, other than milk, under controlled conditions in an institution, and given a wide variety of simple, *natural* foods, could select their own food in such a way that satisfactory nutrition was maintained.** This experiment is not justification for a laissez faire policy by which an adult assumes no responsibility in setting the stage for the child's choices. Rather, it demonstrated that under *certain conditions*, including a full coverage of nutritional requirements in the foods available, freedom from emotional stress and absence of distractions, the removal of pressure and the granting of freedom in the choice of appropriate foods would help children to develop satisfactory food habits. The controlled conditions of the experiment cannot be duplicated in homes where it would be wise to see that children are served meals that consist of foods rich in necessary nutrients, and that the atmosphere at mealtime be free from emotional stress and lacking in distractions.

Acquiring Food Habits: Important Factors. In order to understand the food patterns and habits of a child, we must view them as an integral part of the whole child as he relates himself to his environment. This means concern with his growth, his past history, the customs, habits and expectations of his family, his personal relationships in the home, school and community and the social pattern of his world. As mentioned before, food has many meanings to a child. The particular meanings for a child, when understood, help to reveal the way in which he acquires his food habits and offer a basis for correction if and when correction is necessary.

Every child at birth has the basis for establishing good eating habits, namely, the hunger drive. The gratification from taking food at the time hun-

---

* For discussion of experiments on self-selection of nutrients in rats see Nutrition Rev.[832] and Young.[1015]

** For discussion of applications of this experiment see Davis.[216]

ger sensations occur is the beginning of establishing good eating habits.[756,781] Conversely, frustration in feeding experiences inhibit their development. With this experience as a beginning, the child changes his eating behavior with increasing maturation and experience.

From the early weeks of life *taste discrimination* is present and provides a basis for the development of selective appetite or the liking and disliking of foods. In the infant, taste buds are distributed abundantly in the mouth, on the tongue, cheeks and in the throat. With increase in age, until probably around twelve years of age, they decrease in number and distribution.[556] Thus, with the same food, the taste sensations of young children may differ from those of older children and adults. Also, there are individual differences in the intensity of taste sensation.[994] The sensitivity varies in the same individual from time to time and from one individual to another. Renner[767] says that the keen-sensed individuals are generally the quickest eaters. These differences with age and between individuals of the same age may be responsible in part for individual children's differences in accepting foods.*

Since sight, smell and the feeling of the texture of food in the mouth add to the sense of taste and affect children's reactions to foods, the quality of the food and the combinations of foods will add or detract from the pleasure of the meal. Variety in color and consistency, and pleasing combination of flavors will enhance the attractiveness of meals. The preparation of the foods is also important.

The acquisition of *motor skills* is reflected in the child's manipulation of his food. By the time a child enters school, he has achieved much in this area. (See Chapter 8.) It is important that the form in which the food is served should be compatible with his skill to handle it.

The *social development* of the child also contributes to his food habits. In the school years, as he is breaking away from dependence upon his family and is leaning toward his friends, he drops some of the table manners which he has learned from his family. This is characteristically a period of messy table behavior. Parents need not become distressed, for this is a passing phase and a part of growing up. If parental pressure is applied at this time, it may result only in influencing unfavorably the child's attitude toward food.**

In adolescence the pressure of the social group is strong. Conformity with group practices is important. So it is in the area of eating. The drug-store habit and the attitude of acceptance or rejection of specific foods may interfere temporarily with the practice of good food habits which have been established earlier. The desire for pop and candy bars may be an expression of the emotional need for independence and even defiance as the adolescent is acquiring a sense of identity. A wise parent, who understands the child and his needs, can with ingenuity help direct "what is being done" and provide the means for popularizing desirable habits. Also, during adolescence the heavy schedules of the boys and girls often produce fatigue, with its

---

* See Davis[216] for a discussion of individual differences in the pattern of taste. Eppright[280] gives suggestions for applying the knowledge of taste sensations to feeding children.

** For a discussion of the eating behavior of the child from five to ten see Gesell and Ilg.[347]

depressing effect upon appetite, and irregular or hurried meals because "there just is not time to eat."

Emotions play a role in food habits. We have mentioned the child who overeats to compensate for something which is missing in his life. Children who are happy and secure are more likely to eat well than children who are disturbed by worry, anxiety or discontent.*†

A *healthy child*, all other factors being equal, will eat better than will the child who is not well. However, when he has a cold, or a sore throat, or a toothache, or a greater incapacitating illness, he may not be interested in food. Such an illness, as we have said before, may be the beginning of a chronically poor appetite if the adults fail to appreciate the child's temporary disinterest in food and either urge him to eat or express concern about him. The lack of desire to eat during illness should be respected since it has a real physiologic basis. Children with chronic illnesses and foci of infection, such as diseased tonsils and carious teeth, cannot be expected to have keen appetites.

A child's *physical habits* will strengthen or impair his appetite and thus his interest in and attitude toward food. Regularity and the spacing of meals, satisfactory elimination, plenty of exercise, fresh air and sunshine, and enough sleep and rest to permit recuperation from the activities and stresses and strains of the day are important. There is much truth in the saying "too tired to eat." The tired child, whether he is tired from vigorous exercise or from one of the other many causes of fatigue, is not ready for his meal.

A *balanced diet* is also important. The fats, such as cream, butter, rich desserts and fried foods, should be limited, since fats retard digestion in the stomach. Sweets need to be watched.** As stated previously, thiamine has a definite effect upon appetite.

Food Habits Are Learned at Home.   In his early years the child spends most of his time at home. It is at home that he will acquire his food habits. Parents, in planning for their children, can prepare for them by taking stock of their own food patterns and setting the family food habits in readiness for the children. This is important, for even before the child has moved from infancy into early childhood, he begins to acquire the tastes of his family for the particular foods and food combinations they prefer. He becomes acquainted with sweet foods, with salty foods. If the family likes white bread only, he learns to eat white bread only, both because it is served and because he learns to eat by imitating others. If the family has wide food interests he will have ample opportunity to learn about many foods. If, however, the family list of foods is limited by food prejudices and preferences, he will be deprived of extending his knowledge of foods beyond a very narrow range.

---

* Occasionally children of high school age have difficulty eating breakfast because of emotional tension.

† Rabinovitch[753] points out that food may serve as a symbol for many things in a child including security and comfort.

** Dr. Macy[620] observed that children whose diets were poor had an abnormal craving for sweets. As the diets became well balanced to meet bodily needs, the healthy child voluntarily reduced his sugar consumption.

It is through their early and repeated experiences that children develop interest in a variety of foods and an attitude of adventurousness in trying new kinds. Thus, children are conditioned early in their food habits, some practising wise food selection, some practising poor selection. These childhood experiences with food are reflected later in the selection of food in the school years and in adolescence. Studies of food habits of school-aged children and adolescents indicate that many of them have inadequacies in their diets according to the present knowledge of nutritional needs.[*] Younger children tend to have better diets than older children.[**] Boys tend to have better diets than girls.[†] Adolescent girls tend to fare worst of all.[‡] This points to the need for making it possible for children and adolescents to develop good attitudes toward food and for better teaching in nutrition plus the opportunities for practicing that knowledge.

The atmosphere at mealtime varies in families. In some, it is a time through which to hurry; in others it is a social experience in which enjoyment of good food is joined with good fellowship. Meals are generally more enjoyable in an atmosphere of leisure and relaxation. Mealtime is not a time for scolding, nagging or discussing the day's difficulties and the family problems.

The parents' attitudes toward their children's eating are extremely important. According to Baldwin's[55] study, good appetite was found in homes in which strict disciplinary methods were combined with approval of the child. The type of strictness found in these homes seemed to be a strictness about a few essentials of behavior but not a strictness which completely determined the child's activities. Thus, setting limits on behavior seemed to be psychologically healthful. Strict disciplinary methods were also found in the good table behavior homes but the strictness in these homes seemed to stem from an attempt of the parents to force adult standards upon the child. This excessive restraint seemed to deprive the child of free and spontaneous behavior. A wide acceptance of foods, he reported, was generally associated with abundance of affection and attention.

In a study of food habits of adolescents from different cultural backgrounds, it was found that good food habits are not the result of one single type of family pattern, strict, lenient or intermediary, but depend upon "the parent's adaptability to the needs of a changing younger generation and to a cultural pattern which has no code as yet, but is itself in transition."[417] Thus parents must grow with their children and adapt their guidance according to the stage of development of the child plus the demands of society.

Unwittingly many parents in this country do not always assist children to learn to enjoy desirable foods. Mead[636] discusses the dilemma of the child, in what she calls the average home in the United States, where the child learns, through his parents' attitudes and behavior that the "right" foods tend to be undelicious and the "wrong" foods tend to be delightful. They

* See [281, 581, 742, 853, 892, 901, 957, 1014.]
** See [281, 957, 987.]
† See [100, 892, 901, 1014.]
‡ For a summary of studies see Leamy.[569]

learn this through rewards and punishment meted out at mealtimes. The oft heard remarks "Drink your milk and then you can have your dessert"* and "If you don't eat your vegetables you can't have that candy after dinner" bear evidence to this point. In such instances dessert becomes a bribe and the withdrawal of candy becomes a punishment. A child is virtuous when eating the "right" foods, but he is not expected to enjoy them. Eating the "right" foods and enjoying oneself are not synonymous. Later, when children from such homes have a chance to choose foods for themselves, they have to decide between doing right or enjoying themselves. Since eating the "right" foods has become associated with parental domination, the adolescent may eat undesirable foods as a bold gesture to announce that he has grown up. Thus children with such eating experiences miss the opportunity of laying a foundation of pleasurable experiences with food as the basis for later self-selection.

The foods eaten and the attitudes toward food vary from one culture to another.[691] In order to understand children's food habits, it is necessary, therefore, to know the cultural background of the family** which brings to the family values of foods and the uses made of food in daily living, as, for example, acceptable or unacceptable foods, foods eaten on special occasions, foods associated with religious practices, patterning of meals, eating behavior and the manner in which children learn about food.

Thus good food habits† are learned in an environment which recognizes and permits changing behavior with advancing maturity, which promotes good mental and physical health, provides pleasant experiences with good food, and furnishes an opportunity for learning to make wise food selection. It is a cooperative venture between child and parents in a specific environment.

OTHER FACTORS RELATED TO NUTRITION

To provide children with the food they need for health and growth is not enough. The food must be broken down by digestion into substances which the body can absorb; those substances, such as glucose, fatty acids, amino acids, minerals and vitamins, must pass through the walls of the digestive tract into the blood stream, be carried to the various parts of the body, transmitted to the body cells where they are assimilated and converted into body tissues. The efficiency with which the body performs these processes is not perfect and that efficiency varies from time to time within the individual and varies from individual to individual.‡

Everyone knows of children who, in spite of consuming large quantities of food, remain thin, while other children gain weight on a much smaller intake. It is, therefore, valuable to know some of the factors which influence

---

* We do not imply that all desserts are "wrong" foods.
** See Mead.[635]
† Further discussion and references on Food Habits.[690,691]
‡ This variability is illustrated by long-term well controlled experiment by Hunscher, et al.[449] with children between the ages of four and nine years, on the utilization of calcium. It was found that the retention of calcium varied between 27.4 per cent and 48.5 per cent of the amount ingested.

the assimilation and utilization of food. The possibility of a genetic factor influencing metabolic processes has been stated earlier (p. 52). The need for a balance of nutrients has also been mentioned (p. 117).

Further, the conditions under which the food is eaten influence the use the body can make of it. A leisurely, pleasant mealtime permits proper mastication, which prepares the food for digestion by breaking it up and mixing it with saliva and also makes the normal flow of the digestive juices possible. In contrast, a hurried meal or one fraught with emotional stress and strain is a poor prelude to digestion. Finally, other physical habits—elimination, rest and activity—contribute to the processes of digestion and assimilation.

Elimination.   The elimination of waste products is necessary for the well-being of the whole body. These waste products consist of substances which result from metabolic processes and substances in the digestive tract which have not been absorbed. The organs of elimination are the lungs, the skin, the kidneys and intestines. The lungs excrete carbon dioxide and water vapor; the skin, water and some salts; the kidneys, water, products of protein metabolism and salts; and the intestines eliminate undigested materials, bacteria of the digestive tract, wastes of the digestive process, some salts that have been used by the body and are ready to be removed, and water.

The *amount of urine* excreted varies among individuals and from day to day in the same individual, depending upon the amount of water taken, and environmental conditions which increase or reduce the loss of water through the skin by perspiration. The *frequency of urination* also varies greatly, depending upon the amount of water taken and physiologic and psychologic factors. Boys tend to urinate more frequently than girls. In cold weather children tend to urinate more often than in warm weather. Emotional stress, such as the excitement of the first day at school, or of an approaching contest, will increase the frequency. The frequency of urination is also increased under conditions which cause irritation to the urinary tract, such as concentrated urine or bladder infections. Because of the variability among children in the need to urinate and the variability from day to day in the same child, adults should make it possible for the child to go to the toilet whenever he designates a need.

In fecal elimination, the *amount of feces* depends, to a large extent, upon the diet and water intake. A diet with adequate roughage from a liberal use of fruits and vegetables increases the amount of feces. Small feces are the end product of a diet of foods which leave little undigested residue.

The *normal consistency of feces* approximates that of an over-ripe banana. If the materials in the intestine move too rapidly there is diminished opportunity for water to be absorbed and the frequent, loose bowel movements of diarrhea result. But if the materials move too slowly, excessive water is absorbed through the walls of the intestine, and the hard, infrequent bowel movements of constipation are the consequence. The speed of the peristaltic movements of the digestive tract is influenced by diet and by emotion. Too soft stools, therefore, may be the result of too much roughage, or food which has been too irritating to the lining of the digestive tract, such as berries with too many seeds. Soft stools may also be caused by emotional disturbances. On the other hand, too hard stools may be due to inadequate water, too little bulk or nervous tension.

Fecal elimination generally occurs once a day at a regular time. There is no hard and fast rule, however. Some children have more frequent bowel movements and some have a rhythm of every other day. Regularity in a child's pattern of elimination is more important than the closeness with which his pattern conforms to that of others. Having a regular time daily for the bowel movement, preferably after a meal (since peristalsis is stimulated by eating), and allowing ample time so that the child will not be hurried, will aid in establishing and maintaining good elimination. An excellent time for bowel elimination for the school child is in the morning either on arising or after breakfast. At this time the child is more relaxed after a good night's sleep. There is also less chance of interference in this routine thus timed than during school hours. Children should be encouraged to go to the toilet when the urge for defecation rises. Ignoring this urge may lead to constipation.

Rest and Activity. Both activity and rest are important because of their relation to nutrition and growth. Muscular activity is important in that it improves circulation and respiration, stimulates appetite, aids digestion, improves muscle tone, thereby fostering good posture and normal elimination, and increases endurance, strength and accuracy. The amount and kind of activity for the child should be considered in respect to his bodily strengths and weaknesses, his general physical health, and his stage of development. In addition to large muscle activities, there are the finer motor activities and muscle tensions accompanying mental work.

Activity cannot be continued indefinitely because muscles become tired, so periods of inactivity are necessary to restore them. These periods of rest should occur frequently for children. Rest may not necessarily mean complete inactivity. It may be a change from one type of activity to another so that one part of the body rests while another works, or the tempo of activity may be reduced. For example, a period of folk dancing may be followed by a period of reading or, following a vigorous dance, rhythms inducing relaxation may be introduced. The most satisfactory and prompt recuperation, however, takes place when the muscles are both inactive and relaxed and when there is both mental and physical repose. In the early school years, children can learn the feel of muscles when they are relaxed and how to put them in such a state.

The balance of rest and activity differs for different children. Some require more rest than others, as, for example, the child who has been ill. His muscles have lost some of their tone and are, therefore, more easily fatigued. Such a child needs more frequent and longer rest periods until he has attained his normal vigor once more. Children who are malnourished need additional rest. Some children require more mental and emotional rest and greater physical activity. For children who have been sitting for hours in a classroom, outdoor play is more restful than sitting in a corner reading a book. To plan a child's regimen so as to allow for a balance of activity and rest, it is necessary to know the child, his health history and growth, and his home and school environments with the demands they place upon him.

Sleep. Sleep is the most complete and satisfactory of all forms of rest. It rests not only the voluntary muscles and the eyes but there is also a depression of other tissue and organ activities. The circulation and respiration are slowed. That less energy is expended is indicated by a lower metabolic rate.* More energy, therefore, is available for growth.

Sleep is one phase of the sleep-wakefulness cycle, which, as Kleitman[539] says, can be likened to the crest and the trough of a wave. This cycle is an inborn pattern of alternation of rest and activity. The duration of the cycle and the shape of the wave are affected by experience and training. Thus, feelings and external conditions play a role in determining the characteristic pattern of the sleep-wakefulness cycle of a child. Early in life a rhythm** is established by synchronizing this cycle with the periodicity of day and night, with the changes in light and temperature and with the accompanying "social timetable" of the routine of living which provides stimulation of activities, noises and personal contacts. Important also is the fact that a twenty-four hour body temperature curve is gradually established and usually attains its adult characteristics during the first half of the second year.[540] Physiologic readiness for sleep is associated with a rather sharp drop in body temperature at a particular time.[540] The process of establishing this rhythm, which is easy for some and difficult for others, will depend upon circumstances and the personality of the child. The general requirement, however, is the maintenance of a regularity in the timing of the day's activities, including eating, bathing, playing, etc., initiated by the infant's physiologic clock and later tempered by reasonable adaptation of the child to his family situation and the society in which he lives.

By the time a child enters school the kind of rhythm which has been set will depend upon internal regulatory mechanisms† and his experiences. The degree to which advantage has been taken of the child's daily physiologic and psychologic readiness for sleep will be a factor. According to Gesell[347] the child from five to ten years is still in the process of learning to sleep.‡ He is still having trouble going to sleep and makes certain demands upon his parents for help. Bedtime for the younger school-aged child is still a time of closeness between parent and child, a time when the child is especially responsive and confidential. As the child grows in independence he may resist going to bed, not so much in resistance to sleep itself but to a parent-imposed task.

* For a complete discussion of the physiology of sleep, see Kleitman, N.,[540] and Magnussen.[622]

** For definitions of biologic rhythms and cycles, including those of sleep and wakefulness, see Kleitman.[538]

† Magnussen[622] states that at the present time there is agreement that a center in the hypothalamus is of significance for the regulation of sleep, although as yet there is no complete agreement as to the manner of operation.

‡ By sleep Gesell means a complex of four phases: release into sleep, staying asleep, waking and staying awake.

The quality and quantity of sleep of a child during the growing years varies from child to child and from time to time for each child. It is natural for children to awaken from sleep rested, but for some children sleep is not a very restful, recuperative experience. Children may be unrefreshed after a night's sleep if it is too quiet, too restless or too short. Ordinarily children do not sleep "like a log." There is some bodily movement which varies in amount from hour to hour, from night to night and from child to child. Undoubtedly some of the movement is the result of discomfort that comes from lying too long in one position. Movement during the night, therefore, prevents prolonged pressure on specific muscles and thus contributes to a refreshing sleep. However, too much movement may be tiring.

Several studies* of motility in sleep have been made. From these studies it is learned that at all ages the most quiet sleep occurs early in the night, after which a gradual increase in motility occurs as the night progresses. The children between six and eighteen years studied by Renshaw, Miller and Marquis[768] had on an average 8.7 "active" minutes per hour of sleep.** Within this general pattern for children, each child had his own characteristic pattern of hourly distribution of motility. This individual pattern is very stable in children living under normal routine, free from illness, emotional disturbances, etc. However, motility may be increased by environmental factors.†

The amount of sleep a child needs decreases with age and varies from child to child and from day to day. The young baby sleeps most of the time. As he grows, his waking hours increase so that during the later months of infancy and the preschool years he has a long sleep at night and one nap during the day. By the time he enters school his nap has probably been dropped. It may have dropped out spontaneously, or it may have been forced out by attendance at school. Some schools, recognizing the value of a daytime rest, provide for it in their schedules.

Toward the end of the preschool years, according to Despert,[240] a child sleeps about eleven and one-fourth hours of the twenty-four. Tables of recommended hours of sleep provided as a guide for parents are often misleading because the figures tend to be high. No arbitrary rule can be laid down for older children, since their sleeping needs vary widely. The child's physical and affective makeup and rate of growth, the pace of the daily schedule and activities, satisfactions and concerns with life may contribute to these differences in sleep needs. A child who goes to sleep promptly and awakens by himself, who is energetic and can take the demands of the day in his stride is undoubtedly having enough sleep. On the other hand, the child who has to be called each morning, who takes a long time to go to sleep and who is

---

* See bibliography.[339, 352, 540, 768]

** Using one minute as a unit, an "active" minute represented one in which any movement occurred. See also Giddings.[351]

† Studies have shown increased motility in sleep if the child had been active just before retiring, or if he had listened to fairy tales.[514] Greater motility was also stimulated by sleeping in a room with others when accustomed to sleeping alone,[514] by attendance at movies,[768] by large or heavy evening meals,[352] and by emotional disturbances.[350]

played out early in the day needs to have his twenty-four hour schedule scrutinized. He may need more sleep.

Children when growing rapidly may well need more sleep than when growing slowly. Thus adolescents need plenty of sleep. At times these children are accused of being lazy because they sleep late in the morning, while, in reality, this may be an expression of need. A reasonably early bed hour during school years is necessary for the adolescent since school schedules prevent him from sleeping longer in the morning.

The sleep habits of the school-aged child are built upon the accumulated experiences of earlier years. In sleep, therefore, as in other areas, it is necessary to view the present in light of the past. With this perspective in mind the physical and psychologic factors which contribute to establishing and maintaining good sleep habits can be examined. Being naturally tired but not overstimulated after an active, happy day is a sound basis for good sleep. Consistent but not rigid regularity of bed hour and other routines is an asset. A moderate meal, a quiet, relaxing time before going to bed and freedom from emotional stress and strain or excitement are conducive to quiet sleep. The conditions under which a child sleeps are also important. Quiet, freedom from external stimuli—especially the unfamiliar—and comfort, such as a comfortable bed and warm but light bed clothes, are important. Many of these conditions are more easily achieved if the child can have a bed of his own and, if possible, a room of his own.*

Just as important as providing a good physical environment are the child's feelings and attitudes. It has been stated before that a happy day is conducive to good sleep. How a child feels about himself—and especially in relation to parents, peers and school—is of paramount importance. Anxiety, worries, fears, troubles of the day may prevent him from having a restful sleep.

The child's attitude toward going to bed may be one of pleasant and casual acceptance or one of resistance. The family attitude about sleep affects the child's attitude. Families that have positive feelings toward sleep tend to generate such feelings in the children. Attitudes may stem from the kind of relationship and feeling tone which exists between parents and child. Undesirable attitudes may be fostered by parental overauthority, by too little guidance so that the child is burdened with responsibility for his behavior, by oversolicitude, by much talk about sleeplessness, by suggested fear of the dark or punishment at bedtime. Children will resist going to bed when they feel that by so doing they are being deprived of something. A child with a full and satisfying life will not feel cheated when sent to bed while others of the family continue with their evening activities. During the school years and in adolescence the continuation of good sleep habits is essential, and conditions favorable to a regular and reasonable bed hour need to be maintained.

Fatigue. General tiredness, called fatigue, which is relieved by food and rest, is a natural part of the activity-rest cycle of an individual. If fatigue

---

* Wagner[970] in a study of young orphanage children found that children who slept alone went to sleep more promptly and slept longer than children who shared their beds with others.

accumulates gradually from day to day it becomes chronic. Such fatigue results from disregard of normal fatigue, from illness, from emotional disturbances or various combinations of these.

Factors contributing to fatigue* include inherited constitution, too much stimulation, undue competition, insecurity and compulsion, strained positions while working which might be produced in school by inappropriate lighting and working facilities, poor balance of types of activities, inadequate food** and an over-scheduled life with no time for relaxation and recovery.

In chronic fatigue the body's capacity for work decreases, the tissues become damaged or less fit, resistance is lowered and recovery from fatigue is slow. In childhood fatigue develops more quickly than later because of the immaturity of the tissues and the energy expended for growth.

Different children react in different ways to fatigue, depending upon which system of the body becomes tired most easily. If his digestion is weak, the child reacts to excessive fatigue by loss of appetite, vomiting or diarrhea. In the case of a child with a sensitive nervous system restlessness, overactivity, irritability, sleeplessness, headaches and such conditions will be the first signs. Changes in the circulatory system, indicated by pallor or a dusky color, may appear. Body temperature may become unstable. Almost any acutely tired child is cranky and unreasonable, cries on slight provocation and denies that he is tired. The first results of fatigue are often increased activity and excitability. Later, the child usually becomes listless and inactive. As fatigue progresses, the child may develop dark circles and puffiness under his eyes. He may be unable to control certain muscles, and tremor of the hands or muscle twitches may appear. Speech is sometimes affected, so that the child stammers or stutters.

Teachers[267] have reported cases to show that the tired child in school may demonstrate inability to cooperate in group enterprises, his initiative may be low, and he has short attention span. He may develop a defense mechanism of indifference to his environment.

Children who are fatigued need a carefully balanced program of rest and play in which the three R's, refreshment from sleep, relaxation and recreation are provided in generous amounts. As capacity for activity increases longer activity periods can be tolerated. The chronically tired child should have a thorough physical examination, increased rest, a good diet, with emphasis on the "protective" foods, fewer radio, TV and movie programs and a satisfactory "emotional climate" in the home. Re-read the case study at the end of Chapter 1 in this connection.

EXPERIENCES TO VITALIZE CLASS WORK

1. Plan a day's diet for a kindergarten child; for a high school boy.
2. Visit a school cafeteria.
   a. Observe the room and equipment, the kind and quality of food served, the pro-

* For a discussion of fatigue and relaxation see Rathbone.[758]

** Goodenough[362] reports a study of anger in children in which she found a high proportion of the temper tantrums of preschool children occurring within one-half hour before meals. Fatigue mounts at these times because of need of food.

cedure during the noon-hour, the selection of foods made by the children, the general emotional atmosphere.

b. Observe some individual child to see what actually happens to him during his noon hour.

c. Evaluate what you see from the point of view of nutrition and education.

d. Plan some ways of educating children in the selection of good lunches.

3. How would you explain to an adolescent girl the value of good physical habits of eating, sleeping, activity and elimination?

4. Evaluate your own food habits and trace their origins as far as you are able.

5. Paul is six years old and in the first grade. His mother reports that he takes a long time to go to sleep, is often restless during the night and has to be wakened in the morning. She realizes that something is wrong and asks for help. How would you proceed?

6. Visit a school classroom or recreational group and look for possible signs of fatigue. Enumerate them. Can you recognize the probable causes? Plan a regimen for these fatigued children.

7. A kindergarten child has to go to the toilet about four times during the morning. This has happened for several days. What possible contributing factors should the teacher investigate?

8. A nine-year-old boy is a poor eater. He is not hungry at breakfast and under pressure from his mother eats a little cream of wheat cereal with sugar and cream and some orange juice. At noon he has an hour for lunch. He hurries home clamoring for food, drinks his milk and eats some bread promptly, takes a few bites of egg and vegetable and then wants to go out to play with the boy next door. In the afternoon he raids the ice box. He is not hungry at dinner time, but with pressure from both parents eats a little of everything. By 8:30, his bed hour, he is hungry and has a large glass of milk with ovaltine. What suggestions would you make to the mother?

9. Get relevant facts about the nutrition and routines for your case study child. Evaluate his food habits, his rest-activity cycle. Incorporate this material in your case study write-up.

SELECTED READINGS

Carlson, A. J., and V. Johnson: The Machinery of the Body. 4th ed. Chicago, University of Chicago Press, 1953.

De Castro, J.: The Geography of Hunger. Boston, Little, Brown & Co., 1952.

Gerard, R. W. (editor): Food for Life. Chicago, University of Chicago Press, 1952.

Gesell, A., and F. L. Ilg: The Child from Five to Ten. New York, Harper & Bros., 1946.

Rand, W., et al.: Growth and Development of the Young Child. 5th ed. Philadelphia, W. B. Saunders Co., 1953, Chs. 6, 7.

Spock, B.: The Common Sense Book of Baby and Child Care. New York, Duell, Sloan & Pearce, 1946.

Strang, R.: An Introduction to Child Study. Rev. ed. New York, The Macmillan Co., 1951, Ch. 12.

Williams, J. F.: Personal Hygiene Applied. 9th ed. Philadelphia, W. B. Saunders Co., 1950.

CHAPTER 5

Influences on Growth
(HOME, SCHOOL, CHURCH, CAMPS)

THE HOME AS AN INFLUENCE ON GROWTH

The Home and Family, a Primary Influence.   There is no disagreement among students of child development that, of all the agencies of society which affect children, the home exerts the first and most insistent influence. It is inevitable that the effect of the home should be discussed in many places throughout this book. There are, however, some things which need to be said in a separate unit.

The family provides the child with his *biologic and social heritage*. Through his parents he receives his biologic inheritance which sets his potentialities.* To what extent these potentialities will be realized will depend upon the home, family and environmental influences outside the family sphere. His social heritage comes from the attitudes and experiences of the many preceding generations which have become a part of his parents and other close relatives. Parents bring to their children their past as expressed in their mode of living, their feelings and attitudes. Parents with a rural background may build a pattern of living for their children quite different from that of those who have always lived in a city. An American Chinese family will pattern its life differently from a family stemming from an Italian heritage. Other families will have bits of a number of cultures because of past intermarriages. Parents may bring warmth, affection and spontaneity or lack of these, depending upon their life experiences. They may create an atmosphere of tension or relaxation, domination or acceptance. They may be vigorous and energetic or tired or sick. They may have established satisfactory health habits or poor habits. They may be neglectful of their physical needs and unconcerned about their health, or they may be comfortable in a routine which meets their particular physical needs. So each family presents a unique environment for a child on the basis of contributions from the past. With its background a family sets an environment for the child depending upon its financial status and educational level, its cultural interests, standards and values.

Home is a place where the child's physical and psychologic needs are met. The home

* The effect of heredity has been discussed in Chapter 2.

feeds, clothes and shelters him. Parents protect him from diseases or, through their ignorance or carelessness, expose him to infections which may affect his growth.* They provide (or should provide) him with regular medical and dental supervision either by having a family doctor (or pediatrician, if available and within the financial means of the family) and dentist or by utilizing clinic services in the community. They provide him with a physical space which may be safe or unsafe, comfortable or uncomfortable. This space will influence whether he has rest and quiet, play and exercise, or overcrowding, tension and unrest. Inadequate facilities usually mean inadequate nutrition, too little rest, too much tension. Adequate facilities, if coupled with understanding, should mean good nutrition, sufficient rest, less friction. In this environment he may or may not be protected from accidents** and taught the rules of safety.

Further, parents provide (or should provide) the child with affection, a sense of "belongingness," a satisfactory discipline, a working set of good physical and psychologic habits and attitudes. They set the atmosphere for his moral and ethical standards, his physical well-being, his aesthetic appreciations, his concept of family living† and his philosophy of life in general.[182, 323, 585, 623, 781]

Living space plays a role here, too. The number and kind of people in the home will influence a child's discipline, his cooperation, his tensions and anxieties as well as his satisfactions and joys in family activities, his loyalties and his affections.

---

* Parents may transmit infections through themselves or by employing some infected person in the house. Such diseases as tuberculosis, syphilis, gonorrhea, typhoid fever, respiratory and skin infections are passed on to children. One doctor[519] reports 48 family outbreaks of pneumococcic infection in which two or more members of the family were infected by the same type of organism but in differing manifestations. The person causing the recurring infections invariably was a "healthy" carrier. Thus it is advisable for the family doctor to know his patient's family as well as his patient. Periodic health examinations for the whole family, servants and other adults having intimate contacts with children is a sound procedure.

** Accidents kill more children and young people than any disease. Many more are handicapped by accidental injuries. In 1952 in Michigan 276 children between 5 and 14 years died as a result of accidents. The danger zones for these ages are (1) on the streets as pedestrians, (2) playing around water, (3) at home where a fire occurs, (4) in a motor vehicle, (5) on a bicycle, (6) near firearms. ("Michigan's Health." Michigan Department of Health, October 1953.)

One study[564] of accident repeaters and accident-free children found both groups in good physical condition. In a coordination test with saw and hammer accident-prone children tended to be less controlled and less cautious. Families of accident-prone children had a markedly casual attitude toward injuries. More injuries had occurred among these families and their relatives than among the accident-free families. After the presentation of this study Dr. Ross commented on accidents in camps where she had observed a tendency for children to differ in the frequency of accidents. She noted three types of children among the accident-prone: the show-off, the discouraged, the reckless (resistant to authority, defiant, impulsive). The camp staff worked toward better safety by (1) cleaning up environmental hazards and (2) attempting to understand what went on within the accident-repeater. The same procedures could be applied in the home.

† Education for marriage and parenthood begins in the family, where impressions of the meaning of being a father and of being a mother are learned. Through family experiences the child can learn to think of parenthood as a exciting aim or can, on the other hand, develop negative feelings in this area.

Home is a place for learning: learning about the world, about people, ways of behaving, attitudes toward health, work, people and life in general.

Home is also the place where the child has experiences in receiving, later in sharing and giving, in making decisions, in practicing control over himself and over others. As he grows, the experiences, under the guidance of wise parents, will be such that they are compatible with his abilities and lead him into becoming a participating member of a group, first the family, later the school and the community. Thus, in the home the foundation of his present and future health, both physical and psychologic, are laid.

In the home, consciously or unconsciously, the parents prepare the child for school. This transition from a life of freedom, in which he is treated almost wholly as an individual, into an experience in which he is one of many with its necessary emphasis on the group, can be made an easy one if parents plan well. His habits of sleep, elimination and eating need to be established in relation to his future school hours, so that, upon entering school, there will be no need for readjustments in his routines. A physical check-up, if he has not been having regular health supervision, should be made before school entrance to reveal his physical assets and liabilities. Psychologic preparation is of equal importance. A child who has had contacts outside the home and has played with other children and been taken to visit the school will, all other things being equal, have an easier time adjusting to school life than a child deprived of these opportunities. Some writers believe that the fatigue found frequently in the early school years could be reduced by a more adequate preparation for school.*

After the child enters school the home is still of vital importance. In point of time, the home retains one-half of the younger child's waking time and one-fourth of that of the adolescent.** However, the home preserves more than one-fourth of the influence, since it has the child for meals and at bedtime, both periods well known as more impressionable periods than an equal number of clock hours.

Home is a place for recuperation after the child's daily activities. After a busy day at school the child needs relaxation. The conditions at home determine whether or not he will be able to recuperate from the day's activities and thereby be fresh for the next day's program.

Parents need to grow as their children grow.† A parent who is able to see the world from the child's level as well as from his own and who is flexible enough to adjust his relationships to the child as the child matures will be a satisfactory parent from both the child's point of view and his own.

The child's reaction to his home and his incorporation of it into his own feelings is described later (Ch. 12). Gesell[347] gives a good summary of the developmental increments by which the child gains progressive insight into the meaning of family life. He found that among the children he studied the

* Edwards and Tamblyn[267] found that 65 per cent of children with chronic fatigue in a school in Ontario were in the kindergarten and first three grades.

** This is computed on a twelve months' basis. During the school months the proportion, of course, is somewhat lower.

† See[689] for discussion of family developmental tasks.

child's identification with his home by five years of age has become personal and self-conscious, even to the extent of boasting about his home and his family. By six years, even though the child seems self-centered, he takes an interest in family outings, family secrets, and in paternal and maternal relatives.

Seven [years] in his little serious way has a deepened sense of the family as an institution; he is proud of his home and family possessions; even his negative behavior betrays an emotional strengthening of the family ties. Eight is somewhat less subjective; he is interested in the family as a going concern, and at a festival gathering he is especially anxious that everyone should be having a full share of the good time.[347]

By nine years the child is showing a tendency to be on his own away from his family, yet he shows increased awareness of family standards and a greater sensitivity which denotes a deepening identification with his family. The basic orientations to the family, Gesell says, "are well-nigh complete by the age of ten."[347]

Family Attitudes and Interpersonal Relationships Directly Affect Children's Growth. Important to children are the interpersonal relationships in their homes. These are extremely complex, being made up of the relationships between parent and parent, between each parent and each child, and between each member of the immediate family and any other relative or person living in the household. These relationships are those which can be seen on the surface and those of which we are aware intellectually; but, far more important, they are those based upon emotion and feeling, many of them buried deeply beneath the surface of overt action and operating at the subconscious level. Most important here is the spirit or atmosphere of family life.

In the constant interplay between family members the personality of the child receives its first, and hence its most important impact. Bossard[109] summarizes the contributions of this family interaction as follows: (p. 95) "(a) satisfaction of the desire for intimate response, (b) a stage for the development of the child's ability, (c) the approval of one's kind, (d) the first lessons in living with other persons, (e) determination of personnel attitudes, (f) tools for the acquisition of an education, and (g) living habits."

The child, in turn, makes a contribution to family life which depends upon his individual characteristics, upon the attitudes and feelings of the parents toward the child, and upon the attitudes and practices prevalent in the surrounding culture. Bossard[109, p. 157] summarizes the usual contributions of children to parents as including "(a) an increase in the range and complexity of family interaction, (b) an expansion of family interests, (c) emotional satisfactions of lifelong duration, (d) the opportunity to relive life, (e) the control of human development, (f) insight into life's processes, and (g) insight into the true meaning of life."

Effect of Broken Homes. It is a matter of general observation that unhappiness at home, or the distractions and lack of normal home life affect the quality of children's school work. One study[211] of marks of 300 high school pupils from broken homes and 300 from normal homes showed that the school achievement of the pupils from broken homes was inferior to that of pupils from normal homes. Since the pupils in the two groups were carefully paired for intelligence, sex, nationality, chronologic age and grade, the conclusion was that broken-home background has a deleterious effect upon school achievement. Such home factors as disruption by the death of either parent, divorce or separation of parents, unemployment of the father, and employment of the mother outside the home subject the child to various forms of emotional disturbance and conflict. These distract his attention from his school work, undermine his effort and prevent the most effective application of his abilities.

Teachers can often discover reasons why children are not working up to capacity by making friends with them in such a way as to allow the children to express any anxiety which they may be able to verbalize. At no time, however, should the teacher probe into the private lives and thoughts of her pupils, since, by so doing, she may either further distress the children because they feel they have in an unguarded moment betrayed their families, or because probing may raise to the conscious level thoughts which the children may be emotionally unable to face.

Landis,[561] in discussing broken homes, says that there is a relationship between broken homes and delinquency which is a perfectly logical one. The absence of one parent removes one source of authority;* the remaining member of the family must usually be the breadwinner so that even his authority is absent during working hours. Although recent increases in federal social security coverages have made it possible for many more mothers to remain at home with their children, this is still not possible in many homes.

When the home is broken up because of disagreement (separation or divorce) there is often a difficulty in adjustment for the children because in the conflict between parents an attempt may be made by each to win the child away from the other; the result is often disloyalty to both and a feeling that neither parent stands for high standards of behavior and therefore cannot expect them from the child.

Some idea of the extent of the broken home problem can be gained from the Midcentury White House Conference on Children and Youth[665] which reports that one of every eight of our children under eighteen years of age lives apart from one or both parents.

Position of the Child in the Family. Personal relationships within the family are often affected by whether the child under consideration is an only child, an oldest child, a youngest or a middle child, an only boy among girls or an only girl among boys, the pretty one among ordinary siblings or the ugly duckling, the smart one among ordinary (or average among dull) siblings. Reports of research findings on the effect of each of these factors can be found in numerous child development publications.[242,451,756,905,941] However, the literature is not in agreement about what the effect is of being an "only" or an "oldest" child, or most of the other classifications mentioned above. There is agreement about the fact that children *are* definitely in-

* The effect of this was clearly demonstrated during World War II when absence of the father was reflected in the less effective discipline evidenced, particularly among the boys.

fluenced by these factors, as every clinician knows, but the interplay of circumstances is so complex that it is hard to say that any one of these factors will always produce a known and predictable result.

Only children, for example, have been the topic of many studies which do not agree in their findings. In general, the weight of evidence seems to be in the direction of a better chance for only children to get educational and health privileges, although the literature also indicates that "spoiled" only children do exist and in large numbers, and that, among the privileged upper socio-economic groups, only children are often nervous or delinquent.

The literature agrees fairly well that *oldest children* are somewhat more delinquent than other children (the assumption being that parents learn the job of parenthood on the first child), and that they are more often jealous than other children. Several studies indicate that children in large families have lower intelligences than do the children of smaller families. However, the factor of correlation between large families and lower socio-economic status should be recalled here, as should all of the complex factors which influence growth. On the other hand, oldest children often have very superior personalities because they have learned through caring for younger children how to share family responsibilities. One analyst of Who's Who in America showed that there is a higher proportion of only children in this listing than there is in the general population; also that the highest group of any listed were oldest children in large families where the father had died and the oldest child had had to assume substantial responsibility in the family.

We must not fall into the error of thinking that only children, or oldest children, or only boys, show traits simply because they are only or oldest, but rather because only children live in small families, often of upper socio-economic status; oldest children are first children and have younger parents. These factors, as well as the "onliness" or the fact of being "oldest," are important.

Competition within the Family May Produce Important Emotional Reactions. Most children have conflicting feelings of love and hate (referred to in the literature as "ambivalent" feelings) about their parents on certain occasions.[720,762] Toward brothers and sisters they have these feelings frequently.

Jealousy between siblings, especially of an older child for a new baby, cannot be avoided entirely, even by good preparation for a new baby,[452,475] but is not so likely to endure into the later years of childhood if the children are within the same range of intellectual ability, that is, within five points of I.Q., as when there is a greater divergence of intelligence.[866] It is especially likely to occur, however, if the older child is duller than the younger child, and is almost inevitable if a younger child threatens to overtake, or does overtake, the older in school grade. Murphy and associates[684] consider jealousy as a form of aggressive behavior expressed against a child who threatens the status of another child. This aggressive behavior is likely to be exhibited in bodily attack upon the younger sibling; less frequently, it is expressed by no overt act against the new child, but rather by personality changes in the jealous child which appear at the time of the birth of the new child or soon thereafter. Occasionally, it finds its expression in ignoring the new baby or by denying its presence. In spite of current writings which might lead one to assume that rivalry and hatred are the most characteristic feelings between siblings, MacFarland[607] found these feelings present only occasionally and not as frequently as the more charitable feelings. Unfortunately, the majority of studies to date have centered on the less pleasant traits of personality, perhaps because they cause more trouble.

Parents or teachers need not worry too greatly when children show competitiveness for a place in the family or in the school. It is quite normal behavior. One needs to feel concern about such behavior only when it becomes too intense or vicious, in which case the cure is not an attack upon or disciplinary program with the jealous child. This only convinces him still further that he is not loved, or that he has no status and, therefore, deepens the cause of his jealousy. Every effort should be made to assure him of his place in the family or in the schoolroom, and that there is room in the home and school and in the hearts of the family or teachers for two or more children at once. He may, of course, have a false philosophy of love, believing that any love or attention shown someone else must, of necessity, be taken away from him. In this case, he needs to learn that love becomes greater for being given away, and that the parents or teachers who love or give attention to a new child have even more love and understanding, because of that, to give to the other children already in the family or to the other children in the schoolroom.*

THE SCHOOL AND CHILD GROWTH

Schools Reach All Children Who Are Physically and Mentally Able. Among community influences, the school is the one agency in this country which reaches, by compulsion of the law, all of the community's children. In primitive society no formal school is necessary. The child gains knowledge of the necessary living skills and social codes from his direct contact with his family and the activities of the community. Certain puberty ceremonies and the preparation for them constitute a sort of tribal school, and the examination system is initiation into adult responsibilities and adult privileges. With the development of philosophies and literature, even of the arts of the medicine man, specific and concentrated teaching became necessary in order to keep alive the accumulated heritage of knowledge. This was done, however, on an individual tutorial basis, the learning being limited to a scant few of each tribal group. Even with the art and literature of the Greek civilization, the teaching was still limited to a small social class whose responsibility it became to preserve the cultural heritage and to contribute to it. It has only been in the last century that any type of "book-learning" has been made

---

* Refer back to Chapter 3 for review of materials on effect of the family upon emotional development. Excellent aids to parents in establishing sound relationships with children can be found in Cutts and Moseley,[212] Gallagher,[333] Langdon and Stout,[562] Rand et al.,[756] Symonds,[922] and Thomson.[943]

available to the masses of people. Even today, compulsory education of more than six years is largely limited to the North American continent and to Europe. However, on these continents, and now, increasingly, in Central and South America, the school, as a state-approved agency, is reaching an important sector of the impressionable years of all children.

What Should Schools Teach? This increase in numbers of schools and in attendance does not necessarily mean better education. However, the school has stated certain objectives, among which are not only the teaching of basic subject matter, but also the promotion of health, development of character, and teaching of citizenship. What relationship the school bears to the home, church, and other agencies in this teaching is well stated by Olsen when he points out that we have passed in the first half of the twentieth century, "from a book-centered, through a child-centered, into a society-centered school," and says:

> What, then, is the proper function of the school in this total educative process within the community? How shall the democratic school envision its comprehensive task as society's chief agency for the formal education of youth? Clearly its function is a residual one; its obligation is to start its educative process where those of the other community agencies leave off or prove ineffective; its inclusive purpose must be that of helping children learn with the minimum of time and energy those things they need to know for personal-social-civic efficiency that they do not adequately learn elsewhere.[705]

Next to the home, the most important agency in society for the transmission of the cultural heritage to children is the school. The home as we have seen, transmits vital attitudes, "trains" the child in basic living habits, serves throughout the childhood years as a translator or interpreter of those cultural mores which the child meets outside as well as inside of the home. The school accepts the major responsibility for transmitting and translating or interpreting those aspects of the cultural heritage which have been formalized into "school subjects" such as history, science, etc.* This is its academic job, and the one in which it has little competition or aid from other public agencies.

The schools, however, are no longer limiting themselves to this job. Accepting the thesis that they must develop whatever aspects of personal-social-civic efficiency are not adequately learned elsewhere, the school has accepted a wider responsibility than the mere teaching of academics. This acceptance of wider obligations to children has manifested itself in many ways. "Character education," "education for citizenship," "training for responsibility" are all familiar phrases to educators today.

* Gesell and Ilg,[347] in The Child from Five to Ten say: "The curriculum should not be envisaged as blocks of academic requirements, but as areas of educational opportunity corresponding to the major facets of our culture. These facets correspond to three culture areas. We may well think in terms of these three culture areas rather than in terms of the time honored 3 R's. Three Culture Areas: 1. *Language Arts* (conversation; drawing; writing; spelling; reading; listening; looking). 2. *The Sciences* (mathematics; natural science—physics, chemistry, biology; social science—geography, history, civics). 3. *Personal-social Participation* (creative self-expression; arts and crafts; dancing, poetry, invention, technology, engineering; pre-vocational skills; social cooperation and leadership; aesthetic, ethical and spiritual appreciations)."

The Kindergarten's Contribution.   Soon after the beginning of the century, the kindergarten movement attempted to set up a program which would give careful attention to the physical needs of children, which would make a satisfactory introduction to the formal school through a full recognition of and contact with the homes from which the children came. This movement, in the beginning, had a fairly clear understanding of how schools could function in full light of children's growth needs. Unfortunately, however, the kindergartens were too soon absorbed into the public school systems, there to suffer the restrictions of budget, the pressure of numbers, and, most seriously, the pressure of stereotypy which at that time characterized the public schools of our country. The inevitable result was that, although the kindergarten was able to hold out against the traditional idea that schools should crowd four- and five-year-olds with reading and number work, they were, nevertheless, forced to surrender most of their physical health program and much of their home-school-cooperation vision. The sharply increased numbers of children born from 1942 through the years immediately following World War II have created pressures upon the kindergarten and elementary grades (and as the "tide" moves forward, upon later grades and colleges). These pressures have become acute problems to school administrators and school boards.

The Nursery School's Contribution.   Twenty years after the kindergarten, the nursery school movement was introduced into this country. This movement, fortunately, originated in close alliance with child study laboratories and family-life teaching centers. Its original purposes were (1) to study the growth of children and (2) to serve as a laboratory for schools teaching child development and family life. Inevitably, then, the nursery school came to be an extension of the home upward, rather than, as the kindergarten was, an extension of the school downward. This carried implications of paramount importance in the formulation of nursery school "curriculum" and methods. School became, first, a healthy environment for children, with proper food, proper sleep, and proper toilet facilities. Children received careful physical examinations, daily inspection to prevent the spread of contagious diseases, well-balanced hot meals at noon, rest before lunch, a nap afterward. Special attention was paid to cooperation with the child's home in all details of the day, so that home experience and school experience flowed along for the child in an unbroken continuum. Parents kept in close touch with the activities of the school; the school received daily reports of home activities.

This careful attention to physical activity and to home-school cooperation was, of course, imperative in any school program which attempted the care of very young children. It became a conscious part of the original plan which regarded the physical growth of the child as an important responsibility of the school. The same careful home-school cooperation was worked out for intellectual and social growth as for physical growth. These nursery school programs and such experimental elementary school programs as followed in the wake of child development research have come to be a nucleus for studying total growth patterns, and for experimenting with how schools can meet children's basic growth needs.*

The percentage of primary grades in our country which are proceeding to adjust better to children's intellectual and social needs is genuinely encouraging. Aside from the nursery school, however, with its careful attention to adequate physical examination in order to exclude those with contagious diseases (even the common cold), with its well balanced hot meal and its complete rest period, the physical health and growth needs of school children are being met far less adequately than are their intellectual and social needs.

[**Progressive Education's Contribution.** The Progressive Education Association has achieved a great deal in the reform not only of the primary and elementary grades but also of stereotyped secondary education. Much has been done to eliminate the old "patch-work timetables," and to increase an emphasis upon democratic participation by the pupils, more democratic relationships between teachers and administration, more and better guidance programs, a curriculum which is in much closer relationship to the life of the community, which will more closely meet the demands of the contemporary adult society, and which will, as part of this objective, unify various subject fields. The main changes are in the direction of an attempt to achieve continuity of growth for children through changes in the fundamental purposes or objectives of the school. This is, in general, in line with the increasing awareness of the need of fitting school curricula and school schedules to the growth needs of children of secondary school age evidenced in a number of current writings.**

This means, first, a school setup which provides for the physical needs of young people: freedom from jammed classrooms and halls, convenient locker space, drinking fountains, adequate toilet facilities, some spot in the school where the child belongs, a seat in a room which is his home room, and a place to rest when necessary; adequate lunch rooms, good food, supervised and provided by school authorities and not by commercial concessions; an adequate noon hour set at an appropriate time of the day; a reasonable distribution of academic classes, shop, music, gym or auditorium, and study

* From 1925 on, such centers as the following have been doing outstanding work in this field: Cornell University, Department of Child Development and Family Relationships in the College of Home Economics; Merrill-Palmer School, Detroit; University of California, Institute for Child Welfare Research; University of Iowa, Child Welfare Research Station; University of Minnesota, Institute for Child Welfare; University of Toronto, St. George's School; Yale University.

Some of these were financed, or still are financed, by private endowment. However, a number of public educational institutions have developed child development programs without endowment or private aid. Among these are: The University of Michigan Graduate School of Experimental Education; Ohio State University; University of Nebraska; University of Illinois; Oregon State College; National College of Education; Pennsylvania State University; Winnetka (Illinois) Public Schools; Highland Park (Michigan) Public Schools.

For a good discussion of principles of nursery school education see Read.[759]

** See Bibliography[561, 641, 696, 938] and also Department of Supervisors and Directors of Instruction, National Education Association: Thirteenth Yearbook, 1940: Mental Health in the Classroom, N. E. A., Wash., D. C.

periods; a reasonable load of home work; a reasonable participation in extracurricular activities. These activities should vary, not with what the child is willing to do, but with what his academic ability, his physical health, and his home situation dictate as "good" for him from the viewpoint of promoting his physical, his academic, and his personal growth.

We see clear indications of the trend toward better teacher-pupil relationships in current publications[67,151,153,456,992] which point out that educators are noting and making use of basic mental hygiene concepts. In improved teacher-pupil relationships, for example, we see the influence of pronouncements of psychiatrists and mental hygienists that teachers' personalities leave a marked impression upon children's behavior and attitudes. Poor methods of approach by the teacher can, and often do, produce behavior problems in the classroom.[18] Good methods and an understanding approach on the part of the teacher make school not only a profitable experience for the children, but a joyful experience as well. Doubtless if one were to search for the most important single factor in the teacher-child relationship, one would find that friendliness stands out in simple, direct forcefulness. Teachers are, as a whole, far more friendly in their relationships with children than they used to be, not only because we have a freer conception of education as a whole, but also because of a recognition of the importance of a good teacher-pupil relationship in the child's social and emotional development.

Much Still to be Done. That there is much to be done in the direction of fitting the school to children's needs,* particularly in making school meaningful to young people, is indicated by the American Council on Education. In discussing the proportion of youth who, even now, with our recent large increases in high school and college registration, leave school at the end of the eighth grade or at high school graduation, Bell says:

> Our data suggest that many schools are so organized at present that young people have to go through the whole school program before they can be led to see any genuine value in it. This inevitably creates a sense of inadequacy among the majority of young people who drop out shortly after the completion of the elementary school. The answer is the development of educational programs so closely related to everyday living that each school year, instead of being a means to some more or less remote end, becomes in fact an end in itself.[83]

In summarizing the situation in junior and senior high schools in relation to child development, the Committee on Workshops of the Progressive Education Association says:

> The average junior and senior high school case of discipline is simply a human being in the midst of the uneven and rapid growth of puberty and adolescence who cannot get along sufficiently well with his fellow pupils or adults to avoid conflict situations. . . .
> Among the school practices to be avoided are the following: mechanically applied systems of merits and demerits which finally engulf the wayward, course requirements designed for the 20 per cent who are being prepared for college and applied to the 80 per cent who are not interested, teachers who are utterly uncompromising with the very human nature of youth; lack of opportunity for students to participate in running the school community; subject matter for which pupils can see no use either now or later.[641]

* Witty et al.[1006] point out that our schools typically ignore the facts of continuous growth, particularly in the abrupt changes of attitude and method which occur between the elementary and junior high school, and again between the junior and senior high school.

This committee recommends that schools attempt to provide remedies for these evils through a good individual counseling program, through a program of student participation in school affairs, through stimulating teacher interest in pupils, and through "a very human understanding of the effect of development on behavior." They also recommend special attention to the orientation of entering pupils.

The high school of the future is described by McKenzie[618] as assisting the adolescent to take his place in life by helping him in his developmental tasks, and summarizes these as follows:

    a. Attaining individuality
        (1) Progress toward an organized personality pattern
        (2) An emerging philosophy of life involving a concept of values, desirable behavior, and a place in society
        (3) An understanding of personal assets and liabilities
        (4) A maturing of plans for future living
    b. Adjusting to changes resulting from physical growth
    c. Securing satisfying relationships with age-mates of both sexes
    d. Establishing independence from family
    e. Attaining adult status
        (1) Vocational plans
        (2) Family relations
        (3) Social relations
        (4) Citizenship

He adds that:

Obviously, the wise planning of programs of instruction and the giving of helpful counsel and advice are predicated upon a thorough grasp of the process through and by which individuals pass from childhood to maturity.

If this assistance is to be intelligent, the social and individual goals of the school must be clearly perceived, the levels of aspiration of the adolescent personalities must be known, and the progress of each individual must be assessed from time to time.

Physical Environment of Schools Important to Health and School Progress. Because schools either knowingly or unknowingly affect children's physical health in vital ways we shall turn now to consideration of the role which schools not only do play but could play in providing for children's physical well-being.

Studies such as Harmon's[398, 399, 400] have contributed to an awareness of the importance of the school environment to the health and working efficiency of school children, and to the planning of the environment to fit the needs of the whole child. In his survey of a large number of children in Texas, visual defects were found, which increased with age.* Some children with eye difficulties were seen to assume poor posture at work and had postural asymmetry** which in some instances could be traced to an attempt on the part of the child to relieve his eyes from glare or shadow.[398]

* In the elementary schools 59 per cent of the Anglo-American children had visual defects. Of these, 39 per cent had eye defects not related to refraction. These defects increased from 18 per cent in the first grade to 82 per cent at the end of the elementary years.

** Asymmetry: Body segments were not symmetrically aligned on either side of a vertical line through the center of the body. Line drawn through the eyes did not make a right angle with the vertical axis. See illustrations in[399, 400].

In Harmon's studies some of the children in the upper elementary schools had nutritional defects. About two-thirds of these, or 12 per cent of the school population, were in classrooms where they were being overstimulated by programs which were not related to the physiologic needs, and where activities were beyond their natural physical capacities. Thus not only may the nutritional status of a child impede his educational progress, but also the school may increase his nutritional problem.

About three-fourths of the children in the survey showed evidence of chronic upper respiratory infection. It was found that a certain number of these children in the upper elementary division rooms were so placed in the classrooms that they were being subjected to glare, seating problems and other stresses. For example, when the typical classroom was divided into quadrants, about 50 per cent of the children with chronic infections were found in the rear left quadrant nearest the back windows and thus subjected to unsatisfactory lighting conditions.

The author listed school conditions which possibly contributed to the sensory, nutritional and postural defects, to chronic infections and behavior deviations as follows: improper seating, improper lighting, improper placement of working materials, inadequate stimulation on the one hand, or overstimulation on the other, limitations of desk size or working surface area, improper books, notebooks, paper and other materials, crowding of children at tables, temporary lacks of physiologic, psychologic or experiential readiness.

Later in a study[398, 399] in which health and school progress were observed before and after improving the lighting conditions of the classrooms, evidence was presented to indicate that improper lighting may be an important factor in the life of the school child. Three hundred ninety-six children were given thorough medical and nutritional examinations and visual, psychologic and educational tests in November and again six months later in May. The rooms were rearranged to reduce sky glare and redecorated to secure a better distribution of natural light. During the six-month experimental period the refractive eye difficulties had been reduced by 57.1 per cent, the non-fractive by 90.1 per cent; nutritional difficulties had dropped 44.5 per cent; and signs of chronic infection had dropped 30.9 per cent. At the same time, the children averaged a gain of ten and one-fifth months in educational age. In a school used as a control the mean educational age gain was six and four-fifths months. Thus, it would seem, there is evidence* that improving some of the unsatisfactory conditions in a school environment will make it possible for children to make better progress physically and in their school work.

Healthy School Environment. Schools need to be planned in relation to the development and needs of the particular children who will spend so many hours of their day in school. The site for the school, the plan of the building and equipment for the use of students and teachers are all important. Much is being done to make the modern school functional, adaptable,

* Luckiesh and Moss[502] also found that improvement in school progress followed improvement in school lighting conditions.

esthetic. Many schools are planned to provide for a variety of educational experiences in a healthful environment where space, light, heat, ventilation, toilet facilities, locker space and equipment for work are provided in a manner which allows for safety, health and comfort of pupils and teachers.* However, many children still must attend schools with poor buildings and inadequate facilities.

A child's eyes are of vital importance in his education. When he enters school he begins to use them more and more for close work. Their protection is, therefore, the concern of teachers and school administrators. Adequate lighting,** the placing of work spaces to use the light effectively and the proper selection of materials such as paper and books† deserves careful attention. Factors which produce eye fatigue, such as inadequate light, inappropriate seating in relation to the source of light, glare,‡ too fine work or book print which is too small for comfort, need to be eliminated.

Work space, especially desks and chairs, must be such that a child may sit comfortably in good posture. Placing furniture in the proper relation to the source of light has been mentioned. Movable desks and chairs have an advantage over the stationary kind in that they can be moved about at the convenience of pupils and teachers. The size and construction of the chairs should conform to the size and body proportions of the children using them. (See p. 240 on posture.) Chairs which are too small or too large lead to bad postural habits and all the attending physical and psychologic difficulties. Because children vary in size and build, adjustable desks and chairs are almost a necessity. The chair should be adjusted to the child more than once a year, because of the occasional rapid growth in some children.

In discussing the relationship of the school to children's growth, Ilg§ lists the following as improvements which schools should make if they are to meet the growth needs of children:

1. In the kindergarten and early primary grades there should be a shorter school day or a break in the middle of the week: for example, Wednesday out.§§

* For a review of research in school plants and equipment see Review of Educational Research 25 (1), 1951.

** For appropriate class room lighting see[692].

† For type and size of print see[693] and Chapter 9 of this book.

‡ Most school rooms are planned for right-handed children. Those who are left-handed need to be placed so that their work space is properly lighted.

§ Ilg, Frances, in a lecture at the Merrill-Palmer school, 1946. Ilg is co-author of The Infant and Young Child in the Culture of Today and of The Child from Five to Ten.

§§ An experiment[483] in Richmond, Virginia, between April, 1927, and April, 1928, demonstrated the value of cutting down the length of the school day in the early elementary years. Two schools, serving the same socio-economic group with approximately two hundred and fifty children in each school, began at the same hour, 8:45 A.M., but closed at different times. In School C, the children in the first two grades were dismissed for the day at 12:30 in contrast to 1:45 for the first grade and 2:00 o'clock for the second grade in School B. In School C the third graders left at 2:00 o'clock in contrast to 2:45 in School B. At the end of the year, the gains in weight in School C were 34.3 per cent greater than in School B. School C also had only 225 pupil days lost, while School B had 1677, a 600 per cent greater loss of time in the long-day school. Fewer children in the short-day school were reported fatigued after two months of the experiment, the percentage of fatigued children dropping from 52 per cent to 19 per cent. In the long-day school, the teachers reported 63.5 per cent of the children fatigued. It was suggested that this difference in the

(Footnote continued on p. 166)

2. No marks for tardiness should be given before eight or nine years of age.

3. There should be constant communication between teacher and parent in the early school grades if anything goes wrong with the child.

4. There should be recognition of the difference between the developmental rates of boys and girls, especially in the learning of reading. Boys are more auditory in approach up to eight years of age; girls are visual earlier. Therefore, whereas girls usually learn to read at six to seven years of age, boys should be given simple shop experiences and other such experiences and should not be given much reading before eight years of age.

The school environment and its program should be so planned that everything contributes to the child's efficiency in learning and to his practice of desirable habits. At school the child should be gaining (1) knowledge about himself as a physical being and knowledge of his needs, and (2) experience in providing for those needs. By so doing, he will be ready to assume complete responsibility for himself when the time arrives.

Protection Against Disease. A school program which protects the child from diseases contributes to his well-being. The school can protect the child by encouraging immunization against communicable diseases, which can be controlled, by careful compliance with the Board of Health's regulations regarding all communicable diseases and by early isolation of children who are not well. Early recognition of a sick child* and his removal from the

---

* If a child has any of the following symptoms he should not be in school:
   Red and running eyes
   Running nose
   Coughing and sneezing
   Severe pain
   Dizziness or faintness
   Swelling about the neck
   Sore throat
   Unusual paleness
   Earache or running ears
   Feverish appearance
   Rash
   Nausea, vomiting or diarrhea
   Tiredness, irritability or crossness, or other change in the child's usual behavior.
(Taken from instructions for mothers concerning the spread of acute illness.[179])

(Continuation of footnote from p. 165)

number of tired children may have accounted for the 18.5 per cent more A's in deportment in the short than in the long-day school.

Modification of school days should be made in terms of climate, the hours kept by the great majority of the children's parents, and other such factors laid against the children's growth needs. For example, we frequently find children inside school buildings from 8:45 A.M. to 12:00 noon, and from 1:00 P.M. to 3:30 or 4:00 P.M. For six of the nine or ten months of the school year in Northern climates, this permits only part of the noon hour and week ends in direct enough sunlight to be of any benefit to the child's growth. For rural children who spend, in addition to these hours in school, one to one and one-half hours on busses, both morning and night, their only opportunity for outdoor play is the partial hour at noon and, when recess is offered, the extra half hour of the day thus provided. In some situations we might find a better school day, one which, when weather permits, provide as longer mid-day period for outdoor play than is traditional.

group lessens the chance of spreading infection to others. Most schools have been making a fine effort to control communicable diseases such as diphtheria, smallpox, measles, etc., but they need to do more to check the spread of respiratory disturbances which are so prevalent in the school population. Respiratory infections are the largest contributors to school absenteeism* and can have serious effects upon the health of children. A cold, for example, may lead to an ear infection which may, in turn, affect the child's hearing.** The school can encourage parents to keep children at home during the infective stage. It can also encourage, if not require, their teachers to remain away when suffering from a cold or sore throat.

Physical Examinations and Measurements. Periodic physical examinations, including vision and hearing tests, when adequate, locate weak and strong spots in the child's constitution. When these examinations are used as a basis for correction of defects or deficiencies and when they serve as an educational device to acquaint the child, parents and teachers with the health needs of the child, they become a vital part of the school program. A periodic check of height and weight can, by following the progress of a child's growth, keep the school and home aware of accelerations and decelerations in gains, so that they can plan the child's regimen accordingly, and look for contributing factors in his environment. In a good school program, the doctor and nurse become an integral part of the educational staff.†

The Teacher's Role. Good health provides a teacher with energy to meet the demands of the school day; lack of energy limits her ability to cope with the day's problems and work creatively with her children. She is a better teacher when she is well. Thus it is important that she protect her health by having developed a good set of habits of eating, sleeping and activity. In addition, regular medical and dental check-ups provide the assurance of no physical difficulties or catch them in early stages when they are more easily treated. X-rays of the chest reveal any possible chest infections. Schools which require all teachers to have yearly chest x-rays are protecting both teachers and pupils.‡

In addition to protecting her own health, the teacher can detect the early

---

* A study of absenteeism in the New Haven schools in 1948[593] revealed that 87 per cent of all absences were due to colds, other respiratory infections and diseases of the throat and tonsils. These illnesses amounted to 92 per cent of all the illnesses of the children.

** In a Hartford County, Maryland, conservation of hearing program[413] chronic conduction deafness was nearly always associated with previous upper respiratory infections.

† These two, plus the teacher, can form a team which watches the status and progress of each child and works with his family in maintaining his health. If possible, conferences about each child in which information is exchanged and integrated will make each adult more effective in providing a good school experience for a child.

‡ Cases of teachers acting as a source of tuberculous infection have been cited.[392] For example, a man with unrecognized tuberculosis taught chemistry and led the band in one school. When the children in this school were given the Mantoux test (to indicate tuberculosis infection) 15.72 per cent of the children in the school had a positive reaction. For the boys in the band, who had a closer contact with the teacher, the incidence of a positive test was twice as great as that for the whole school population.

beginnings of sickness or nutritional deficiencies* provided she knows her children well, knows the early symptoms of illness and deficiencies and is a keen observer.

The teacher also has a role to play in helping the child to understand his physical needs. She can guide him in understanding the reasons for their importance and, serving as a model through her behavior and attitudes toward eating, sleeping and all the other physical habits, she can encourage good practices and attitudes in her children.

Health Education. The school can play a major role in the health education, including nutrition education, of children and adolescents. It can supplement the learning in the home, or, when the home fails in this function, the school can be the primary agent in providing the child with information and positive attitudes regarding his health. Thus the school can help him to assume responsibility for his own health in a reasonable, healthful manner. For some this means reinforcing already learned habits, for others it means changing habits. This can be done through presenting information in a way which is meaningful and acceptable to the child by teachers who not only can give the information, but can do it convincingly and with an understanding of the beliefs, attitudes and behavior of the families of their pupils. In order to make this information functional, experiences for demonstration and practice are essential. Children can learn about their growth and that of others while being weighed and measured.** While receiving first aid a child can learn the reasons for such procedure. Physical examinations and vision and hearing tests can also be made meaningful to the child rather than just a routine which is a nuisance. Nutrition education can be geared to the rest of the school program, to the school lunch, to the strengths and weaknesses of the diets of the children, to community resources. Trips can be made in the

---

* The Subcommittee on Medical Nutrition, Division of Medical Sciences of the National Research Council, has prepared a list of symptoms and signs of early nutritional deficiencies, classified according to persons capable of observing them.

Teachers and parents may observe the following symptoms and signs suggestive of early deficiency states:

Children	*Adolescents*
Lack of appetite	Lack of appetite
Failure to eat adequate breakfast	Lassitude and chronic fatigue
Failure to gain steadily in weight	Lack of mental application
Aversion to normal play	Loss of weight
Chronic diarrhea	Loss of strength
Pain on sitting or standing	History of sore mouth or tongue
Poor sleeping habits	Chronic diarrhea
Backwardness in school	Nervousness and irritability
Repeated respiratory infections	Burning, prickling of skin
Abnormal intolerance of light (photophobia)	Abnormal intolerance of light
Abnormal discharge of tears	Burning or itching eyes
Bad posture	Abnormal discharge of tears
Sores at angles of mouth	Muscle and joint pains (muscle cramp)
	Sore, bleeding gums
	Sores at corners of mouth

Journal of the American Medical Association, *118:* 615–616, 1942.

** One school[188] had 13- to 18-year-olds follow their growth progress on the Wetzel Grid and discuss factors which might be contributing to deviations in their growth pattern. As a result they were motivated to improve their habits when it seemed advisable.

community: perhaps to see a produce market in a large city, the sanitary control of the water supply, a public health laboratory, the canning or freezing of food, an example of scientific farming. Thus the many facets of health education can be made a vital part of the school program and of real significance to the child.

Nutrition education has been shown to be effective in improving children's eating habits. One study[370] demonstrated improved selection of school lunches after a group of fifth graders had a nine months' unit in nutrition which included a variety of experiences relating to nutrition. Another study[988] demonstrated improved food habits following a school nutrition program which was a part of the total school program. It was integrated with the day-to-day teaching and learning and also with the community health program. It was developed with the cooperation of the teachers, after careful observations had been made in the school and the community so that it would fit the needs of the children. These illustrate two different ways in which a school can teach nutrition effectively.*

Contributions of the School Lunch. The school lunch can have both health and educational values. It can contribute to the health of children if it provides the proper share (one-third) of the day's food requirements, if it is planned to share in the total day's requirement by supplementing the home diets, if it is prepared well under sanitary conditions and served attractively, and if it is eaten in leisure in comfortable surroundings. For all children a substantial lunch means energy for the afternoon's work and food to grow on; for some it may mean the only good meal of the day.

As well as giving the child necessary nourishment, the school lunch can offer other advantages. It can extend the child's knowledge and liking for a variety of foods; it can help the child to establish standards for food and for table behavior by observation of others and by guidance from teachers. It can be the place where he practices that which he has learned about health in his various school experiences. It can also be a force in the community for the promotion of better food habits. For a school lunch to achieve these objectives it needs to be an excellent regimen well planned, well supervised, and made a part of the total school and community program. All school cafeterias do not, unfortunately, measure up to these criteria and, therefore, contribute little to the real nutritional needs of the child and less to his education.

HOME AND SCHOOL MUST WORK TOGETHER FOR BEST RESULTS

Home-School Cooperation Depends upon Mutual Understanding. Home-school understanding and cooperation are generally accepted as basic to smooth continuity of growth as the child moves from the home into the new and different environment of the school. This is important not only as he enters kindergarten (or nursery school) but also as he moves back and forth between home and school throughout his formal educational experience.

* For nutrition education on elementary and secondary school levels see Goals for Nutrition Education[236] and Activities for Nutrition Education.[596, 597]

The school must remember, however, that not every parent sees eye to eye with the school or with every other parent in his ambitions for his child. As long as we remain a democracy the parent has a prior right over the State in determining many things about his child. No parent, under our law, may neglect a child's food, clothing or shelter, nor may he abuse his child or contribute to the child's delinquency. Nor may any parent keep a child out of school during school age; but the parental attitude toward the school may sabotage anything the school might try to do for the child.

Fortunately, however, only rare parents have any atittude but a constructive one toward their children, so that, given even a modicum of encouragement from the school, cooperation with the school is dependent only upon parental understanding of what the school is trying to do. Teachers and school supervisors must overcome their characteristic attitude that everything right with the child can be attributed to the efforts of the school, whereas everything wrong with him can be attributed to his parents. They must also overcome a characteristic tendency to feel that, in any difference of opinion between home and school, the school is always right whereas the parent is always wrong, or ignorant, or negligent. The home, on the other hand, must realize that the school serves many children and cannot always make adjustments to all the needs of any one child. Even crowded schools, however, under good principals and good teachers, manage to make fairly adequate adjustments to the needs of individual children.

Plans for home-school contacts should be a conscious part of the program of any school which even pretends to function as a promoter of development in children. Some communities now require at least one visit each year to the home of each pupil. Occasional schools provide a time, even to dismissing early one day each week, or providing substitute teachers one-half day each week, when the regular classroom teacher can visit homes. A number of schools have frequent days when parents are scheduled by special individual invitation to spend the day in the school; sometimes they are invited to participate in the program.

School Report Cards as an Aspect of Home-School Cooperation.　Parents should be kept informed of school regulations as well as of the individual progress of their own children. A formal report card, requiring the parents' signature, is the usual system, but many schools are revising the traditional form of their report cards. An occasional outstanding school calls a parents' meeting from time to time to discuss such matters as the form of report the parents consider desirable and the teachers find practicable. Such use of parent-teacher meetings for active discussion of school policies, which so intimately concern both teachers and parents, injects a meaningfulness into school-parent clubs which many such clubs lack at present. Some schools have experimented in the early primary grades with the abandonment of any form of formal report to parents. This seems to work in situations where parents understand the reasons for such a program, and where some personal conference with the parents at periodic intervals keeps the parents informed about the child's progress and adjustment. It fails wherever the move is made without sufficient understanding and support from the parents, and wherever the children and the parents are left "dangling," without any progress reports or information about whether the child is "making good," or not. Most parents are interested parents; they want their children to learn to adjust to the school job, since they realize that, in a certain sense, success with this job predicates success with "life" jobs; they want to cooperate with the school in seeing that the children do learn how to make this important adjustment. The school which fails to utilize this interest not only misses an excellent opportunity to serve its community, but it loses invaluable information about individual children which would make its work substantially more efficient.

The School Curriculum Extended into the Home.   A proposal made by the Committee on Workshops of the Progressive Education Association[641] is the use of home projects as a means of improving home-school understanding as well as a means for teaching young people family relations. The projects must, however, be carefully chosen and so set up as to increase home cooperation rather than to arouse antagonism. A boy should not be led to quarrel with the judgment of his father over the exactly "correct" use of tools because the shop teacher has been overstereotyped in his instruction. A girl who learns to look down upon the old-fashioned or "unscientific" methods of her mother's housekeeping, instead of to cooperate in the general task of household management, has not only been taught meaningless techniques, but has also been encouraged to destroy the only foundation upon which good homemaking can possibly exist, viz., harmony among the family members. School projects sent into the home must always have in mind a sympathetic understanding of the standards and techniques of the individual homes and must encourage, rather than discourage, parent-child harmony.*

OTHER AGENCIES AND EXPERIENCES AFFECTING THE LIVES OF CHILDREN

Many Other Agencies and Experiences Also Teach.   As we have suggested elsewhere, some teachers and school administrators are inclined to limit their thinking about developing citizenship in children to the role played by the school. They tend to neglect the nonschool influences which operate during school age and which are often far more potent than the school in forming habits and attitudes. Nonschool agencies always did, and still do, have a vital function to play in the education of children for life.

That the school is only one of the community agencies which teach citizenship, or which affect the lives of children, both while they attend school and after they leave school, becomes evident when we consider the number of

* Excellent suggestions for the building of school programs in personal-social development, in home-making and family relations courses, and in social science courses are contained in the report of the Committee on Workshops of the Progressive Education Association, in the publications of the National Council of Parent Education, the Federal Bureau of Home Economics, in the reports on Adolescent Study of the Institute of Child Welfare of the University of California, and other publications of the Progressive Education Association in addition to those cited.

children who pass beyond the influence of the school at a comparatively early stage in their development toward mature adulthood.*

We may gain a partial insight into the number of agencies other than public schools which touch the lives of children when we consider the religious, social, welfare, recreational and other agencies, federal, state and local, which exist for the welfare of children: churches, Sunday schools, young people's organizations, settlement houses, hospital clinics, private doctors and hospitals, boards of health, visiting and public health nurses, visiting housekeepers, public welfare organizations, children's aid and placing societies, orphanages, juvenile courts and detention homes, public and private guidance clinics, public libraries, art museums, science museums, children's concerts, the radio, television, the newspapers and comic strips, newsstands with magazines good and pernicious, public and private recreational centers, camps, scouts, Y.M.C.A. and Y.W.C.A. and similar organizations. These are only some of the agencies in urban centers. Rural areas have 4-H clubs, rural youth organizations, church organizations, county health and welfare, and other social agencies.

Many of these agencies prove, upon analysis, to be concerned with the care of children in the bottom sector of our population—the ill-fed, ill-clothed, ill-housed. Many are concerned with the prevention or correction of delinquency or other problem behavior. Some are caring for children from broken homes; some are nursing sick children back to physical health. A few, working beside the school, the church and the home, are broadening children's horizons, developing their talents and appreciations, and providing enrichments for body and mind. Some, like radio, television, movies, the comics, are both destructive and constructive, depending upon the quality of what they offer; but, whatever the offering, these four influences have multiplied their power over children in a geometric ratio in recent years, as we shall see in Chapter 6.

CHURCH

As we proceed further with the constructive forces in the lives of children, we find the church the largest organization, besides the school, which attempts to guide standards and attitudes of children. Whereas medicine, public health, recreational programs and the like take primary responsibility for the physical development of children, and whereas schools take primary responsibility for intellectual development, the church is regarded as the organized agency whose chief responsibility it is to oversee the spiritual development of children. There are many academic schools which exist under the control of the Church rather than of the State.**

* Although by 1950 all states required school attendance at least up to 16 years of age, the Midcentury White House Conference on Children and Youth[665] reports that enforcement of school attendance up to these years is still lax in most communities.

** It is also true that nearly all schools take some responsibility for physical and for character development as well as for intellectual growth. Of course, as we have said repeatedly, the family is of all agencies the most influential and responsible for the physical, informal intellectual and spiritual development of individual children.

Many Families Leave All Formal Spiritual Training to the Church.
Many modern families do little about formal spiritual training of children,
tending to turn that responsibility over to the church if they give it any attention at all. Family worship is no longer widespread. Many so-called
"modern" families find themselves embarrassed and awkward at any mention of God or of cosmic or mystical forces. Fortunately for the development
of the children in these homes, there is usually a well-defined and clearly
practiced "social philosophy" and a high sense of "ethics." This being true,
the children gain in these homes fairly clear beginnings in ethical practices
and fairly adequate social viewpoints. They do not, however, as a rule, have
any help in the verbalization, and hence clarification, even of such principles
as the parents themselves verbalize. They receive little or nothing of the inheritance of the racial tradition or mores, as represented in Bible stories or
stories of Church saints. They are likely to grow up with the conception that
there is no wisdom or strength in the universe beyond themselves, or, at least,
beyond mankind. Many such people find themselves getting along quite
smoothly until some crisis of life arises. It is in the crises that most people
find themselves in need of explanations of life and death, and of a Source of
Strength beyond the human. They have none of the solutions for life crises
which the race has accumulated and which it passes on through religious
tradition. Lacking this, they have deficient strength with which to meet major
life crises.

Sensing this need for fortification in periods of crisis, sometimes sensing,
even though they do not have it themselves, that there is some viewpoint
or contact which can enrich daily living, many parents who do not themselves
belong to or attend church send their children to Sunday school. All parents
who find strength in religious practices wish to have their children find the
same strength. There is, therefore, a fairly high proportion of children who
are at least exposed to the influence of the Church. This proportion has been
increasing since World War II, as has the proportion of families who join
churches.*

Churches Do Not Always Use Good Educational Methods. The religious concepts or ideas which many children have are confused and distorted. Unfortunately, these distortions are not often evident to the adult
who has unwittingly instilled these ideas. Although many churches now use
trained teachers and good educational devices in their Sunday schools,
many still fail to do so.

Results of poor teaching in the past can be seen in Brown's[129] study of
college students. He carefully balanced in the study the ratio of Protestants,
Jews and Catholics. Eighty-nine per cent of these young people had changed
their childhood concepts of God; 96 per cent had experienced conflict in
their own minds about childhood religious concepts, but 7 per cent had preserved the childhood ideals. The first doubt for many of these young people

---

* Many newspaper and magazine articles since 1950 report this trend, based upon
figures which show church membership in nearly all denominations increasing more
rapidly than the increase in population.

is traceable to the death of someone whom they considered useful and necessary, and which led them to question, "Why should a just God take away
this one and leave so many useless people alive?" Some questions arose when
disaster befell someone whom they regarded as not deserving it, whereas
they felt that all about them wickedness went unpunished. These young
people were still laboring under the idea of an irrational, whimsical God,
and needed to come into possession of a far wider concept of Life and Universal Law. Prayers which are not immediately answered arouse doubt in
the person who is so limited in his conception as to think that it should not
rain on a given day because he wants to go to a picnic. That ten thousand
farmers may be praying for rain never occurs to him. Many young people
trained by poor methods had retained childish anthropomorphic concepts
of God and of their own relationship to Him.

One of the best writers on religious education for children, Ligon,[592] says
that healthy-minded religion should help children to work out the following
problems at the following ages:

Two to four:	Confidence in people and things
Four to six:	Cooperation
Six to eight:	Sensitiveness to criticism
Eight to ten:	Fear of failure
Ten to twelve:	Positive attitude toward goodness
Twelve to fourteen:	Venturesomeness in work

He does not wish us to understand that these are the only problems in which
religious education should help children, since he is acutely aware of the need
of introducing children to the concept of God at an early age, but he does
wish us to understand that words and stories alone are not enough in the
early education of children. We must see that they *experience* basic religious
conceptions in situations so life-like that the necessary lessons are learned and
desirable attitudes developed.

If Brown's group, mentioned above, proves a fairly adequate sample of
young people, and clinical experience indicates that it is, then it becomes important to see that religious concepts are taught in childhood in such a way
that they can stand the test of modifications which experience must give them.
Only in this way can religious concepts keep abreast of the growing life experience of the individual. This does not mean half-formulated ideas, but
rather, that God should not take on anthropomorphic outlines, being "an
old man with a white beard, sitting on a throne," passing judgment on each
good and each bad act, handing out rewards and punishments by whim or
upon being bribed or wheedled. This is actually the concept which many
children get from formalized church-school teaching.* That God's rewards
and punishments follow orderly law, or that God is a Spirit far more om-
niscient and omnipresent than is possible for a person sitting on a throne in

* Based upon several years of church-school samplings made by the Merrill-Palmer
School in religious education experiments.

the sky seems impossible for many young people trained on dogmatic parrotings of Bible quotations which are beyond their comprehension as children.

It is because of this type of meaningless teaching that many children come to hate Sunday school and to put up a weekly battle about going. Part of the difficulty is due to rather haphazard teaching by volunteer teachers who have no special training. Many of the more modern Sunday schools are employing trained teachers and are offering freer programs, with dramatizations of Bible stories and other group socialized experiences which give children not only the inheritance of a knowledge of the Bible, but also a practical experience in cooperation and teamwork, in "Love thy neighbor as thyself." Young people's groups are offering many types of activity, not only as social experiences for the young people themselves, but as services of the young people's groups to the church and to the wider community.

Some Churches Are Using Modern Methods with Excellent Results. The attitude of the children in one small city church* was completely changed in two months by a new pastor. Instead of having to "hound" the children into Sunday school, within two months this pastor had the children of his church not only attending enthusiastically, but also bringing in their friends and neighbors. He accomplished this mainly by conducting a separate high school service which duplicated the adult morning service, except that the young people themselves organized into a church with deacons and elders, served as ushers, choir, verse readers, collection takers, etc. Paralleling the adult service in time, he also conducted a children's church in a small adjoining chapel in which the children were ushers, verse readers, choir, pianist and collection takers. Only one adult was present at these children's services. This was a mother or father who told a story in place of the adult sermon. This proved an excellent means for stimulating not only active interest but for establishing a habit of participation which, at least as long as this particular experiment has lasted, has led to continued interest and participation through adolescence and into adulthood.

This plan, which was developed in several different communities several years ago, has become a practice in many communities with excellent results. There seems to be an increasing understanding on the part of religious leaders that religion can become functional and vital to children and young people only when the precepts are carried into practice, and that it is part of the business of church-schools to see that this happens both in the family life of the child and in his relations with the wider community.[660]

Church-school projects which cooperate with other agencies in the community are doubly useful in teaching teamwork and group spirit in a world in which cooperative work in the home is diminishing. In the old days of weaving, baking, washing and cobbling in the home, parents and children worked together on projects which were clearly necessary for the well-being of all. Few of these chores remain in the modern home to teach such cooperative production for the good of all. Schools help somewhat by the cooperative projects which they create. However, these projects are usually

* New England Congregational Church, Aurora, Illinois.

centered around the children themselves, promoting the learning or the housekeeping or the play interests of the participants. Sacrifice for an ideal, or for people not in your own immediate group (and, therefore, from which you do not yourself, as a member of the group, reap benefit) is not frequent in the life of the weekday school. Teaching of this wider sacrifice seems the realm of the church-school.

This should not be misunderstood as indicating that modern educators assume that activity programs are the most important part of spiritual education. There must be spiritual counsel, knowledge about the great basic principles of faith and insight, and about great spiritual leaders. There must be time for and the habit of prayer.*

SUMMER CAMPS

From 1900 to 1941 the spread of summer camps for boys and girls was rapid and steady. Nearly every state now boasts dozens, ranging all the way from the free camps for underprivileged children, supported by newspapers, Rotary clubs and Community Chests, to the expensive private camps, which charge $75 to $100 per week and provide every sport and living luxury. Children of all ages, from two-year-olds through adolescents, attend. Preschool camps are, however, a fairly recent development.

There are not only twenty-four-hour-a-day camps, but innumerable day camps, or playgroups where supervised recreation is the program.

Summer play schools have, since World War I, demonstrated the feasibility of group programs for children, which offer excellent physical care and informal educational opportunities to children whose summers would otherwise be spent in crowded city slum homes and on the streets. New York City has led in these programs, which are usually centered around settlement houses. Such programs provide a hot noon-day meal, carefully planned for nutritional value, mid-morning and mid-afternoon milk or fruit juices. Daily naps and showers are gladly accepted by children from hot, overcrowded homes where no one goes to bed until the coolness of late evening hours has tempered the heat of the rooms, and where baths are not easy to get. Creative play, arts and crafts opportunities, story and reading activities all help to provide a well-balanced day. Children characteristically gain weight under these programs, returning to academic schools in the fall in far better physical and psychologic condition than would otherwise be possible. For the numberless children who cannot leave crowded cities for summer camps, these play school projects provide a type of care which is invaluable for the children's growth and well-being.

One of the greatest contributions of these play schools and of nursery schools to education in general lies in their recognition of the importance of parent education and the cultivation of parental cooperation. Talking over with parents physical examinations, daily schedules, food values, the pro-

* Fahs[286] says that if children are to be taught the experience of mysticism, they need leisure as well as activity and book knowledge.

Fig. 23. Camp can be a good experience for children and a laboratory in child development for students.

gram of rest in relation to the children's growth and well-being often leads to talk about children's individual personalities and adult-child relationships. Visits by parents to the schools, planned parental participation in the school day, invitations to parents to "come to lunch with us," to help plan and conduct trips, to drop in on extemporaneous plays and other story-hour projects all help to make the parent feel at ease in the school, to give an opportunity for informal, friendly teacher-to-parent and parent-to-teacher education. Such cooperation helps the school to adjust the day's program to the needs of each child as determined by the exigencies of his home life, and also helps parents to plan such adjustments as are feasible in the home program to fit around the school activities. Thus home and school work together, day by day, to achieve a successful summer of growth and well-being for the children. There is much of the home-school relationship in these programs which could, and should, be adopted in winter school programs to promote a genuine improvement in the total growth and well-being of children.

Camp programs range all the way from a detailed scheduling of every half-hour of the day to informal play-and-do-as-you-please programs. In view of the rigid scheduling demands made upon most children during the school year, there is a desirable tendency in the direction of freer programs in the more modern camps.

Camps exert a considerable influence upon the life of the modern city child.[17] Probably their greatest contribution, if they are well run, is physical. The sunshine and out-of-door play, the healthy appetite for meals, and the regular hours of sleep often make all the difference in a child's physical stamina for the following winter. Many children lose some actual weight in an active summer of camp life, only to gain much more than the amount lost as soon as they get back home. Many children, however, gain steadily after the first week of adjustment; particularly do underprivileged children gain in camp. Unfortunately, many of the undernourished children from crowded city slums which offer neither play space nor rest are the children who get only ten days or two weeks in camp. The more privileged children who have play space and plenty of food at home, and many of whom have, in addition, a "cottage on the lake," are the children who get six or eight weeks in camp. Camp also makes a contribution to most children's physical skills. Riding, hiking, swimming, and skill games widen the repertory of physical skills, and sharpen interest in physical play. It trains the child for life by training his body, increasing his love of exercise, and developing his self-confidence. As the child learns to overcome physical fears in swimming, riding, and overnight hikes, he learns much about overcoming psychologic fears. Courage can, perhaps, be defined as that which one possesses when one has overcome fear. Thus, in increasing command over the body and in overcoming fear, the development of physical skills makes an important contribution to mental health.

Camps also exert a strong influence on social adjustment and moral values. Because children live for twenty-four hours under the influence of camp counselors and are required, not only in play but also at meals and during rest and sleep hours, to adjust to other children, progress in social adjustment is often rapid. Camp promotes the weaning from dependence upon parents which is an important part of total social growth. Close living with people other then the family teaches self-control and consideration for others as they cannot be taught at home. Parents, by virtue of the fact that they are parents, are always *with* a child and *behind* him, no matter how badly he behaves. People outside the family have no such obligation and can withdraw support or companionship whenever the personal relationship becomes inconvenient or disagreeable. Many children find self-discipline in camp for the first time, and discover that the only way to get along with others is to temper what one pleases to do with consideration for the rights and wishes of others.

Another contribution of camps, as well as of good schools, lies in teaching children joy in work. Satisfaction in a job well done, the ability to put forth continuous effort in work and to find creativity in doing so is one of the basic, unshakable foundation stones of the truly healthy personality. In camp, the summer of constant effort may be crowned by the ability to swim 50 yards. Housekeeping, waiting table, and other "work" can become fun as the child does cabin duties in a group and as preliminary to hours on the beach.

Thus work becomes fun, play aims at a goal of perfection, and a "passion for excellence"* is achieved for many children who would not develop it otherwise.

A CASE ILLUSTRATING INTERAGENCY COOPERATION

The following letter from a hospital psychologic clinic to a school nurse indicates the type of information which can be gained in one clinic contact and one home visit by the clinical social worker. This child was referred to a children's hospital by the school nurse who worked in a school district where no medical or psychologic examination is provided by the school. The nurse felt that an effort should be made to discover why Evelyn was having trouble with her teachers. In the hospital where the clinic was conducted medical examinations were preliminary to referral to the psychologic clinic. The distance from the clinic was too great to permit a consistent follow-up by the clinic personnel. Unfortunately, Evelyn's school system had no special classes for mentally retarded children. It was necessary, then, that in spite of her mental age she should find whatever academic adjustment possible. She had failed often enough that at ten years ten months she was just entering the first half of the fourth grade when the case came to the attention of the school nurse.

The letter also demonstrates the kind of interagency cooperation which is possible in the care of children.**

Dear Miss M——:

As our hospital social worker has perhaps informed you, we saw Evelyn F. in our Out-Patient Clinic at the Children's Hospital yesterday. We gave her an intelligence test. At a chronological age of 10 years 10 months she scored on a Revised Stanford-Binet test 7 years 6 months, giving her an I.Q. of 69. Her medical examination was negative except for evidence of malnutrition and for the need of a check on her eyes.

Evelyn does not present a very promising picture as nearly as I can see. She is one of those border line intelligences which always find it difficult to get on in school. Complicating this there is not only a very bad dietary condition, but also a number of fears which make her cling to her mother or any available adult. Since it is so long a distance for the mother to come in and since correction of this sort of thing takes a considerable length of time, I am wondering if it would not be possible for you to carry on for us.

The mother apparently has very little understanding of correct food. To provide adequate food on the budget available will take a good deal of help. I also gather that even when the right foods are available Evelyn refuses to eat them. According to their report the child's diet yesterday was as follows:

Breakfast: 1 cup of coffee, one piece of bread
Luncheon: peanut butter sandwich and a piece of pie
Supper: mashed potatoes, bread, tomato preserves

* L. P. Jacks' phrase. Mr. Jacks is a leader in the camping and recreation movement.
** The National Society for the Study of Education Forty-third Yearbook on Adolescence[696] contains an excellent discussion of the inter-relation between the school and other community agencies. (p. 327)

It is our feeling that a higher intake of calcium and vitamins might help to make her somewhat less distractable in attention and less flighty.

The essential need psychologically is for her to adopt a more mature role—learning to bathe and dress herself, learning not to run to her mother every few minutes for physical attention, learning even to participate in some of the household activities. If you could help the mother and the child to get her to assume a role more equal to her mental age and less like that of a two- or three-year-old child, it would be of some help.

There is a possibility that some of Evelyn's insecurity is traceable to the fact that she does not understand that the present father is a stepfather rather than her own father. I asked her mother to clear this up. There seems some confusion between the record that we had and the mother's own statement as to whether Evelyn is an illegitimate child. If you have any opportunity to check this and find that she is illegitimate it may be possible that the mother's own attitude toward this would convey some insecurity to the child.

There seems evidence, as we mentioned above, that she needs eye correction. We have made an appointment for this for next Wednesday. I understand that our social worker will get in touch with you about providing for her glasses.

The child is to return to Dr. N. at the Medical Clinic in four months.

If we can be of further service please call upon us.

Sincerely yours,

This case was followed through by the school nurse who was able to get good cooperation from the mother. Evelyn proved to be an illegitimate child who had been legally adopted by her stepfather. The mother seemed on the whole to accept this situation without conflict, although she overprotected Evelyn in an attempt "to make it up to her" for not giving her a legitimate own father. She realized that overprotection was a handicap to the child and soon succeeded in helping Evelyn grow up to her mental age. As this occurred Evelyn became more able to give attention in school and in other ways to benefit from the school program. A better balanced diet gave her more physical vigor. This, combined with her more grown up behavior, improved her play relationships with other children. Thus we see home-school cooperation and interagency cooperation solving a problem of growth and adjustment as nearly as it was possible to do in such a case.

EXPERIENCES TO VITALIZE CLASS WORK

1. A. Invite into your class two or three successful mothers of school-age children. Encourage them to discuss:

   a. What happens to their children before they get off to school in the morning?
   b. What happens to them during the noon hour?
   c. What happens to them after school and until they go to bed?
   d. What happens to them over week ends?
   e. How much work or home responsibility does each of their children carry?
   f. How many clubs do their children belong to? How many special lessons do they take?
   g. How much do they listen to the radio? To television? To what programs? With what resulting effect? (Preserve this information for discussion of Chapter 6.)
   h. How often do they go to the movies? What kind of movies? With what resulting effect? (Preserve this information for discussion of Chapter 6.)
   i. How many of their children go to church school? Receive religious instruction at home?
   j. How much spending money or allowance does each child have? What does he do with it?
   k. What hobbies does each child have?
   l. What part have the fathers been able to play in the care and guidance of these children?
   m. What occasions arise for discipline? What kind of discipline seems to work best?

n. Discuss with these mothers some of the recommendations for routines and discipline found in your readings. How practical do they prove to be?

B. If the mothers cannot visit your class, have two or three members of the class visit one home each and obtain the same information. Bring it to class for discussion.

2. If you are doing a case study, gather the above information for your child.

3. Contrast the following two school schedules for "fit" to children's growth in your community. Consider the job of getting the school work done, sunshine hours, frequency of bad weather, number of children who go home for lunch, age of children involved, predominant working hours of fathers (as this relates to family meal hours and bed-time) and other relevant factors.

School A (Elementary)		School B (Elementary)	
8:45	School opens	8:30	School opens
9:00	Classes begin	8:45	Classes begin
10:30	Recess—Mid-morning milk or fruit juice or cracker	12:00	Dismissal
10:45	Classes resume	1:00	Classes resume
12:00	Dismissal	2:30	Recess
1:30	Classes resume	2:45	Classes resume
2:30	Recess (if good weather)	4:00	Dismissal
2:45	Classes resume		
3:30	Dismissal		

4. Contrast the following schedules for high school pupils:

Child X in School C (Senior high school)		Child Y in School D (Senior high school)	
8:15	English	8:45	Mathematics
9:00	Gym	9:30	Spanish
9:45	Study hour	10:15	Study
10:30	Shop	11:00	History
11:15	Mathematics	11:45	Lunch
12:00	Spanish	12:30	Shop
12:45	History	1:15	English
1:30	Lunch	2:00	Study hour
2:00	Study hour	2:45	Gym
2:45	Dismissal	3:30	Dismissal

5. Visit an old school and a modern school. Observe and compare how the building, grounds plan and facilities of the two provide for effective learning and healthful living.

6. A. Recall your own childhood. Did the school you attended make any genuine attempt to win the good will, understanding and cooperation of your parents? If so, with what result? If not, why not? Outline a practical home-school program which would help children both at school and outside of school.

B. If you are doing a case study, get this information for your child.

7. A. Recall the Sunday school you attended as a child. Plan a desirable Sunday school program for that church which would meet the spiritual growth needs of the children who attend. How would you select leaders who understand the needs and interests of children of various ages? What equipment and program would be feasible in that church?

B. Visit the Sunday school attended by your case study child. Evaluate as well as you can how well the program fits his stage of development and his needs.

8. Do any of the agencies in your community sponsor camps? What type of children do they serve? If your community does not sponsor children's camps, either get a copy of the American Camping Magazine or write to the American Camping Association (343 Dearborn St., Chicago, Ill.) for catalogues of several different types of camps. Discuss the programs of these camps for adequate fit to the ages and backgrounds of the children served. Discuss any experiences you have had with children's camps.

SELECTED READINGS

American Council on Education: Helping Teachers Understand Children. American Council on Education, 744 Jackson Pl. N. W., Washington, D. C., 1945.

Association for Childhood Education International: Using What We Know for Children in the School, the Home, the Community. Washington, D. C., Association for Childhood Education International, 1951.

Bossard, J. H. S.: The Sociology of Child Development. New York, Harper & Bros., 1948, Chs. 3–12, 15–20.

Chenoweth, L. B., and T. K. Selkirk: School Health Problems. Revised ed. New York, Appleton-Century-Crofts, Inc., 1953.

Honigmann, J. J.: Culture and Personality. New York, Harper & Bros., 1954, Chs. 13 and 14.

Horrocks, J. E.: The Psychology of Adolescence. New York, Houghton Mifflin Co., 1951, Ch. 2.

Hymes, J. L., Jr.: Effective Home-School Relations. New York, Prentice-Hall, Inc., 1953.

Landis, P. H.: Adolescence and Youth: the Process of Maturing. Revised ed. New York, McGraw-Hill Book Co., 1952, Chs. 9, 22–25.

Rand, W., et al.: Growth and Development of the Young Child. 5th ed. Philadelphia, W. B. Saunders Co., 1953, Ch. 2.

Wheatley, G. M., and G. T. Hallock: Health Observation of School Children. New York, McGraw-Hill Book Co., 1951.

Witmer, H., and R. Kotinsky (editors): Personality in the Making: Fact Finding Report of Midcentury White House Conference on Children and Youth. New York, Harper & Bros., 1953, Chs. 9, 11.

Influences on Growth—*(Further Community Factors)*

EFFECT OF THE CULTURE

As subtle as the influence of the home, and as ever-present, is the influence of the culture* in which the child lives. As a Hindu, a Chinese, a French-man, a New Englander, a Western white, an Indian, or a Southern Negro, certain expectations and patterns of what one does or does not do surround one from birth. These expectations and patterns may take the form of modifications of the physical form, like binding of the girl's feet in the older Chinese culture, or stretching the neck in certain African tribes. In the average American group, for example, it consists of a certain athletic development for boys with emphasis upon height and musculature, and of a certain emphasis upon feminine curves for girls. The short, undermuscled boy feels the impact of his undesirability as does the lanky, uncurved girl.

The culture usually attempts to mold not only physique but also habits, character and personality. Five meals a day in some parts of Europe, three in the United States; certain diets for Italians, others for Frenchmen are all typical in their respective locales. In the development of specific habits, our middle class American way of life

includes a deep respect for cleanliness, for property, for sexual control, and for rapid achievement. Children resist these values. Therefore our training levies heavy demands upon the young child.**[222]

Every culture, for example, makes demands of some sort upon very young children in exacting control of eliminative processes. Times, places and circumstances regarded as proper for elimination differ. Important in child training is the age at which control of elimination is expected. We have some evidence, for example, that the age at which our American children have been trained for the toilet upon the advice of most pediatricians and parent-educators during the 1900's to 1940's was somewhat too young. Current advice is to permit the child greater freedom in this learning. In

* Bossard[109] defines the culture in simple terms as (p. 119) "the sum total of the ways of doing and thinking, past and present, of a social group. From the standpoint of the child, culture is the social heritage to which he is born and in which he is reared." Herskovits[419] says (p. 147) that "culture is the learned behavior of a people."

** See later (Ch. 12) for more about the effect of culture on the development of personality.

many countries there is little if any pressure for early achievement in control of elimination, yet children seem to adopt the pattern of the group at a fairly early age.

As children grow older, every culture places upon them expectation of self-care in various degrees and at various ages, of participation in the life of the community, of economic independence or contribution to the group life, of marriage and child rearing. Too often these expectations are imposed regardless of the individual child's ability or constitutional make-up. Until recently, for example, the United States has had no place for any but the muscular, aggressive male. The contribution of thinkers, artists and other introverts was not utilized as in Europe. For this reason, much art and literature, and even, until the turn of the century, much science was lost in the welter of aggressive action which dominated the cultural expectation for boys. More than this, great unhappiness and maladjustment existed for the "misfits." Since the beginning of the acceptance of art and literature, and of scientific or scholarly pursuits, this particular loss and unhappiness has decreased. But today's American culture has its own emphases, many of which still ignore individual equipment or functioning. Until we can come to recognize each child's peculiar capacities and resistances, until we can develop a culture of understanding and tolerance, we shall go on losing socially valuable output and creating socially destructive unhappiness and maladjustment.

Within the framework of our characteristic "American" culture in the United States* we find that the demands of the social group upon the child vary from the family to the gang (the standards of the gang often coming into conflict with those of the family), and from the gang to the standards of boy-girl or other behavior in adolescents. Murphy[684] gives a clear discussion of the meaning of these changes in standards of behavior or group mores. Children learn one pattern of behavior and one set of standards for moral and ethical beliefs in the home. These must be adjusted later to those of the gang and neighborhood; and these, in turn, must be worked out to fit the demands of intimate, personal relationships in adolescence.

Even within the family, the child finds that he must adjust to differing standards as he grows, since one type of behavior will be expected at one age, another at a later age. For example, nearly every infant, whether he was wanted before his birth or not, is soon loved by his parents. He experiences a period when he is the adored center of at least his mother's universe. At eighteen months to two years he becomes "the run-about child," getting under foot when his mother works, getting into everything, asserting his own ego in temper-tantrums. He experiences a period when discipline, thwarting and restrictions are inevitable, a period when even the calmest adult finds himself "on edge" at times. Ordinarily, there will be many periods still when the child is thought "cute" and receives admiration and affection, but the conflict of being in the way and being adored in turn is present for most children. This is heightened if a new baby is on the way or already present, in which case the child sometimes experiences a strong feeling of being in the

* See Davis and Havighurst[222] and Martin and Stendler[630] for excellent case studies.

way and a nuisance in the household. Relief from this feeling comes when he is out of doors and hence no longer under foot. This is not at all destructive in his growth, since to be too much adored in the family circle sometimes means that the child cannot leave it; to be somewhat unwanted, at least at times, gives one the courage to seek satisfaction outside.

Upon entrance to school, a number of things may happen. If the child is quick to smile, to obey orders, and to learn school routines, he often experiences a renewal of mothering affection from his kindergarten or first grade teacher. If he is troublesome to have in the group of children, slow to fit into routine and not particularly lovable, he may exact rebuke and a further sense of isolation from the adult world. In any case, the majority of children do not stay entirely lovable in the eyes of most teachers very long. The result is often scoldings from teacher and principal, rebukes from neighbors and sometimes even from the police, warnings from the parents to keep out of trouble, "or else." Some children, in spite of competition with other children in the family for a place in the sun, feel through all of this a secure affection from their parents, and hence find these conflicts with the world not too unbearable. Others, failing to feel confidence in their place in the family, find "belongingness" only in the approval of the gang. This may lead to a bid for status in the gang either on the basis of bravado and "wickedness" or on the basis of constructive accomplishments as a good ball player or a champion model-airplane builder. The good of society and the mental health of the child lead us to hope he will make the latter rather than the former adjustment.

In any case, he reaches adolescence. Here he almost inevitably goes through a period of ridicule from adults for his awkwardness; he is expected to be grown up in judgment and behavior, yet is denied what, in his eyes at least, look like grown up privileges of independence from supervision. Parents and teachers make "last minute gestures toward control"[684] which sometimes takes on the aspect of desperate attempts to teach all the lessons of self-control and good judgment which the adults fear were not learned earlier. Conflict with adult authority is often even more acute than it was between two and four years. However, the young person may be able to save his face with the adults if he gets good enough school grades, or is prominent enough in school activities, especially if the activity is football. There is a diminishing group of parents with whom the most effective "face-saver" is getting a job and paying board at home. Meanwhile, the adolescent's own inner urges take him into the realm of socializing, shopping-for-mate activities which prove in direct conflict with the activities which serve as good "face-savers" with the adults.

Murphy summarizes these demands of the culture as follows:

1. He is expected to be cute and beautiful, the idol of the family, from birth to two or three.
2. He is expected to keep out from underfoot and give the adults a chance to take care of the new baby (this experience may come at any time from two to six in most families).
3. He is expected to sit still in school and learn to read and do numbers (beginning elementary school).
4. By his own age group he is expected to prove that he is male and is independent of the grown-ups.

5. The girls expect him to learn to dance and look nice and drive a car (early adolescence).
6. The school expects him to throw all his energy into winning for the ———— High School. His parents expect him to get the best marks.
7. He is expected to find a job, either to support himself or to contribute to the expenses of college or vocational school in order to prepare for a job later.
8. He is expected by his bride to love her day and night, and by the world to concentrate his energy on "making good."

This brief list is intended not to be inclusive, but merely to suggest the variety of demands imposed upon the growing young person by a society which progressively asks him to be the center of attention, to get out of the way, to accept absolute authority, to show his independence of authority, to sacrifice himself for the larger group, to be self-sustaining and independent, to love passionately and to achieve financial success.[*684]

Mead says that "American children are growing up within the most rapidly changing culture of which we have any record in the world, within a culture where for several generations, each generation's experience has differed sharply from the last, and in which the experience of the youngest child in a large family will be extraordinarily different from that of the first born. . . . So long-standing and so rapid have been these processes of change that expectation of change and anxiety about change have been built into our character as a people. Our homes have become launching platforms from which our children set out on uncharted seas, and we have become correspondingly more anxious that they should be perfectly equipped before they go."[666, p. 84]

It seems clear that, within the family or in the school and community, the child's behavior and attitudes, standards and beliefs are constantly being molded in directions dictated by the particular culture in which he grows up. Let us examine further some of the specific influences in the community which mold his growth as a community member.

SOCIO-ECONOMIC STATUS

Effect of Socio-economic Status on Physical Health and Growth. Socio-economic status is important because it determines to a large degree the paucity or abundance of those conditions in life which are conducive to healthful living. Many studies[**] in the past have pointed to the fact that material well-being affects physical development. Investigators have accumulated evidence by comparing private and public school children by grouping children according to the family income, according to the occupation of the parents, or the type of neighborhood in which they live. Still other investigators have studied the effect of changing the environment. Meredith[653] has summarized the evidence presented in American studies for boys seven and ten years old. Using several studies, he concluded that white boys of the professional and major managerial classes are taller and heavier than those of the unskilled and semi-skilled classes. The difference between the two classes averaged one inch in height and three pounds in weight. As Meredith states, the explanation of differences in height and weight between different socio-

* For other conflicts see Figure 21.
** For summarization up to 1934 see Sanders.[805]

economic groups is not known, but diet, housing conditions, health practices, occupational demands and selective mating are possible contributing factors. Sexual maturing as indicated by menarche occurs earlier in better than in poorer socio-economic levels.[663]

The effect of environment upon the health of children is not always easy to determine since illnesses during childhood are predominantly acute infectious diseases and acute respiratory diseases which affect both rich and poor. It is the chronic diseases which come later in adulthood* which show a class differential, with a higher incidence in the poorest groups of the population.[252] However, Downes[252] points out that the incidence of rheumatic fever, pneumonia and tuberculosis bears some relationship to income. Poor environment in some way contributes to a higher incidence of these. Fiedler,[290] in a study of young public school children with learning defects, found that the great majority of them were underprivileged children. It has been said that poverty is one of the basic causes of malnutrition. This is borne out by the Spies studies that were mentioned in Chapter 4.

In discussing the environmental trends among the American Negroes, Michelson[662] states that the greater incidence of tuberculosis and syphilis, higher mortality rate and more illness among the Negroes than the whites in the United States can be associated with factors which go to make up the Negroes' poor socio-economic status. In the last three decades improvement in the Negroes' general health and a lowered mortality rate have accompanied increased health facilities and some improvement in their living conditions. However, there are still wide discrepancies between the health facilities and living conditions available to Negroes and whites. Much needs to be done in this area before a marked improvement in the well-being of the Negroes can be expected.

We must realize, of course, that the poor physical condition of low income children springs from more than their actual food, shelter and medical care. Several factors may contribute. Some of the parents of these children are themselves suffering from long-term malnutrition and chronic disease and therefore lack the vigor and ambition necessary to improve their condition. Some are the not-quite-normal intellects of the population whose low intelligence prevents them from raising their economic status and from understanding the needs of their children and providing for them. Some are the victims of social and economic forces. In many instances the contributing factors are multiple. The poor physical condition of children in low income families may therefore be due to a complex of hereditary, nutritional and social factors.

Effect of Socio-economic Status on Emotional and Social Development. There are many factors in socio-economic status which affect children's emotions and attitudes. Crowded, dilapidated homes, inadequate clothing and other evidences of "inferior" status leave certain marks on children. They cannot have the sense of personal adequacy which comes from the feeling that one can be proud of one's home, that one's clothes are as good as

* These chronic diseases may have some of their roots in the growing years.

those of others, that one's father is a "success." They cannot, especially in adolescence, feel "equal" to asking any girl they choose for a date, or to asking any boy in the class to "come home and meet my family." False standards of snobbish over-valuation of material things is not involved here. Children from modest homes can and should be proud of the real values of such homes. But to be conspicuous for the holes in one's clothes, or because one cannot produce a dime for morning milk leaves a deep mark on any child's feelings of self-adequacy. Davis says in the Proceedings of the Midcentury White House Conference on Children and Youth[666] that when a family has known stress from hunger, cold and inadequate shelter they often react with a learned fear of deprivation which colors family reaction thereafter. In some families, for example, it leads to pressure upon the children for early and rapid attainment and for conscientious work habits.

Habits of cleanliness and tidiness are far more difficult to acquire in homes where there is no running water, where the rats and cockroaches overrun one's best efforts to fight them off, where there is only one outfit of clothing each and that is of cheap, hard-to-keep-clean-or-pressed material, and where there is no drawer space or closet space in which to keep anything. Respect for property rights is much harder to acquire in families where no one child owns anything "of his very own" but where, for example, any available clothing is put on the child who needs it most at the moment. (See further discussion of this in Chapter 14.)

On the other hand, there are certain pressures upon the more privileged children. Middle and upper class children are subject from early childhood to the pressure for success in life and for social acceptance by "the right people." Hence, they come to fear failure, not only in the accomplishment of long-range "life" goals but also in the accomplishment of immediate goals. The underprivileged child has no such expectation of success, hence little of the same kind of fear of failure. Especially in school, success is demanded of children in quite different proportions depending upon family status in the community. Middle and upper class parents put constant pressure upon their children for school success, whereas the lower class parent more readily accepts special classification in retarded classes, quitting at the end of the eighth grade, etc.

Although "social class" does not stamp all individuals within that class with the same patterns of behavior, there are certain experiences common enough to the different "social classes" to warrant comment. Davis and Dollard[215] found in an analysis of over one hundred Negro adolescents in the deep South that children of underprivileged Negro homes are punished physically more often and more severely than are children in more privileged homes. Characteristic was the mother who said, "I can't understand why he is so bad—I licks him all the time." The investigators felt that children governed by this type of well-intentioned but severe discipline give more blows than average children because they receive more. They learn early the emotional satisfaction which accompanies violent expression of emotion; they learn too, that beatings and fights are rarely fatal, whereas middle and upper class children are continually taught the danger of overt aggressive behavior. Aggressive children in slum areas are encouraged to be still more aggressive so that they may become capable of looking out for themselves. In "nicer" neighborhoods the aggressive children are suppressed as rough and hard to get along with. Sexual exploration does not bring the loss of social status for lower class children that it does for other children, since, for the underprivileged child, sex is usually an open book in his home. Such children are much better informed, much less repressed about sex and elimination.*

In certain matters, however, like amount of friction and emotional strain, Davis and Dollard[215] found children within each social class differing more widely from each other than one class differed from another class. This means that some privileged children showed more strain and greater emotional tension than most underprivileged children showed. There were harmonious and happy homes as well as divided, tense and quarrelsome homes in all socio-economic classes.

Two studies seem to indicate that more mental disorders are found in the youth of poor rather than good communities. Among boys examined in Washington, D. C., for the Armed Forces, Hadley[390] reports there were one and one-half more rejections for personality disorders from a slum than from a good housing area.** In Boston among 60,000 selectees in the winter, spring and summer of 1941 to 1942, Hyde and Kingsley[455] reported a significant increase in mental disorders and psychopathic personalities from the best to the poorest communities.

Housing and Health. Housing is one of the indices of the economic status of a family. Bad housing is a symptom of low economic status and does not exist alone. It is accompanied by inadequate food and insufficient medical care. As Chalmers[174] phrased it: "Just as people live in a one-room house, so it might be said that they are clothed and fed in a one-room manner." Because housing is part of a constellation of economic and social factors, it is difficult to say that bad housing, *per se*, produces retardation in growth or conditions which make it difficult for the child to develop. However, poor housing means poor chances for children, as shown by a comparison of four slum areas and four good areas in Chicago.† In comparison with the good areas the poor areas had twenty times as much juvenile delinquency, twelve times as many deaths from tuberculosis, four times as many deaths from pneumonia, three times the amount of truancy and two and one-half

---

* The relationship of delinquency to socio-economic status has been reviewed in Carr-Saunders, et al.[171] Helpful material will also be found in the summaries of Recommendations for Action, Report of the National Conference on Prevention and Control of Juvenile Delinquency, U. S. Gov't Printing Office, Wash., D. C., 1947; Erikson;[282] Martin and Stendler;[630] Harsh and Schrickel.[406]

** Data obtained from 1940 Housing census and physical examination findings of 5,800 boys.

† From the Chicago Housing Authority in Children and Youth at the Midcentury, Midcentury White House Conference on Children and Youth; Chart 28 in A Chart Book: A graphic presentation of social and economic facts important in the lives of children and youth.

times as many infant deaths. Fuerst and Kaplan describe one slum area in Chicago. "Rats, mice, roaches and other kinds of vermin infest more than half the buildings; stoves and makeshift arrangements are the only means of heating for nearly 85 per cent; almost seven-eighths of the individual flats are dilapidated or are in dilapidated structures; a little less than half the houses lack bathing facilities; toilets in good condition amount to less than one per dwelling for every other building."[328, p. 178] Such houses are breeding places for disease, accident hazards, barriers to good habits of eating, sleeping, elimination. They are frustrating to parents who want a better life for themselves and their children. These are extremely bad conditions. Many other children live in conditions not as bad but still not adequate for a good life.*

Poor housing with its poor facilities, crowding and poor environment make the establishing of good health habits very difficult, if not, in some instances, impossible. Poor toilet facilities may interfere with regular elimination. A quiet, pleasant atmosphere at meal time may be prevented by the hurry, noise and confusion that result from too many people in too small a space. Sleeping facilities may be limited. Children frequently must sleep together in poorly ventilated rooms. Under such conditions it would be a rare child who could get up in the morning feeling refreshed and ready for the day's activity. Under such circumstances children develop fatigue. This fatigue will be enhanced by the noise and confusion and the inadequacies of diet.

The basic principles of healthful housing may be grouped under three broad headings: (1) meeting the physiologic and psychologic needs of the individual, (2) protection against contagion, (3) protection against accidents. Meeting physiologic needs involves temperature regulation, ventilation, light, protection against excessive noise, and provision of adequate space for exercise and for children's play. Meeting the psychologic needs involves adequate privacy for the various members of the family, opportunities for normal family life, facilities for doing the household tasks without undue physical and mental fatigue, opportunities for normal community life, facilities for maintaining the cleanliness of the house and the family and living in accordance with the prevailing social standards of the local community. Protection against contagion involves safe and adequate water supply, adequate toilet and sewage facilities, absence of vermin, sanitary conditions in the vicinity, provision of facilities for keeping milk and food fresh, and provision of sufficient space in sleeping rooms to minimize the danger of infection by contact. Protection against accidents includes a safe dwelling, elimination of fire hazards, protection against the danger of electrical shocks or burns, protection against falls or other mechanical injuries, and protection of the neighborhood against automobile traffic hazards. Housing which conforms to these principles provides an environment for healthful living.**[741]

* In an environmental and sociologic study of rheumatic heart disease in two different types of communities in Connecticut, factory and residential, crowding in the home seemed to be a factor associated with the disease.[752]

** For planning houses for family living see Gutheim.[385]

Child Labor Affects Development. Child labor is another index of economic status of the family. Folks defines child labor as

... any work by children that interferes with their full physical development, the opportunity for a desirable minimum of education or their needed recreation. It is the employment of children in any occupation at unfit ages or for unreasonable hours, or under unhealthful or hazardous conditions, or while the schools which they should attend are in session.[298]

In spite of the progress made in protecting children from work that would be detrimental to their health, child labor still exists. The "sore spots" are among share croppers and migrants. Many children as young as eight or ten years are working.[1018] In addition, among the migrant group, whether the children themselves work or not, they frequently live in unfavorable conditions because of their mobile life* with indequate housing and sanitation. They often miss out on education** and an opportunity to develop a feeling of being accepted by and belonging to a community.

In all parts of the country many teen-agers are working today,† most of them combining work and school. In many instances this work is not classed as child labor, for proper part-time work can be an asset rather than a liability.‡ However, school work often suffers and health may suffer if a teen-ager's schedule of work and school is too heavy to allow for adequate rest and recreation. Schools and families should provide wise guidance to youth in making a decision to work and in selecting the type of employment. Sound labor standards include: (1) no work during school hours or in factories until a boy is at least sixteen, (2) no hired work outside of school until fourteen and (5) no hazardous work until eighteen years.[963]

RURAL AND URBAN ENVIRONMENTS

Urban Life Usually Means Greater Nervous Strain for Families. One of the most striking contrasts in type of environment in which children live is that between urban and rural. It would seem reasonable to assume that cities, roughly in proportion to their size, represent the antithesis of rural conditions. Whereas the country is typified by physical isolation, the city is crowded; in the country the family is a center of many activities; in cities public and private organizations of many kinds at least partially supplant functions of the family. In cities contacts with humanity supersede contacts

---

* Some children travel long distances. In Arizona children were found working who have come from Idaho, Washington, Wyoming and Texas.[962]

** In a study[962] of children, mostly 10 to 15 years of age, working in agriculture during school hours it was found that 70 per cent had not made normal school progress. Forty per cent of the 14- to 15-year-olds were in the 4th grade or below. Twenty-six per cent had not been in school for about a year. A few had never been to school.

† In 1952 it was reported that over one-fourth of the 8 million teen-agers in the U.S.A. were working, twice as many as in 1940. Most of them also attend school. More high school-aged youth were applying for full time work permits than in the past five years. More youth are dropping out of school. Seven times more children under sixteen were out of school in rural areas than in cities.[963]

‡ Such part-time work as baby sitting, a paper route during school months and almost any job not requiring night hours or too hard physical labor during vacation months will make children more responsible and will contribute to their desirable growth.

with nature; differentiation of economic classes and specialization of economic tasks which rank and grade men are prominent with resulting disparities of opportunity and their accompaniment of competitive living. The complexities and competitions of city life produce nervous strain of a type not usual under rural conditions. *

Both City and Country Offer Certain Advantages to Growth. The country, rich with open spaces for imaginative play and with nature lore, domestic animals, and chores to do, offers a type of physical exercise, and of character-forming opportunities not to be found in larger cities. City parents envy rural parents these environmental factors. On the other hand, rural parents envy city parents their libraries, art museums, lecture series, theaters, concerts, schools, music conservatories and markets for buying food, clothing and other necessities. The urban teacher wishes for the nature lore of the country as a background for biology, botany, etc. The rural teacher envies his city colleague the same educational facilities which the rural parent envies the urban parent. It can be supposed that these physical, psychologic, and social differences between rural and urban environments produce differences in the pattern of development of rural and urban children and necessitate different kinds of educational programs for these children.

It is difficult to evaluate differences between rural and urban children. In the first place, no clear-cut boundaries between urban and rural life exist. One merges into the other. A sector of urban life, such as a hotel or a mansion, may be located within a rural area. Both rural and urban populations are heterogeneous rather than homogeneous. There are in both types of environment differences in socio-economic status, racial differences with their varied cultural patterns, and varied hereditary strains. We must remember, too, that there are good rural and poor rural environments as well as good and poor urban environments. These variables must not be overlooked in a discussion of the effects upon children of rural versus urban life. Perhaps the very complexity of the problem accounts in part for the limited information available. **

Physical Health May be Affected. There seems to be little information about the relative status in physical growth and health of urban and rural children. The information available comes from studies in the thirties and early forties. Just how applicable the results of these studies are to the children of today cannot be stated. As far as child care is concerned, it is known that even today the rural child and his family have less adequate facilities than urban children and their families. One out of four counties in rural areas is still without a full-time public health nurse, although the situation

---

* Merrill and Eldredge[659] point out three ways in which the family tends to differ in the urban and rural community: namely, differences in fertility (more children in rural families); differences in the gainful employment of women (more urban women work away from home); and differences in family stability (higher divorce rate in urban areas).

** Baker, et al.[53] studied a Midwest small town and suggest that it is a good environment for young children. Stott[903] in a Nebraska study found that small town and rural parents tend to favor strict control of adolescent children while urban parents tend to favor more leniency and freedom.

is improving.* Children living in isolated rural counties receive only one-fourth as much health supervision as children in or near the biggest cities.** Farm dwellings are in poorer condition than non-farm dwellings. In 1947 two-thirds of the farm houses had no running water. Only one in five had indoor plumbing.† Thus, some conditions for some rural children are not favorable for health, but, on the other hand, the children of the slums and poor neighborhoods in cities and towns are also handicapped. A child can have a life which will promote physical health and growth in either type of environment. The reverse may also be true.

General Intelligence Ratings for Rural and Urban Children.   It seems clear that children in cities measure higher on intelligence tests than children in the country, and that children in good country districts measure higher than children in poor country districts. The rapid expansion of the central or consolidated school since 1940 has greatly improved school opportunities in districts where the population can afford it and are alert enough to vote the change from isolated, one-room schools.[173a]

There are probably two factors involved in the poorer showing of rural children on intelligence tests. For several generations the alert and ambitious families tended to migrate to the cities. In the 1940's there was a substantial movement of families away from big cities and into suburbs so that children could have better play and school opportunities. This probably means that urban and suburban children come from slightly superior stock. But there is also a second factor of environment; the school terms are in general shorter in rural districts because of poor financing of schools, the need for children to do seasonal farm work, muddy and snow-blocked roads and other difficulties of getting to school. Rural teachers are generally less specialized than urban teachers, the rural teacher still frequently having to teach all subjects in several grades, whereas urban teachers often teach only one subject. Subsidiary educational facilities, like libraries, museums, etc., are also at a minimum if not altogether lacking in rural areas.

It should be noted, however, that in only certain types of intelligence tests are rural children conspicuously slower than urban children, namely, in pencil and paper tests, in those involving coins, streetcars and other experience to which city children have greater access, and in distinctly verbal tests. These tests account for about half of the 10-point IQ difference in favor of urban children found in one study.[500] Test items involving practical problems showed much less difference between the two groups. This indicates that a considerable portion of the difference in intelligence rating between rural and urban children can be regarded as due to experience factors.

* Data from Child Health Services and Pediatric Education. New York, The Commonwealth Fund, 1949.
** In Western Canada a demand for better health facilities in rural areas has resulted in the passing of health legislation from which the Manitoba Plan came into existence. This plan provides for preventive services in communities.[464a]
† Data from Census Bureau in Chart Book: Child and Youth at the Midcentury. A graphic presentation of social and economic facts important in the lives of children and youth.

School and Home Programs Differ at Least to Some Extent   Differences in environment of rural and urban boys and girls should have a real significance for teachers in planning their school programs, since school programs should always be based on an understanding of the environment in which the children live. Such consideration will in some instances, at least, necessitate one kind of program for rural children, another for urban. For example, Sanchez[804] emphasizes the importance of relating school activities to the daily interests of rural children. As these interests and activities differ from those of city children, so, too, should the content of the school curriculum of rural children differ from that of city children.

Parents, too, must adapt care and education to the neighborhood in which they live. City parents fall, quite naturally, into a habit of "leaning" upon city facilities. They take advantage of music and dancing teachers, of art and riding lessons, of children's concerts, etc. In apartment neighborhoods play space is at a premium, so children are urged into scout programs, Y.W.C.A. or Y.M.C.A. projects, and week-day church clubs. Wanting to "keep children busy" and "to give them every opportunity," parents frequently allow the city child to schedule most of the hours of every day in the week. With no logical chores to do there are few opportunities in cities to give children meaningful, regular work to do. "Made" work is useless for teaching a sense of responsibility, since children have no sense that such work is needed. Therefore, they argue, it doesn't matter whether they do it or not. Rural parents, on the other hand, may fall into the error of isolating their children too much from group experiences on the one hand, or, in order to provide group experience and good (consolidated) schools, may find themselves in the same position as urban parents with overscheduled, overtired children on their hands.

INSTITUTIONAL ENVIRONMENT

Institutional Life.   "It is an unfortunate fact of our society that a certain number of youngsters will find their way into institutions, either because their homes are unable to provide for them, or because no other homes are available at the time, or because their own actions have brought them into conflict with the law. Institutional life is not a normal life for a child. To the extent that children in institutions are removed from their homes and parents and thrown into twenty-four-hour-a-day confinement with others in mass, they exist under special duress."[189, p.5]

Cohen goes on to explain, however, that in institutions where good medical and psychologic facilities exist and where the staff who handle the children day by day have real understanding of child needs much can be done to promote desirable physical and psychologic development. The institution of tomorrow will give as much consideration to the emotional life of the children as it does to food, clothing and shelter. The institution, he says, (p. 177) "will be a permissive environment in which the child will feel free to express himself, and through this expression to work toward a satisfactory resolution of his difficulties." This ideal institution will be organized to provide for compatible age groups and for individual attention. It will place emphasis upon full participation of the youngsters in planning for program and in determination of procedures and rules which affect their conduct. The personnel of such an institution will be selected primarily for their will to serve children and their love for them. They will be given continuous training for their jobs.*

MOVIES

Physiologic, Emotional and Moral Effects of Attendance at Movies. Movies, in spite of acute competition from radio and particularly from television, still occupy enough time in children's lives that they should be considered here. A number of studies indicate that movie attendance tends to fatigue many children with resultant effect upon the quality of their sleep. Certain types of movies have a detrimental effect upon health and conduct if attended too often. This effect is greatest at puberty, probably because the predominating theme of most movies is love, a theme of great interest to, but little understood by most young adolescents.

Many children suffer eye fatigue. Many become excessively excited over certain scenes, although there are wide individual differences in this. To some nervous children movies of an exciting sort are the final factor which tips the balance, thus causing more nailbiting, loss of sleep and loss of weight than would be experienced with no movie attendance. This effect is heightened if the movies are seen at night, just before the child goes to bed, particularly if they keep him up past his usual bedtime.[309, 478]

Evidence that children are influenced by what they see in the movies is given by Healy and Bronner,[414] who say that delinquents in their studies exhibited much more interest in movies than did their non-delinquent control group. They report that movie attendance by the delinquents was to a large degree a temporary escape from unpleasant situations and unhappiness, but a few of the delinquents stated that they did derive ideas from gangster or other crime pictures which served as a pattern for their own delinquencies.

We may conclude that children tend to react emotionally, physically and morally to movies. As they become older, with changing interests, widening experience and somewhat less "realistic" reactions, their emotional and physiologic responses are somewhat less violent. However, it is clear that too frequent attendance at movies may prove far too stimulating to a nervous or high-strung child. If such a child attends movies at all there should be definite restriction upon the type of movie he is allowed to see.

Movies in Education. Charters[175] reports that motion pictures "stir powerful ambitions, good and bad; develop permanent ideals, high and low; and crystallize the framework of life careers," and therefore have strong potentialities for good as well as evil. Peterson and Thurstone[724] have shown that children's values and attitudes can be changed dramatically by well planned movie experiences. They report that good motion pictures have definite and lasting effects on the social attitudes of children.

* Redl and Wineman[762] (1952) discuss characteristics of desirable institutional or group care for certain types of disturbed or unmanageable children.

There is little question that sound movies, appealing as they do to the ear as well as to the eye, are a dynamic force in education wherever they are used. The multitude of educational movies now available and in use at all levels of formal and informal education is evidence of their possibility for positive benefit. Many universities now operate studios for the production of educational movies in nearly all possible subject-matter areas. Few modern elementary or secondary schools now lack movie devices and access to extensive educational film libraries. Almost no college or university fails to use movies extensively in at least some of the subject-matter divisions. Few adult education programs would think of operating without movies and other visual aids. It must be remembered, however, that in spite of all that is being done with educational movies, children still spend considerably more time listening to the radio, viewing television at home and attending commercial movies than they do on classroom radio, television and movies.

THE RADIO AND TELEVISION

Radio.   Radio, as an important influence in the development of children, began to command much time and attention in the late 1920's and has influenced an increasing number of children since then. Levenson and Stasheff[580] (1952) report that there are currently operating in the United States more than 2700 radio stations, and that realistic business men spend over $400,000,000 yearly for the use of radio time to sell products. In the early 1950's there was a substantial drop in radio listening in areas where television was available,* although radio was still listened to somewhat in television homes, and was still commanding large amounts of time in the many areas still without television. There was in the United States in 1952, according to Cooley[197] an average of one radio set for every two persons.

Extent of Radio Listening among Children.   There were many surveys of the extent of radio listening during the 1930's and 1940's. These report the average amount of time per day spent by elementary and secondary school children listening to radio as ranging from one and one-half[792] to as much as three hours.[186] Jersild[475] points out that this is on the average about one-seventh of the child's waking time, and over the total week, almost as much time as he spends in school. These studies indicate that most of this listening is done in the late afternoon and early evening, the most popular hours being between six and nine-fifteen,[367] that children listen not only to the so-called children's programs, but to many adult programs as well. Surveys[975] show that about one-third of the programs best liked by children were designed not for children but for adults. Children listen to such a variety of programs that the only sense in which a program can actually be said to be a child's program is that children listen more universally at certain hours, so that whether a program will have a child audience is largely a matter of the hour at which it is broadcast rather than of the content.

* Hofstra College reported a survey of New York suburbs showing "a tremendous drop" in radio listening in most television families, with smaller drops in movie attendance and in reading.

What Children Listen to on Radio.   There seems considerable agreement among the studies about what type of radio programs have been found to be popular. Exciting stories are especially attractive to children.[580] Among the children's programs which rank high in favor are a number devoted to adventure and crime, as well as certain comedians on adult programs. Brown[129] reports a study made by his students of 2500 boys and girls in grades five, eight, ten and twelve. They found in both the fifth and eighth grades that the mystery play ranked first, with comic dialogue and skits and dramatic plays almost equally popular. By the senior year, the girls had lost interest in the mystery plays but continued to listen to the skits and plays. Senior boys retained interest in the "thrillers" more than girls and continued to like comic dialogue, but gave less time to plays and skits. Classical and semi-classical music is more popular in the eighth than in the fifth or twelfth grades; popular music increases steadily in favor from the fifth through the twelfth grade. Classical music at no time had more than one-third the listeners that semi-classical music had, or more than one-fifth of the listeners that popular music had. Boys listen to current events and political speeches more than girls do.

In general, preferences in radio programs seem to cut across lines of sex, of intelligence and of socio-economic status, certain programs being equally popular with boys and girls, with bright and dull children, and with rich and poor. In general, however, boys show a somewhat higher preference for crime and violence programs than do girls. Fairy tales, make-believe, nursery rhymes and folk tunes, and other children's hour programs directed toward younger children prove, upon investigation, to be reaching their audience, since they are more popular with children less than nine years old than with children more than nine years old. *

Effect of Radio upon Children's Emotions.   The effect of radio upon children's emotions seems less clear than the effect of movies. However, few writers deny that radio and television have a profound effect upon the attitudes, taste, feelings and buying habits of children,[1002] the effect being evidenced by the buying fads for Hopalong Cassidy and Space Cadet costumes seen everywhere. There are several studies,[309, 477, 479] however, which point out that, although some fears seem traceable to the radio, the number of fears so stimulated seems small compared to the sources of fear elsewhere in the child's life. Children seem to become hardened with age to the stock devices used on the radio to arouse suspense and create excitement, although certain children react badly. Clinicians occasionally recognize tensions and nervous habits which are aggravated by certain radio programs. Eisenberg[271] found among the unfavorable influences of radio upon children nightmares based upon radio plots. Probably more significant, however, was interference with other developmental activities such as reading, since children tend to listen passively to the radio rather than to spend time reading. As we have

* For further discussion of children's radio programs see Jersild,[475] Lazarsfeld,[568] and Witty.[1002]

said before, this unfavorable competition applies also to radio's interference with out-of-door play.

Probably the chief damage done to children by radio and television is loss of sleep. Getting children to leave the radio or television to go to bed is a current problem of great extent in the modern home. Conflict between parents and children about which programs the children should listen to is also frequent, though it seems to be more frequent in homes where parents are above average in educational background than in homes of below average status. Listening to radio programs seems to interfere with school "home work" among children who are above average in school work less than it does with poorer students. This seems natural, since the better student likes to study better and would resist giving up the radio in favor of study less than would the poorer student. It is unfortunate that this is so, since it sets up a vicious circle: poor school work, dislike of study, greater resistance to giving up radio, more radio, poorer school work.

Extent of Television Viewing: Its Effect upon Children. Since 1947–48 television has become an increasingly potent force in the lives of children.* Levenson and Stasheff[580] report that at the beginning of 1952 there were in the United States fifty areas served by 108 television stations. There were, however, in 1952 a total of nearly 18 million TV sets tuned to these 108 stations.[197] It is predicted that the ultra-high frequencies will accommodate some 2000 TV stations in the United States in time.** In television areas surveys have shown as high as 94 per cent of the children aged ten and older viewing television an average of 3 hours or more per day.[580]† This is not much more time than is (or was) spent on radio, but the current impression among writers is that the absorption in TV while listening and looking is more intense than for radio, and consequently the emotional impact is somewhat more severe. As with radio, the hours per day spent with television are proving for many children to be an interference with out-of-door play hours, with meal hours, with restful sleep, and with school work.

The United Parents Association of New York surveyed membership homes and reported[580] that as the number of television sets doubled (which they did in one year) the per cent of school failures also doubled, jumping from 10 to 20 per cent. Even seven-year-olds showed loss in study habits, loss in other than TV recreation activities, adverse effect on eating habits and on emotional well-being. Nightmares and difficulties in getting to bed affected the eight- and nine-year-olds. About one-eighth of the eleven- to thirteen-year-olds were adversely affected in school marks, recreation and eating habits. Teachers in many TV areas report that children with TV in their own homes or with access to it in other homes show drowsiness and inatten-

---

* Cooley[197] (p. 6) reports that "Television was given official blessing and sent on its commercially sanctioned way July 1, 1941."

** Marx et al.[682] (1953). This small book also contains an excellent bibliography on radio and television.

† A mail survey of 500 Chicago television homes reported by Billboard. Reviewed in Levenson and Stasheff. A Stamford, Conn., survey showed that although only 50 per cent of the student body had TV in their own homes, 79 per cent watched it regularly.

tion in school and come to school with homework poorly prepared or not even attempted. Opticians report, however, that eyesight need not suffer, even from two or three hours a day of TV viewing, if the distance between viewer and screen is at least six times the height of the screen, and if proper focus and a proper degree of contrast and brightness are maintained.*

Quality of TV Programs: Their Effect upon Children. In the early years of television commercial programs for children were among the most successful financially of all programs. In 1949, for example, 18 per cent of N.B.C. broadcasting was devoted to programs for children. Programs planned for children were, on the whole, carefully guarded for quality under a voluntary censorship by the major TV companies. Many good programs grew up and have on the whole persisted during the five- to eight-o'clock "children's hours." There has, however, with pressures exerted through competitive advertising, been some deterioration of these programs,** part of which is associated with the introduction of ancient Western films. A survey by the Southern California Association for Better Radio and Television† found on television programs scheduled between six and nine o'clock in the evening 91 murders, 7 hold-ups, 3 kidnappings, 10 thefts, 2 cases of arson, 2 jailbreaks and other similar episodes.

Good or bad as the children's programs may be, the fact is clear that children do not confine their TV experience to these programs. There is no doubt that children in large numbers listen to the programs after eight or nine o'clock in the evening, thus not only losing sleep, but spending time viewing programs which the broadcasters themselves admit are not meant for children's eyes.‡ Although many of these programs are excellent from the artistic and the informational points of view, many are crime thrillers or other forms of undesirable emotional stimulants which result in nightmares or restless sleep for at least some of the children who view them.

Opinions Differ about Seriousness of Effect of Radio and Television. There are differences of opinion about how good or bad such emotional experiences are for children. Some educators, psychologists and psychiatrists, among them Dr. Bruce Robinson, psychiatrist and Director of the Child Guidance Bureau of the Newark, New Jersey, public schools,§ are inclined to counter the acute concern of some parents and educators about radio and TV programs in general. They not only emphasize the good quality of many programs and the outstanding contributions both media have made and continue to make to formal and informal education, but are also of the opinion that children and parents must be selective in their choices from among the programs available. This is a necessary lesson to be learned in many areas of life, namely, selection of foods, books, magazines, movies, musical

* Levenson, *ibid.*, p. 454.
** Gould, J.: The Low State of TV. New York Times, October 19, 1952.
† Reported in Levenson and Stasheff, *ibid.*, p. 453.
‡ Levenson and Stasheff, *ibid.*, p. 450. For other references to children's interests in television and the effect of television upon children see Dunham,[262] Maccoby,[619] Seagoe,[825] Witty.[1002]
§ Quoted in Levenson, *ibid.*, p. 453 f.

programs and friends. Another point is made, too, in pointing out that there is much personality development to be achieved in this process of learning to be selective, in discovering that rest, proper meals and well-prepared school work are better than too much TV. There is much, also, to be worked out in family relationships as parents and children solve such basic problems together at the elementary and junior high school level, thus laying sound foundations for the solving of problems in adolescence. An additional point is made that children, especially urban children who are limited in the amount of exploration and creative outlet available, can get certain emotional release through vicarious excitement and action on radio and TV.

There seems little disagreement that good radio and TV programs can benefit children if they do not interfere with other desirable growth experiences. There is considerable difference of opinion about the benefits to be gained from vicarious emotional living through the more exciting and "thriller" programs. The Tenth District (Los Angeles) of the California Congress of Parents and Teachers surveyed some 300 pediatricians, sociologists, neuropsychiatrists and psychologists with a consensus of opinion as follows (Levenson, *ibid.*, p. 452.):

"90 per cent said that radio crime programs have a detrimental effect on children; 93 per cent said radio thriller shows and programs ending in suspense have a bad effect; 81 per cent said that present day radio programs contribute to children's delinquency or anti-social behavior."

Radio and Television in Education. The immense potential of radio and television as educational devices is generally recognized.* In addition to the radio stations they have maintained for many years, a number of universities and colleges now have their own TV stations, and more are taking up the option offered by the Federal Communications Commission on the band of TV frequencies laid aside for the exclusive use of educational programs. Several states now have TV as well as radio rural chains for the broadcasting of programs of an educational nature. Several universities are using live TV shows or movie briefs over TV for classroom teaching in several subject-matter areas. Some secondary and elementary schools have TV sets as well as radios so that appropriate broadcasts can be brought into the classroom. Many schools use selected TV shows viewed away from school for the basis of classroom discussions. This is particularly useful for current events and civics discussions, as well as for homemaking programs. There seems little doubt that both formal and informal educational agencies will continue to expand their use of this medium as an educational device. It is to be hoped that in time parents, teachers and producers may work together to educate children's tastes in TV as well as in the other mass media.**

* For detailed current bibliography on educational uses of radio and television see Federal Security Agency, Office of Education, Division of Health, Education and Welfare: Radio and Television Bibliography. Bulletin No. 18, 1952.

** The International Seminar on Education and the Problems of Everyday Living called by the National Ministry of Education of France, at Sèvres, France, June-July 1954, recommended that parents, teachers and boards of education in all countries work together and, wherever possible, with the industry to improve the quality of radio and TV programs.

NEWSPAPERS AND MAGAZINES

Comics Are Children's Dominant Reading Preference.   The child's enjoyment of the sensational in movies, radio and television is reflected in his choice of reading material. How much time children spend on "reading" as contrasted to time spent on radio was revealed by one study[1012] of Middle Western children. Children under twelve were spending only from 35 to 40 per cent as much time on reading as they did on radio. Martin and Stendler[630] say that it is safe to assume that a large part of this "reading" time is spent on comics. They go on to add, however, that, fortunately, in school a considerable portion of the child's school day is spent in reading of fiction and non-fiction, and that this, in competition with comics, radio and TV, forms an important source of guidance for the child's behavior. In a survey of 2500 children in the fifth, eighth, tenth and twelfth grades, Brown[129] reports that for all grades and both sexes, the comics lead the list of newspaper readings by a wide margin. Less than 1 per cent of the fifth graders paid attention to foreign news. Encouraging to note, however, is the fact that by the eighth grade 23.7 per cent read foreign news; by the tenth grade 32.3 per cent, with a slight drop to 29.4 per cent in the twelfth grade. Apparently, school programs in current events, or some other influence, wakens some high school students to an interest in world affairs. Political news also rose in interest in the tenth grade, where 40.3 per cent of the children read it. Editorials and signed columns, however, were practically ignored at all levels, being read by only 8.3 per cent even of the seniors.

Witty[1002] studied the interest in comics of 334 children in grades four to six. He found, as Brown had, that comics were the most popular of all reading pursuits. The boys read many comic strips, an average of four comic magazines *regularly*, and four more *often*. Girls read an average of one and one-half comic magazines *regularly*, and two and one-half more *often*. This absorption with comic strips in the newspapers and with comic magazines is yielding to the captivating power of television. Folger[297] reported as early in the history of TV as 1950 that although the comics offer an inexpensive way of filling certain needs for children there are indications that television is filling these needs in better fashion. In one Brooklyn elementary school a study showed that 60 per cent of the boys and 50 per cent of the girls preferred television to books, movies, radio and comics as leisure time activity. In fact, comics was fifth in popularity among the above media, with only 7 per cent of the boys and 4 per cent of the girls preferring them as first choice.

Josette Frank[315] in writing about comic strip characters, points out that, even though children say they like funnies because they are funny, actually the comic characters are by no means comic.* They are, rather, with few exceptions, "serious fellows, intent on dangerous adventure and noble deeds." Methods used by these characters for accomplishing the dangerous adventure and the noble deeds vary from magic, through fantastic, to pseudo-scientific and "just plain violent" means. Motives for the behavior of the

---

* With the introduction of Pogo, "the funnies seem once again to be getting funnier." (Newsweek Magazine, July 7, 1954.)

characters vary from dedication to justice and war on crime to personal quest of adventure. But, whatever the method and the motive, the end result is always that "good triumphs over evil, virtue is its own reward, and evil-doers are undone by their own foul deeds." Frank adds: "We have not come far from the morality of the copy-books, after all! The form is different—and how much more enticing!"

Not All Effects of Comics Are Bad. Witty[1002, 1004] has cited evidence which should serve to reassure adults about the effect of comics upon children. He studied the 10 per cent of children who read the comics most in one school, and contrasted these with the 10 per cent who read them least. He found their intelligences almost exactly comparable, the "most" group averaging 107 in I.Q., the "least" group 105. The general reading interests of the two groups were quite similar. Some of the individual children who read comics most had "rich, varied and generally commendable" reading programs.

R. L. Thorndike[944] gives further reassurance about the effect of comics upon children. He studied the word content of the most popular four of the comics which appear monthly. In 1940 these, by circulation, which runs into millions, proved to be *Superman, Batman, Action Comics,* and *Detective Comics.* Contrary to the usual idea that comics are largely pictures, he found that the actual average vocabulary count in each of these magazines was near 10,000 words. He concluded: "The child who reads a comic book once a month through the school year (and this represents a very moderate dosage), gets about as much wordage of reading as he gets from even the new fourth or fifth grade reader" (p. 110). Although a number of slang words were included in this wordage, the bulk of the vocabulary was straight English. Many hundreds of the words used were words which children need to encounter as they expand their reading vocabularies. He assured us that comics do provide a substantial amount of reading experience at about the difficulty level of upper elementary school or even junior high school reading.

He added, however, that the word question of comics should not be the only matter to concern us. The content and ideas are also important. "Whether the comics provide exposure to a viciously distorted and unreal world, whether they merely provide a rather innocuous way of wasting children's time, or whether they provide a needed vicarious release for tensions and aggressions which are built up and unexpressed in the world of reality is a *vital* question. It is also a *moot* question. . . ." (p. 112).

Influence of Other Magazines. Magazine reading (other than comic magazines) seems to follow a different curve of interest from that found in newspaper reading, since magazine reading seems to command a somewhat more serious attention. Brown[129] reports magazine interest for the same group of children for whom the newspaper interest was reported above. Twelve per cent of fifth grade children reported that they read some magazine regularly, whereas 74.9 per cent of the high school seniors read at least one magazine regularly. *Popular Mechanics, Boy's Life,* western stories, detective magazines, and *The American Boy* were popular in the above order with children in the eighth and tenth grades in this study. Brown also reports that, although studies show boys and girls attending movies in about equal numbers, no movie magazine appeared in the first five choices of magazines for the boys, whereas movie magazines consistently ranked first in choice with the girls. *True Story* and *True Confessions* ranked high for the girls; western and detective stories for boys. One needs only to look at the assortment of twenty to thirty movie magazines, fifteen to twenty westerns, twenty to thirty magazines of the true confession type on any large magazine stand to appreciate the tremendous consumption of such magazines. Young people between fifteen and twenty-five buy more of them than any other age group. We seem to need some sort of action here on the part of adults comparable to the actions which have done much to clear up and improve movie and radio offerings.

The Total Effect of Mass Media.   Martin and Stendler[630] point out that the total impact of mass media upon children is even greater than the impact of each medium considered separately. The possibility of these media, they point out, for propaganda "is frightening" if forces for evil should come to control them. These authors say that (p. 501) "Our only safeguard against such a danger lies in intelligent listeners. Only as children receive help and practice in analyzing the values and techniques in mass media can we be assured of such a safeguard." Another author[872] asserts that the schools have a definite obligation to help educate children in selective use of mass media and to learn to express opinions about some of the poor quality programs. Even more important, this author says, is the obligation of schools (and we would add here, of families) to teach children recreational and avocational interests and habits which can be counted upon to fill their lives with constructive activity and which leave time and interest for only the best of the programs or materials offered by the mass media.

Witty[1004] suggested that we should study the all-around recreation programs of children with a view to broadening recreational interests, and thus competing with the influence of bad comics and poor movies, radio and TV programs. In the specific field of reading interests he suggested such competition to comics as The Disney Readers, The Story Parade Adventure Books, and The New World Neighbors.*

OTHER RECREATIONAL ACTIVITIES

Brown extends his discussion of the recreational activities of young people beyond that of newspaper and magazine reading. He reports a study[473] of the recreational activities of thirteen communities scattered all over the United States, noting that in this study the home proved the preponderant place in which leisure time was spent. For young men community centers, parks and playgrounds were second, but for young women commercial amusement places were second. The school ranked fifth in the total, being only slightly more important than the street as a place of recreation. It would seem from this that the school is missing an opportunity to influence the lives

* The Disney Readers and New World Neighbors are published by D. C. Heath & Co.; The Story Parade Adventure Books by Grosset-Dunlap.

of its students. This same study indicates that, although the church is making excellent attempts to provide for the recreational life of its young people, in these thirteen communities studied, its influence was not yet of great importance. There is also evidence that too much time is being spent by young people as spectators rather than as participators in sports.

Bell comments on youth's need for proper recreation as follows:

> The United States has, with more or less justification, acquired the doubtful distinction of being the 'most criminal' of all the civilized nations of the world. . . . The need for more effective and comprehensive recreational programs in most of the urban and rural areas in the United States reminds us of Mark Twain's observation that everybody talks about the weather, but nobody seems to be doing much about it. So far as our data are concerned, this seems particularly true in farm areas, where one out of every five young men interviewed reported that his principal leisure time activity was loafing.[83]

A report of the Committee on Youth Problems of the Office of Education[357] indicates that one fortunate and long range effect of the depression of 1929–1939 was the wholesome effect it had on general leisure activities, compelling young people to turn from commercial activities to the simpler and less expensive self-activated recreations, such as crafts and other creative outlets, dancing at home to the radio, picnics, playground sports, etc. W.P.A.-financed recreation programs probably had something to do with this and with the development of libraries, museums, settlement houses and other recreational centers. As the W.P.A. programs were terminated many of these projects were taken over by the communities in which they were set up.

The spread of *children's libraries* in many cities and towns provides not only a place where children can read but books which can be taken home. *Children's museums* furnish centers for the development of educational and nature hobbies. *Settlement houses* offer clubs for underprivileged children where they often have gymnasium and pool, game rooms, crafts, hobby groups, but mainly a place in which to meet friends away from the crowded and often sordid homes as well as off the streets and away from pool halls. *Boys' clubs*,[112] not unlike settlement houses, have made a splendid contribution to constructive use of leisure time. *Boy Scouts* and *Girl Scouts, 4-H Clubs, Y.M.C.A.'s* and *Y.W.C.A.'s* are among some forty organizations serving youth in this capacity.[21] In fact, this is only an enumeration of the more widely known organizations. A preliminary report to the American Youth Commission of the American Council on Education listed no fewer than 330 national nongovernmental youth-serving organizations.[721]

Expenditures for public recreation have increased rapidly in this country from less than one million dollars in 1907 to hundreds of millions today. This looks as if the public were giving youth a great deal. And so it is; but this expenditure seems wise in the face of current city and rural conditions which have placed young people in a position where commercialized recreation, slum living and temptation to delinquency are overpowering. During World War II and the ensuing inflation, particularly the inflation since the beginning of the Korean war in 1950, the situation changed from one in which young people could find little if any work, to one in which they were in great demand at high wages. Problems of bored unemployment changed to problems of unwise expenditure of intoxicating amounts of money. Whether the situation be one of unemployment, or of too much money to spend, it seems evident that adults bear a heavy responsibility for providing wholesome recreation and for developing sound tastes in the use of leisure time.

In this chapter we have seen that community factors outside the home, school, church and camp exert an extremely important influence upon child growth. Parents and teachers are accustomed to thinking of the importance of the factors discussed in Chapter 5; they are less familiar with the ones discussed in this chapter. Group social work and recreation programs, as well as the work done by juvenile courts and other social agencies, and particularly by our churches, are contributing much to child growth. Not until all of these agencies can work in close cooperation with parents and teachers will we achieve the best that child development can contribute to children.

EXPERIENCES TO VITALIZE CLASS WORK

1. Survey your community (either the one you are now in, or your home community) in order to learn what facilities there are for: (1) Examination and care of children's health. (2) Minimizing accidents and spread of communicable diseases. (3) Educating children in physical hygiene and good health habits. (4) Wholesome recreation outside of school hours for (a) young children, (b) pre-adolescents, (c) adolescents. (5) Provision of adequate fresh fruits and vegetables the year around at reasonable prices. (6) Locating and caring for crippled children, subnormal mental cases, especially gifted children, children with special sensory defects, epileptics, and other children needing special education and attention. (7) Control of movie programs, particularly on Saturday afternoon; control of radio and television programs, particularly between five and eight o'clock in the evening. (8) Library services to children; public concerts for children; opportunities for development of interest and ability in art; and the development of other interests and abilities which enrich living by providing constructive use of leisure time. (9) Detection, correction and prevention of delinquency.

2. Visit a newsstand that carries comic magazines, and get a collection of these magazines for study. Summarize these, along with the comic strips in your daily papers, listing both good and bad influences they might have upon children.

3. Listen to the radio and television programs available to your community between five and eight o'clock P.M. Discuss those programs to which children might be listening, for possible effect upon children.

4. Investigate the current literature (from 1950 on) for material about the effect of community factors upon child growth and development.

5. Select several case studies from Davis and Havighurst on the selected reading list. Present them to the class for discussion.

SELECTED READINGS

Bossard, J. H. S.: The Sociology of Child Development. New York, Harper & Bros., 1948, Chs. 13, 14, 24–28.

Davis, A., and R. J. Havighurst: Father of the Man. Boston, Houghton Mifflin Co., 1947.

Harsh, C. M., and H. G. Schrickel: Personality Development and Assessment. New York, Ronald Press, 1950, Ch. 8.

Jersild, A. T.: Child Psychology. New York, Prentice-Hall, Inc., 1954, Ch. 16.

Landis, P. H.: Adolescence and Youth. Revised ed. New York, McGraw-Hill Book Co., 1952, Chs. 4, 6, 12, 18–21.

Martin, W. E., and C. B. Stendler: Child Development: The Process of Growing Up in Society. New York, Harcourt, Brace & Co., 1953, Chs. 6–16.

Martin, W. E., and C. B. Stendler: Readings in Child Development. New York, Harcourt, Brace & Co., 1954, Parts 2, 3, 4.

Smiley, D. F., and A. G. Gould: Your Community's Health. New York, The Macmillan Co., 1952.

CHAPTER 7

206-232

Growth and Use of the Body—*(Physical Growth)*

We have given evidence to show the interrelation between physical and mental growth. A child truly is ". . . a compound of tissues, organs, fluids, and consciousness."[170] He is not an aggregate of separate independent parts but rather a whole to which each part contributes and in which each part is intimately affected by other parts. The ability to adapt oneself to change within and without the body, to combat disease or deprivation, to meet new and difficult situations, is the result of activities of all parts of the body. This adaptive function is necessary for the optimum development of an individual both mentally and physically. In order to understand how a child adjusts to his internal and external environments it is necessary to have some understanding of his physical development.

GROWTH IN SIZE

The Pattern of Growth in Height and Weight.   The pattern of growth in height and weight is characterized by alternating periods of faster and slower growth as indicated in Figures 1 and 7 in Chapter 1. Thus it follows the general principle that growth does not proceed at an even tempo. The first period of fast growth occurs in infancy; the second period, known as the pubescent spurt, occurs in early adolescence and is closely associated with approaching sexual maturity. It is under endocrine control.* Following this second spurt growth slows down and, especially in height, ceases at maturity. During the growth years an individual increases in height about three and one-half times and in weight about twenty times.

The child who has reached school age is already in that middle period of slower growth. During the elementary years the child has been growing less in height each year (Fig. 24) until nine years if a girl and eleven years if a boy. Generally girls grow faster from nine to twelve years with a peak in the twelfth or thirteenth year; boys grow faster from eleven to fourteen years with a peak in the fourteenth or fifteenth year.** In weight (Fig. 25) the school-aged child increases in momentum slowly each year until girls reach a peak

---

* See discussion under endocrines.
** Average age of maximum growth according to Shuttleworth[851] is 12.56 years for girls and 14.8 years for boys; according to Nicholson and Hanley[702] 11.51 and 13.77 years, respectively.

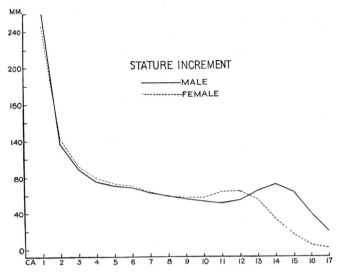

Fig. 24. Annual mean increments for standing height for boys and girls. From Simmons, K. The Brush Foundation Study of Child Growth and Development. II. Physical Growth and Development. Monogr. of Society for Research in Child Development IX, No. 1, Society for Research in Child Development, National Research Council, Washington, D. C., 1944, p. 43.

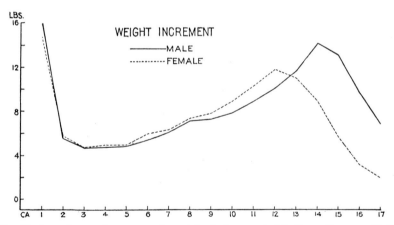

Fig. 25. Annual mean increments for weight for boys and girls. From Simmons, K. The Brush Foundation Study of Child Growth and Development. II. Physical Growth and Development. Monogr. Society for Research in Child Development IX, No. 1, Society for Research in Child Development, National Research Council, Washington, D. C., 1944, p. 44.

at about twelve and boys at about fourteen years. The peak in weight tends to lag behind that of height by six months or more.[851, 899] Thus many children have a brief "filling out" period after their rapid growth in height. During this pubescent spurt girls may gain seven times more weight than during their prepubescent years.[852] Boys in one study[899] generally gained slightly more than twice as much in height during the two and one-half to three and

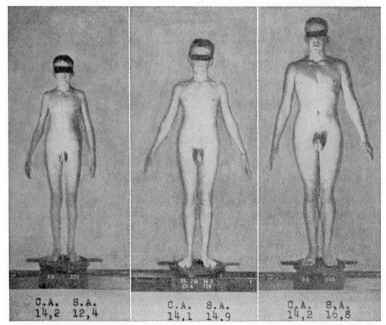

C.A. S.A.
14,2 12,4

C.A. S.A.
14.1 14.9

C.A. S.A.
14,2 16,8

Fig. 26. Three fourteen-year-old boys who differ in degree of sexual maturity and size. (Greulich, W. W., et al.: Somatic and Endocrine Studies of Puberal and Adolescent Boys. Monogr. National Research Council, 1942. Wash., D. C.)

one-half year period of rapid growth* as they did in the preceding and following periods covering two to four years.

Growth in height generally ceases somewhere between sixteen years and the early twenties.** Growth in weight for the average adolescent probably stops in the early twenties.

As stated above, the *timing of pubescent growth in height and weight is related to progress toward sexual maturation.* Indicators of this progress are menarche (first menstruation) in girls, growth of penis and testes in boys and pubic and axillary hair. Studies† demonstrate that children of the same chronologic age who are farther advanced toward sexual maturity are taller and heavier than those who are maturing more slowly. Figure 26 illustrates this difference in size that accompanies difference in degree of sexual maturity. While all three boys are fourteen years of age, the one at the left is physically still a boy while the one at the right is a man. In one study[244] among the fourteen-year-old boys, the postpubescents were 4.6 inches taller and 22.6 pounds

* Stolz and Stolz[899] divided the adolescent growth period into three sections: prepuberal, puberal and postpuberal. The puberal period is the period in which maximum growth rate occurs.

** Brush Foundation figures[858] give fifteen to twenty years for boys and fourteen to eighteen years for girls. These Cleveland children can be considered above average economically and socially. See also Randall[757] on army population for terminal gains in the early twenties.

† See Stolz and Stolz,[899] Dimock,[244] Simmons and Greulich,[859] Shuttleworth,[851] [852] and Richey.[783]

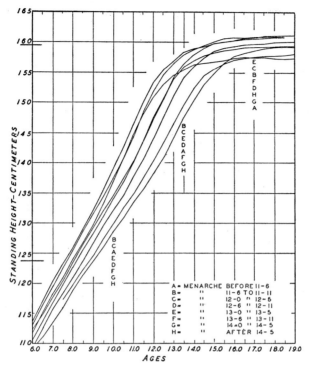

Fig. 27. Growth trends in average standing height for each of 8 groups of cases men-struating at different ages. (Shuttleworth: Monograph of the Society for Research in Child Development, Vol. II, 1937, National Research Council.)

heavier than the prepubescents; in another study[783] the average twelve-year-old girl who menstruated before her thirteenth birthday was 4.34 inches taller and 24.58 pounds heavier than the average girl who did not menstruate until she was at least fourteen years old. That faster growth is associated with earlier menarche is demonstrated in Figure 27. When curve A, which represents the growth in height of girls who menstruated before eleven years and six months is compared with curve H which represents girls who menstruated after fourteen years and five months, it is easy to see that the growth in height of girls represented by curve A is faster (steeper slope) and the period of growth is shorter than the growth in height of girls represented by curve H.

The beginning of the pubescent spurt of growth and its peak are closely timed with age of first menstruation in girls[852] and genital development in boys.[899] The initiation of the period of rapid growth in height generally occurs sometime between two and one-half to three and one-half years before menarche and the year of most rapid growth sometime within the two years preceding menarche. For example, according to Shuttleworth, girls who menstruated for the first time at eleven years had their year of most rapid growth in the preceding year between their tenth and eleventh birthdays. Those who menstruated for the first time at fifteen years, however, had their most intensive growth between twelve and one-half and thirteen and one-half years. Some of the later maturers show relatively little acceleration through this period. Boys, according to Stolz and Stolz,[899] have their greatest gains concurrently with increase in the size of the genitalia.

The greatest gains in weight are also related to stages of sexual maturation. For example, the average girl in the Shuttleworth[851] study had her greatest gain in weight about three months before she began to menstruate.

This relationship between progress in sexual maturation and progress in height and weight indicates that the maturity of a child must not be disregarded when evaluating his growth.

Progress in Height and Weight. According to the Stuart and Meredith norms[*][915] 80 per cent of the newborn boys range in height from 18.9 to 21 inches and in weight from 6.3 to 9.1 pounds; newborn girls range from 18.8 to 20.4 inches and from 6.2 to 8.6 pounds. By five years, when they enter kindergarten, the boys will be 40.8 to 45.2 inches tall and will weigh 35.5 to 46.7 pounds; the girls will be 40.5 to 45.4 inches tall and weigh 34.8 to 49.2 pounds. According to these same norms one might expect a so-called average boy[**] to gain 9.7 inches and 14.7 pounds in the first year, 4.8 inches and 5.5 pounds in the second year, 2.5 inches and 5.5 pounds in the sixth year, 1.9 inches and 5.9 pounds in the tenth year, 3 inches and 14.6 pounds in the fourteenth year (around the time of the peak of the pubescent spurt) and 0.3 inch and 2.8 pounds in the eighteenth year. Girls will make somewhat similar gains in infancy, the preschool years and early school years but by ten years they are gaining more than the boys (2.3 inches, 6.5 pounds). In the fourteenth year girls have passed their peak of growth, gaining 1 inch and 9.3 pounds, and by the eighteenth year have stopped growing in height and are gaining only .8 of a pound in weight. These figures speak for themselves in indicating that averages tell a trend in decelerating growth with a slight acceleration during pubescence, but they do not tell the story of the growth of any one child. Difference in the timing of sexual maturation accounts in a large measure for the obscuring of individual gains in late childhood and early adolescence. During the period of puberal growth boys have been observed[899] to gain in height anywhere from 4.76 to 11.77 inches with an average of 8.35 inches and in weight from 7.2 to 64.8 pounds with an average of 39.9 during a period of 2½ to 3½ years.

Progress in height tends to be more regular than progress in weight. In the latter, children may show more irregularities, more periods of no gain and sometimes loss. Weight is more variable because it includes soft tissues and water as well as bone and is easily susceptible to external factors. Because the environment contributes greatly to the evenness or the unevenness of progress in weight, those who are responsible for a child's environment in the home,

---

* Norms to 5 years are based on measurements of a group of healthy white children of northern European ancestry living in or near Boston, for the most part of lower economic status but all under regular health supervision. Beginning at 5 years they are based on similar studies in Iowa City of children almost entirely of northwestern European descent and predominantly from the professional and managerial classes.

** Using the median values in these norms.

school and the community, and for planning to meet his needs can do much to smooth or disrupt the even tenor of his progress in weight.

Progress in height can also be considered in terms of achievement toward mature height. Fifty per cent of mature height is achieved for boys at 2.2 years and for girls at 1.7 years; 75 per cent by 8.9 years for boys and 7.2 years for girls; 90 per cent by 13.7 years and 11.4 years respectively for boys and girls; and 99 per cent of mature height at 16.4 years and 14.6 years respectively. Thus children have acquired at least two thirds of their height by the time they begin school. Girls mature in height faster than boys.[702]

Individual Differences. Individual differences in height and weight are apparent at birth and continue throughout the growing years. Differences are noticeable in size and in the pattern of children's growth both between boys and girls and between children of the same sex.[*] Observe the differences in the three fourteen-year-old boys in Figure 26. The degree of variability changes from time to time. Differences in size tend to be greater during periods of more rapid growth.[654] During the elementary years when growth is slower and during the college or late adolescent years when growth is tapering off, individual differences can be expected to be less than during the late elementary and early high school years.

The child's individual pattern of growth tends to become well established during the second and fourth years and to become regular during the years of steady growth in middle childhood.[915] Tall children tend to remain tall, short ones short in relation to other children as they grow.[**] However, some children change gradually but consistently in these respects throughout the school years, becoming quite different than would have been anticipated.

Even during the pubescent period an individual's relative position tends to be kept.[899] However, some may emerge from this period shorter or taller than might have been expected. For example, the child who matures early with his or her rapid increase over a short period of time may emerge as a small person even though he or she entered the phase larger than the average.[915] (See Fig. 28B.)

In the pattern of growth boys and girls generally gain about the same amount in height between four and ten years and in weight between five and eleven years.[858] Girls, then, during the pubescent spurt of growth have a temporary superiority over boys. Girls pass through this period of most rapid growth and reach mature size about two years before boys.[†] Figure 28 A and B illustrate this sex difference in timing. The girl (B) has completed her growth in height at about fifteen, the boy (A) at seventeen.

Differences in timing and length of the pubescent spurt are well demonstrated by the California Growth Study.[899][‡] Some boys had an early begin-

---

[*] See Chapter 1.

[**] One study[459] of children observed through twelve years of age has demonstrated that heavier children at birth tend to weigh more and (to a lesser degree) are taller in childhood than those with a smaller birth weight.

[†] See p. 206.

[‡] The onset of the puberal period (see p. 208) was found to extend from 10.5 to 14.5 years and ended anywhere from 14.2 to 17.5 years. It lasted from 2 to 4 years.

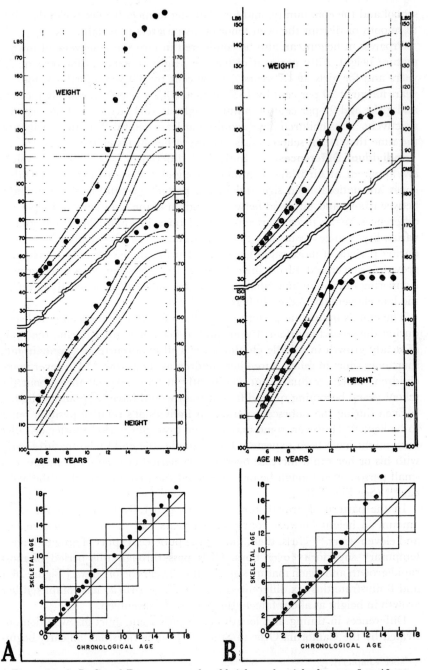

Figure 28. A, B, C and D present graphs of height and weight for ages 5 to 18 years against norms representing percentiles 10, 25, 50, 75 and 90. They also present skeletal age plotted against chronologic age as determined by the Todd inspectional method of evaluating films of the hand and wrist. Figure 28A shows the growth and skeletal development of a boy who was advanced in both measurements at all ages, but particularly during

(*Plates C and D on following pages*)

ning, some a late one; some a short period, some a long one. During this period growth for some was rapid and dramatic, for some moderately intense and long, for a few intense and long, and for another few neither intense nor long. Thus boys have varied growth experiences during these years. Some early developers become short, some medium, some tall in stature. Some late developers also become short, some medium, and some tall. See Fig. 28 A and Fig. 28 C and D. A is a fast grower. C and D represent two different patterns of slow growth.

The majority of children who begin their pubescent spurt earlier tend to grow faster and complete their growth earlier (see Fig. 28A). At maturity they may not be taller than late maturing children, as is seen in Figure 27. The late maturing children, on the other hand, tend to begin later and grow more slowly. (See Fig. 28 C, D.) They are not necessarily shorter at maturity. In fact some are taller than those who mature early.* Thus later maturing children may catch up eventually with their faster developing peers. This may be comforting to a child who is growing slowly and is concerned about it, and also to his parents and teachers. An understanding that there are different paths to the same end and that being taller, shorter, stockier or slenderer than peers can be "normal" for children can provide adults with the knowledge which will equip them to understand each child and to be able to interpret his growth to him. Children frequently need reassurance that they are normal, especially when their time schedule of growth is somewhat different from most or when they differ in size or build. This is especially true during pubescence.** Children can be misjudged as over or under weight when their rate of maturing is overlooked. Such misjudgment may lead to ill advised attempts to regulate weight by diet. Both physical and psychologic harm can be done either by increasing or reducing the food intake of a child when such a procedure is not indicated by his growth pattern.

Factors Contributing to Individual Differences.   Variables which contribute to differences in height and weight include family-line heredity, of which race[336, 648] is a part; socio-economic status,[653] which encompasses diet, health, living standards and family surroundings; climate;[786] and emotions[990]

* Bayley.[74]
** See Chapter 1.

---

adolescence. It is to be noted that he was somewhat advanced in maturation, as indicated both by skeletal age and by making his maximum gain in both weight and height in his 13th year. The presence of pubic hair at 12 years and axillary hair at 14 years adds further confirmation to his slightly advanced maturation. The greater deviation from his original percentile position in weight than in height during the adolescent years indicates that accompanying his early and vigorous adolescent growth, this boy also became relatively obese.

Figure 28. B presents the growth and skeletal development of a girl who matured early and rapidly. She not only attained her maximum growth very early but terminated it early and rapidly so that she became a relatively shorter and lighter person at maturity than would have been anticipated. Her early pubescent growth was accompanied by early appearance of pubic and axillary hair, by menarche at 10 years, 8 months and by rapidly advancing skeletal maturation after 9 years of age. In respect to these attributes, she had attained approximate adult maturity at 14 years of age.

(Continued on next page)

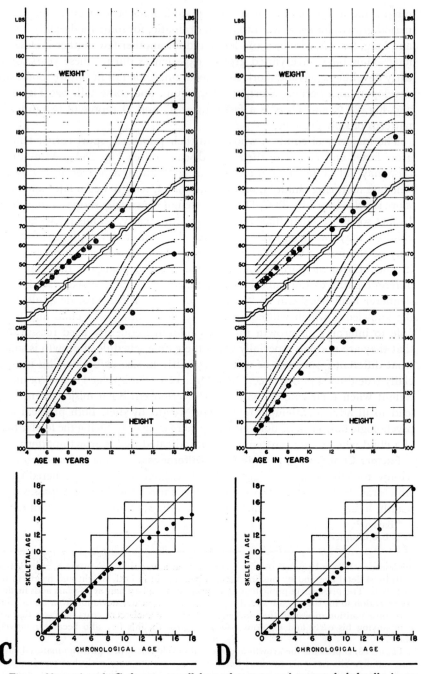

Figure 28 continued. C shows a small boy who grew and matured skeletally in an expected manner up until about 9½ years of age after which he lost position in weight, height and skeletal development. He had clearly become much retarded by the age of 16, after which his height and weight curves suggest a very late but adequate pubescent growth. This boy showed the first appearance of pubic hair at 17 years and still had no

(Continued on next page)

—in fact, all the extrinsic environment of the child.* Growth of an individual child is, therefore, dependent upon the interaction of heredity and environment. Heredity sets the potential for growth; health and environment, including nutrition (see Chapter 4), determine the degree to which that potential is achieved.

The Use of Height and Weight in Evaluating Physical Status and Progress. Height and weight are frequently used as criteria for judging physical status and progress.† The adequacy of growth is determined by assessing both the child's status and his progress. Status is determined by comparing his growth with that of other children; progress is determined by comparing the child with himself from time to time through the accumulation of serial measurements. Population norms or standards provide the means for evaluating status. The effectiveness of the use of these standards depends to a large degree on the selection of the particular standard and the interpretation made of the comparison. Different standards represent different groups of children, that is, children of varying hereditary and environmental backgrounds. As stated in Chapter 1, the standard chosen needs to be one compiled from a group of children with backgrounds and living conditions similar to those of the child being evaluated. More recent standards are preferable to older ones since the children of the present decade are taller and heavier than those of the twenties or thirties.[649] Because of the sex differences in growth, standards for boys and girls are separate. A satisfactory standard, in addition, includes not only an average but also a range, thereby indicating a broad

---

* Children in a superior socio-economic environment generally are taller and heavier than children of comparable age who live in less favorable circumstances.[653] An example of racial differences is the shorter stature of Japanese children than that of American children.[550] Racial differences have a strong environmental component, however. Japanese children born and reared in the United States have been found to be taller than those born and reared in Japan.[877] American Negro children, when compared to white children of all socio-economic levels combined, are similar in height and weight.[648] Studies of Negro infants[651, 822, 823] seem to indicate that Negro newborns tend to be somewhat smaller than white newborns, but those from families of the lower middle class have growth curves similar to those of white infants from the same class. Birth weights of Negroes in 1950 were higher than those reported earlier.[822] Children in the tropics tend to be lighter than those in colder climates.[786] Emotional disturbances can slow up growth.[92 327, 990] Atomic bombing has been demonstrated to interfere with growth.[378]

† See Krogman[550] for an excellent discussion of the measurement and interpretation of height and weight in children.

---

axillary hair at 18 years. These features correspond quite well with his apparent maximum growth in the 18th year and his 3 years' retardation in skeletal age at this time.

Figure 28. D presents data for a boy who was not only consistently small but somewhat slow in maturation as indicated by retarded development in the hand and by the appearance of pubic hair at 13 years and axillary hair after 14 years.

These four cases were selected to illustrate some of the many varieties of individual differences in the patterns of growth and development which are encountered among relatively healthy individuals. (From studies of health and development conducted by the Harvard School of Public Health; through the courtesy of Dr. Harold C. Stuart).

pathway of normality. This pathway of normality may be expressed in terms of an average and standard deviation or in terms of percentile rank.*

Standards are used more effectively when progress and status of the child can be observed concurrently. This can be done when standards are represented as curves which give the pattern of growth for a large number of children over a period of time. Such, for example, are the Iowa curves,[466] the percentile curves of Stuart and Stevenson[915] and those of Meredith.[652] The Iowa curves (see Fig. 19, p. 73) consist of three curves for height and three for weight. For height the three curves represent the average, plus one and minus one standard deviation. For weight they represent the sixteenth, fiftieth, and eighty-fourth percentiles. The Stuart and Meredith percentiles give the 10, 25, 50, 75 and 90 percentiles for height and weight from birth to eighteen (see Fig. 28). The Meredith percentiles cover the ages of four to eighteen. The spaces between the percentile curves are indicated as zones of varying degrees of tallness or shortness and of lightness or heaviness. All of these series of curves are drawn on coordinate paper so that actual height or weight, as may be the case, can be plotted against chronologic age. When a child's series of measurements are plotted, a comparison can be made between the individual curve and the group curve. Unless circumstances interfere with his growth pattern a child will tend to maintain the same relative position with respect to his age group from time to time except during the pubescent spurt when differences in the timing of the spurt of growth may produce changes in relative positions in individuals' curves.

The Fels Composite Sheet[876] provides another way of following growth progress by plotting standard scores.** Evenness or unevenness of the horizontal line indicates steady or unsteady growth as compared to that of other children.

Yet another device for evaluating height and weight, the Grid-Graph formulated and developed by Wetzel,[980, 982, 983, 984] is a reliable height-weight-age gauge of individual progress. It consists of two parts (see Fig. 29). The first, on the left, is a channel system of nine channels on which height is plotted against weight and which represents gradations in build from slender on the right to stocky on the left. These channels are crossed at regular intervals of ten units (isodevelopmental lines) which are incremental units. The second part, on the right, is a grid for plotting developmental levels against chronologic age with a series of curves, auxodromes, representing the

---

* When averages and standard deviations are used, approximately 68 per cent of the children measured might normally be expected to fall between plus and minus one standard deviation; approximately 95 per cent will fall between plus and minus two standard deviations.

In a standard based on percentiles, measurements are ranked according to magnitude from the smallest to the largest as they would be found in any typical series of 100 children. The middle point or median is represented by the fiftieth percentile. Half of the children might normally be expected to fall between the twenty-fifth and seventy-fifth percentiles, which are equidistant from the median. Eighty per cent of the children might be expected to fall between the tenth and ninetieth percentiles.

** Standard score represents the difference between the normative value and actual value at a particular age divided by the standard deviation for that age. Any norms with standard deviations may be used.

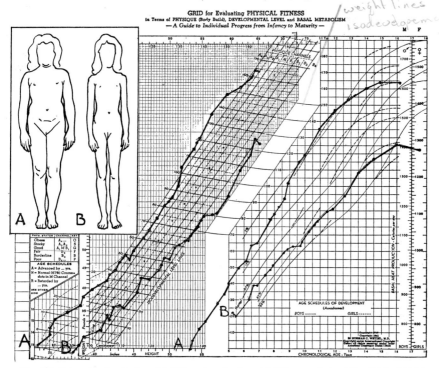

Fig. 29. Progress of a stocky girl (A) and a slender girl (B) recorded on the Wetzel Grid, showing differences in build, changes in physical status, and differences in speed of development. (Copyright by Norman C. Wetzel, by National Education Association Service, Incorporated)

speed of development from slow to fast. Healthy development travels channel-wise from about six years to at least eighteen.* "Cutting across" two or more channels is a signal for careful scrutiny of a child's growth.[550]** A healthy child's speed is about twelve levels a year or one a month throughout the ten to fifteen school years. A child's curve will be expected to parallel one of the auxodromes. The particular one will depend upon his schedule, whether it be slow, average or fast.

Figure 29 illustrates the use of the Grid. The height and weight of two girls are plotted, one from five to sixteen years, three months, and the other from five years, four months, to seventeen years, six months. Girl A has always been stocky and for a time became overnourished† but has returned to the A channel which undoubtedly is her "preferential path." The shift to the left may have been the result of a number of factors, namely, too much food, too little activity, a temporary emotional disturbance and, perhaps, a

* While the Grid covers ages two to six this seems to be a period of relative instability in body build. Wetzel also has a Baby Grid[981] which covers the period of infancy to around two years. See Rand, et al.[756]

** Wetzel's criterion for significant deviation from a child's own path of growth of one half channel for ten developmental units may be too fine since many healthy children have been shown to cut across channels.[335]

† By overnourished we mean an excess of intake over output of energy.

slight hypothyroidism. Her return to her channel followed a correction of these imbalances. The curve at the right indicates (1) that her schedule was faster than that of most children; (2) that it was steady except for a shift between eight and fifteen years. The other girl (B) of slender build has moved to the extreme right, out to B_4, the area of poor physical status. The curve at the right indicates that she is on a slower schedule than girl A. Her progress has been somewhat unsteady. Girl B has a history of illnesses, small appetite, and much activity. She is an example of a child who has been "in the red" in her energy balance. This grid can be useful in studying an individual child in order to ascertain whether his progress is satisfactory for him. Marked deviations from channel or auxodrome call for a physical examination and an evaluation of his environment and habits.

An interesting method for determining normal weight for children between five and eighteen has been devised by Massler and Suher[634] in which they use the measurements of calf girth and height.* Normal weight for boys and girls can be determined by calculation or without calculation by the use of a nomogram.

Growth in Size Has a Qualitative Aspect.   To know that a child is large or small or that he is growing slowly or rapidly is insufficient. We are also interested in the quality of his tissues, the proportionate growth of bone, muscle, fat, and body segments and thus in the build or physique of the child. A large child may not be a better child, for a small child with muscles firm to touch, promptly and adequately responsive to stimulation and with straight bones that contain a good store of minerals will have an advantage over a large child with flabby muscles and poorly mineralized bone. An increase of a pound in weight may mean that a pound of good muscle, a pound of poor muscle, a pound of fat or even a pound of water has been accumulated. Because of differences in the timing of growth of the different parts of the body, weight increases in the early years may have a different meaning, qualitatively, than similar increases later. Much of the increase in infancy, for example, is due to growth of the brain and vital organs; much of the increase in adolescence is due to growth of bone and muscle.

Components of Weight.   The components of weight vary in their proportion to total weight with age and between children of the same age. For example, at birth about 25 per cent of the total weight can be attributed to muscle, 16 per cent to the vital organs and 15 per cent to the central nervous system whereas at maturity muscles, viscera and the central nervous system will represent approximately 43 per cent, 11 per cent and 3 per cent respectively. Two children may weigh the same, yet one may have relatively large muscles and the other relatively more fat.

The accumulation of muscle and bone follows the pattern of growth of the

* The formula $\dfrac{(\text{Calf girth})^2}{K} \times \text{Height}$, was derived on the basis that the human body may be represented by an irregular cylinder whose specific gravity, under ideal conditions of tissue balance, approximates 1.0. K is a correction factor for the irregularity of the cylinder and differs between boys and girls. Calf girth was found to be directly and closely related to the body build of a child.

body as a whole with accelerating periods in infancy and early adolescence,[598] lagging somewhat behind total body growth during infancy and childhood but compensating for this later in adolescence. Subcutaneous tissue (largely fat), on the other hand, has a sharp increase in infancy, steady loss during childhood and a marked sex difference in early adolescence when it increases for girls and decreases for boys.[774, 775, 914]*

There are also changes with age in the distribution of fat in that after twelve and one-half years fat tends to decrease on legs and arms, increase in waist and chest, and in hips tends to increase in girls and decrease in boys.[774] Thus there are readjustments in amounts and position. Even when height and weight change little in later adolescence, shifts in the relative proportions of bone, muscle and subcutaneous tissue take place. Thus changes in absolute and relative amounts of muscle, bone and fat result in changes in body contours.

As stated in Chapter 1, some boys differ from the regular trend of growth in fatty tissue by having a period of plumpness as they pass from childhood into early adolescence. In the California Adolescent Study,[899] it was found that some boys had a conspicuous accumulation of fat around the nipples and over abdomen, hip and thighs. These differences, which suggested male-inappropriate development, lasted from one to three and one-half years and was psychologically disturbing to the boys.

Early maturers have more fat (as measured on the calf of the leg) than late maturers.[774] Boys are consistently larger in muscle and bone and girls in fat.[777] It would seem that increase in weight during adolescence means relatively more increase in muscle for boys and fat for girls. This has significance for adults in understanding sex differences both in appearance and in physical performance.

Changes in Body Proportions and Form. It is obvious that small children differ from adults not only in size but also in body form. The growth pattern of muscle, bone and fat discussed above suggests why the characteristically chubby baby changes to the thinner and "wiry" preschool child and gradually acquires a body build which becomes characteristic for the individual. In the process of growing up changes occur in body proportions and contours and the characteristic sex differences in body form emerge.

In *body proportions* the baby's head is large, his legs and arms are short in comparison with those of an adult, and his shoulders and hips relatively narrow. During growth the proportions of head, trunk and legs change.** The growth pattern of the different parts of the body, except for the head, which completes most of its growth before the school years, is similar to those of height and weight in trend but differs in timing and in degree. There are also similar sex differences and similar differences between early and late maturers.

* Girls reach their peak at 15.5 years; boys reach their low point at 14.5 years.[774]

** The head changes from one-fourth of the total length at birth to about one-sixth at six years and about one-eighth at maturity. Legs change from about three-eighths of total length at birth to about half the total length at adulthood. Legs increase in length almost five times from birth to maturity, head twice and trunk three times.

During the elementary years* boys and girls become more slender in arms and legs at a diminishing rate. This slenderizing trend stops at around seven years for the trunk but continues in the extremities. The sex difference in the width of shoulders and hips in which adolescent girls generally have relatively broader hips and adolescent boys relatively broader shoulders begins back at this time for girls when they begin to increase their hip width relatively more than their shoulder width. Boys do not as yet show any increase in relative shoulder width.[657] These differences become noticeable during the adolescent growth spurt.[74, 75]

This adolescent growth spurt does not occur simultaneously for all parts of the body. For both boys and girls[851, 852] increase in leg growth is one of the earliest signs that childhood is ended. The maximum growth for stem length or sitting height,** width of chest, shoulders and hips which occurs about the same time follows leg length and while this is the pattern for most children, some have a different sequence. For girls, these increases generally come within a year preceding menarche.[852] For boys the peak of increments comes within the period of maximum genital growth.[899] Sex differences in shoulders and hips have been mentioned above. Whether a boy or girl is an early or late maturer has some effect upon shoulder-hip relationships. The effect is greater among boys than girls. Early maturing boys tend to have broader hips; late maturing boys tend to have slenderer hips and longer legs. Late maturing girls have a tendency to be broad-shouldered. A longer growing period frequently emphasizes the growth of shoulders.

Body proportions and the amounts of the three tissues and their distribution contribute to an overall *body form*, *build*† or *physique* which is a vital part of an individual's uniqueness. Body form may be designated in various ways. For example, individuals may be classified as slender to stocky, as having "soft roundness," "muscular solidity" or "linearity-delicacy"‡ in varying degrees and proportions or as varying in the degree of masculinity or femininity.

It would seem that differences in physique may be recognized at a fairly early age for many children, since there is evidence in two studies,[263, 395] using different methods of typing physique, that build tends to be relatively constant in childhood.§ However, some children will change in build, as has

* These studies were done on children 4 to 11 years old. See Meredith and Sherbina,[658] Meredith and Culp,[656] Meredith and Meredith.[657]
** Measurements include head and trunk. The first is taken in a recumbent position, the other in an erect position.
† Body form, build or physique is studied by various methods: relating certain anthropometric measurements by the use of indices[656] or by factorial analysis,[446] by somatotyping in which the individual is rated according to the relative degree of three components, endomorphy, mesomorphy and ectomorphy,[840] by rating on an audrogyny scale which indicates the degree of maleness or femaleness of an individual.[77]
‡ Terms for endomorphy, mesomorphy and ectomorphy, respectively, given by Dupertuis.[253]
§ Hammond[395] noted that adult types could be distinguished in children from 5 to 18 years. Dupertuis and Michael[263] using Brush Foundation height and weight data on children from 2 years to 17 years and somatotyping the subjects as young adults found that the somatotype as indicated by measures of height and weight remains fairly constant, at least for ectomorphs and mesomorphs, throughout childhood into young adult life. There is evidence from an anthropometric survey in the Army[701] and the Minnesota study of semi-starvation[566] that this constancy does not necessarily hold for adults.

been shown in some of the cases in the California Adolescent Study.*
Body build has a significant role to play in the evaluation of weight, as
indicated earlier. Two children of the same height will vary considerably if
one is of stocky build and the other of slender build. To expect each to weigh
the same would badly penalize one or the other. One study[263] indicates that
children with "muscular solidity" (mesomorphic) tend to be heavier, shorter,
reach their peak in puberal growth spurt in height-weight earlier, and grow
faster than those with "linearity-delicacy" (ectomorphs). Mesomorphs in the
California Adolescent Study tended to be stronger than ectomorphs.[495]
Juvenile delinquents in one study[359] had a higher mesomorphic rating than
nondelinquents. Sheldon[841] related temperament to somatotypes in young
men, but to date no work is reported on children. These examples indicate
the interest in the study of the role of body build in an individual's life. In
relating build to behavior or performance it must be remembered that body
structure is only one in a number of contributing factors.

BODY FRAMEWORK

The frame of the body consists of the bones bound together by tough bits
of connective tissue called ligaments to form the skeleton. To this skeleton
are attached the muscles. Thus the bones and muscles serve as support in
holding the body together and as protection for the organs of the body. The
bones of the head protect the delicate structure of the brain so that pressures,
bumps and blows from without, unless very severe, do not damage brain
tissue. The bones of the chest protect the heart and lungs and the pelvis acts
as a support for the abdominal organs. The working together of muscles and
bones makes locomotion possible. The bones not only serve the function of a
framework and a protection for the more delicate body structures, but also
are the seat for the manufacture of blood cells and provide the body with a
store of calcium which can be drawn on when other parts of the body require
additional calcium for performing their functions.

Bone Development.   Most bones develop from a cartilaginous model**
which is laid down early in prenatal life. This cartilage is gradually replaced
by bone beginning at ossification centers from which it spreads concentrically.
Through intricate cellular processes, the organic form is established and
minerals, predominantly calcium and phosphorus, are deposited. The mineral
salts give hardness and rigidity to bone; the organic material provides its
tenacity. The process of replacement of cartilage begins early in embryonic
life and continues until the skeleton has reached full maturity.†

Bone growth takes place at the edge of existing bone, not by expansion
from within. Bones grow in width by adding new bone at the outer edges
underneath the periosteum, and long bones grow in length toward each end

* See Shuttleworth[850] for pictures of boys showing constancy of build and one case in
which build changed from endomorphic to mesomorphic between 9.9 and 16 years.

** The exceptions are those which develop in a membranous area, as is true of the bones
in the vault of the skull.

† Ossification centers appear from the middle of the sixth week after fertilization until
twenty years. Most primary centers appear before birth; most secondary centers appear
after birth.[703]

of their cartilaginous models. In long bones another ossification center appears at the ends of the cartilaginous model and is called an epiphyseal center of ossification or epiphysis.* While a long bone is growing there remains a non-calcified area, observable in an x-ray, between the shaft or diaphysis and the epiphysis. New bone is produced by cellular activity at the edge of the diaphysis of this area. At the same time the ossification of the epiphysis continues. Growth of the long bones is terminated when the epiphysis and diaphysis is fused, as is seen in the top finger bones of the hand illustrating fusion age in Fig. 30.

Bone development continues throughout the growing years and is not completed generally until the individual is in his twenties. In the early years the skeleton has many aspects of immaturity that distinguish it from that of an adult. In the young child all of the cartilaginous model has not been replaced by bone and larger spaces between bones exist at the joints. With more space between the ends of bones at a joint and longer and less firmly attached ligaments, the child has more flexibility in certain movements, all of which give him the appearance of being "double jointed." Immature bones also have proportionately more water and protein-like substances and less minerals. Thus young bones are less resistant to pressure and muscle pull and, therefore, more liable to deformity. In the school years sitting for long periods in ill-fitting seats and at inappropriate desks may lead to postural defects of the back. Growing bone also has a rich supply of blood. Thus growing bone not only receives a steady supply of bone building materials but also will be subjected more readily than mature bone to any infecting organism which may be carried in the blood stream.

As bones grow they pass through a series of regular changes from small spherical dots to the characteristic form of each bone at maturity. These changes can be observed by x-rays taken at intervals of time. Figure 30 illustrates the same stage of development (first appearance) in three bones, namely, the epiphysis of the radius, the epiphysis of the ulna and the sesamoid** of the thumb, but at widely different chronologic ages and the beginning of the final stage of bone development (fusion). Note also the appearance of other epiphyses, of carpal or wrist bones and the change in the size and shape of the bones. The sesamoid bone announces approaching menarche in girls since it generally appears within two or two and one-half years[143, 296] prior to menarche.† The beginning of the fusion of shaft and epiphysis of the last phalanx of the second finger is also related in time to menarche. Bone development in the hand is completed with the fusion of all the epiphyses and shafts of the bones, for girls generally in the seventeenth year and for boys in the nineteenth year.

Bones may record metabolic disturbances resulting from severe illness and

* In Fig. 30 note the two bones of the arm, the radius and ulna, in the second hand from the left. At the end of each is a smaller bone. These small bones are epiphyses.

** The sesamoid is that small round bone seen at the joint at the base of the thumb. It can be seen more clearly in the fusion-age hand.

† Among Brush Foundation children in Cleveland[143] it appears in girls at 10.1 ± 1.1 years and in boys about two years later at 12.6 ± 1.1 years.

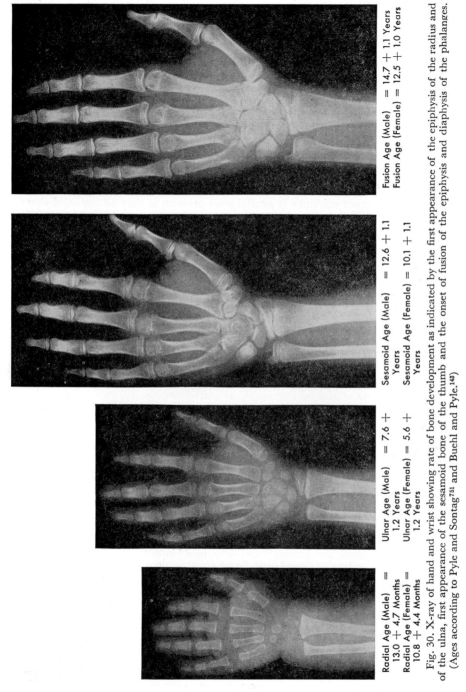

Radial Age (Male) = 13.0 + 4.7 Months
Radial Age (Female) = 10.8 + 4.4 Months

Ulnar Age (Male) = 7.6 + 1.2 Years
Ulnar Age (Female) = 5.6 + 1.2 Years

Sesamoid Age (Male) = 12.6 + 1.1 Years
Sesamoid Age (Female) = 10.1 + 1.1 Years

Fusion Age (Male) = 14.7 + 1.1 Years
Fusion Age (Female) = 12.5 + 1.0 Years

Fig. 30. X-ray of hand and wrist showing rate of bone development as indicated by the first appearance of the epiphysis of the radius and of the ulna, first appearance of the sesamoid bone of the thumb and the onset of fusion of the epiphysis and diaphysis of the phalanges. (Ages according to Pyle and Sontag[751] and Buehl and Pyle.[143])

other adverse circumstances and also changes taking place in the early stage of recovery from malnutrition by the **appearance of bone** scars or transverse lines on certain bones. Such scars or lines indicate that normal growth has been interrupted.[403, 380, 273]* Some children after a severe illness will show bone scars, others of comparable age and with illness of the same severity will show none. The reasons for these individual differences of response are not known at present.

Children differ in skeletal development as they differ in height and weight although the process of maturation is less subject to fluctuations than is that of growth. Girls are skeletally ahead of boys. This difference becomes progressively greater so that upon entering elementary school girls are approximately a year ahead of boys; upon entering high school they are approximately two years in advance.[296] There are also fast maturing and slow maturing children of both sexes.** American Negro infants tend to be skeletally more mature at birth than white infants of comparable birth weight.[184] During childhood, although no direct evidence is available at present, it may be assumed that Negro and white children of comparable socio-economic status are similar in the process of their skeletal maturation since their reproductive maturation is similarly timed.

The density or degree of mineralization of bone which can be revealed by the depth of the shadow in an x-ray† also differs in children and in a child from time to time. The cause of the fluctuation of density, undoubtedly associated in some way with calcium metabolism, has not yet been ascertained. Certain behavior characteristics have been noted to accompany lightly mineralized bone.‡ These individual differences between children of the same and opposite sexes have implications for all adults who live or work with children.

The assessment of skeletal maturation, as stated previously, can be done by x-ray examination of the joints of the body and comparison with a standard time of appearance of ossification centers, changes in bone contours and finally union of epiphysis with the diaphysis. The growth of the bones of the hand and wrist is considered by many to be a satisfactory representative of the growth of the skeletal structure as a whole.§ Bone development of the body, therefore, can be evaluated by inspection and comparison with a standard x-ray picture of the contours of the ends of the bones of the hand, of wrist bones and epiphyses and of progress toward union of the epiphysis with

---

* See discussion in Greulich and Pyle.[380]

** There is evidence that heredity[773] and endocrines[993] influence bone growth. Likewise skeletal maturation may be slowed down by adverse conditions. See Greulich et al.[378] on the development of children in Hiroshima and Nagasaki, Spies et al.[883] on children with nutritive failure and Weiner and Thambipillai[978] on the progressive difference with increasing age between a group of West African Negro children and an American white group.

† A less dense or less well mineralized bone is indicated by a lighter shadow in the x-ray film.

‡ Todd reported: "So frequently do we find lightly mineralized bones in the highly strung child, who is prone to fatigue, restless, often very alert, irritable, poorly adjusted, apprehensive and fearful, with deficient powers of attention and concentration, that we have come to suspect deficiency in mineralization as the physical counterpart of this emotional maladjustment. But one should point out that one is dealing not with cause and effect but merely with two aspects of a constitutional handicap."[950]

§ X-rays of all the joints gives a more complete picture but such a procedure is not always feasible.

the shaft of the bone. Standards used are Greulich and Pyle,[380] which is a revision and extension of the standards of Todd[949] and Flory.[296] The degree of maturity is expressed in terms of skeletal months or years. In the more recent atlas of Greulich and Pyle each bone is assessed so that symmetry of development may be observed. Thus any imbalance can be observed. An imbalance will prompt investigation of the health history of the child to find contributing factors. The range of development can be observed easily by plotting from time to time the least and most advanced centers as well as the average. Such a graph is termed a "Red Graph" and the method is termed the "Red Graph Method" for observing symmetry or asymmetry in skeletal development. A child's progress toward maturity is more important than his status at the time of the x-ray.*

*Skeletal development can be used as an indicator of physical maturity.*** The use of the skeleton in determining bodily maturity is important because (1) its maturation extends over the whole period of development, (2) the process can be observed by the use of x-rays and (3) its development is closely related to the development of the reproductive system which is assumed to be a reliable indicator of general bodily maturity. This assumption is based on the fact that many changes in tissues other than those of the reproductive organs, including skin, hair, sweat glands, distribution of subcutaneous fat and muscle growth, occur at pubescence. The degree of reliance that can be placed on the skeleton as an indicator depends greatly on the degree of harmony in a child's development in all its parts. Naturally, the value of any tool in assessing development depends on the manner in which it is used.

Knowledge of the skeletal development of a child aids adults in understanding a child and being appreciative of his behavior and needs. An adult can further be of service to a child by interpreting to him his development. The value to the adult of information regarding a child's skeletal development rests in its relationship to other aspects of development. For example, it is a more reliable indicator of growth in height during pubescence than is chronologic age.† Because skeletal age is closely related to the percentage of mature height attained at a particular age it is possible to predict, with fair accuracy, how tall a child will be at maturity if his skeletal age and height at the time are known.[75, 79] The concern which fast-growing girls and slow-

---

* For example, a child in a period of twelve calendar months may progress twelve months in skeletal age. In such a case his progress in skeletal age is in keeping with his progress in chronologic age. On the other hand, if he gains only four months in skeletal age during the same period, his skeletal growth is lagging behind. If his gain were fifteen months his bone growth would be progressing at an accelerated rate.

The range of normality in the Greulich-Pyle Atlas is considered to be ± 2 standard deviations. The majority of a group of radiologists, asked to give their opinion of the skeletal age limits of apparently normal 6-year-olds, gave 5–0 to 7–0 as the limits.[443]

** Nicolson and Hanley,[702] deriving a maturity score for over-all adolescent physiologic maturation, found that skeletal age 12.75 is the second best single measure of adolescent maturation in girls. To determine general body maturity separate assessment of each system would be most satisfactory, but this is not yet possible.

† Stolz and Stolz[899] found that the range in skeletal age at the onset of the puberal period of growth in height in which maximum growth occurs was less than half the range in chronologic age. The average skeletal age at the onset was 13 years.

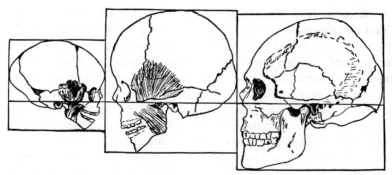

Fig. 31. Skulls of newborn, six-year-old boy and adult drawn in their natural proportions. (Brash, J. C.: The Growth of the Jaws, Normal and Abnormal, in Health and Disease. The Dental Board of the United Kingdom, London, 1924, p. 147.)

growing boys register about their size can be relieved for a tall girl if she can be assured that she will not grow much more and for a short boy if he knows that he still will add some inches to his stature. The approximate age of menarche can be anticipated by knowing a girl's progress in skeletal maturation.* Boys also who are on a slow or fast schedule in skeletal development may be expected to be slow or fast in sexual maturation and may differ accordingly in their interests and attitudes during the high school years. As is true with height, sexual maturation more closely follows skeletal maturation than chronologic age.** This is indicated in Fig. 26 of three fourteen-year-old boys who differ in size, genital development and skeletal age.

Thus an adult who is following the growth of a child and is watchful of skeletal age progress can provide more adequately for his needs and can help that child to understand and accept his own particular pattern. By so doing the adult can ease the child's social adjustments and further his school achievements.

Development of the Head. The relatively large head of the young child has been mentioned before. Not only does he have a relatively larger head than an adult but also a relatively larger brain case and relatively smaller face. As he grows the facial part of the skull grows faster than the cranial portion and thus the face assumes more prominence. At birth the relationship of face to cranium is one to eight; at five years it is one to five. Facial growth makes considerable progress during the school years so that the ratio is reduced to one to 2.5 at maturity. Figure 31 demonstrates these changes. Along with the more rapid growth of the face the features gradually assume their mature characteristics. The development of the skull is associated with the growth of other structures of the head, and these structures affect the growth of the skull at different periods. The brain and the eyeballs in infancy, air sinuses during infancy and childhood, the teeth during the

---

* See Buehl and Pyle[143] and Simmons and Greulich.[859] In the Brush Foundation Studies[859] early average and late menarcheal groups could be differentiated by skeletal assessment prior to puberal acceleration in height and weight. Menarche generally occurred when girls reached a skeletal age of 13 years.

** Greulich et al.[379] and Greulich and Pyle.[380]

eruption of the permanent teeth, and the muscles in later childhood and adolescence, have their effects upon the proportional growth of the head.

Development of Teeth. At the time of birth the twenty deciduous (baby) teeth and the first permanent teeth (six-year molars) are developing in the child's jaws. Both the enamel, or outer portion, and the dentine, or inner portion, are forming. By the time the tooth erupts the enamel is fully formed. The dentine, however, continues to form until the root is completed, which occurs sometime after eruption. The development of the deciduous teeth including the crowns and roots is completed between three and four years. The calcification of the 32 permanent teeth begins at birth with the beginning of calcification of the first or "sixth-year" molars and continues through infancy, the preschool, and the school years. The third permanent molar or "wisdom" tooth does not complete its growth until sometime between eighteen and twenty-five years.*

Tooth development is influenced by heredity, prenatal conditions, nutrition, illness and certain endocrine factors. Materials that are necessary for the development of teeth of good quality are calcium, phosphorus, vitamins A, D and C.

Like bones, teeth can register various misfortunes in health during the growing years. Enamel is laid down regularly and rhythmically in layer after layer so that a series of rings** is formed, somewhat like tree rings. If this process is undisturbed these rings are regular; if disturbed they are accentuated. If these disturbances are severe enough, they may produce lines which can be seen with the unaided eye. Any health mishap will be reflected, of course, in the particular teeth whose enamel is developing at the moment. Permanent teeth will, therefore, reflect disturbances in infancy and the preschool years. For example, an imprint left by measles at three years of age may be found on a child's permanent incisors when they erupt. The growing tooth, therefore, reflects through its growing enamel and dentine the normal and pathologic variations in metabolism.[817]

Eruption of Teeth. The appearance of the first tooth is an occasion of great rejoicing in the family. This first tooth is generally a lower front tooth which erupts around six months. During the first two or three years the other deciduous teeth appear.† A quiescent period follows until about six years when the first permanent tooth erupts. This tooth does not replace a first tooth but appears behind the second deciduous molar. Because it may appear before the loss of any deciduous teeth, it may not be recognized as a permanent tooth and may be neglected. Even before this six-year molar appears and as the permanent teeth are developing in the jaw beneath the deciduous teeth, the roots of the latter are gradually disappearing by the process known as resorption. When a permanent tooth is ready to erupt only the crown of the temporary tooth above it is left; the tooth becomes loose and

* Chronology of deciduous and permanent teeth from Kronfeld[552] and Kronfeld and Schour.[553]
** These rings are generally microscopic in size.
† For time of eruption of deciduous and permanent teeth see Stuart and Stevenson.[915]

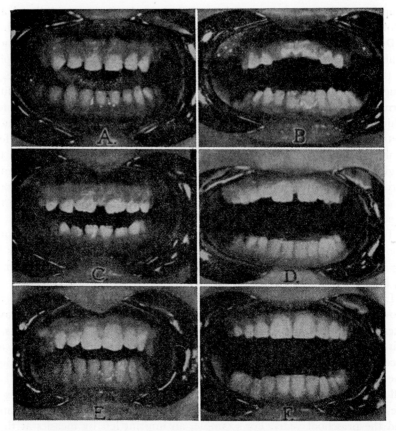

Fig. 32. Photographs of the front teeth of a child showing normal transition from deciduous to permanent dentition: A. At about 4½ years of age, showing spacing of deciduous teeth. B. At about 6½ years of age, showing loss of deciduous central incisors and eruption of lower permanent central incisors. C. At about 7½ years of age, showing eruption of permanent lower lateral and upper central incisors, space between and angle of upper central incisors. D. At about 8 years of age, showing eruption of permanent upper lateral incisors and beginning of closure of space between upper central incisors. The lower incisors are aligned by the action of tongue and lips. E. At about 10 years of age, showing further eruption of upper lateral incisors and closing of space between upper central incisors. F. At about 11½ years of age, showing eruption of permanent cuspids, and correction of the angle of the incisor teeth. (From Schour, I. and Massler, M.: The Development of the Human Dentition. Journal of the American Dental Association, *28:* 1941, p. 1158.)

drops out. When the child enters school, at six years of age, he may have all of his deciduous teeth but more often he has lost some of his front teeth which have been replaced by partially erupted permanent incisors. Perhaps he will also have his sixth-year molars. During the elementary years he will be passing through a stage of mixed dentition when he will have both deciduous and permanent teeth in his mouth. By looking at Figure 32 it can readily be seen why Dr. Broadbent calls this the "Ugly Duckling stage." From six to twelve years the child goes through the process of replacing old teeth with new ones which, at first, look out of line but, with the correct order of eruption, are later pushed into place by the eruption of nearby teeth. Therefore, he acquires a mature look by twelve years of age. By that time he has all his permanent teeth except his "wisdom" teeth. Wisdom teeth sometimes fail to erupt because of failure to develop or because of lack of sufficient space in the jaw. An insufficient increase in the growth of the jaw during pubescence is probably responsible for the latter condition, termed "impacted teeth."

The teeth erupt in characteristic sequence with wide individual differences in timing. A child, however, tends to be consistent in timing, being slow, average or advanced in the eruption of both deciduous and permanent teeth.[915] Because of this wide variability in eruption time there is no need for concern when children are a little behind schedule. Girls generally cut their permanent teeth somewhat earlier than boys.[453] There are familial differences. In some families children cut their teeth early; in some families they cut them late. In other families one child may have an early eruption schedule and another a late one. Further investigation regarding the factors associated with the time of tooth eruption is needed.

Dental Caries. Tooth decay is a serious problem in the United States. Relatively few children escape it in some degree. The wide scope of this disease has been indicated by surveys in various parts of the country.* Dental defects were the cause of rejection of 20.9 per cent of the men drafted for the armed forces of the United States in World War II.[799] Surveys show that the incidence increases with age as noted above. Dental decay attacks the rich and the poor alike.[537] It tends to run in families.[535, 536] American Negroes tend to have less tooth decay than whites.[291] Girls tend to have more permanent teeth affected than boys.[291] Some communities have more caries among their population than others. The lower incidence seems to be associated with the presence of minute amounts of fluorides in the water.[533, 534, 803]

Because of the damage which may result from tooth decay much research has been undertaken in an attempt to discover the cause of dental caries and thus take measures to prevent them. This is not a simple matter since many factors are involved which undoubtedly include body metabolism and oral environment.** There is full agreement that dental decay begins at the outer edge of the enamel and progresses inward. There is agreement that bacteria in the mouth are necessary for production of dental caries. There is controversy, however, as to whether the primary agents produce acid and etch the enamel or act upon the protein substance of the tooth and thereby cause disintegration. The most widely accepted view is that acid forming bacteria are responsible for carious destruction of the enamel. These bacteria act on carbohydrates, especially sugars, to produce the acid which in turn produces the decalcification of the tooth. Most investigators agree that there are degrees of tooth resistance or susceptibility to dental caries which is developed primarily during formation and maturation of the tooth. Hence

---

* Finn,[291] in summarizing the prevalence of dental caries, quotes in a survey of children that 25 per cent of 6-year-olds had some caries; 97.8 per cent of 14-year-olds had carious teeth.

** See Shaw[838] on nutrition and dental caries and Cox[205] on oral environment.

the structure of the tooth is important and all factors contributing to healthy tooth structure have significance in preventing dental decay.

In the prevention of tooth decay natural rather than highly refined foods, a well balanced diet rich in protective foods, and limited consumption of sugar and other sweets have proved to be beneficial.* This is borne out by observation of lower incidence of caries in primitive peoples. When their natural diets are replaced largely by refined foods, including sugar, the incidence of caries increases.** Studies of institutional children have shown that they have less tooth decay than children living in homes.[953] The food habits, including foods eaten, regularity of meals and lack of sweets and soft drinks between meals, of the institutional children may have been a contributing factor. Decrease in dental caries was noted in several countries during World War II,[643, 875, 952] and in Norway, where the observations were continued, an increase again after the war. The reduction was greatest in young children and in the teeth of the older children which matured during the war. Again, the common cause appears to be a difference in food habits. In England the diet of the children improved in spite of restrictions. Milk had been made available at reduced cost at school. Margarine was fortified with vitamins A and D; bread was fortified with calcium carbonate. Pregnant and lactating women were given increased rations of milk, cod liver oil and fruit juice. Refined carbohydrates were limited. In Norway the most pronounced change was a decrease in refined carbohydrates, including sugar and all kinds of sweets, meat, more less highly refined flour, potatoes, vegetables and fish. Daily intake of milk and cod liver oil was more regular. Between-meal eating of cookies and sweets practically disappeared.

Thus food habits are important in the prevention of dental caries.† Adequate care of the teeth is also of significance. Regular visits to the dentist will make it possible for him to detect and care for carious teeth at an early stage. The regular brushing of teeth is another measure which, although it will not assure freedom from decay, will remove particles adhering to teeth, help to keep them clean and also may improve blood circulation in the tissues around the teeth.‡

Other measures which can aid in reducing caries are the provision of drinking water containing very small amounts of fluorides during the formative period of teeth, or topically applying a fluoride compound to the teeth.§

* One study[384] has demonstrated differing effects of sweets according to consistency. Eating sticky candy, e.g., caramels, was followed by increase in caries while a sugar solution or chocolate bars effected no change. Increase was greater when the candy was eaten between meals.

** See Toverud.[953]

† Health supervision and education can do much to promote eating habits in mothers and children that will aid in protecting the teeth of children, as seen in Norway.[953]

‡ One study[308] has demonstrated that regular and vigorous brushing of the teeth after taking any food, or, if brushing were not possible, rinsing of the mouth thoroughly with water resulted in a reduction of caries.

§ See Knutson[543] and Cox[204] for review of literature.

After 6½ years during which fluoride has been added to the water in Grand Rapids, Michigan, the reduction in dental caries ranged from 66.6 per cent in 6-year-olds to 18.1 per cent in 16-year-olds. Similar reductions have not been observed in Muskegon, Michi-

Many communities with "fluoride free" water are adding fluorine, one part per million parts of water, as a public health measure.

Jaw Development. The development of the jaw is closely associated with that of the teeth. There is rapid growth while both the deciduous and the permanent teeth are developing and erupting. During the time of deciduous dentition (the first three years) the pattern of the face is being established. After that time, change in the face consists more or less of a proportionate increase in size rather than any marked change in proportions.[124] Growth of the jaw may be adequate or inadequate to allow for the proper placement of the teeth. If growth of the jaw at any time is inadequate, the teeth may not erupt, may appear in an unusual order or may force their way into too small a space, resulting in crowding or irregular alignment. Then again, a jaw may grow more than is needed to accommodate the teeth and wide spaces between the teeth will result.

The growth of a normal face is orderly and symmetric. Occasionally, however, one jaw may grow more rapidly than the other so that the teeth of the two jaws do not fit together properly; such a condition is designated "malocclusion." For example, the lower jaw may grow more slowly in width than the upper jaw, so that the grinding surfaces of the upper and lower teeth do not meet and the lower front incisors, or biting teeth, will be crowded and will not fit behind the uppers as they normally should. The lower jaw may grow too slowly in depth, resulting in a deep overbite of the upper teeth. Figure 33 on the left shows good occlusion, on the right shows malocclusion.

Irregularities may be of the types that correct themselves during development, such as the normal sequence of the position of the teeth during the "Ugly Duckling State"; they may be within the range of normal variation and thus not interfere with the function of the teeth; they may grow steadily worse. As in all aspects of growth, there are individual differences in the pattern of growth of children's jaws.* It is advisable, therefore, that the development of the teeth and jaws be watched carefully at regular intervals beginning around three years of age by a dentist who understands the developmental process. Such a regular examination will make it possible to follow the child's development and make regular appraisal of dentofacial growth as a part of the "whole child." Sometimes it is necessary to assist nature by applying pressure provided by suitable bands or wire placed in the mouth. The jaw of the child is quite plastic, which makes adjustment possible.

* See Sillman.[854]

---

gan, where the water supply remained "fluoride free." It can be noted that the children who had had water with fluorides throughout their lives had a higher reduction of caries than older children who did not receive fluorides in their early years.[225] The value of fluorides persists into adulthood.[803] In another demonstration (Kingston, New York) physical examinations have revealed no deleterious effect of the fluorides upon the health of the children.[812]

The topical application of fluorides to the teeth is recommended shortly after the eruption of the teeth,[542] on the basis of the fact that young enamel is the most permeable. However, one study[541] has shown reduction in caries after topical application of sodium fluoride in young adults averaging 25 years.

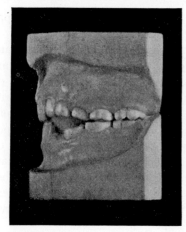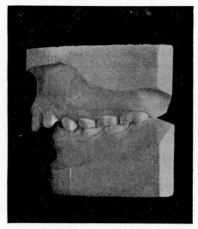

Fig. 33. Impression of teeth of 2 six-year-olds showing good occlusion and malocclusion.

Good or poor occlusion may be due to developmental, local or genetic factors.* Premature loss of a baby tooth may cause irregular eruption of the permanent tooth. However, malocclusion does not always follow the premature loss of a tooth.** Congenital absence of teeth will retard jaw development.[123] Thumb sucking may cause protrusion of the upper front teeth.[591,856] A serial study[856] of a group of children from birth to fourteen years of age showed that thumb sucking tended to affect those with poor bites but had little or no effect on those with good bites. Spontaneous correction has been observed after the activity is stopped, even as late as eleven years of age.[856]

The value of well-developed, symmetric jaws, with teeth of good quality and good appearance is immeasurable in the school years and in adulthood. Such a condition contributes to the physical and mental health of the child and adult. The ability to chew well, and the absence of centers of infection aid in maintaining physical health. An attractive set of teeth and good facial contour increase one's self-confidence, and the proper alignment of teeth contributes to satisfactory speech.

The development of the jaws is stimulated by exercise; namely, sucking in infancy and later chewing. This exercises the muscles of the jaw and stimulates circulation.

Chest. At birth the chest is rounded, the shoulders are high, and the neck is short. During childhood, especially between three and ten years, it broadens and flattens, and the ribs change from a more horizontal position to a more oblique one. The shoulders drop and the neck appears to lengthen. If the bones of the chest do not become firm enough to withstand pressures, chest deformities may result which crowd the lungs. Such a condition may reduce the efficiency of the respiratory function.

* See Krogman,[549] Sillman.[855]
** Lewis[590] found the timing of the loss of the tooth in relation to the development of the jaw important. Sillman[855] cites cases which indicate the importance of a family history of good or poor occlusion.

Vertebral Column.   The vertebral column or spine grows until the early twenties. It is a flexible rod which at birth has one curve. A curve at the neck appears when the child begins to lift his head. At the time of walking another curve, the lumbar, appears in the lower part of the back. These curves of the back are produced by the pull of muscles. With such a flexible rod, it can be understood how easily the spine can be twisted out of shape by unequal pull from opposing muscle groups. Such a state can develop through fatigue or habitually bad habits of sitting and standing. The flexibility of the spine decreases slowly with age, with the process of fixation (stiffening of the spine) beginning in childhood but proceeding very slowly into maturity.

Pelvis.   The pelvis, consisting of the hip bones and the sacral bones, is relatively much smaller in the infant than in the adult. As children grow the pelvis increases in size, broadens and becomes less vertical. In infancy and throughout prepuberal childhood pelvic measurements for boys tend to be larger for the overall structure; for girls they tend to be larger for the inner structure including the inlet. A child tends to have a persistently distinctive pelvic shape.[772] Growth changes of the female pelvis are especially noticeable during pubescence.[381] During infancy and childhood the pelvis consists of a number of separate bones joined by strips of cartilage. The parts of the hip bone do not unite until about ten years in girls and fourteen years in boys.[813] The union of the sacral bones is completed between twenty-five and thirty years.[371] While the pelvic bones are still not united children and young adolescents should be protected from possible strains produced by carrying very heavy loads or standing for a long time without rest.

Extremities.   At birth arms are longer than legs, but before growth ceases this relationship is reversed. The hand of the child differs from that of the adult not only in size but also in shape. The short, stubby fingers in the child's hand are due to slower growth of the last two bones of the fingers. These bones grow vigorously in the later years of the grade school period.

The legs of a newborn child are short and flexed and the soles of the feet are directed toward each other. As the infant grows his legs straighten. By the time the child enters school at six, his legs and knees should be straight.

Meredith[650] has summarized the research on the length of the foot. In the twenty years or so of growth the average boy's foot grows from 3.2 inches to 10.3 inches. Girls' feet are smaller than boys' feet,* and reach mature size earlier. Individual differences increase with age from 1 inch during the first year to 2 inches at ten years and to 3 inches at adulthood.

The pubescent spurt of growth of feet, according to a study by Davenport,[214] tends to occur before or during the spurt in stature, or as the author states it, a boy will usually go into men's shoes before he goes into men's trousers.

According to Robinow et al.[789] the arches of the foot are well developed at a relatively early age, before five years, and the height of the arch varies considerably from child to child. Whether children they studied had high or low arches seemed to be determined by genetic factors. More information

---

* Girls' feet are smaller than boys' by 0.1 inch at birth and 1 inch at maturity.

is necessary before judgment can be made about the relative value of high or low arches in resisting the strains of life.

Muscles. Muscles, in conjunction with nerves, are responsible for all bodily movements, voluntary and involuntary. Attached to the skeleton and activated by nerves, they make it possible for man to maintain an upright position, to change that position and to control his environment through the manipulation of matter.

Muscles are also involved in the movement of the organs of the body, movements which, for the most part, are unnoticed but which, nevertheless, are necessary for life. Thus, we breathe, the heart beats, food is digested, and waste is eliminated. Eliminative activities change in the young child from involuntary acts to acts controlled by the will. The muscles of the eye operate to produce binocular vision and depth perception. Facial muscles, attached to the skin, make the face mobile and give it the ability to respond to the outside world and, in turn, give some clue to others in solving the human equation. Speech also owes its existence to the functioning of the muscles of the face and throat.

Muscles play a necessary part in maintaining body balance. Attached to the bones by tendons (tough, fibrous material), they hold the various parts of the skeleton in place. The changes which take place in balance as children grow can be attributed, in part at least, to the activity of various muscle groups. Body balance, good or poor, is dependent upon the quality of the muscles and their function. Thus, muscle tone, that state of readiness to act, contributes to the mechanics of the body. The intimate relationship of bone and muscle makes it possible for muscles to contribute to the growth of the skeleton. This is particularly noticeable in the face, where the muscles used in mastication play a part in molding the jaw and in stimulating circulation.

Muscles increase in weight about forty times from birth to maturity. At birth they constitute about one fifth to one fourth of the body's weight, in early adolescence about one third and in early maturity about two fifths. During the school years considerable muscle growth takes place. However, it lags behind growth in size but compensates for this lag in late adolescence. An adolescent, therefore, who is fully grown in height and in sexual characteristics is not necessarily fully grown muscularly. This has implications for adult expectations for adolescents and in planning programs for them.

After birth, no new muscle fibers are acquired. Muscles grow in size by increase in length, breadth and thickness of fibers. The muscles also change in composition and in their attachment to bones. In comparison with adult muscles, the muscles of the very young child contain relatively more water and less solids and proteins. They are more delicate and less firmly attached. They are not completely under voluntary control. The immaturity of the muscles and their innervation are reflected in awkwardness and inefficiency in movement in young children, in the erratic change of tempo of movement, in inability to sit still for long, as noticed in young elementary school children, and in their fatigability. Small children tend to fatigue more easily than adults but also recover more rapidly. Thus frequent rest periods and changes in activity throughout the day's program are advisable during childhood in order to bring different muscle groups into play and to relieve fatigue.

Children differ in their muscle equipment and efficiency. Boys generally are more muscular than girls. Some children have broad, thick muscles which give them advantage in muscular strength; others have the type of muscles which make them agile and successful in activities requiring motor skills. Some children have muscles which fatigue especially easily. Such differences are worthy of consideration in planning programs for children in the schools. The same child may differ in his muscular abilities at different times. After illness a child's muscle tone is generally lowered. More rest and less strenuous activity during the convalescent period, which usually extends beyond his return to school, will give his muscles an opportunity to recuperate from the effects of the illness and the period of inactivity necessitated by it.

Good development of muscles and nerves provides potentialities for increasing steadiness of movement, speed and accuracy, strength and endurance during the growing years. Thus a child as he matures and practices his emerging abilities can acquire strength, efficiency and grace of movement.

Strength. Strength* has been shown to increase with age, with changing tempo and differences in its patterns of growth. While boys are somewhat stronger than girls,[495] both make similar progress until about thirteen years, after which boys increase their rate of growth in strength while girls decrease their rate. Thus the sex difference becomes pronounced.**[495] For boys the beginning of the spurt of growth in strength† comes about the time they reach a skeletal age of fourteen years, and generally lags behind the spurt in height and weight. Strength is less closely related to height, which has its spurt of growth about one and one-half years prior to that of strength,[899] than to weight. Growth in strength continues in the third decade.[108]

Girls generally have their spurt of growth in strength in the year preceding menarche.[495] By thirteen their growth in strength is slowing down very appreciably. By sixteen years of age practically all boys are superior to the average girl. As in other phases of growth, girls mature earlier than boys and thus at the same chronologic age girls are farther advanced toward their terminal strength than boys.‡ Jones concludes that the evidence regarding

* As measured by grip and pull up and thrust.

Meredith[654] gives grip norms for boys from birth to eighteen years. Bookwalter[108] gives norms for boys between nine and twenty-four. The California Adolescent Growth Study,[497, 498] in which children were given a battery of tests for a period of seven years, included measurement of strength by dynamometers, tests which involved propulsion of the body, and measurement of motor ability by the Brace test.

** Jokl et al.[489] using shotput tests found similar relationships between the strength of boys and girls. While boys were always stronger than girls, there was a fairly even progress for both sexes until about eleven. After puberty the rate of increase for boys greatly exceeded that for girls.

† At the beginning of adolescence hand strength is relatively greater than shoulder strength. The latter has a longer period of acceleration.[495]

‡ For example, at thirteen years boys had reached approximately 45 per cent of their terminal strength in pull and thrust; girls had reached 75 per cent in pull and 90 per cent in thrust.[495]

sex differences indicates that these differences in strength have primarily a biologic basis, but, in addition, cultural expectations operate to increase motivation and practice in boys and diminish it in girls.

Early maturing individuals are generally superior in strength to the late maturers.[*] This is most marked in boys around fourteen and one-half and girls at thirteen years of age.[495] The superiority of early maturing boys continues into later adolescence; this does not hold for girls. Early maturing girls tend to drop below the average maturing group. The lag in the puberal spurt of strength behind that of other physical measurements is more noticeable for the early than for the late maturers. The late maturers in the California Adolescent Study tended to be "as strong as they looked"; the early maturers were not as strong as their size implied. Jones,[495] in commenting on this, points out that while the late maturing boys, with their slower pattern of growth, may have a more closely synchronized physical development and thus escape some of the strains incident to rapid growth, the early maturing boys, with their rapid and in some ways less well-integrated growth, often gain an early advantage in athletic competition and in associated prestige.

Further, children may vary in strength because of differences in physique. The relationship of physique and strength has been mentioned earlier in the chapter. Some children are consistently strong or weak from eleven to seventeen; some reach maturity stronger, some weaker. A strength score at eleven is not necessarily a good indication of strength at maturity.

Endurance and Skill.   Changes with age and sex differences in endurance and skill have been demonstrated by Jokl and his associates.[**][231, 488] They found that in endurance, as measured by a 600-yard run, both boys and girls improved about equally from six to thirteen years. After thirteen years of age the boys continued to improve; the girls lost in efficiency, so that, between seventeen and twenty years of age, they were no better in their performance than the six- to eight-year-olds. The decline in efficiency was noted not only in the running time but also in the condition of the girls at the end of the performance.[†] This rise and fall in the physical endurance of girls and the difference in endurance between boys and girls in adolescence needs to be considered in planning physical activity programs for children.

In the 100-yard run, as a measure of skill, the boys showed a steady increase until eleven years of age, a distinct slowing down between eleven and fourteen years, followed by another period of steady increase from fourteen to

---

[*] Dimock[244] also found this to be true. See Chapter 8.

[**] They studied three components of muscular performance, skill, endurance and strength, in children from five to twenty years of age by using 100- and 600-yard runs and a 12 pound shot put throw.

[†] The six-year-old girls recovered after two to five minutes. The ten-year-olds had a much longer recovery time. They felt more tired, breathing was more labored, and they were unable to talk for a few minutes. The fourteen-year-olds were uncomfortably tired, with forced respiration and frequently a pulse rate of 180. Their recovery time was even longer. They did not attend to ordinary work for an hour following the run. The eighteen-year-olds were exhausted. For hours, and often for the rest of the day, they were weak, tired and incapable of doing any physical or scholastic work.

eighteen years. The girls improved steadily to eleven years. Beyond that age their skill remained stationary.*

Thus, pubescence in girls practically brought the developmental progress of physical efficiency to an end. In boys the rate of progress was retarded,** not stopped. The authors base their interpretation of the effect of pubescence upon the work done by Selye, who states that the organism possesses a certain amount of "adaptation energy" which is mobilized in various emergencies. No doubt pubescence and physical activity represent physiologic "strains" which are capable of taxing the adaptation energy of the body to the utmost. They conclude that such a demonstration of a physiologic tendency of temporary or permanent interruption of the growth of physical working power is an important "biologic hint" that during the pubescent growth period children should be protected from unnecessarily strenuous activities which lay undue stress on the reserve energy of the body.

Muscular Fitness. The fitness of muscles depends upon their structure, plus the use that is made of them. Muscles respond readily to good physical care, including food, rest and activity. Satisfactory balance between activity and rest is essential for the well-being of muscles.

That many children in the United States are not acquiring muscular fitness is indicated by a study†[548] testing the strength of abdominal and back muscles. The children tested fared less well than comparable European children.‡ The authors indicate that American children, in contrast to European children, live in a highly mechanized society. Many are taken to school in car or bus, many use elevators, many are spectators rather than participants in activities. They have too few natural means for muscular activity. Careful planning for adequate physical activity, therefore, is needed in many homes, schools and communities.

Posture. Good posture, or good body mechanics, is good body balance. Good body balance is control and coordination of the movements of the body, so that movement is easy and graceful. The body is, in some ways, like a machine; its parts are accurately adjusted to one another. If all the parts

---

* Shock[847] offers as a physiologic reason for the relatively reduced physical performance of girls in adolescence differences between the sexes in the functioning of the circulatory system. In adolescence the increase in blood pressure in girls is less than in boys. Girls also, in comparison with boys, show a smaller rise in blood pressure after exercise.

** Other studies have noted similar changes in rate of growth at pubescence. Jones[493] reported a lag in motor ability around a skeletal age of fourteen years. This was the time when most boys were becoming postpubescent. By fourteen and one-half years improvement occurred. Espenschade[283] demonstrated a lag in many motor tests between thirteen and fourteen years of age. Dimock[244] found a decrease in rate in the period when boys passed from prepubescence to pubescence, and preceded the period of most rapid growth in size.

† See also (in mimeograph form) Kraus, H., and Hirschland, R. P.: Health and Muscular Fitness. From the Institute of Physical Medicine and Rehabilitation, New York University–Bellevue Medical Center.

‡ In urban and suburban areas 56.6 per cent of healthy children between six and nineteen years failed in at least one test; 16.4 per cent failed in more than one. In contrast 8.2 per cent of children in northern Italy and southern Austria, comparable to the American children, failed in at least one test; 0.3 per cent in more than one

bear their proper relationship one to another, body function can proceed effectively without stress and strain. If, however, some part of the body is out of correct position, there is additional wear and tear which lowers efficiency and may even, through inducing fatigue, affect feelings and attitudes.

Posture can be an index of physical and mental health. Poor posture may indicate lack of physical vigor; good posture is likely to be a characteristic of a healthy, energetic child. Furthermore, the child who feels inadequate gives himself away by his posture, just as the adequate child, full of enthusiasm for life, expresses his joy and enthusiasm through his body.

Good control of the body and its effective use in physical activities is dependent upon body alignment and the health and activity of the bones, muscles and nerves. The body is subject to the laws of gravity and, in order to maintain good posture with a minimum of muscular effort, the body must be arranged as nearly as possible symmetrically about a vertical line passing through the center of gravity. If a part of the body extends too far on one side of this line, it must be balanced by another part extending in the opposite direction. If a body in good balance is viewed from the side, the line of balance passes through the ear, the center of the shoulder, the hip joint, knee, and a little in front of the ankle. Strong bones, firm muscles and kinesthetic perception* contribute to maintaining this position.

Each child has not one but a series of postural patterns which differ according to activities,** health and feelings. Underlying all of these, however, are basic similarities which are the resultant of hereditary and environmental forces. Body balance also varies as the child grows. (See Fig. 34.)

The baby begins while lying on his back or stomach to "unroll" the "coiling" which has been his intrauterine position. He first learns to balance his head, then to sit erect, to stand and finally to walk. Back curves appear concurrently with this progress. The first curve in the neck region appears when he holds his head erect; the curve in the lower part of the back, the lumbar curve, gradually develops with standing and walking.

When a baby is learning to stand, he is very unstable and his instability continues into the preschool years. Every baby has bowing of the legs, which, all other factors being equal, straightens in due time after he begins to walk. The toddler has knock-knees and some degree of pronation,† a prominent abdomen and, in proportion to the prominence of the abdomen, a lumbar lordosis (exaggerated lumbar curve). In one study[790] of posture of children between two and twelve, the authors refer to this period as the "ugly duckling" stage. Most of the conditions which they studied, unless exaggerated, namely knock-knees, pronation, lordosis, slumped back and hyperextended

* The ability of feeling muscle contraction and relaxation or knowing what a muscle is doing which makes it possible to "get the feel" of good body balance. Metheny.[661]

** Because balance will differ according to the way in which the child is using his body, it is necessary to observe and evaluate how a child manipulates his body in all kinds of situations from sitting to activities requiring fine balance. Observing a child as he stands in a laboratory is not enough. He must be observed in motion as well.

† Pronation refers to a position of the foot in which the weight in standing is borne heavily on the inner side of the foot resulting in prominence and sagging of the foot in the area of the ankle; the heel is tilted outwards.

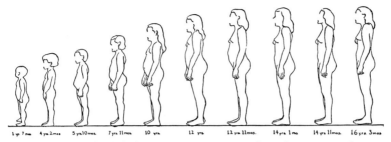

Fig. 34. The posture of a child from one year, seven months to sixteen years, three months showing changes in body balance accompanying growth.

knee,* improved with age. Knock-knees and pronation tend to disappear earlier than the prominent abdomen and lordosis.** The ability to bend over and touch toes while knees are straight is simple for the young child and easy for the later adolescent, but, between eleven and fifteen, many children who have no evidence of muscle or joint tightness cannot achieve this.[520] The relatively longer legs of this age is suggested as the possible cause. The preadolescent child's varied activity undoubtedly contributes to the better all-round postural development.[725]

In the adolescent period between twelve and seventeen years tendencies which have begun earlier tend to become fixed and thus the characteristics of the adult posture appear. The abdomen flattens. The typical dorsal and lumbar curves emerge. The pelvis is tilted slightly upward in the front and downward in the back instead of forward as in earlier ages. These changes can be noted in Figure 34.

Adolescents present marked differences in their postural patterns both in activity and in repose. They may be graceful when active yet awkward in repose; they may be awkward in action. Some acquire good postural habits, some poor habits. Many factors may contribute to these differences. The generalized type of preadolescent interest has often changed to concentration of interest in one or a few activities. The spurt of growth varies in its intensity. It was pointed out earlier that a fast growing individual tends to have a relatively longer lag between development in size and strength than one growing at a slower rate. A fast growing individual may not, therefore, be muscularly strong. Footprints may show a temporary sagging of the muscles of the foot.[314] Girls may become aware of their breasts and try to conceal them by holding their shoulders forward. A tall adolescent may slouch to conform more closely to the size of his peers. All these conditions may be temporary or they may lead to permanent postural habits. On the other hand, there are many incentives to acquiring good balance. The desire to excel in sports, to be physically attractive and to perfect the motor abilities which contribute to social success all motivate the adolescent to learn good

* Hyperextension is a condition in which the knees are pushed back beyond their normal position.

** Kendall et al.[520] say that the condition of the knees and feet improves by six or seven; the protrusion of the abdomen changes noticeably at about ten or twelve. Prominence of the shoulder blades seems to be typical of children around eight years of age.

body balance. This period, therefore, is very important, and is the strategic time, both physically and psychologically, to emphasize postural correction and to teach the principles of good adult posture.

Postural defects may occur any time during development. They may be due to an exaggeration of posture typical of a developmental stage or to a failure to outgrow a particular stage as, for example, pronation, which is natural for a young child but which should be outgrown. Conditions which demand attention at all ages are exaggerated natural anterior-posterior curves of the spine, lateral spinal curves (scoliosis), chest deformities, flat feet, cramped toes, and poor balance due to a general lowered muscle tone. Early recognition and treatment is important because of the greater plasticity of the bones of younger children and because the poor postural habits have not had time to become firmly established. A child will not outgrow a real defect in posture but rather learns to live with it. Sweet says:

. . . generally it is easier and more comfortable to rest and move with a deformity than against it toward correction, and in the young, growing child, with his elastic tissues and his great skill for learning new, substitute stances and movements, deformities, even though considerable, rarely cause sufficient discomfort to make their correction mandatory.[920]

Factors Influencing Posture. A sound, healthy body is the firm foundation upon which good postural habits are built. Such a body is the result of interaction of hereditary potentialities with experiences. A number of factors in living are important including freedom from illness and defects, sleep, relaxation, adequate food, good digestion, elimination, adequate clothing, diversity of play activities and interests, and good mental attitudes and habits. Most of the factors mentioned above have been discussed elsewhere in this book. It will suffice to mention a few of the environmental influences. Clothing can allow for freedom or can be restraining. Light, loose clothing permits freedom of movement. Shoes and stockings may affect foot posture. It is believed that many of the numerous foot defects of adults can be traced to improper shoes or stockings worn during childhood.* Shoes should be of adequate length and width to fit the foot properly. They should be sufficiently flexible to allow movement of the foot but firm enough to serve as a suppport when walking on hard surfaces. The heels should be of a height that will not interfere with good body balance. Stockings should be one-half to three-quarters of an inch longer than the foot.[287] Stockings frequently become too short for children because of shrinking and because of rapid growth of the foot at certain ages.

Sleeping and working conditions need to be evaluated in terms of their possible effect upon posture. Beds of ample length, firm, flat mattresses, light and nonrestricting bed-clothes contribute to good posture as well as good sleep. Desks and chairs should fit the child, so that his feet are flat on the floor, knees at a right angle, back supported by the back of the chair, and the distance of the desk from the chair such that he can lean forward

* In one study[527] 72 per cent of foot defects in children were traced to outgrown shoes.

from the hips when working. The top of the desk should be about level with his elbows when he sits erect and slightly tilted. Comfortable chairs of the correct size and construction will encourage good sitting habits. Lighting should be so placed in relation to desk and chair that he can see his work without distortion of his posture.

Adult's Role in Aiding Good Body Balance.   Since good body balance is learned and some factors in life aid while others hinder a child's progress, adults have a real responsibility in setting the stage for the child. It is the parents who see that the environment in the home makes it possible for the child to practice good body balance. His bed, his chair at the table, the place where he reads and works are set for him. In the early years parents are responsible for his clothing. They are the ones who watch to see that he has not outgrown his clothes, that they fit properly and do not impede his activity. Later, as he becomes more independent, his own selection is influenced, in part at least, by the standards set up by his family. He learns his postural habits in his family. Here he unconsciously acquires his way of manipulating his body in all kinds of activities, from doing the daily chores to playing. He also imitates mannerisms of sitting, standing, walking, etc. from others in the family.

Parents can be aware of early tendencies by careful and regular inspection. He can be watched in action and in repose. Parents also can provide regular physical examinations by a doctor who will watch for the beginnings of postural difficulties. For example, early recognition of inequality of leg length may prevent a permanent scoliosis. Cramped toes, or red spots on the feet may indicate improper fitting of shoes or stockings. Parents under the guidance of a physician also can see that early physical defects are prevented or corrected as far as possible.

Parents can create the right attitude toward posture. To do so parents need to have the right concept of posture. Good balance cannot be achieved by emphasizing one part of the body to the exclusion of others. Frequent reminders to "put your shoulders back" or "sit up straight" do infinitely more harm than good. Children either resent them or become too self-conscious. For most young children good diet, sleep, a variety of activities and a happy atmosphere are all that is needed. Later on, children may need instruction in body mechanics to improve their posture. The point of attack will depend upon the interests of the particular child.

Parents may also cooperate with the school in its endeavor to protect their children's health and thus promote good posture. An appreciation of the school program and a willingness to reinforce the practices of the school at home make for success.

The school has a parallel role with that of the parents. The planning of the environment and the program in terms of the school's contribution to learning good postural habits is important. Lighting, seating, ventilation and work materials can be planned to eliminate unnecessary fatigue and permit the practice of good postural habits. The program can be planned to minimize fatigue by frequent changes in activities, frequent opportunities to move about and the elimination, as far as possible, of noise and confusion. The school can contribute further to the development of good postural habits by providing (1) a program of health protection and prevention of early defects and (2) a well balanced physical education program planned according to the child's stage of development and flexible enough to meet the differing needs of individual children. Time should be provided for helping individual children to learn to control their bodies and to use them in the easy rather than the hard way. Here, as at home, the attitude of the adults toward posture will do much toward creating a satisfactory attitude in children.

ORGANS AND FUNCTIONS

Some Pertinent Facts about Organs and Functions. The body performs its work more efficiently as development proceeds. As a child grows the heart beats more strongly, more slowly and more regularly; respiration becomes slower, deeper and more regular; food takes longer to pass through the digestive tract and digestion is not as easily disturbed; the bladder can retain urine longer; body temperature becomes more stable; the composition of the blood remains more nearly constant.* Because of this increase in efficiency older children and adults can adjust to changes in environment and in routines more easily than young children. In the early school years children acquire considerable physiologic stability so that they can adjust to reasonable changes in temperature; their temperatures will not shoot up so easily in response to emotional and digestive disturbances. Periods of work and play gradually become longer without inducing fatigue. The foods which are given sparingly in the early years, because they may produce diarrhea, can be increased gradually during the school years. Throughout childhood, therefore, the demands which adults make of a child must be compatible with the ability of his body to perform work.

The activity of the *digestive tract* has an intimate relationship to growth since the fundamental process of growth, conversion of food into tissue, is primarily dependent upon adequate digestion. Foods which will interfere with digestion and absorption, or which crowd out essential foods, have no place in a child's diet, for the growing child cannot afford to lose the necessary growth promoting substances. Changes in the kinds and amounts of food for a child will accompany increasing maturation and growth in size of the digestive tract, which continue into early adolescence. In the latter half of childhood, which falls in the school years, the child's stomach capacity is still a little less than two-thirds that of his parent or his adolescent brother.

A difference in the rate of growth of the *heart* and the body as a whole during the school years has significance for adults working with children. Between four and ten years the heart has a period of slower growth. During these years the heart is smaller in proportion to body size than at any other time during the growing years. Washburn[976] states that heart lag in pre-

---

* For pulse rate, respiration rate and body temperature between two months and eighteen years see Iliff and Lee.[458] For a discussion of changes in pulse rate, basal metabolism, blood pressure and the physiologic adjustments after exercise during the adolescent period see Shock.[847]

adolescent and early adolescent years may account for the frequency of functional heart disturbances at these ages. Certainly at these ages children should be discouraged from participating in activities, either work or play, which place too heavy demands upon their hearts.

The *ears* and *eyes* are such valuable assets in an individual's life that protection of them at all ages is important. The ear is well developed at birth. The inner and middle ear have practically reached their adult size by the time the child is born. One difference between infants and adults which has particular significance is that of the difference in structure of the Eustachian tube, which connects the ear with the throat. In the young child this tube is short, wide and straight, affording a relatively easy passage for bacteria from the throat into the ear. This may account, in part, for the higher incidence of ear infections in young children than in later years. All necessary precautions should be taken in childhood to prevent ear infections which often lead to the impairment of hearing.

The *eye* continues to develop throughout the growing years.* The infant is usually farsighted. This farsightedness decreases during childhood. Binocular vision (single vision with depth perception) is slowly developed, often with temporary setbacks up to the age of six or eight. Many individuals never do achieve this high degree of vision.[334] When binocular vision does not develop and the child has double vision the condition is called "crossed eye" or strabismus. It appears, ordinarily, at about two years of age, and at first is periodic, being most obvious when the child is excited or nervously exhausted. If strabismus persists and becomes constant, the child, in order to relieve himself of the double vision, will either cease using one eye or use the eyes alternately. In both cases, he is deprived of accurate depth perception, which interferes with his judgment of distances. Damage to the good eye may result from the strain placed upon it. Because such a child develops faulty visual habits, this condition should be recognized and treated early, if possible before it is time for the child to go to school. Correction at an early age protects vision and spares the child the humiliation of being different from other children. The health of the eyes is related to the general health of the child, to nutrition, to environment** and to the use of the eyes in health and in illness. Children need larger print than adults, and frequent relief from close work, as we shall see later in Chapter 9.

The pattern of growth of the *nervous system*, in terms of weight, has been discussed in Chapter 1. We shall not attempt to discuss its anatomy and physiology here since we believe that it is more profitable at the present time for students in child development to approach the study of the nervous system through the observation and interpretation of children's behavior.† The

---

* See Gesell et al.,[349] Keeney,[515] and the National Society for the Prevention of Blindness, Inc. Publications, 50 West 50th Street, New York.

** For a discussion of environmental factors influencing the eyes see Chapter 5.

† Much is being learned about the physiology of the brain and changes during its development through the use of electroencephalograms. The patterns of brain waves of young children and of adults differ. The student is recommended to investigate this field and watch its progress.

reader is, therefore, referred to the chapters dealing with motor and intellectual development.

Reproductive System. The reproductive organs,* which are immature at birth and remain so during the early years, have most of their growth during the school years** beginning somewhere around ten years of age and reach maturity when reproduction is possible. Active, mature spermatozoa are not usually found until fifteen or sixteen years; conception is uncommon before sixteen years.[915] Sex differences are well established by birth and all during development these differences are noticed both in appearance and in developmental progress. The most important differences are the so-called sex characteristics: the primary sex characteristics which have to do with the reproductive organs themselves, and the secondary sex characteristics such as the distribution of hair, contour of hips, depth of voice and size of breasts. The role played by the endocrine glands in influencing the development of the reproductive system has been discussed in Chapter 2.

Boys and girls, as stated in Chapter 1, differ in the age at which the body changes characteristic of approaching sexual maturity begin. These changes begin later for boys than for girls, as shown in Figure 35.

The sequence in the development of external sexual characteristics for boys begins with the growth of the testes and penis.[776, 899] The first appearance of pubic hair occurs at the onset of the growth of the testes for some and follows the beginning of accelerated genitalia growth for others.† Axillary hair follows pubic hair, after the latter is well developed, and in turn is followed by facial hair. The "masculine" pubic hair contour, diamond shaped with hair extending up on the abdomen, appears toward the end of adolescence.[915] Hair on other parts of the body appears generally in adulthood and varies widely in degree and location.[771] The timing of these changes is an individual matter.‡ Note the differences in the development of the three fourteen-year-old boys in Figure 26.

In one study[899] the onset of growth of the testes began anywhere from ten to thirteen years,§ and their accelerated growth was completed from about fourteen and one-half to eighteen years.§§ Growth of the penis and development of pubic hair had been completed during this interval. On the average it took four and one-half years to complete this development. According to Kinsey[530] first ejaculation generally occurs in the fourteenth year. Mature, motile sperm appear later.[303] Changes in the voice, due to growth of the larynx, occur around fifteen.[915] A knowledge of these phases of growth as well as his changing size and an understanding of his own particular pattern will help a boy to accept himself and probably will alleviate his concern if he is one of those who mature late.

---

* Primary sex organs of the male are testes, epididymes, seminal vesicles, prostate and penis; those of the female are the uterus, ovaries and vagina.

** See Figure 2 in Chapter 1.

† See Stolz and Stolz[899] and Reynolds.[776]

‡ Schonfeld[816] in a study of 1500 boys in New York City found that they entered the pubescent period anywhere from ten to sixteen years. With such a wide variation an average age has relatively little significance.

§ Mean age: 11.8 ± .78 years.   §§ Mean age: 16.4 ±.88 years.

WHEN BOYS AND GIRLS MATURE

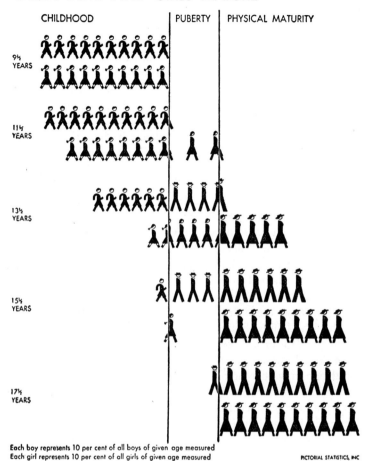

CHILDHOOD | PUBERTY | PHYSICAL MATURITY

9½ YEARS

11½ YEARS

13½ YEARS

15½ YEARS

17½ YEARS

Each boy represents 10 per cent of all boys of given age measured
Each girl represents 10 per cent of all girls of given age measured

PICTORIAL STATISTICS, INC

Fig. 35. When boys and girls mature. (Keliher: Life and Growth, D. Appleton-Century Company.) It is assumed that puberty represents the period of pubescent changes and that physical maturity means postpubescence, not functional reproductive maturity.

In girls sexual maturation begins with breast development. Pubic hair soon appears, followed by menarche after which breast changes are completed. Menarche generally occurs after pigmented curly pubic hair is present in moderate amounts[779]* and about the time of the appearance of axillary hair.[915] Prior to menarche changes in the vaginal secretion and in the type of bacteria in the vagina occur.[377,734] During this period the hips broaden with the growth of the pelvic bones and subcutaneous fat in that region. The maturation changes up to and through menarche, according to one study,[702] took a little over five years.**

* The mature female pubic hair contour is that of an inverted triangle.
** In this study[702] the average age in years for the beginning of breast development was 10.6 ± 1.2, for the terminal stage 13.9 ± .09, for first appearance of pubic hair 11.6 ± 0.9 and for menarche 12.8 ± 1.1 years.

Menarche occurs for many girls in the United States in their thirteenth year,[779,702,143]* but may occur anywhere from eleven to sixteen.[279] A few girls may begin to menstruate earlier or later than these ages. Reynolds[779] describes one girl who began to menstruate at ten and one-half years as having adult body configurations, mature breasts and pubic hair development at that age while another girl at thirteen and one-half years, who later menstruated at sixteen, had only begun breast and pubic hair development and still had immature body configurations. Such differences may have psychologic significance for girls.

Individual differences in the timing of menarche here and in other parts of the world may be attributed to a number of factors including endocrine, genetic and environmental factors. Daughters tend to follow the pattern of timing of menarche of their mothers.[368] Sisters are more alike in their age at menarche than unrelated girls.[769]** Menarche is later in the tropics than in a temperate climate.[277]† The role that climate plays is probably due not to climate alone but to a constellation of factors.[663] Environmental factors including nutrition may well account for differences attributed in the past to race.‡ Michelson[663] found that all American Negro girls, irrespective of socio-economic status, had a higher menarcheal age than white girls but when comparisons were made between Negro and white girls of the same socio-economic status the difference did not exist.§ Further, he found that in the North of the United States, Negro girls have an earlier menarche than in the South, and, in turn, those in the South have an earlier menarche than those in the West Indies.

That nutrition may be a factor is indicated by the delay in sexual development reported by Stefko[893] in Russia following World War I which he attributed to malnutrition resulting from famine. During World War II in Greece[965] and in Holland during the hunger months amenorrhea was prevalent.§§ The earlier onset of menstruation in more recent generations[368,663,670] which accompanies accelerated growth in height and weight[649] and earlier menarche in the United States, with its higher standard of living, than in

---

* At a skeletal age of thirteen years.[859]

** Early sexual development of boys has been found to run in families.[972]

† Mean age of menarche of a Nigerian group of girls was 14.2 years while that of an English group was 13.7 years.[277] In Java menarche was found to occur between 14 and 16 years.[681] Observers have been unable to find evidence of precocity among natives of Japan, British India or Egypt.[681]

‡ Mills[670] lists ages of menarche for girls of different races, giving authors and dates of studies.

§ When all Negro and white girls were compared, the menarcheal age of Negroes was 13.09 ± 1.2 years and of whites 12.86 ± 1.04 years. Menarcheal age for "better-to-do" Negro girls was 12.85 ± 1.14 years; for white girls attending Abraham Lincoln High School in New York it was 12.86 ± 1.04 years.

Ramsey[755] found no difference between Negro and white boys in the age of appearance of pubic hair (13.3 and 13.6 years), first ejaculation (13.8 and 13.8 years) and first recognition of voice change (13.7 and 13.4 years).

§§ Amenorrhea is absence of or abnormal cessation of menstruation.

In Rotterdam and The Hague during the hunger winter of 1944–45, 50 per cent of the women had amenorrhea and almost 60 per cent of the remainder had irregular menstruation. This condition cleared up when more food was available.[868]

parts of Europe and Asia[670] also lend evidence to the probable importance o nutrition and living conditions in general.

For a time after its onset menstruation, part of a cycle of events under endocrine control (see Chapter 2), may be irregular and periods may even be missed.* Knowledge of this expected irregularity in adolescence will allay fears and anxieties in girls who may consider themselves abnormal because their menstrual cycle does not follow the proverbial twenty-eight day period. Also girls need to understand that they may differ one from another in their pattern of regularity and length of period. Some will be relatively regular, some irregular.** Some will have a short menstrual flow, some a longer one.†

Menarche does not mean the achievement of sexual maturity. For most girls menstruation begins before the ovaries are capable of producing ripe ova. Ovulation tends to occur before the uterus is sufficiently mature to support pregnancy.‡ Thus conception seems to be an unlikely possibility for a time following this event. There is, rather, a period of adolescent sterility for most, the length of which varies with individuals.[37]§ Menarche is, therefore, one of the maturity indicators of the reproductive system, a landmark along the way to becoming an adult woman. Since menarche is an indicator of approaching maturity, those who look forward to becoming grown up may welcome it, while those who are not ready psychologically for what maturity entails may resent it. Family attitudes and cultural backgrounds§§ will influence the attitudes of a girl. It is wise for teachers and others who may be teaching and counseling to have a good understanding of the process of sexual maturing and of the social and cultural forces which may have played a role in molding a child's attitudes and feelings about this process.‖ Equipped with these understandings the adult can be helpful in promoting the development of mature individuals.

Summary. Physical growth, as we have seen, is not only growth in height and weight but includes all those changes within the tissues and organs of the body which make it possible for the child to be healthy and to use his body with increasing effectiveness as his life unfolds. The degree of effective-

---

* In a study of girls from 10 to 18.5 years[769] the cycle varied in length from 10 to 250 days with a mode of 27 days and a mean of 29.8 ± 8.1 days. In the first year the mean was 32.01 days; in the fourth and fifth years 29.03 days. In the first year there were many more skipped periods than later. These "skips" tended to account for the differences in the average length of cycles. These results are similar to those of Arey.[33]

** In the study noted above[769] none of the 100 girls were absolutely regular. Standard deviations ranged from 2.9 to 12.9 days.

† Reymert and Jost[769] found a range of 1 to 14 days with a mean of 4.85 ± 1.68 days.

‡ See Ford and Beach.[303]

§ Animal studies[408,1013a] have demonstrated that first menstruation and the attainment of ability to reproduce do not coincide. Ashley-Montagu[37] discusses the evidence for adolescent sterility in man. Cooperman[200] in following the morning and evening temperatures of two girls for three years, found that their temperature curves for 12 to 18 months following menarche differed from the mature type of curve.

§§ See Abel and Joffee[2] for an excellent discussion of attitudes toward menstruation according to cultural backgrounds.

‖ For a discussion of the relationship of physiologic sexual maturation and sexual behavior see Ford and Beach.[303]

ness achieved is dependent upon the processes of growth and maturation and the quality of body tissues. Good bones, firm muscles and sound organs are invaluable as a basis for a happy, satisfying life.

A knowledge of how children grow, namely, the sequential changes, and the variability in the rate of growth from time to time and from child to child should give every adult who lives or works with children a basis for understanding the individual child. Thus, the adult can set the stage for the child, fit his activities to his maturity and rate of physical development, remove obstacles to development and provide him with the necessary prerequisites for growth.

EXPERIENCES TO VITALIZE CLASS WORK

1. The following are the measurements of the height and weight of a boy. Plot these measurements on one of the standard curves discussed in this chapter. Evaluate his status and progress. Write a letter to his parents interpreting his growth to them.

Age	Height	Weight	Age	Height	Weight
3	39.0	33.5	8	50.2	54.7
4	41.5	36.9	9	53.0	61.8
5	44.3	40.6	10	55.8	69.9
6	45.9	43.1	11	60.3	86.7
7	48.5	49.0	12	64.6	108.0

2. Look up the meaning of the words puberty, pubescence and adolescence. Check how they are used in the various reference books on Child Development you have read.

3. The school dentist has asked you to assist in presenting to a group of parents an educational program which will:
   a. Make them aware of the need for better dental care for their children.
   b. Point out factors contributing to poor dental conditions including dental caries and malocclusion.
   c. Help them in gaining the cooperation of their children in correcting and preventing dental defects.

What information would you assemble and what methods of presentation would you employ?

4. Observe the posture of children in a high school. Have the students ample opportunity for learning good body balance? Discuss this from the point of view of school equipment, of schedule, of the programs for health protection and physical education.

5. Considering the physical development of children of these ages plan a program of games involving physical activity for a group of (*a*) seven-year-old boys and girls, (*b*) thirteen-year-old boys, (*c*) fourteen-year-old girls.

6. Have someone in the class go through last year's file of the magazine Today's Health, looking for information on physical growth and development and report to the class.

7. Plan a talk to pubescent girls interpreting to them the bodily changes occurring during pubescence and what these changes mean to them in terms of physical habits and social and emotional adjustments.

8. A teacher of first grade said to you that she was not interested in the physical development of the children in her group because they presented no problems. What would you say to her to help her understand the importance of the development of children at this age and the need for her to be aware of the physical well-being of her children?

9. Get relevant facts about the physical development in terms of status and progress of your case study child. Evaluate his growth and maturation, his posture, his physical abilities. Incorporate this material in your case study write-up.

SELECTED READINGS

Carlson, A. J., and V. Johnson: The Machinery of the Body. 4th ed. Chicago, University of Chicago Press, 1953.

Chenoweth, L. B., and T. K. Selkirk: School Health Problems. 4th ed. New York, Appleton-Century-Crofts, Inc., 1953, Ch. 2.

Krogman, W. M.: A Handbook of the Measurement and Interpretation of Height and Weight in the Growing Child. Monogr. XIII (3). Fayerweather Hall, E., Northwestern University, Evanston, Ill., Society for Research in Child Development, Inc., 1950.

Metheny, E.: Body Dynamics. New York, McGraw-Hill Book Co., 1952.

Ministry of Education and Central Office of Education: Physical Education in the Primary School. Part I. Moving and Growing. London, Her Majesty's Stationery Office, 1952.

Shuttleworth, F. K.: The Adolescent Period: A Graphic Atlas. Monogr. XIV (1). Fayerweather Hall, E., Northwestern University, Evanston, Ill., Society for Research in Child Development, Inc., 1951.

Shuttleworth, F. K.: The Adolescent Period: A Pictorial Atlas. Monogr. XIV (2). Fayerweather Hall, E., Northwestern University, Evanston, Ill., Society for Research in Child Development, Inc., 1951.

Watson, E. H., and G. H. Lowrey: Growth and Development of Children. 2nd ed. Chicago, Yearbook Publishers, Inc., 1954.

CHAPTER 8

Growth and Use of the Body—(MOTOR CONTROL)

Importance of Motor Development and Motor Learning.   In primitive life control of bodily coordinations and the acquisition of good motor skills was basic to survival in fending off predatory animals, securing food and finding shelter against the elements. Today highly developed motor skills are less crucial to immediate survival, but they continue to be highly influential in the social welfare of growing children, as we shall see in social development (Chapter 12), since the social development of preadolescent and adolescent children includes motor skills as an important component. In everyday adult life, too, physical skills are important to smoothness and efficiency of movement in dressing, doing daily household chores, driving a car, building or creating most of the things used and enjoyed in life. For many people fine hand skills provide the means of earning a living; to a diminishing group, physical power and strength provide a living. To everyone of every age joy in the use of the body in sports and games, in social dancing, in out-of-door recreations of many kinds provides a variety of interest and activity which assures relaxation from the accumulated and increasing strains of modern living, and the exercise which is one of the best guarantees of sound health, both mental and physical, not only throughout childhood, but throughout life.*

To the psychologist, control of one's own body means the beginning of self control in general. In bringing his own body under control the child brings under control the most ever-present piece of his environment. Having controlled this most obvious part of himself, the child finds it easier to bring his temper and other emotions under control. This, coupled with the aspect of emotional and tension release of vigorous physical play, is of vital importance to the adolescent as he faces the problem of keeping his sex drives under control.

Thompson[941] says that motor skills are complex and involve almost every aspect of the child's psychologic status, being ultimately related to perception and intelligence, to previous learning and present motivation, to emotional stability, and to social relationships. Horrocks[442] says that in adolescence as

* In the many books on old age which have appeared recently (Cavan,[172] Lansing,[565] Stieglitz[897]) emphasis is placed upon the effect of early acquired habits of physical activity in preserving vitality and physical mobility. Older people will continue to exercise if they have a love of it from earlier age.

well as at other periods of growth strength and physical fitness status have far-reaching implications for social and emotional development. He points out that actual structural or functional change is only the beginning from which stem social behavior and attitudes toward oneself and others and toward many things which the adolescent feels have value for him.

Understanding of the Entire Growth Cycle Important to the Understanding of Any Part of It. In order to understand any stage of development one must understand the entire growth cycle. If, for example, one is interested chiefly in the school age period, one will find in the earlier grades children who are still in the preschool period of development in body, in mind, or in some aspect of personality. A few children will be lagging behind their chronologic age in all areas of growth. Unless one understands something of the nature of earlier growth one cannot best help these lagging children to catch up. Again, one must understand the aspects of growth which still lie ahead, or one cannot best prepare children to make the desirable smooth transition from present to future growth stages. We shall, therefore, attempt to trace some of the major areas of growth through the infant and preschool period, then through the prepubescent and pubescent, and finally through the adolescent and into the early maturity periods. Our immediate concern will be with growth in control and use of the body as a whole.

Equipment for Learning Possessed at Birth. Perhaps the most conspicuous thing about a newborn baby is the fact that he has, in nine months of intrauterine life, grown from the two cells which met at conception into a complex human body able to maintain the major life functions of breathing, moving, eating, digesting, and eliminating apart from the mother's body. He has the impulse to grow and to learn and the mechanism with which to do both. He has inherited certain bodily and mental qualities; he has already been influenced by the environment of his mother's body for nine months of important development. He is not the "tabula rasa" which Locke claimed children to be and upon which, he claimed, could be written anything we wish. He is, however, an extremely impressionable being, subject to the physical, intellectual and emotional forces around him. His physical and mental well-being for life are largely made or broken within the first few years of his life.

MOTOR GROWTH: GENERAL BODILY CONTROL

Learning to Use the Body. Early Beginnings. One of the most interesting of the learning patterns to follow is the achievement of general bodily control which leads to upright walking and the later skills which use the entire body. From the beginning of random, jerking, uncoordinated movements the infant gradually picks out those which prove satisfying and useful.*

Control in general proceeds from control of the whole body to control of

* See Bayley[78] (1941), Blair and Burton[93] (1951), Garrison[337] (1952), Horrocks[442] (1951), Rand et al.[756] (1953), and Thompson[941] (1952) for detailed patterns of motor development and current bibliographies.

the various parts, from the less well differentiated to the finer movements. It also proceeds from head and neck through the torso and into control of arms and legs.* Newborn babies have little general muscular control. Even a three-months-old baby needs his back and head supported while being carried or handled. However, within the first few weeks most babies learn to pick up their heads if placed on a flat surface face downward. The lift will be wobbly and temporary, control of the neck muscles being so undeveloped that the head may fall forward with a thump.

Muscular strength and coordination proceed so rapidly, however, that by four to six months of age most babies, placed face downward on a table, can lift head and chest and, by wriggling the elbows under them, can hold this upward lift for some seconds at a time. The head and neck muscles co-ordinate well enough by three or four months that babies, held up so that they can see over one's shoulder, will survey the scene for several minutes on end, only dropping the head occasionally for rest. This head and torso control are good enough by four or five months to permit most babies to sit upright with comfort if they are supported by pillows, and the length of the sitting up periods are gradually increased as muscular strength improves. Babies become fretful or cry when fatigued, and will thus give the sign for change of position and muscular rest.

Sitting for short periods without support is usual among babies of seven or eight months.[345] By nine or ten months babies can sit upright for in-definite periods. Some babies can stand with help at nine months, and nearly all babies can do so by twelve months.

Locomotion, or getting from place to place, really begins with the muscular strengthening and controls learned during the first weeks of life. Stretching and pushing of arms and legs are essential exercises for the young infant. Babies can turn from side to back or side to front by three or four months, can flip completely from back to front or vice versa by six or seven months if free of clothing. Crawling, or hitching along on stomach or back, has usually been discovered as a means of locomotion by six to eight months. Creeping, or moving on all fours (hands and knees, or, occasionally, hands and feet) follows crawling, although some children creep without crawling. Many children of eight or nine months cover ground rapidly with a sideways hitch-creep-sit technique, scooting along on one hip with the two hands and opposite foot as propellers.

Pulling up onto the feet by means of a chair or table leg often accompanies this period of creeping, and many children learn to pull up some days before they learn how to let themselves down to a sitting posture again. From this standing up with the help of support, the baby begins gingerly side-stepping back and forth around chair or crib, or whatever object is providing the support. At this stage of learning peoples of many cultural traditions offer

---

* The assumption that all behavioral development occurs from a generalized total pat-tern to specific responses must, according to Carmichael,[167] be taken with great caution. In a careful and complete analysis of studies of fetal behavior he states (p. 120): "Certainly the late fetus has an elaborately organized and in some respects quite specific response mechanism. To some stimuli the relatively early fetus makes quite definite responses."

babies special aids in the form of walkers of one kind or another. Present understanding of the psychology of learning, however, strongly recommends that the baby be left to his natural development without dependence upon artificial aids. Mastery of the art of standing, balancing, and hence walking taxes muscular strength, produces a good many falls, is slow, and therefore requires a good deal of courage and patience. If the satisfaction of getting around from one place to another is made too easy by mechanical aids the child may lean too heavily upon them and hence his progress may be retarded.

After walking has been fairly well mastered and has produced the genuine satisfaction which will fix it in behavior, however, presentation of kiddie car or tricycle will offer a fascinating new means of getting around and will extend, rather than limit, the child's range of body skills. Especially helpful to the thrill of adventure and self-confident control of the body are two-wheel scooters given to the child as body balance and running skills develop. Fortunately for the development of both physical skill and psychologic adequacy, bicycles are demanded by most children of six or seven to eight or nine years of age. Traffic hazards in some communities are great; the parent must, therefore, see that lessons of self-care in traffic have been well learned before bicycle freedom is given. With the help of most public schools, this is learned, as a rule, by seven. However, the riding should be limited to uncrowded areas until the child has complete mastery of his vehicle.

Independent walking, as does each stage of motor development throughout the growing period, appears at a comparatively wide range of ages, and illustrates nicely the arguments against a too rigid adherence to standards of measurement. The average age of independent walking, determined by wide studies of many children, seems to be somewhere between thirteen and fourteen months. Some children walk as early as nine or as late as eighteen months; an occasional child walks at seven or eight months.[70, 345, 756] Fast growers on the one hand walk early; slower growers later. Yet both are probably developing at a "normal" rate, that is, a rate desirable for that individual child because it is a rate compatible with his total development.

Factors Influencing Age of Walking and Later Motor Skills. Acquisition of walking skill, like the achievement of most motor skills, depends upon a number of factors. Probably first is good physical health and adequate bone and muscle development. Plenty of space for general locomotion activities is important along with the opportunity to use the space freely without too much interference from adults. Also conducive to rapid learning are clothing which permits freedom of action, and shoes which are well-fitting and have firm but flexible soles.

General intellectual development used to be considered one of the factors most closely associated with age of walking. Normal development of the nervous system and normal intellectual alertness are indeed closely correlated with normal age of walking and of all motor development, yet delayed walking or other delayed motor development does not necessarily indicate retarded mentality since there are, as we have seen above, many other reasons why children may prove slow in these developments.

Emotional factors are important. Severe accidents may produce timidity; illness may rob the child not only of physical strength but also of normally active aggressiveness; too great anxiety on the part of adults that the child may hurt himself may make him overanxious about the dangers of the bumps without which bodily skill can scarcely be achieved. Too great concern lest he prove late in learning to ride a bicycle or do other motor stunts, or too great enthusiasm about first successes will frighten timid or self-conscious children away from further effort. Children, however, need the enthuisasm and en-couragement of adults in all their learnings, the warning here simply meaning that overenthusiasm may place too great emphasis upon the necessity to succeed and may frighten some children. A few children, lacking a vigorous interest in learning new things, may prove slow in acquiring motor skills because they have no need to get about, since everything is brought within their reach and they like the coddling better than the adventure involved in finding things for themselves. In learning all motor skills, children need health, vigor, opportunity to experiment, freedom to adventure, and the satisfactions of adult encouragement. The accomplishment of the first inde-pendent walking or of learning to ride a bicycle or to drive a car is rightly celebrated in the lives of most children. These accomplishments, whether the parents are consciously aware of the fact or not, represent a sort of "com-mencement" or "graduation," and are "certificates" of good physical and psychologic development if they occur near the normal age.

General Bodily Control Proceeds Rapidly.   From the widespread legs and the wobbly struggle for balance which characterize the first walking of most babies, there gradually develops a smoother gait, followed by ability to run or trot about. *Climbing* up and down stairs depends upon opportunity to practice and, of course, the steepness of the stairs, but most babies can negotiate passage upstairs by a creeping-hitching method at about the time they walk easily. Depending upon the steepness of the stairs and the banister aids, most children acquire the adult method of ascending and descending by alternate feet on successive steps by three and one-half or four years of age. Climbing on low inclined planks, packing boxes, jungle gyms, fences and the like is usually well established by three years of age if children have access to such equipment.

Hopping on one foot, skipping, jumping, standing on one leg all come before school age if normal opportunity and freedom are allowed. Most books on kinder-garten and primary practice suggest hopping, skipping, jumping, and gallop-ing as appropriate group activities for five- and six-year-old children, saying that younger children cannot master these accomplishments. This is good theory, since many children do not prove able to do these things earlier. However, Gutteridge[387] gives us some interesting figures in this connection. She reports that among the 2000 children from two to seven years studied by her, jumping was a skill in which 42 per cent of her group rated well at three years. At four and one-half years 72 per cent were skillful, and at five years 81 per cent were proficient. Jumping from a higher level to a lower is in evidence in individual cases from two years on. Jumping over an obstacle presents a different hazard and appears to call for a different stage of ability and practice. Individual children of four years find this difficult, and use less mature methods of attack. A long jump is attempted by some individual children from five years on. From six years ability in such stunts as high jump and broad jump improves rapidly.

Children are six years old before the majority of them can hop skillfully. The range of ability is wide, since among six-year-olds one may find every level of hopping skill from refusal and inability to excellence.

Galloping is a skill not as a rule seen in three-year-olds; but many four-year-olds practice it and many five-year-olds are able to do it fairly well, although not until six and a half years are most children really skillful. Children appear to have different ways of learning to gallop. Most seem to introduce a galloping step into their running or to pound on the strong beat of the music. Only later do they learn the basic movement of throwing the weight on to the forward foot when galloping. When children become skillful in galloping they introduce many variations and are found to be galloping sideways and backwards and to add gestures or vocalizations while in motion.

Skipping enters later than galloping into a child's motor repertory. At four years of age only a few children are able to skip; by five years many children are able to do so, while at six years nearly all children have learned this basic step.

Children of two become very skillful in the management of kiddie cars or tricycles, steering, backing, turning with speed and accuracy. Three-year-olds are facile on tricycles and often on two-wheeled scooters. Four-year-olds push and turn wagons, complicated foot-operated automobiles and airplanes with great skill. Five-year-olds sometimes roller skate fairly well, and, with practice, can perform the complicated footwork involved in some dance steps. Seven- and eight-year-olds are often graceful, speedy and agile, being able to master quite complicated dance steps.

In the use of the nursery school and kindergarten slides Gutteridge found that 54 per cent of her three-year-old children could slide well, the percentage rising to 71 for four-year-olds, and to 96 for five-year-olds. The difference in the height of the slide did not appear to make a marked difference in proficiency except in the early years. From four years of age the majority of the children were successful at any usual height of slide. Interest in stunts on apparatus in gymnasium or on the playground increases rapidly from five years throughout the elementary school years.

Skills Characteristic of Early Primary School Years. *In learning to throw and catch a ball* we can see a steady pattern of development. Gesell introduces his discussion of throwing skill by saying:

Throwing involves visual localization, stance, displacement of bodily mass, reaching, release, and restoration of static equilibrium. Skill in throwing a ball requires a fine sense of static and dynamic balance, accurate timing of delivery and release, good eye-hand coordination, and appropriate functioning of the fingers, as well as the arm, trunk, head, and legs, in controlling the trajectory of the ball.[345]

Gutteridge offers interesting evidence of the extent of ball-playing skills which younger children have mastered. She reports that, although children of two and three years were often found practicing the throwing a of ball, no two- or three-year-olds were rated as throwing a ball well, and only 20 per cent of the four-year-olds were so rated. From five years to five years six months, however, 74 per cent could throw well and at the latter part of the same year 85 per cent were proficient. The range of ratings in throwing is wide at all ages, for even at six years of age it covered the scale from awkwardness to excellence in ball throwing. She reports that children of four years were rated as awkward in attempting to bounce a ball. It was only at five years that 45 per cent were proficient while at six years six months 61 per cent were able to bounce a ball well. The range of achievement in bouncing was also wide. It virtually covered the whole scale of achievement at every age level. In ball catching only 29 per cent were proficient at four years, while at five years 56 per cent were able to catch a ball and at six years the percentage was 63.

Ball playing is so universal a game in the United States that skill in handling balls of all kinds is almost a *sine qua non* for good gang contacts in the elementary school years. Simple ball playing which requires little in the way of complex team work is somewhat popular even in the primary school years, although chase and run games occupy more of the time of children of this age because they are more skillful in running than in throwing and catching. Team ball games are extremely popular with upper elementary school boys who, at that age, not only possess good throwing and catching skills, but also are attracted to complex team play.* Touch football is popular even with girls in the upper elementary and secondary school years. Soccer is especially popular with high school and college girls. Basketball, volley ball, tennis, pingpong, and other ball games which require accuracy of timing hold the interest and develop the skills of children throughout preadolescence and adolescence.

Strang[905] gives an excellent summary of general bodily skills characteristic of children at entrance to school (five and six years of age). Running, dancing, and climbing are given as activities which afford much pleasure and profit to primary children. Children begin jumping rope between five and six years, can walk a chalk line or the top of a fence and can balance on roller skates, but have trouble with single blade ice skates. Most six- and seven-year-olds, however, can manage ice skates. If previous lessons of balance have been learned on two-wheeled scooters, some children can ride small bicycles at six or seven.

Most children of seven or eight can roller skate gracefully and ride bicycles skillfully, the grace and skill or ease being a stage of learning which has passed the first stages of mastery. In roller skating and bicycle riding, as in climbing, we see evidence of an early stage of learning in which the motor habits have not quite smoothed out, viz., the stage of tumbles, tight muscles, and awkwardness. Later, with practice, comes a stage of rhythm in all motor learnings. The clumsiness of the eighteen-months-old child in walking,

* See Social Development, Chapter 12.

passes into the awkward, flat-footed run of the two-year-old; and this passes into the increasing skill and balance of the three- and four-year-old; but one seldom sees the flow and ease of movement which are referred to as grace in walking or running until the child is five. So it is in roller skating or bicycle riding. Piecemeal, step-by-step movements which are characteristic of the first stages of learning flow with time into the self-assured, relaxed rhythm of movement which we call grace. Kingsley[528] points out that once a skill is acquired up to the level needed for proficient performance, continued practice will make it operate more smoothly as an integrated whole. Accessory or waste movements will be eliminated, fatigue will be reduced, speed and accuracy will be increased, and increased emotional satisfaction in the use of the skill will result.

Many children never go on past the stage of awkwardness in their motor learnings, partly because they do not practice enough, but partly, too, because self-consciousness and negative attitudes grow up which keep the child from freeing himself as he moves. It is important in all dealings with children to see that no adult approach is allowed which would cause feelings of inferiority or self-consciousness to "tie up" motor skills. Ridicule, sarcasm, scolding, or laughing at children's clumsiness in the early learning stages, or at the inevitable slips which cause dropping of objects, stumbling, or falling, may cause an emotional blocking which can result in tense movement and awkwardness throughout the child's life. Instruction in motor skills can, through pointing out more efficient procedures, cut down waste movements and keep poor habits and false accessory movements at a minimum. Children must practice any new skill with satisfaction if learning is to proceed rapidly. The teacher can do much to keep motivation at a high level, and to help the child to retain self-confidence in his ability. Unless there is a defect of muscles or nerves or bone structure, grace and free-flowing, rhythmic bodily movement should become the possession of every child. No child should be robbed of the joy which can be found in skillful bodily movement, of the social contacts it can provide during the preadolescent and adolescent periods, or of the contribution which adequate exercise and bodily expression can make to general mental as well as physical health and vigor throughout life.*

The Elementary School Years. Joy in the use of the body is normal for children throughout the elementary school period. Extremely popular are running, chasing, jumping rope, hop-scotch, hikes in the woods, roller-skating, bicycle riding, swimming, and all other forms of physical activity which are outlets for energy. Most children from six to twelve are problems to the adults who are responsible for them because of the insistent vigor of their movements, their inability to remain quiet in body or voice, their concentration on physical play and rough-housing.** In motor skills, as in in-

---

* Mahler[623] (p. 50) says: "Motor release is the most important and soundest device of the growing child to serve ego growth, obtain balance, and form and always available safety valve against anxiety."

** Blair and Burton[93] (1951) comment that the school-aged child's new physical power and his concentration on "rough-house" activity may intensify conflict between adults and children at this age if parents and teachers do not make provision for them and do not allow the freedom needed.

tellectual skills (see Chapter 11), the elementary school years prove to be a period of practice in the perfection of lessons already learned, and in the extension of new skills. Interest in the use of their own bodies is so dominant in this period that children as a rule devote much more time to this than to the use and manipulation of tools or toys like blocks or dolls, popular as these toys are. Strang aptly summarizes the situation by saying, "An eight-year-old will probably prefer tag to toys."[905]

Children of this age have the need to push themselves into the type of new learnings which require courage. We find that they are constantly "daring" each other and taking "dares." Stunts, like walking high and narrow fences, performing on a high bar or trapeze and games like "follow the leader" are so characteristic that most writers fail to attribute such behavior to any other age. At very early levels, however, children tend to "stunt" in any field of motor activity as soon as they master a skill. Two- and three-year-olds use slides "belly-buster" or backwards, as soon as they have conquered the usual "slide-on-the-seat" method. Common observation of any group of preschool children or even of one-year-old children will corroborate such findings as Gutteridge's or Gesell's that children scarcely learn to walk with reasonable balance before they begin such "stunts" as running on tip-toe, running with arms held high above the head, and later, whirling to make themselves dizzy. In all types of motor skills we can expect from an early age variations in such directions as speeding and the addition of difficulties of balance or coordination not inherent in the original nature of the skill itself.

This seems a general principle in motor learning. Jersild[475] reports that as children grow past the preschool years into the elementary school age, they develop not only more expertness and versatility, but also more speed of movement and greater strength. Goodenough[365] found a steady increase in motor reaction time from $3\frac{1}{2}$ to $11\frac{1}{2}$ years of age. Jenkins[472] found a steady improvement in several athletic stunts like short dashes, ball throwing and broad jumping between ages five and seven.

Jones[503] found what we all observe in children, that once the basic mastery of any skill has been achieved, concentration upon the mastering of the skill lessens and the skill tends to be used in more imaginative play or for work or other use. One can see a six- to eight-year-old child concentrating on riding a bicycle, learning to get on, start, stop, balance. Once learned, however, the skill is utilized to run races, to speed up the journey to school, or for some other purpose. At first the joy lies in mastering the learning, then in using the skill to some end. Only occasionally will renewed concentration on learning itself occur, and this will be when some new stunt is being learned: backing the tricycle, turning sharp corners with the bicycle, throwing a new curve on the ball, making one-handed catches or scooping up grounders. If we are to make physical education programs useful as well as interesting to children, we must help them to enlarge the variety of skills as well as to amuse themselves by using skills already mastered.

Adolescence   In the adolescent period, as in the preadolescent, there is still a paucity of material on the development of motor performance.

There are a number of observations of the width of a broad jump, or the height of a high jump, or the speed of a hundred-yard dash for children at various ages. Little has been done in the observation of patterns of acquisition of motor skills at the elementary and secondary school ages. One of the best of the observations of motor performance characteristic of adolescent young people and of the relation of these performances to body type or stage of growth, is that of Espenschade, whose work was part of the extensive, long-term study of adolescent children at the University of California under the direction of Harold E. Jones. In a survey of current literature in relation to the motor performance of older children, Espenschade notes that, "It has long been recognized that older, taller and heavier children are stronger and in general more proficient in activities than are younger, shorter and lighter children."[283]*

Although Espenschade[283] found that there were sex differences in motor performance in favor of boys at all ages, the differences between boys and girls were greater for the older than for the younger children. Munn,[683] in a careful survey of the literature, explains the fact that boys in our culture are somewhat superior to girls in many types of motor performance at all ages. He says that there is evidence that girls, given the same training and practice in motor performance, learn as rapidly as boys do. Although there are differences in skills at all levels, there is little or no difference in basic motor learning ability, especially in such fine motor skills as typing, watch making, surgery, and piano playing. The skills in which there is probably basic difference in ability are those which require great muscular strength, like the shotput, football, and the broad and high jumps.

There are differences of opinion about this, however. Evidence seems to indicate that with intense practice and interest men and women can do motor performances on the whole about equally well, the difference in the skills achieved being in large part due to the practice and interest involved. These, in turn, are largely the by-product of cultural expectation, the girls in our culture being encouraged to do "girls' games" and "girls' jobs," the boys being encouraged to do those things expected of men. Our culture puts a premium on physical prowess for boys during adolescence, whereas, with certain exceptions girls reflect the expectation that they will be "feminine" in interests and activities. Tyron[958] found that fifteen-year-old girls who were not good at heterosexual relationships found a certain prestige substitute in "being good at games."

Espenschade found that, probably because of both maturity and cultural factors, girls taper off in motor performance at around fifteen years of age, whereas boys do not taper off until seventeen or eighteen years. The maturity factor is related to the fact that biologic maturity is a stage at which motor strength reaches its maximum potentiality.** Kuhlen[554] says in connection with the tapering off of interest in physical activity characteristic of girls in

---

* Recall here the material on strength and endurance in Chapter 7.
** Dimock[244] found that boys of thirteen who were biologically mature were stronger than boys of fifteen who had not matured.

the United States culture (p. 49): "This does not necessarily imply that physical educators should consider physical education for girls a lost cause. Large differences from program to program might be expected in the enthusiasm with which girls respond—and the differences will largely correspond with the degree to which feminine interests are considered."

MOTOR GROWTH: DEVELOPMENT OF FINER MOTOR SKILLS

Like the development of larger muscles and of gross bodily control, the development of the smaller muscles and of fine motor skills proceeds in an orderly pattern. Controls of eye muscles, and of hands and fingers progress from the random uncontrolled movements of the tiny infant to the finely controlled skills which make reading, writing, drawing and fine mechanical work possible.

Control of Eyes. Few people realize that children are not born seeing, but that they must master two very fine muscular processes before light can be focused on the proper spot of the retina for keen vision, or before the two eyeballs can be turned into position to gain a true picture for each eye. The detailed steps by which these two muscular skills are mastered can be found elsewhere.[756] The fact important for a teacher or parent to know in this connection is that most children do not perfect the art of turning both eyes together upon an object until several months of age, and some children still have difficulty as late as three or four years, looking straight-eyed one moment, and cross-eyed or wall-eyed the next. Some children suffer from strabismus as late as six or eight years, as we saw in Chapter 7. Defects of eye control which occur as late as this, however, should have the attention of an eye specialist, as should even eighteen-months-old children whose eyes have become fixed at the wrong angle.

The finer control of tiny muscles which govern the lens in the focusing of light is pretty well mastered by five or six months of age. At least, the normal baby gives evidence of being able to see an inch cube at four months, and specks of dust or hairs on a rug at six months. One-year-old children delight in picture books which have one or two simple animals or figures on a page. By two and one-half years children spend ten to fifteen minutes or longer looking at picture books and listening to simple nursery rhymes. They cannot concentrate on one page more than a brief moment, however, but will want to move from page to page rapidly. The art of focusing the light on the retina and at the same time carrying the eyeballs horizontally across the page is still so difficult for many six-year-old children that they can read simple primers only by tracing the lines of the text with their fingers as an aid to the eye in keeping the place. Eye control proceeds rapidly from six years on, however, and increase in the eye controls as well as in span of perception which permit increase in speed of reading are possible well into adulthood for people of normal vision or who are properly fitted with glasses.

Control of Hands and Fingers. At birth one of the most characteristic of the random movements is a constant fanning of the hands, the fingers and thumb spreading and closing alternately. From this, apparently, develops not only strength of the individual muscles but also a gradually increasing voluntary control over them.

Even at three or four months most infants have not yet learned that what they do with their fingers has anything to do with the retention of a rattle. They grasp by chance, and let go by chance. However, they are beginning to make some important connections between what they see within reach and the fact that contraction and extension of certain arm and finger muscles brings the seen object into possession. At three months a proffered toy will usually throw the baby into excited movement of arms, legs, and head, but there is as yet no selection from these random movements. Close observation, however, will reveal that once this learning is initiated, even a few trials lead to a start at selecting right from wrong movements, and in a few days arms begin to do more of the reaching while head and legs do less. Gradually eye-hand coordination becomes more effective and by four to five months most babies will reach directly with hands, closing in upon the coveted objects with a fair degree of accuracy. At six months to seven months many babies reach and grasp effectively with one hand in the lead. Nearly all babies have achieved this by nine months of age.

Gesell[347] corroborates the pattern of learning in reaching and grasping, and emphasizes the role which the thumb plays in the development of efficiency in the use of the hand. He calls this use of hands for grasping *prehension*, a term which should become familiar to students of child development.

One of the most interesting things to note about the hand of the newborn baby is the complete uselessness of the thumb in hand action. Characteristically the thumb lies flaccid in the palm of the hand, being fanned out as the fingers spread, but seeming to have no "character" of its own. The Darwinian grasp, characteristic of the hand action of newborn babies, is a "monkey" grasp, using the four fingers, but not opposing the thumb unless by chance the testing rod is inserted between thumb and fingers. Effective use of the hand depends not only upon eye-hand coordination and proper extension and flexion of arm and finger muscles, but also upon the development of the "pincer" technique which uses the thumb in opposition to the fingers in grasping. Early reaching and grasping under voluntary control at three to four months takes place by the "palmar scoop" (Gesell's term) method in which the thumb is still ineffective and objects are scooped up by the four fingers and side of the palm. The thumb "takes on character" and becomes effective in the "pincer" technique at about six to eight months, at which time babies can pick up objects with a dainty finger and thumb grasp.

By eighteen months accurate reaching for near objects has become automatic. In reaching for objects beyond arm's length, however, much body balance is required. Even four-year-old children tend to push one set of muscles in improper balance to others, hence are awkward and immature in reaching. Not until six years for most children is the art of body balance so well in hand that the child can reach for objects beyond arm's length with ease and assurance.

Certain Behavior Problems Belong to the Age of Learning to Use Hands.
At around six months of age, when the "pincer" technique of prehension has
become effective for picking up tiny objects, and when the eyes have mastered
focus upon tiny near objects, the eyes and hands have learned to work together.* The happening together of these growth accomplishments produces
a characteristic behavior problem. Parents of babies of this age are often
troubled by the "baby's dirty and dangerous habit of putting pins, specks of
dust, hairs into his mouth." Occasional psychologists explain this "behavior
problem" as an evidence of the baby's natural inclination to eat dirt. Understanding of growth patterns, however, makes it quite easy to explain as the
by-product of a focusing of several patterns of learning and a natural practicing of new learnings which in themselves are thoroughly desirable. If one
looks upon such behavior as a troublesome problem which indicates perverse
instincts, "treatment" is likely to be instituted, and tension on the part of
the parent is almost inevitable. If it is regarded as the exercise of naturally
desirable learnings, the answer is simply to see that the baby has a clean
place to play and plenty of desirable and safe objects to manipulate and to
put into his mouth.

A second "problem" is characteristic of the period when skill in use of the
hand is proceeding at a rapid rate. Restless hands, if deprived of objects to
manipulate, almost inevitably concentrate upon exploring the body to which
they belong. All babies explore their own bodies, tugging hair and ears,
grabbing toes, rubbing stomachs, exploring genital organs. As the most
everpresent environment, the body offers the most convenient object for exploration and manipulation. Babies should be permitted to discover the
confines of their own bodies, part of which inevitably includes occasional
touching (for girls) or touching and tugging (for boys) of the genital organs.
If this behavior is not singled out for emotional excitement or made the focus
of a disciplinary battle, and if normally desirable manipulation toys are
provided, no "sex" problem will arise. Exploration of the genitals is a very
usual type of behavior in infants and young children[345, 544, 585] and should
assume little if any greater significance in the development of the infant than
manipulation of ears, hair, or toes.**

Since interest in manipulating the genitals is short-lived in children whose
physical and psychologic well-being is progressing as it should, children who
masturbate (or handle genitals) in school should be called to the attention of
the school doctor for an examination to reveal any possible adhesions or

* Eye-hand coordination, the use of eyes and hands in coordinated movement, has a
growth history of its own which we shall not elaborate here. So, also, has hand-mouth coordination. This material can be found in Rand.[756]

** Some schools of psychology will dispute this. Freudians teach that manipulation of the
genitals, along with sucking at the mother's breast, and other infantile behavior is highly
significant in the development of the sexual life of the individual. That it is normal behavior and occurs in the development of all children, we agree. That the steps of development in this area are of great significance to adult sexual functioning, being of definite
positive value if "grown through normally" and of serious negative value if handled unwisely in the infancy period, we also agree. Our object here is to minimize emotional
tension on the part of the parent, and to "normalize" in the mind of the parent what the
Freudians call "infant sexuality." For further discussion of this see Chapter 14.

ɔther irritating physical cause of the behavior. If no doctor is available, the teacher should suggest to the child's parent that a physical examination and care might relieve the trouble. Care should be taken in approaching parents on this subject, however, since, in spite of fairly general sound sex education for the generation who are now the parents of school-entrance-aged children, many parents still cannot face any conversation in the area of sex, and are so emotionally disturbed by it that they are unable to take necessary steps toward the correction of unfortunate sex habits or attitudes.

Many children masturbate because they have stumbled upon the possibility in the early babyhood explorations of the body and have been dealt with unwisely, thus making the habit assume an undue significance. As in thumbsucking among school-age children, it often indicates too little interest in a more constructive use of the hands, or such unfortunate treatment of the habit in babyhood that it has persisted. In this case there would be implied the need to wean the child away from such concentration on himself and his own body and into an increasing satisfaction and pride in using his hands and his mind for other things. Occasionally the habit results from a deep need for affection or for status with one's family. This latter is a rather delicate area for a parent conference, but if this seems to represent the child's difficulty, one can at least suggest a greater demonstration of affection and somewhat more frequent praise of the child's efforts, perhaps less punishment. In any case a teacher can provide some of the love such a child needs. Occasionally the habit occurs in an overindulged child who refuses to curb any desire. In this case a more consistent and firm discipline may help. It is clear that a teacher must know which is required—more discipline or more praise—before she recommends either.

A third problem, again associated with the period of rapid increase in use of hands, is that of thumbsucking, a habit which is found very frequently among American children and children of Northern Europe.* If a child is still sucking his thumb when he enters school the teacher should make every effort to interest him in the use of his hands for more constructive purposes. She should also do everything possible to make the child feel emotionally secure in his new environment, and should quietly expect that the habit will stop as time goes on, namely, as the child learns more satisfactory "grown up" ways to find his security and his place in the world. In this, as in any case which requires special understanding of the child, contact with his parents is essential. The teacher needs to know, if possible, what gave rise to the habit (although most parents do not know), what the relationship of affection and discipline is between the child and his parents, what opportunity he has had to learn a more satisfactory use of his hands, and the other facts without which she cannot possibly deal intelligently with the child. Children who are finding reasonable satisfaction in the use of their hands, whose affectional security is sufficient, and who are not clinging to babyhood for some reason or other do not suck their thumbs past four years of age. (See effect of thumbsucking on teeth in Chapter 7.)

* Discussion of causes for thumbsucking can be found in Rand et al.[756]

Preference in Use of Hands. A question which arises frequently in education is whether or not to compel the use of the right hand. Some educators feel that this is a right-handed world; therefore, all children should be trained to use the right hand. Most educators today agree that right-handedness should be encouraged but not forced if the child shows a consistent preference for the use of the left hand.

There is still a definite difference of opinion as to the bases for handedness. One group of writers[356,711] feel that the basis is a neurologic one, that one hemisphere of the brain is the seat of motor control for the opposite hand (or foot), and that interference with a child's "dominant" handedness often results in interference with motor speech or other fine motor controls.* Other writers[234,426] stress the fact that exact conclusions about the bases of handedness are hard to establish, since social and cultural factors enter the life of the child so early that they may be the reasons for the high percentage of right-handedness. Hildreth[426] points out, for example, that there is considerably more ambidextrality (use of either hand) and left-handedness among boys than among girls. Since girls are more tractable and less resistant to adult and other cultural pressures, she reasons, the social pressure to eat and write with the right hand influence girls more; hence handedness may be due primarily to social or cultural factors.

Whether handedness is a result of genetic, neurologic factors or of social and cultural pressures, it is clear that the vast majority of the population learns in fairly early childhood to use the right hand. Percentages of left-handed in the populations have been found by various studies to be around 4 or 5 per cent[264] in writing, eating and other socially conspicuous activities to 6 or 7 per cent in ball throwing or other such free play activities. Orton[711] reports that a small percentage of children seem so dominantly left-handed that attempts to change them can be successful only with unreasonable discipline which results in some children in an unbalanced condition akin to mental chaos. He says, and several writers confirm this, that possibly 20 per cent of children can be trained to use either hand without much strain. It is, perhaps, this group of children, who respond without apparent damage to insistence upon use of the right hand, that has deceived some writers into insisting that all children should be forced to use the right hand.

There is some additional confusion in the issue of handedness because it is clearly evident that nearly all babies use either hand with almost equal skill (or lack of skill) in the earliest months of life[221,348,426] and do not consistently prefer one hand over the other until around 12 to 18 months. Increasing preference and use of one hand proceeds as the child becomes more practiced

---

* Orton[711] and many neurologists defend this point of view. The writers of this book have known many cases of stuttering associated with forced use of the right hand in children who seem to be strongly left-handed. When this was the cause of stuttering, a release of pressure for use of the right hand and freedom to use the left hand resulted in correction of the stuttering. Jersild[475] points out that in such cases it is difficult to determine whether the stuttering is the result of interference with natural hand dominance or the result of parental pressures of the sort that would push a child to this extent. He says (p. 175): "The fact remains that a change in hand preference as the result of pressure from others may, in individual cases, have unwholesome consequences."

in manual skills. Hand preference becomes quite stable in nearly all children after six years of age.

Whatever the genesis of handedness, one fact becomes clear and is agreed upon by the vast majority of writers, namely, that, as was said earlier, right-handedness should be encouraged but never forced. Thompson[941] (p. 267) says, "A decision to change a left-handed child to right-handedness should be considered a major readjustment for the child, and a program not to be instituted without serious caution and psychological planning." Jersild[475] points out that whatever difficulties the left-handed may suffer in a right-handed world, they (p. 172) "are minor compared with those of the child who has a strong natural bent toward left-handedness, or who gets a long start in learning to prefer the left hand, and then is compelled to shift to the right hand. The interference and thwarting which such a shift involves may have many unfavorable after effects."

One additional factor teachers should remember in dealing with left-handed children who are beginning to learn to write. Every effort must be made to teach these children to establish a proper direction for reading and writing. (See Chapter 9 for details.)

Further Growth in Fine Motor Skills. Most babies begin to learn to feed themselves by reaching for the spoon and helping to hold the cup before one year of age. Most children of three, if chair, table, food, spoon or fork, and plate are right, can feed themselves without many spills on chin or tablecloth.

Little children cannot be expected to chew hard things with the mouth entirely closed and to observe perfect table manners. However, gobbling and gulping, smacking and smearing are unnecessary even for two-year-olds after the first preliminary stages of motor awkwardness are over. The baby "fist grip" on spoon or fork can be left behind by three-year-olds. Use of the knife for cutting and spreading is usually not possible before five years. Many children cannot cut any but the tenderest meat until they are six or seven years old. By ten years of age they have good control of their utensils and need help only occasionally.[347]

If clothing is made easy enough and if either a small toilet or steady step with which to reach the adult toilet is provided, children of three can usually take care of themselves for urination. This does not mean that the child is free of bed-wetting or even entirely free of accidental daytime wetting of clothes at this time. Davis and Havighurst,[222] in a careful study of practices in toilet training in middle class American families found that (p. 102) "up to the age of four or five, bed-wetting is to be expected in many children. As a rule, no child should be regarded as a confirmed bed-wetter until after six years of age." Widelegged trousers and underwear simplify urination for boys, though width of leg should not be such as to expose the penis when the child sits, or to encourage a too frequent handling of the penis. Elastic bands in panties permit girls to slip them down easily, but should be watched to see that they are not too tight around the waist for comfort, or too loose to stay up. Both sexes need to be taught how to go to the toilet, to urinate so as not to soil the toilet or floor, and to keep clothing dry in the process. Bowel movements and wiping afterwards need supervision until six or seven years of age, not only because the child's motor skill is indequate to do the job well, but also because the parent will wish to keep track of bowel elimination, its time, quantity, and character, for the sake of health. All children must have acquired efficiency in self-care at the toilet before entering school, and should be taught to report to the mother if daily bowel elimination fails to occur. In training children for cleanliness great care should be taken to see that the training is not begun too young and that use of coercion and of shame or other forms of punishment is avoided. The psychologic repercussions of such methods are serious.[222,616,756]

Many mothers, busy with the care of younger babies, turn the chore of toilet procedure over to school-aged children without adequate check, only to find illness following in the wake of constipation. Quite frequently mothers think children have developed "dirty habits" when they find underwear soiled with feces, whereas all that is wrong is that the child has not yet learned how to wipe himself properly or has failed to appreciate the need of doing so. Here, as so often happens, is a "behavior problem" which is due to the fact that some learning is taken for granted when the child has had no opportunity to acquire that learning.

As in self-care at the toilet, self-help in dressing and undressing depends upon the type of clothing. Tiny, hidden buttons and hidden fastenings are impossible for little fingers to handle. Complicated belts and back buttons are too much for even school-aged children to handle. Simple yet warm clothing both for indoor and for outdoor wear is now available in many attractive designs for both boys and girls. If clothing is simple enough, four- to five-year-olds can manage the whole job of dressing except tying the bowknot on their shoes. The bowknot is a complicated learning achieved by most children only at six or seven years of age. Simple zipper, one-piece, out-of-door play suits can be managed by four-year-olds, but galoshes, even when comfortably large, challenge five-year-olds. Most five-year-old children can take a bath with help on neck, ears, genitals, and back, and help with drying. Such help with the bath or inspection of ears and neck is necessary well into preadolescent years.

Hand Skills Preliminary to School Work.   Skills in manipulating pencils, scissors, and other materials preparatory to school work are accomplished by many children today before entering kindergarten since parents or nursery schools are providing opportunity to practice these learnings. Most children do little creative work with clay, paints, and the like before three, if by creative work we mean taking an initiative in design. Scribbling with pencil, crayons, or paints, or smacking and rolling bits of clay are usual activities of two-year-olds. Covering a page with color delights three- and four-year-olds, who occasionally produce some quite telling effects. Consciously formed designs do not, as a rule, come before the late four- or early five-year period. Some four-year-olds who have older brothers or sisters in first or second grade will attempt to copy the drawings of man or house or the formal pattern designs which they see in the older children. Such crayon or paint work is seldom spontaneous in preschool children. If given ample materials and opportunity, however, the four- to five-year period is one in which scribbling and painting or cutting begins to take on constructive form. Lacking this opportunity, children who enter kindergarten at five usually have to do the preliminary scribbling and messing by way of first steps before constructive form develops.

Before a teacher can be intelligent in guiding children through such learnings she must understand the steps by which such development takes place. Gesell[345] describes it clearly, having traced it in his studies of babies at Yale University. A baby of a year will cling to a pencil with his fist and scribble imitatively. Eighteen months of age finds most children able to make vertical strokes with a pencil. At two they begin to imitate horizontal strokes. By three years, Gesell reports an ability to inhibit and to delimit movements in both spontaneous and imitative drawings. At this age the child's strokes are better defined, more specific, and less repetitive. At four he can give concentrated attention to the drawing of an isolated detail. He copies a circle and a square now, and can combine a horizontal and vertical stroke into a cross. At five he wields crayons with considerable assurance, and can draw a fairly recognizable man. He is sure of vertical and horizontal strokes, especially downward ones, but is still uncertain in oblique strokes, especially upward ones. He can copy a square and a triangle, but not yet a diamond, which he masters only at six or seven years of age. (See relevance of form discrimination to this in Chapter 9.)

Hand Skills at School Age. From six to twelve years of age control of arm, shoulder, and wrist muscles improves rapidly, reaching almost the adult level of perfection at twelve. Control of fingers progresses more slowly, however, and the fine control necessary for speedy writing or for delicate and rapid finger manipulation of musical instruments is not accomplished by most children before twelve years of age or later. Motor control continues to develop well into adolescence both in total bodily skills, as we have seen, and in finer coordinations.

The fundamental to accessory theory, taught for years in education and educational psychology courses, is on the whole substantiated by researches in the child development field. The larger muscles reach skillful control before the smaller muscles do. Fine sewing, detailed drawing, reading of small print, should be delayed until the child is eight or ten years old. We must not forget in our planning for young children, however, that even the finer controls, like eye movements and prehension, achieve a tremendous amount of their development in the first five years of life. Opportunities to scribble and "paint," to cut, and to mold clay, as well as opportunities to button one's own buttons, wash one's own hands, and to help with simple household chores should not be neglected in the preschool years.

From this it can be seen that children are not, upon entrance to school, prepared to write with anything but large movements, or to draw detailed objects on small pieces of paper. Smooth, legible, rapid *handwriting* is one of the most important tools for other learning and for the expression of learning which the school teaches. Most schools begin this teaching in the first grade. The first problem becomes one of getting the child's writing to be legible regardless of its size. There is some argument as to the form of beginning writing, some teachers claiming that manuscript (printed) writing reduces the child's confusion because he is learning to recognize letters in printed form in his reading. Other teachers claim that the child who learns manuscript writing only cannot read or write in the cursive style which is usual in handwriting. Freeman[321] suggests the use of manuscript writing at the beginning, but a change to cursive writing in the second half of the second grade.* Speed in writing should be reserved for the time when the child has conquered the muscular coordinations necessary to legibility, order on the page, and reduced size of letters. This is not included as a goal in most school curricula until grades 4 to 6. There are, however, many standards for judging what children have been found capable of doing in the various grades.[905]

In a study in grades 4, 5 and 6, Rowley[798] found that there was no significant difference in native motor ability, as measured by tapping tests, between slow and fast handwriters. The differences between slow and fast writers was attributed to training factors, and the conclusion was drawn that slow writers could be greatly improved by remedial training.

It is a matter of common observation that, although there is a close relationship between intelligence and complexity of motor skills which the individual can achieve, many high grade feeble-minded children become superior in handwriting. One explanation of this probably lies in the interest factor. Feeble-minded children cannot master arithmetic or the other school subjects which require a high type of perception. They can achieve the motor skill necessary to copy material in handwriting. Since they can find some success in this area, they find satisfaction in the task and tend to practice much more than do children whose time and attention are absorbed by the subjects which challenge higher levels of perception.

The background of development in *drawing* has been portrayed as a consistent pattern by studies[89,397] which have been made of young children's drawings. At first, children explore whatever medium they are using, experimenting with ways of handling paint or crayon. This is partly learning how to keep the paint from running up their arms as they stand at the easel, partly finding how hard a stroke is necessary on the crayon, partly a sheer acquisition of finger and hand control. Most children will remain happy for some time with experimentations in how one color looks against another, will produce simple masses of color or scribble, often filling a whole page, or declaring themselves "done" with only part of the page filled.

Some effort to produce designs of line or color or both occur for children who have freedom to experiment at about three or three and one-half years of age. Once finished, children will often name what they have done. Only at four, however, will most children attempt to draw or paint an object from a conscious idea. "Now I'm going to draw a rain cloud," or "I'll make a

* A good discussion of the values of manuscript writing will be found in Conard.[194]

pig." A fatal mistake, which kills most children's interest in drawing or painting, is to make primary school children "copy a vase" or "draw this bunch of carrots." Drawing from imagination, like "painting the story we have just heard" or "drawing a picture of the trip we have just taken" is quite different. Here, the children are free to use whatever art technique they possess in the free portrayal of objects or situations as imagined. Emphasis on art in the primary grades, says Strang,[905] should be on gradually increasing technical control both of art media and of the child's muscles, upon improved accuracy of perception of form and color, and upon the development of creative imagination.

Block building also follows fairly definite patterns of development.[482] First, children simply carry blocks and manipulate them in irregular masses. By two or three years they place the blocks in regular rows or piles, building very simple structures like enclosures. Following this, structures become more complex, and by four or five years children use blocks as part of dramatic play. At five or six years only do children try to duplicate actual structures they see around them. As in many learning skills, children deprived of opportunity to play with blocks until five or six years, at that time go through the stages characteristic of younger children though, of course, more quickly.

Construction work with wood, too, follows a pattern for most children. First they must learn to use the tools. A two- or three-year-old child will spend considerable stretches of time simply pounding nails into a mat or soft block. Older children, first exposed to a work bench, will enjoy pounding nails, holding a board to saw along a line, and in other ways learning to manipulate the tools. Only when children can handle the equipment fairly adequately do they enjoy "making" things. At four years, for example, they like to pound three or four pieces of wood together for a wagon or chair or airplane. At five or six they produce a more acceptable piece of work, and there will be in the product some vague similarity to the boat or table the child set out to make. If compelled to "make" objects, or to shape materials to too fine a pattern, before the basic skills of hammering, sawing, and the like are fairly well mastered, the child is likely to become too discouraged and give up shopwork in disgust. Building of doll and birdhouses, bookends, and fairly recognizable model airplanes follows for most children at six to nine years of age. Most first graders can participate in the building of rude houses, backdrops, and traffic signals for a play village.

Untidy, careless work in any manual skill should not be tolerated; yet, to drive children to a standard of perfection which they do not yet have the maturity or background of practice to achieve results in making them hate rather than love manipulation of materials. Rapid growth in use of tools occurs from eight or nine years on for children who, in their first experiences, find joy and success. This is especially true, needless to say, for children who have some special talent in such work. Most upper elementary and junior high school programs find children delighted with the shop and the cooking laboratories. Some children before high school become quite skillful, being already more adept than most adults.

Clay modeling, too, proceeds through first steps which consist of simply handling, patting, pounding, and rolling the material itself. Only at six to nine years of age can most children make anything but the most rudimentary paperweights, or birds' nests full of eggs. Bowls, animals, candlesticks with handles, and so forth follow only when the basic "feel" of the clay has been attained. Thus, as in general bodily control, we find children mastering certain basic skills before using them in play or to execute ideas.

IMPLICATIONS FOR EDUCATION

In light of the review of studies on the growth of control of the body, certain suggestions to the field of education would be in order. To thoughtful educators who observe children closely, what follows will offer little new. There still persists in general educational practice, however, much that is in direct conflict with what is known of the growth of children. Hence it may prove worth while to make some suggestions.

In the Nursery School. The schedule should be free; the activities offered should encourage climbing, balancing, pushing, pulling, and other large muscle coordinations. "Drawing" and painting should be on large sheets and free to progress through the scribble and experimenting stages. Clay work should allow for pounding and manipulation without expectation that anything at all complicated will be produced. Cutting at three years is mainly getting success at free slashes, and at four years is only beginning to follow a line. Block building follows simple patterns and only at four years grows more complicated. Rhythms must not tax children by demanding galloping or other complicated forms of movement.

Toilet facilities should be fitted to the size of the children, should be immediately available, and adequately supervised. Play space should be on the same level or not more than one flight of stairs away. If a roof is used, elevator facilities should be ample and safe.*

In the Kindergarten. Modern kindergarten teachers are quite accustomed to two groups of entering children: (1) those who do, and (2) those who do not have familiarity and skill with manipulative materials; and (1) those who do and (2) those who do not have the practice and independence which make possible self-care in removal of wraps, toilet procedure, and taking out and putting away materials. These teachers are also prepared to handle the child who has good general bodily skills in running, climbing, hopping, skipping; they should be prepared as well to help those children who are awkward, undeveloped and unskilled in rudimentary bodily movement. This is true also of handwork and the finer muscular skills. Children who lack preliminary experience with clay, paints, scissors, and pencils will need to do the preliminary experimenting which many other kindergartners will already have done.

* National Association of Nursery Education, University of Iowa, has two publications on standards: (1) Some Ways of Distinguishing a Good Nursery School; (2) Essentials of Nursery Education. See also Read, K. H.: The Nursery School. 2nd ed. Philadelphia, W. B. Saunders Co., 1955.

The evidence on the development of handedness is clearly against forcing the use of the right hand in any child who seems persistently awkward in using it or who seems nervously disturbed by the necessity of giving up the use of his left hand.

Primary Grades.   Every first grade teacher is familiar with the children who have manual experiences which make writing an easy next step, and also with those children so inexperienced in the use of their hands that writing readiness is obviously lacking. Such children must begin at the beginning, scribbling, learning vertical and horizontal strokes, and the like, as well as becoming familiar with the "feel" of paper and pencil. These steps for normally intelligent children will be passed through quickly, however, and skill may develop so rapidly that any given child will stay "behind the class" only a few days. Children of retarded intelligence will, of course, remain longer in the preliminary stages.

In the first grade small writing or drawing movements cannot be expected of any of the children. Through the first and second grades art work should allow for free, large movement, and fine work which calls for detail should not be expected. School bands in the early grades are made up largely of percussion instruments, since most children of these ages are not capable of note playing on other instruments.

Plenty of provision should be made for free bodily movement. Seats should not be nailed down, but should permit free use of floor space for creative projects. Opportunity to hammer and saw, to daub and "mess," should be offered. Playgrounds should be available, and recess hours should be such that young children do not have to compete with older children for space or for equipment.

Upper Elementary.   Grades three through six are the ones in which writing skills are perfected. Finer control over eye movements combined with increasing skill in form perception permit a gradual reduction in the size of print used in readers. At twelve years most children have no difficulty in reading newsprint. (See also Chapter 9 for further information about size of print.) Some schools now use either especially printed children's newspapers or regular newspapers as a basis for class discussion in fourth and fifth grades. Children appear able to handle a certain amount of this without strain. Details of design and finer shadings and lines are possible in art work. Many children in modern schools learn to play musical instruments with a fair degree of skill. Long hours of practice on musical instruments should be avoided, however, since children of this age need much outdoor play. Between eight and twelve years of age rapid increase in bodily control makes possible more complicated rhythm work and dancing, games requiring exact throwing and catching of balls, and other tests of skill. This is a period when keen interest in competition leads many school people wisely or unwisely to encourage competitive track meets and other forms of individual athletic matches.

Physical skills are of such importance at this age that much social contact centers around them.* The boy who cannot throw a ball or run fast becomes a group liability. The girl who does not roller skate or ride a bicycle with skill is likely to have a lonely time. Children who do not develop these skills offer a problem to the teacher or group worker. We have a lead from the L. K. Jack study** and from the experiments of the Institute for Juvenile Research in Chicago** which suggest the wisdom of individual coaching to improve skills which will prove useful in helping children to make group contacts.

Depending upon experience and interest, many girls as well as boys are fairly adept during the elementary school years in the use of hammer and nails, saws, and shovels. Boys as well as girls can carry dishes of soup or glasses of milk or cans of paint water, can straighten up a disorderly room, putting books, crayons, and so forth away neatly. Greater freedom in dress and movement for girls in the past quarter century has largely done away with the idea that girls are less interested in vigorous physical activity than boys. Until adolescence they scoot, swing, climb, run, skate, and ride with wide individual differences, but in general almost as skillfully as boys. Boys, on the other hand, with recent emphasis upon camp life, are proving to be skillful in dishwashing, cooking, bedmaking and mending. Self-consciousness about what is boy's work and what is girl's work seems to be largely the product of adult-implanted ideas which help to preserve a cultural tradition. However, boys as a whole seem to be somewhat more inclined naturally to more vigorous physical pursuits, whereas girls quite spontaneously tend to doll play and similar feminine activities.

Junior and Senior High School.   With the suggestion from our review of the literature that the peak of physical skills for girls occurs around fourteen to fifteen years of age, we might assume that programs which appeal to interest in physical skills would be wisely emphasized in the late elementary and early junior high school years. It still remains to be determined whether the slacking of physical skills for girls after this age is a change in potential motor abilities or a reflection of inadequate physical education programs in later junior high school and in senior high school. It is more likely, however, to be a reflection of our cultural expectation that girls become less active and more feminine as they reach sexual maturity. Careful planning of physical education programs adapted to the girl's growing interest in femininity will without doubt capture more interest than is now evident, and may do much to stabilize at this age a genuine love of bodily activity which will last through life.

The implications of the Espenschade[283] study for boys is clear. Boys continue to improve in physical skills, at least through the seventeenth year. It is obvious that boys carry the potential motor capacities for continuous improvement of physical skills throughout high school if the high school provides a program which can develop these capacities. Undoubtedly the cultural pattern which sets a premium upon sports and enhances the prestige of the

---

* Further elaboration of this idea and what teachers can do about it can be found in Millard[668] (1951).
** Described in Chapter 12.

outstanding athlete has a good deal to do with boys' interest in continued improvement.

Even though boys' interests and skills develop consistently throughout adolescence, it should be remembered that there are wide variations of physical maturation within any group of junior and senior high school boys, with consequently wide variations in skills. Stereotyped programs at this age may place some boys under strain while failing to challenge others. Moreover, whatever the level of skill for any individual boy at any given time, changes occur rapidly at this time, and skills may be very different at the end of a semester than they were at the beginning. Great flexibility of physical education programs should exist, allowing for much individual variation in level of skill at any one time, and also providing for each individual to change his participation as his abilities change even if this change must be made within any given semester's program. In any highly organized team sport, or in activities requiring highly developed individual skills, care should be taken to classify participants according to their skills so that a maximum of satisfaction may be obtained by the young people.

There is a further reason for variation in school patterns and expectations in junior and senior high school physical activities. Many children at this age find themselves "out of things" not only because of physical immaturity and awkwardness but because of heart defects, orthopedic (postural and bone) defects, or lagging energy due to rapid growth or poor nutrition. If a too great premium is placed upon motor skills, such children develop keen feelings of inferiority because they may fail to gain the prestige or confidence necessary for enough social contacts to provide social learnings. Thus, there may be added to a motor handicap a social handicap as well. Some plan should be kept in mind for helping such children to develop other skills which will be useful to them socially. Painting, story-telling, music, craft work of all kinds, and interest in nature can all be called upon to help.

Whether or not the tapering off of girls' physical skills at adolescence is innate or the product of cultural expectation is, perhaps, immaterial. That boys and girls differ in athletic interest and skill at an age when interest in each other becomes especially keen is of significance in our planning for them. Programs planned for boys and girls together should demand only such simple motor skills as folk dancing or certain group games of low organization.

EXPERIENCES TO VITALIZE CLASS WORK

1. Look up the topic of Motor Control in the current literature (since 1950). What findings corroborate or refute the material in this chapter?

2. Observe a physical education program in an elementary school. Was there enough of the right kind of equipment for the age group you saw? Was there too much equipment? What did the children do with the time they were there? Were they improving their physical skills? Were there adaptations for individual differences of strength, skill and interest?

3. Observe a physical education program in a junior high school. Answer the questions in (2). Also observe whether the program fits both the boys and the girls. Were differences in program made to accommodate the wide ranges in physical maturity?

4. For each of the above observations report the general level of motor ability of the children. Is it at, above, or below average? What scatter of ability did you observe in each group, viz., how wide was the range of individual differences? How can a teacher (class-

room or physical education) adjust the program best to meet the gross motor needs of the individual children in the group? How long is it reasonable to expect kindergarten children to sit still? Fifth graders? High school pupils? In view of this what adjustments in schedule and teaching methods are necessary from primary to intermediate grades? From intermediate grades to high school?

5. Can you see how an understanding of the causes for thumb-sucking, masturbation, etc., can be of use to primary school teachers? Discuss, as a case study in class, some child or children who suck thumbs and/or masturbate in school. Where did the habit originate? What treatment have the family and former teachers used? With what results? Can you recommend some more effective treatment?

6. In what way does an understanding of the acquisition of early hand-control help a primary teacher to understand and, therefore, to guide the acquisition of handwriting skills? Select some child who is having special difficulty with handwriting. What causes his difficulty: poor motor skill? bad initial methods in handwriting? unfortunate attitudes? Whatever the cause, trace, if you can, its origin. What can be done to help the child learn?

7. Same as 6 for clay work, painting, cutting and pasting.

8. How much and what kind of toilet supervision should be given kindergarten children? How much and what kind of supervision with wraps? With putting away playthings? Do you think a kindergarten parent-teacher meeting might benefit from a discussion of clothing appropriate for school? Of attitudes and training to help children care for themselves at the toilet? Of cooperation between home and school in putting away toys? Suggest other topics which might be of benefit to both parents and teachers.

9. If you are writing a case study, get as much as possible of the information outlined in 2 through 8 for "your child."

SELECTED READINGS

Blair, A. W., and W. H. Burton: Growth and Development of the Preadolescent. New York, Appleton-Century-Crofts, 1951, Ch. 4.

Collins, L. B., and V. S. Blanchard: A Modern Physical Education Program for Boys and Girls. New York, A. S. Barnes Co., 1940.

Garrison, K. C.: Growth and Development, New York, Longmans, Green & Co., 1952, Ch. 6.

Gesell, A., et al.: The Child from Five to Ten. New York, Harper & Bros., 1946, Ch. 2.

Horrocks, J. E.: The Psychology of Adolescence: Behavior and Development. Boston, Houghton Mifflin Co., 1951, Ch. 10.

Millard, C. V.: Child Growth and Development in the Elementary School Years. Boston, D. C. Heath & Co., 1951, Ch. 5.

Rand, W., et al.: Growth and Development of the Young Child. Rev. ed. Philadelphia, W. B. Saunders Co., 1953, Ch. 8.

Strang, R.: An Introduction to Child Study. Rev. ed. New York, The Macmillan Co., 1951, Chs. 14, 18, 22.

Thompson, G. G.: Child Psychology: Growth Trends in Psychological Adjustment. Boston, Houghton Mifflin Co., 1952, Ch. 7.

CHAPTER 9

Growth of Sense
Perceptions and Judgments

INTELLIGENCE: GENERAL CONSIDERATIONS

What Is Intelligence? We shall not review here the controversies over what intelligence is, since students using this book will doubtless be taking separate courses in educational psychology. In general, we shall consider intelligence as that sector of human life through which the individual learns about the things, people, and situations around him, and by means of which he deals effectively with them*

Intelligence Testing. There is a wealth of material in the research field dealing with the growth of intelligence as measured by the standard intelligence tests, or as tested by success in academic work in school. We shall not cover the discussion of intelligence tests here, since this area is covered in other courses in education.**

As far as the measurement of intelligence is concerned, we would like to call attention to one mistake now prevalent in public school use of intelligence tests. It is a fairly general practice to give children intelligence tests upon school entrance as a basis for classifying them for academic work. Most of these tests are group tests, administered to a group of several to fifty children at one time. Only in a small percentage of the cases are the findings of such a group test checked by an individual test. As a rule, even though teachers are told to watch for evidence that children may need reclassification, it is a usual thing for the children to remain in the original classification until entrance to junior or senior high school, when a reclassification occurs.

There is a good deal of evidence presented in the various Yearbooks of the National Society for the Study of Education, the Yearbooks of the Department of Supervisors and Directors of Instruction of the National Education Association, and other research publication journals that (1) group tests are a good rough screen, but classify individual children incorrectly often

---

* Goddard[361] defines intelligence as "the degree of availability of one's experiences for the solution of immediate problems and the anticipation of future ones." A fairly complete discussion of theories of intelligence can be found in Piaget[731] (1952).

**An excellent discussion of intelligence tests and what teachers and parents should know about them can be found in Thompson[941] (1952).

enough to prove seriously detrimental in the lives of many individual children, (2) even individual tests of younger children are so often inaccurate that their results should be rechecked from year to year, and (3) that ratings on intelligence tests (IQ's) change somewhat as physical, emotional, and educational changes occur. The application to educational procedure seems clear:

> If we give a child an intelligence test when he enters the first grade, we cannot be sure that the IQ obtained at that time will remain a good index of his ability throughout his school career. The validity of an IQ depends, among other things, on its recency, and more especially is this true of very young children.[73]

Why the Teacher Needs to Understand the Steps of Intellectual Growth.
If the lay person were asked what he considered the business of the school to be, he would probably make some remark about teaching people to be intelligent. The teacher cannot, however, bring her own intelligence effectively to bear on the training of "intelligent" behavior in her pupils unless she thoroughly understands what stage of intellectual development any given pupil is in, what steps he has already taken, what steps lie ahead of him, and especially what steps he should take in the immediate furture while under the supervision of this particular teacher. In the past and still too often at present teachers have depended for their teaching content entirely upon the detailed steps of the official curriculum handed to them from the superintendents' office. These curricular prescriptions are well set for the average performance of the mass of children. However, they ignore the individual child. They bind the teacher by the page by the day. Teachers can be free only through understanding of the process of intelligence which it is their main business to develop. We shall, therefore, devote most of the next three chapters to presenting some of the current knowledge about the steps by which intelligence grows.

A Schematic Way of Thinking about Intelligence. In discussing the specific patterns of how intelligence develops, some help may perhaps be obtained from seeing the various aspects of intelligence in relation to each other. Figure 36 serves as one way of picturing this relationship.

No intelligence would, of course, be possible apart from the body in which it lives, and through which it expresses itself. Without a sound brain and nervous system, intelligence cannot exist or develop except in a most primitive or rudimentary fashion. Although there are cases of fine intelligence existing in badly deformed or paralyzed bodies, the usual pattern of development of intelligence in the great mass of children depends in an important way upon the use and control of the body's bones and muscles.

Intelligence is entirely dependent upon the sense organs (eyes, ears, taste, smell, and touch organs) for development. A serious deficiency in one of these may not impede intelligent behavior too much, but serious defects of more than one prove fatal to the intellectual development of nearly all children.*

---

* For an outstanding study of the relationship of hearing to the development of reason see Templin[932] (1950).

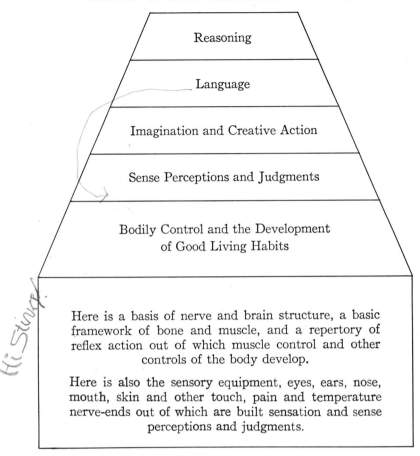

Fig. 36. A device for picturing how the various areas of intelligence are interrelated.

Helen Kellers are rare, indeed. On the basis of what comes to the child's intelligence through his sense organs he builds increasingly accurate interpretations of the world around him. In other words, he builds increasingly accurate sense perceptions and judgments. In proportion as these interpretations become accurate he becomes able to deal with the objects around him.

The building of conceptions and ideas, of imagination and creative action, is an important step in the improvement of the quality and usefulness of intelligence.

The development of language is one of the most important human means of improving and of expressing intelligence, since the child learns to interpret and to react to the world about him far more rapidly when he has the help of verbal coummunication with people more experienced than he is.

Throughout our recorded history and in all of our literature, reasoning has been generally considered the crowning achievement of the intellect, the supreme evidence of man's intellectual superiority. It is an outgrowth of the other foundation skills, dependent in very important ways upon them. Even language exists in man's repertory of behavior mainly as a tool for reasoning.

If the training of the intellect is an important business of the school, then training of each of the foundation structures which lie beneath intellect's supreme accomplishment, viz., reasoning, is to be considered important business of the school. This means specific training in bodily development and control, in good living habits, in wide and accurate sense perceptions and judgments, in language facility, and in reasoning itself. Any school which fails intellect in any of these areas cannot be said to fulfill that first job for which it was created and for which it continues to be financed.

Differences in Rate of Intellectual Development.   There is an exceedingly wide variation in rate and ultimate level of intellectual development, ranging from low grade idiocy through outstanding genius. The causes for these differences are both hereditary and environmental, as was pointed out in Chapter 2.

Defective grades of intelligence are often accompanied by (or caused by) defective bodily conditions. From the medical point of view, feeble-mindedness is often defined as

> . . . a state of incomplete or pathological development of the organism which is significantly reflected in subnormal or abnormal structure and function of the central and autonomic nervous systems. This in turn limits the growth of intelligence which is manifested in educational, behavioral, and social incompetence.[248]

Heredity or accidents of prenatal or early childhood environment produce the from 1 to 2 per cent* of the population who are incapable of profiting from instruction. The degree of incapacity to learn varies from the idiot through the moron. Doll[248] defines these as follows (p. 873):

> The idiot is grossly retarded in mastering the rudiments of selfcare, the beginnings of linguistic expression, and the simplest forms of occupational activity. The imbecile masters these but makes no progress in scholastic subjects. The moron may learn the scholastic rudiments (up to the fourth grade) but rarely makes appreciable use of such accomplishments.

Since the lower grades of these children offer such difficult problems of care in the home, and since none of these grades of intelligence can profit from the usual public school instruction, nearly all states make provision for caring for them in state schools for the feeble-minded. Here special educational programs are set up which utilize concrete materials, situations, and the endless repetition necessary. Morons can usually be given some degree of occupational competence in the simple work tasks.

Morons should not be confused with the lower levels of so-called normal intelligence, the latter being a large group (estimates run as high as 15 to 20 per cent) of children who, because of their inherent level of development of intelligence, cannot proceed through school at the usual rate of one grade

---

* Estimates differ from 0.3 per cent to 4 or 5 per cent, depending upon methods of selection used. Percentages vary significantly depending upon age, locale, sex, degree of deficiency used as definition, and the like.[248]

each year. Although rural, small town, and parochial schools often cannot make provision for these children, most larger school systems have special classes for them which provide for less academics and more concrete learning than the usual curriculum.*

In contrast to the feeble-minded and slow to learn are the gifted in intelligence—those who develop more rapidly and to higher levels than other children in thinking, reasoning, and making judgments. Rated in terms of I.Q. those children who measure 140 or over are 4 or 5 of every 1000, those who measure 130 or over are 8 to 10 out of every 1000.[667] These children do not always turn out to be adult geniuses[936] since some able people are not trained to make the best of their abilities or do not take a desirable amount of responsibility for the use of training and ability they possess. Genius, too, is made up of other talents than sheer intellect, the creative abilities being at the root of much outstanding accomplishment. However, superior children as a whole remain superior "despite the fact that some of the individual cases have not held their own. As a rule, the bright child remains bright."**

Heredity as well as early environment is of importance in the origin and development of gifted children as it is for the feeble-minded. The majority of gifted children stem from families of professional status who are leaders in their communities. In Terman's[933] study of children in California who possessed I.Q's of 140 or over, 51 per cent were of British descent, 17 per cent German and Austrian, 10.5 per cent combined Jewish stock, 6 per cent French, 4 per cent Scandinavian. These percentages must be interpreted in light of the percentages of these stocks present in the California population. Negroes, Mexicans, and Chinese were found among Terman's genius group. Jewish children predominated in Hollingworth's New York City genius group.[430]

Gifted children have relatively fewer physical defects such as defective hearing, mouth breathing, headaches, or other symptoms of nervousness.[667] Terman's study showed that, other things being equal, gifted children are in better physical health than an unselected group. Gifted children go to school early and advance rapidly through the grades.[667] Of Terman's group, 85 per cent skipped one or more half grades. In terms of mental age, however, gifted children are seldom if ever in the grade which would utilize their ability even approximately near its maximum capacity. Social contact factors have, quite wisely, led most schools to keep these children with a group of children somewhere near their own chronologic age. The American Association for Gifted Children[16] says (p. 17) that "there seems to be (in 1951) an increasing tendency to enrich the curriculum for the gifted child rather than to accelerate him in school." Many schools meet at least part of the the need of gifted children for more and better training than the average

---

* A most competent summary of research on the education of exceptional children covering 1900 to 1950 can be found in Nelson.[698] For excellent coverage of education for handicapped children see Baker[50] (1953), Fiedler[289] (1952), Heck[415] (1953), and Kirk and Johnson[531] (1951).

**American Association for Gifted Children: The Gifted Child.[16] (1951, p. 29). See also Terman and Oden: The Gifted Child Grows Up[936] (1947), Witty[1003] (1952).

child by offering enrichment of curriculum and individualized instruction. Many of these children come from families that can and do afford private school instruction.* Gifted children stand out in their school work in such areas as debating, history, composition, literature,** grammar, general science, geography, civics, reading, and arithmetic. The weakest subjects of gifted children are those requiring manual coordination or dexterity such as handwriting, art, and handiwork.[667] They often take lessons outside of school in such special activities as music, drawing, painting, dancing, and languages. Gifted children show far more favorable social development than do unselected children.[933]

In summarizing the capacities of gifted children Strang[906] says (p. 134)

> The truly gifted person is usually endowed with a superior body and mind. His physical vitality and his mental ability enable him to cope with strains and stresses, and to correct undesirable emotional conditions or personality trends. Perhaps he is better equipped with "psychological antibodies" than the average person. Another asset, from the standpoint of mental health, is his superior capacity for self-diagnosis.

She adds, however, that like other children, the gifted must be considered and treated as individuals.

DEVELOPMENT OF SENSE PERCEPTIONS AND JUDGMENTS

As was said above, intellect grows in most important ways through the constant accumulation of impressions which come into the central nervous system from the surrounding world by means of the sense organs and the central nervous system. One may see and hear, smell and taste and feel, but sensation alone is not enough. Until, through experience, sensation comes to have meaning and to be understood, one's reaction to the world remains unintelligent.† One does not automatically judge the size, shape, distance, or other qualities of objects; one learns to judge them. Probably one of the clearest differentiations between a mediocre and a brilliant person is to be found in the speed and accuracy with which he "sizes up" situations and in the discrimination with which he reacts to them.

The Newborn Baby Must Learn to Use His Sense Organs.   The newborn baby has visual (for seeing), auditory (for hearing), olfactory (for smelling), gustatory (for tasting), touch, pain, and temperature sense organs.‡ Impressions come in to him through his sense organs but he does not interpret these impressions. An important part of learning in the first days and weeks of postnatal life consists of learning how to use the eyes to see with, the ears to hear with, the nose to smell with. Once the infant has learned to see and hear

---

* For an excellent discussion of school adaptations to gifted children see Miles,[667] pp. 931–935. See also The Gifted Child[16] (1951). This book contains a wide coverage of studies and bibliography on the gifted child as well as recommendations for education of the gifted.

** Over half of Terman's group had learned to read before starting school. Their parents had seldom coached them but had simply answered questions and showed an interest in the child's interests.

† This will be explained more fully later.

‡ Recall from Chapter 7 the state of maturing and of readiness to function of the sense organs at and immediately following birth. Also see Zubek and Solberg[1020] (1954).

and to use his other senses his intellect begins to store up a multitude of impressions from the outside world. Also important not only to the intellect, but to the development of personality and emotional reactions as well, are the impressions which come to the baby from his own body. Feelings of hunger, of fatigue, of need for movement; feelings of well-being and security or of discomfort and insecurity are among his inner impressions. All these sensations and impressions reach his intellect and build the bases for later intellectual behavior.

We do not know just how much newborn babies see or hear or taste or smell or feel. They have no language but the cry or relaxed well-being, a start or jerk or reflex action with which to tell us their reaction to the various stimuli which affect them. We have many excellent studies of the sensory equipment and sensory reactions not only of neonates (newborn children) but also of fetal (intrauterine) reaction.*

Sensory Equipment and Beginning of Development.   It is fairly well agreed that, although the neural mechanism involved in hearing, taste, and smell are developed in the late fetal months,[166] babies do not have full use of their sensory equipment at birth. In most sensory areas like temperature, taste and smell, however, fairly accurate discrimination is displayed within a few weeks of birth. Part of the sensory inadequacy at birth is due to the fact that the baby has not yet learned how to control the muscles involved in vision and hearing. Part of it is due, too, to the lack of experience which leaves the baby without meaning or understanding of things he does see and hear, taste and feel. So inadequate are these sensory abilities that young mothers sometimes become panic stricken thinking their babies are blind or deaf when they fail to focus eyes intelligently or to give evidence that they see or hear some special stimulus.

The Sense of Touch and Pain.   The sense of touch seems to be the most nearly perfect in functioning at birth,[744] a slight touch on the cheek setting up the sucking reflex, or on the nose causing a closing of the eyes. Bath temperature which varies much from lukewarm causes crying and struggling, and all writers agree that the temperature around a baby should not vary markedly or he will give evidence of discomfort. He does not, however, react strongly to temperature variations applied to small areas of his body, and he seems fairly insensitive to pain like that caused by blisters or scratches.

Studies[247] show that infants do not respond to needle pricks or electric shocks in the first four or five days of life, but that they learn to respond within eight or ten days. Colic pains cause screaming by six or eight weeks of age, and from then on children seem to suffer pain much as adults do. They, of course, express pain and the fear that severe pain arouses by screaming. The progressive lessons in courage and self-control in the face of pain which our culture tries to teach begin in most instances around two or three years of age when parents try not to appear too concerned over minor injuries, and even try to encourage children to stop crying. By the age of five or six most

---

* A comprehensive study of the literature on development of the sense organs appears in Carmichael.[166]

children have already developed a substantial margin of self-control when in pain. In some primitive societies boys have already become stoics by the time they are ten years old. Our training in gang experiences disciplines boys not to cry when hurt, and even pokes fun at girls who cry too easily. The child who remains in an infantile stage of reaction to pain through indulgence and oversympathy from parents, or through missing gang discipline in this regard, suffers a severe handicap in later life. Lessons in courage when in physical pain are fundamental to the later learnings about courage in the face of difficulty, defeat, and other psychologic pain. However, such lessons must not be overdone, since nothing shakes the emotional security of a child more than to be in genuine pain or danger and find himself without sympathy and support.

The Sense of Smell. The neural mechanism for the sense of smell is developed before birth.[166] Avoidance of strong odors like petroleum or oil of amber and the quieting of crying when a drop of milk or perfume was presented to the nose led earlier writers to assume a greater sensitivity in smell than has since proved to be the case.[166] Investigators on the whole[246,745] have found that although infants seem to react to intense odors they do not react to olfactory stimuli as adults do. However, year-old children frequently sniff flowers or other objects in imitation of adults, and two- or three-year-old children seem as reactive to unpleasant odors in a room or neighborhood as are adults. There are individual differences in sensitivity to odors as there are in taste. As children mature both senses can be trained to detect small differences in odor or flavor.

The Sense of Taste. Opinions about the development of the sense of taste in infants differ. Most experimenters report that sweet flavors are reacted to first. Salty, sour, and bitter tastes are distinguished with more difficulty.[166] The fact that preschool children will take cod liver oil directly from the spoon and reach out to lick off the last drop makes some people wonder if the sense of taste is not defective even at that age. However, this latter instance is only one of many which indicate that children will accept a wide variety of tastes such as cod liver oil, turnips, liver, and other strong tastes if these tastes are offered without prejudice. They will, however, refuse them if the adult makes his own distaste for such foods evident.

The Sense of Hearing. The neural mechanism for hearing appears to be well developed at birth but amniotic fluid in the Eustachian tubes keeps the baby deaf for a few hours after birth. Once the amniotic fluid is cleared, babies react to sharp, sudden, harsh sounds. Within ten days reaction is elicited by the tick of a fairly loud watch or by the human voice. Pitch discrimination and reaction to other complex sounds probably does not exist in infants,[744] but develops later. There is evidence that acuity of hearing continues to develop until it reaches a maximum in pubescence.[770]

The child's development in reaction to music and to spoken words will be discussed later in Chapter 11. What he learns to like or to dislike in the way of sounds seems to be a product of (1) his own sensitivity to sound, (2) a reflection of the tastes of the people about him. Some children have a lower threshold of sound (are more sensitive) than others. Occasional nursery school or primary children will hear the hum of an airplane engine several seconds before the average adult, or will call the attention of older children and adults to bird calls or other sounds not noticed by them. An occasional child has "absolute pitch," and can identify any given musical note correctly; some children have a far lower difference threshold of sound even than adults, and can, therefore, detect finer differences of tone or sound than the average adult. Apparently these differences are in part native, and in part due to early training. Preferences in sound seem largely determined by training and pattern set by admired adults or peers. Much can be done, and is being done, in nursery schools and in elementary and secondary schools to train children to love good music, to enjoy nature sounds, to appreciate fine speech, and in other ways to improve their reactions to sound.

The Sense of Sight.　　The sense of sight is probably the least perfect of the sensory reactions at birth, and seems to be the slowest in reaching full maturity. The neural mechanism for sight begins to develop in very early fetal life, and continues to develop until well after birth.[166] Although a certain amount of muscular control of the eardrum tension is necessary to hearing, this seems to be acquired fairly easily. The muscular processes involved in obtaining accurate vision are more complicated, and therefore take longer to acquire.*

However, complicated as are the muscular adjustments of vision, most infants have sufficient control over their eyes to see larger objects, like the approach of persons, within two or three weeks. The baby may see his mother's approach before he has come to associate her with physical comfort. We can be sure that he sees her or any other object only when he starts wriggling or stops crying or gives some other sign when she approaches. Both the psychologic association of meaning ("mother means comfort"), and the control of eye muscles necessary to see an object as large as an approaching person have been accomplished by most babies within two months of postnatal experience.

Most babies have acquired fine enough control over the mechanisms of vision and of reaching by four or five months to enable them to see inch cubes as evidenced by their attempt to grasp them. This depends upon grasping and reaching accomplishments, and it is quite possible, as before, that he sees such a fine object before he can give us sure evidence in his behavior toward it. The same is true of his picking up pins and specks of dust at seven to eight or nine months, this being dependent upon a development of the pincer technique of using the hands, and upon being on the floor where such small objects come within his range. However, we have this final evidence that by seven to nine months the actual mechanism for keen vision, at least of near objects, is almost perfectly developed and almost perfectly under control. This represents a great deal of learning.

However, even though babies of six or seven months have learned momentary control of the mechanism of near vision, this control is still so imperfect

* See Zubek and Solberg[1020] for a description of what these muscular processes are.

at school entrance that no strain should be put upon it. In view of the clear-cut demonstrations which the children themselves give us of their ability to see tiny, near objects, most people have generally accepted the idea that children of six years can see as well as anyone. The eyeball does not gain its full weight until after seven years of age, or its full development until several years after that.[571] As we saw in Chapter 7, the young child is farsighted as measured by adult standards, although he has a wide range of focus. He tends to look closely at objects, often holding things quite close to his eyes in order to make objects look larger. He should not, however, spend much time looking at small things close by. Schools which require such close fixation over long periods of time may be encouraging nearsightedness.

A study made in England by the British Association for the Advancement of Science through a Committee to Inquire into the Influence of Textbooks upon Eyesight set up the following standards for type:

24 point for children under 7 years

18 point for children 7 to 8 years

12 point for children 7 to 9 years

11 point for children 9 to 12 years

10 point for children from 12 years up*

What Is Meant by Sense Perception?**   A sense perception is a sensation which is understood. In other words, the sight seen or the sound heard

* Report of the Eighty-Third Meeting of the British Association for the Advancement of Science, Birmingham, England, 1913 (London, John Murray, 1914, pp. 268–300).

A more careful study which considered size of type in relation to length of line was reported in 1931 by Buckingham[141a] who recommended for second grade children: 12 point type in lines $2^7/_{16}$ inches to $3^1/_2$ inches long with three or four point leadings (3.25 or 3.60 min. interlinear spacing). This study did not consider whether this type setup would be optimal for continued reading.

** Kingsley[528] discusses perception as follows (p. 261): "A large part of our learning is accomplished through perception. In the first place, we learn directly about things by observing them. In addition to this, perception often plays an important part in other learning activities. It fuses with action. . . . It is essential to learning by imitation. It furnishes the experiences that promote understanding and augment reflective thinking. Without it we could have no memories, no imagination. It is the initial step in most of our emotions. Through perception we learn, and without perception there could be no learning except possibly that of the most primitive and meager sort. But what is probably not so fully realized is the fact that we also learn to perceive." And again (p. 266ff): "Our perceptions do not come ready-made. They grow, and in growing they change. They are enriched in detail and become more definite, refined, and specific. Like action, under repetition they tend toward economy of performance by the elimination of superfluous adjuncts. . . . The principal modifications are alterations in the sensory patterns, changes of meaning, reduction of cues, and greater adroitness in detecting small differences." Later he states (p. 274): "Just as we acquire motor skill through repeated action so we acquire skill in perception by repeated perceiving."

is recognized. It is difficult to draw a sharp line between the nerve development which makes it possible for accurate sensations to reach the brain on the one hand, and the almost immediately accompanying psychologic interpretation of the meaning of these sensations on the other hand. However, we can see this difference in the occasional individual who has the neural development and the muscular adjustments necessary to translate sound waves into nerve impulses and in turn into consciously felt sensations of sound, yet who lacks the necessary neural mechanism by which associations are built up. Such a person cannot, therefore, learn to interpret the meaning of the sounds heard. He could hear a human voice, but could not understand what the sounds meant. He would have auditory sensations as the result of words spoken to him, but he would have no perception or understanding of the meaning of the sounds. Such a person is called "word deaf." Few normal adults experience raw, uninterpreted sensations, because when brain and nervous system are normal, experiences build up so rapidly that even new, previously unknown sounds, carry meaning to us at once as "sounding like" something already known. The unexpected and unfamiliar bugle of a Rocky Mountain elk, for example, may for an instant remain meaningless to the novice, yet almost at once the fertile mind of the normal adult produces previously experienced associations: "That is a strange animal call," or "That must be a coyote yelping."

How Perceptions Develop. Young children, limited in experiences, often know raw, or uninterpreted, meaningless sensations. Yet, so fertile is the human mind, and so rapidly do experiences and associations build themselves that children of two are already past the stage in which they frequently experience sights, sounds, or other sensations for which they fail to have some associated meaning. The infant of a few weeks has already connected the feel of hands lifting and tending him with the comfort which follows, and will stop crying at the touch of his mother's hands even before the comfort has been produced. At first the baby's understandings are limited to the things and experiences which come within the range of his immediate environment. Feeding and other physical actions, his mother's face and the touch of her hands and his own physical sensations seem to make up his conscious world. But as voluntary control over his eyes and other parts of his body develops his range of conscious awareness widens. Sounds, too, come to have wider meaning for him, and he can be seen listening intently to the sound of a bird chirping, a car siren, a piano tone. Eventually he learns to interpret the sounds which are spoken language, and as this becomes possible his understanding of and knowledge about the world advance rapidly. Touch opens new worlds to him and voluntary reaching and grasping are followed by eager manipulation of every object which comes within range.

The Correlation of Perceptions into Meaningful Wholes. Not only is the child in his first year of life learning the use of eyes, ears, touch, smell, and taste, and rapidly building associations around each of these; he is also tying the sense perceptions from each sense together with those from the other senses into meaningful wholes. Something with a handle and which looks round, smells like celluloid, tastes a certain way, makes a certain noise when waved about: all these together become the familiar rattle. A certain face plus a certain voice, plus the feel of certain hands ministering comfort: these come to mean Mother. Another face plus a different voice plus strong tossing about for fun come to mean Father. All this occurs purely as sensations plus associated meanings and certain exceedingly important emotional tones. No spoken language, no calling of names is involved in this aspect of the building of perception. A rattle is not the spoken or as yet clearly heard word "rattle"; it is simply a sight, a touch, a taste, a smell, a rattling sound. Mother is not in the early stages "Mother" or "Mamma"; she is something seen, something heard, something felt. And so with the rest of the world around. One soon learns to suck on a bottle in order to obtain something which can be swallowed with resulting comfort inside one. One does not try to eat Father; one wriggles in anticipation of a romp when Father appears. And so the building up of intelligent reactions to things and situations goes on.

Names for objects and actions soon follow, but are a separate mental process and not to be confused with the building of the fundamental sense perceptions. Accuracy in judging the qualities and uses of objects develops quite apart from the naming of them. As we shall see later, children can react accurately to color as demonstrated by sorting of colored cards or blocks and by uses of color in painting some months before they can name any but the primary colors. On the other hand, children can glibly recite, "One, two, three, four, five, six" long before they have any clear perception of the meaning of "three" or "four."

Perception of Size. After the first awareness of general objects and situation is fairly well established there follows a breaking down of the general reaction into more specific parts. An infant will react to a tiny doll bottle with the same reaching expectancy that he uses to react to his own full-sized bottle. As yet size of objects has not been separated out from the other qualities like shape and general appearance. A year-old baby may occasionally be seen to reach for the moon as eagerly as for the ball in his play pen. Distance has as yet no separate meaning to him. Mistakes of size, shape, weight, and the like are still being made by children of three to five years, involving even common objects with which they are in general thoroughly familiar.

What size means, viz., that a large object occupies more space than a small object and will not, therefore, fit into the smaller object, is a concept foreign to infants. One of the favorite toys of eighteen-months- to two-and-one-half-year-old children is a nest of four-sided, hollow cubes which fit into each other. To the eighteen-months-old child, they are only blocks to handle and throw or to stack by chance. But in time he finds that some of them slip inside the others. With help a two-year-old child will learn to call the one which goes inside the other "little," and the one which goes outside "big." Eventually he will learn that the one which goes inside all of the others is the "littlest" and the one which will not go inside any of the others is the "biggest." By two and one-half years most children can look at the cubes and

Fig. 37. Sequin form board. (Courtesy of C. H. Stoelting Co.)

without trial and error pick the biggest, then the next biggest, and so on to the littlest, either placing them inside each other accurately or stacking them into an orderly graduated tower. From such toys or from the kitchen cupboard pans and covers they can learn that size is a property which all objects have, that it means the amount of space the object occupies. At the same time they are usually learning the conventional language names: "big," "little," "large," "small," etc.

Confusions of size persist in occasional instances for most children even into the fifth year. In play three-year-olds may be so carried away with the imaginative house play with doll furniture that they will temporarily submerge the as yet imperfectly formed judgments of size. One can see them for a moment forgetting to realize the size of tiny doll furniture and attempting to sit on it themselves, only to look surprised, and often a little sheepish, because they failed to react accurately to this quality of the object. A three-year-old can be seen trying to ride his tricycle through an opening too narrow or too low for it. Probably because the child sees himself less than he sees other objects he usually misjudges his own size later in his development than he does the size of other objects. Four-year-olds, for example, can be seen trying to sit in an adult chair as an adult does, back against the back and feet on the floor, and looking puzzled because they cannot fit themselves into this position. Although these misjudgments are not typical of daily play, such instances show us that perception of size is not automatic even at four years of age.

Perceptions of Shape: General Forms. Judgments of shape must, like those of size, be learned. Oddly enough, we do not see shape instinctively any more than we do size, but rather, we must learn how to react accurately to the factor of shape. A two-year-old child, given a form board (see Fig. 37), almost at once catches the idea of placing the figures into the available holes, but he will try to fit the pieces indiscriminately, pushing the square into the round hole at random. He will select the smaller pieces for the smaller holes, and the larger pieces for the larger holes, but will confuse the shapes, trying to put the star in the hole meant for the cross, the half circle in the space meant for the elongated diamond. Most children cannot use such a form board with accurate discrimination of both size and shape until they are four years old.

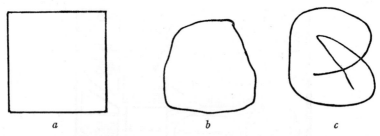

a   *b*   *c*

Fig. 38. *a*, Square to be copied. *b* and *c*, Squares as drawn by children of mental age less than four years.

Children differentiate squares, circles and triangles first, diamonds, crosses and more complicated shapes later. One test in the Binet Mental Test Scale (revised by Terman in 1937) requires the child to copy a square at age five, using pencil and accomplishing one correct drawing in three trials. Most children of less than four years of mental age scribble, or produce a cornerless drawing resembling an irregular circle (Fig. 38). Until after four years of mental age they fail to see the difference between their own drawing and the clearly marked square which serves as a copy.

Perceptions of Shape: Letter Forms and Other Fine Shapes. Ability to discriminate between letter forms is fairly well in hand by five years, since some children of five can recognize many of the letters of the alphabet when printed in capital forms, and can, before their sixth birthday print, in staggering sizes and alignments, the letters of their own names. This facility should not be coached or pushed, however, into "reading" and "writing," since to do so would place undesirable strain upon all but the most exceptional children. Even six- and seven-year-olds have difficulty in making such fine discriminations of form as that between "p" and "q," "b" and "d," "3" and "E," and such similar word forms as "hat" and "hot." Great patience is necessary in helping children to take such an important step in the lowering of their difference thresholds of form discrimination as the above and hence to prepare them for reading and writing. Children who are conspicuously slow may be lacking in the general experience with a wide variety of objects which teaches hand and mind to analyze detail and to react discriminatingly to small or subtle differences in form. Children make rapid progress in the differentiation of small differences in size and shape throughout the elementary school years, ages six to twelve. Even three-year-old children enjoy a simple two-piece jig-saw puzzle. Six-year-olds love such puzzles with around ten to twelve fairly large pieces. Children of nine to twelve years rate puzzles among their dominant interests, and the jig-saw puzzle of increasing complexity continues to hold interest as a challenge to accurate form discrimination throughout adulthood if the puzzle is complicated enough.

Aids to Learning about Shape. Children a generation ago had many natural opportunities to explore objects and thus to develop accurate perceptions of size and shape which those children who live in city apartments or slums lack today. Playing with mother's pots and pans in the kitchen, "helping" to wash dishes, or to bake, roaming about through the several rooms of a house and about the yard, listening for bird sounds, playing in sand and digging, keeping pets, etc. were all experiences which contributed to children's knowledge of the properties of objects. A small apartment, with a maid to do what little housework there is, or the restricted environment of a city slum deprives children of many of these natural learning experiences. We have been compelled to find substitutes. "Educational" toys have been created and nursery schools and kindergartens have given much attention to providing experiences which train sense perception. Montessori's equipment and the many "educational toys" to be found on the market today were designed as foundation training devices for familiarizing children with sizes, shapes, textures, sounds, and so on, emphasis being placed upon training reaction to the finer differences in bigness or littleness, in graded sounds, and the like. Definite training in recognition of finer and finer gradations of sense reaction in all of the sense fields seems to help children to benefit from school work, if this training does not go so far, of course, as to make the child so sensitive to sounds and sights and touches and smells and tastes that he cannot live in the ordinary world. Reaction to too low thresholds of stimulation or to too fine differences of stimulation can produce the neurotic who cannot bear a musical note a tiny degree off pitch, or a dish of food which is slightly different in flavor.

Confusions in Direction in Reading and Writing. Some children suffer a longer period of confusion in reading and writing direction than do average children. They confuse "saw" and "was," for example, or they "mirror" letters or words in writing longer than most children do. Some confusion in direction is natural, since it is merely convention which requires us to move from the left to right side of a page instead of, say, from top to bottom, as the Chinese do. Prolonged confusion, however, is likely to mean confusion about general direction, and this is often related to handedness (see Ch. 8). Naturally left-handed children find movement from right to left easier than the conventional direction, since movement from the inside to the outside seems more natural for either hand. Right-handed people swing naturally from left to right in reading and writing. Left-handed people or those who have a tendency to left-handedness seem to "feel" naturally a right to left direction. Such children require much more practice in the fixing of direction of eye movements in reading and of hand movements in writing than do average children. It is important in the early attempts to read and write not to let practice in the wrong direction occur. Teachers should watch children who lean toward left-handedness to see that they practice correct direction from the beginning. They should also watch to see that the left-handed child* places his paper for writing on the northeast, southwest oblique (see Fig. 39) so that the left hand can proceed naturally across the page with the hand held below the writing. If the left-handed child places his paper on the northwest-southeast oblique, as do right-

* Children of five can distinguish the right from the left hand in themselves, but not in other people.[345],[935]

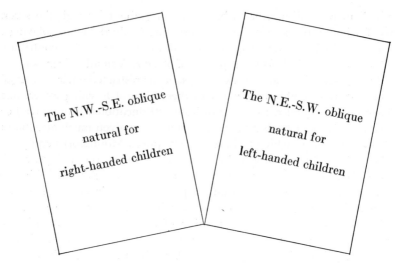

Fig. 39. Positions of paper for right-handed and for left-handed children.

handed people, there is nothing left for him to do but write "upside down" the hand placed above the writing and the wrist twisted. Left-handed children can, and should, learn to write as legibly and as rapidly as right-handed children, but they can do so only with proper help. They can also learn to read as well, but only with proper help in establishing direction of eye movements.

Observations of form and the ability to reproduce what is observed in a drawing develops in such orderly manner[27,364] that at least one shortcut to the measurement of mental age has been based upon it. The Goodenough scale for judging mental age from the drawing of a man is based upon the observation that children draw one or two of the most familiar things in their environment (man, house, etc.) in characteristic form at given stages in the development of form discrimination. Drawings characteristic of first grade children (see Figs. 40, 41) show definitely characteristic developments in form discrimination, ability to produce perspective, and utilization of detail.

Perception of Color. Reaction to color is another of the learnings in the process of development of sense perceptions, since it is another of the fundamental qualities of objects. Whether or not tiny babies react to color as such is a matter of dispute.[178] By two or two and one-half years there is clear evidence that children react not only to the fact of color but also to specific colors, since they can sort colored disks with reasonable accuracy and are even beginning to name certain specially favored colors. Whether preschool children prefer red or blue or yellow seems undecided, since available studies differ in their findings. At least one study[13] indicates that color preference is related to the feelings of the individual child. Studies differ as to the color named most frequently and with most accuracy by preschool children.[190,447] Most of the fundamental and familiar colors are prop-

Typical First Grade Figures
Selected from Children's Booklets
and Movie Strips —

Fig. 40. Typical first grade figures selected from children's booklets and movie strips. (Hughes & Stockdale: Childhood Education, March, 1940.)

erly named by kindergarten age, or can be learned easily at that time. Boys will have a greater tendency to confuse colors than girls, partly because 8 to 10 per cent of males are red-green color blind, whereas only 2 per cent of females are so afflicted,[873] and partly because our present social tradition expects boys to pay less attention to colors than girls do. There are wide

Cows in a Barn

Hen and Chickens

Chickens in a Pen

Our New Calf

Fig. 41. (Hughes & Stockdale: Childhood Education, March, 1940.)

individual differences in sensitivity to colors, some children seeming to be captivated by colors early in the preschool years, others remaining comparatively indifferent to them.

The Child's Sensitiveness to Color, as to Other Properties of Objects, Can Be Utilized to Advantage. All sensitiveness to size, shape, color, and the other properties of objects can be developed by good teaching into a source of genuine intellectual curiosity and into a widened aesthetic awareness which will be of value throughout life. Much of this teaching consists of providing the experiences which will lower thresholds of difference, and should be such as to result in emotional satisfactions in such activity. Babies of a few months appreciate toys which are colored, while children of two to three years enjoy clothes which are "pretty," or a room which is colorful. Picture books which are attractive can, from twelve to fifteen months of age, begin an interest in books which serves as an excellent background for learning to read upon school entrance, and for the joy of reading throughout life. Paints and a place to daub with them should be available not only to preschool children but to children throughout childhood and adolescence. Teachers can do much to heighten the child's sensitivity to color and to teach him wise and creative use of color in his everyday life.

Perceptions of Textures. Judgments of texture also develop largely during the preschool period, although, in this as in all sensory reactions perfection and discrimination can be refined throughout life. Children of one year through three years are notorious "handlers." They wish to touch and to explore everything about them, the hunger to perfect manual skills and the eagerness to learn all the properties of objects leading them to examine everything with which they can get into contact. One of the properties they are thus investigating is texture. Hard, soft, rough, smooth, slick, or furry—all "feels" are welcome to the fingers and to the mind to which all these awarenesses are new and fascinating. Most children of two to five years would not only enjoy but would learn much from a scrap bag of textiles, empty spools, and other odds and ends. Clay to model, or bread dough in the kitchen helps children of primary and early elementary age to satisfy the continued urge to handle textures. Children of all ages along with adults enjoy finger painting, in which one "messes" on paper with the whole hand, thus producing pictures with free flow and often beautiful rhythm. This satisfies not only the urge to feel textures, but also the urge to produce something creative.

Perception of Weight. Judgments of weight are inaccurate for several years because accurate judgment of weight depends upon accurate judgment of size and a wide variety of experience with materials. Weight, in other words, is dependent upon the size of the object and upon the weight of the material of which the object is made. As adults we have forgotten the painful experiences by which we learned to judge the weight of objects and by which we learned to make the necessary muscular adjustment before picking things up. One reason why children drop things so often is not only that their hands are still clumsy, but that they frequently fail to make the appropriate muscular adjustment necessary in order to hold on to things. As a general rule, small things are light and big ones heavy. Preschool and primary aged children will, therefore, make little muscular preparation when picking up small objects and much adjustment when picking up large objects. However, a small object which is made of a heavy metal or other heavy material, requires the muscular adjustment necessary to lift a heavy object. The child, having failed to appreciate this, drops such objects until he learns which materials (how they look and feel) are the heavy ones per unit of size. Similarly, one sees young children making elaborate muscular adjustments preliminary to picking up a large balloon-like beach ball, only to throw themselves over backward as the ball fails to use up the muscular pull. Thus they learn that some big objects are light and require little muscular pull, and gradually they learn which materials are light as well as which ones are heavy.

Weight judgments depend, then, upon knowledge of the factors which usually make up the weight of objects, namely, size and density of material. They also come, in time, to mean the kinesthetic "feel" which goes with the handling of objects. The exact amount of muscular tension, and the exact feel in the joints of the body come to be part of the perception (or meaning) of weight. So orderly is the development of this perception in the experience of average children that judgment of weight has been used as a test of intelligence. These tests of weight discrimination are spread over several years of mental age and serve to indicate that judgments of weight are improving in fineness of discrimination throughout childhood. This is also true of all other perceptions and judgments, viz., that the first obvious conquests of knowledge occur in the preschool years, but that an increasing skill in judgment as evidenced by constantly lowering difference thresholds or fineness of discrimination occurs throughout childhood.

Perceptions of Distance.   Judgments of distance are even more complex than judgments of weight. The farther away an object is the smaller it looks, the less definite its outlines, the less saturated its color, and the slower its movement. Preschool and primary school aged children, looking down at traffic from a tall building, are enchanted with the toy world which lies below. Until told, they sometimes fail to realize that below them lies a world of full-sized automobiles and street cars and people which look diminutive only because they are far away. Through such experiences as this, and through watching cars approach or retreat, they come to learn that the smaller a standard-sized object looks the farther away it is. Through experience they learn the other qualities of the objects by which one can judge their distance away. In traffic the pedestrian must learn these judgments accurately, and usually comes to use loudness of sound of cars as an added index by which to judge their distance. One soon learns to vary these judgments according to circumstances. On foggy days cars which are quite close are blurred in outline and, therefore, seem farther away than they are. This, added to the fact that the driver sees less well than usual, multiplies traffic-pedestrian accidents. Persons who have learned distance judgment in the high clear air of the mountains are in serious danger of traffic misjudgments in the denser and often more smudgy atmosphere of a low altitude industrial city.

As in the judgment of weights, adults have usually forgotten that judgment of distance is not instinctive but is learned. Some radical change of conditions like the above is usually necessary to recall to mind the complexity of learnings upon which our judgment of distance is based. It is small wonder, then, that young children so often misjudge distances badly. One sees them pushing a tray too close to the edge of a table with consequent breakage, jumping from heights too great and getting hurt. It takes a good deal of understanding on the part of the adult not to laugh in amusement, or to be irritated, or puzzled at this type of misjudgment.

Characteristic also of inability to judge distance is inability to judge depth accurately. Recall from Chapter 7 that children are slow to develop binocular vision or single vision with depth perception. Two-year-old children, in the learning process, will lift a leg elaborately to step over the edge of a carpet or linoleum; or they will run a finger wonderingly over a figured material commenting, "It looks rough; it feels smooth." They have not yet learned when a change of line means a change of surface, since in some instances it does and in some it does not. The edge of a step, for example, means both a change of line and a change of surface; a pattern on dress material means a change of line without a change of surface. The change of line at the edge of a rug or linoleum means enough change of surface to trip you up, but not enough to require a lift of leg equal to ascending a step. Only with time and experience can children learn that change of depth or surface can be judged by the depth of shadow, by the difference in color intensity, or the angle and play of intermediate lines and surfaces.

Perception of Time.   Judgments of time, like those of distance, never become really accurate. We are, at any age, limited by our experience with time. Yesterday, a year ago, five, ten or fifty years has meaning to the adult who has lived that long. One hundred years sets us to computing historical dates, as does 1000 years. But a light year in distance, or a million years in geologic time are vague concepts indeed. So it is with children. What they have experienced repeatedly becomes meaningful; what they have not yet lived through is meaningless. A new child in the nursery school cannot understand that Mother will come "this afternoon" because "this afternoon" has no meaning for him. He can understand, however, that "we will have our orange juice, then we'll play a long time (when waiting for Mother it will seem long to him), then we'll have a story, then lunch, then we'll have our nap. Then it will be afternoon and after we've played some more Mother will come."

Even for the three- and four-year-old, afternoon is "after lunch." However, more clear-cut events, separated by more dramatic incidents like going to bed and the change from light to dark and back again, stand out. "Yesterday," "today," "tomorrow," are clear to most four-year-old children.* Four-year-olds can grasp accurately the meaning of "day before yesterday," "day after tomorrow," "last week," even "next week." Dramatic events like "last Christmas," or Easter, or birthdays stand out, and are appreciated as events. However, how long it will be until Christmas is nebulous to most four-year-olds unless the time is within a few weeks and the stores give evidence of preparedness. "Summer when we go to the lake," or "Winter when we wear

* Ames,[23] in a systematic compilation of verbal expressions of time used by young children, found words indicating the present first used at twenty-four months, the future at thirty months, and the past at thirty-six months. General divisions of the day (morning, afternoon, evening) were not used correctly until four years; days of the week at five years; months at eight years. Her children were not able to tell time until seven years of age.

galoshes," or "Spring when the leaves come out" are becoming clear in the late preschool period.

For the nine-, ten-, and eleven-year-old child, time falls into sequences of years through which they have lived, and into some judgments of historical time. Reynolds[780] tells of a group of eight-year-olds who were not sure whether George Washington was mentioned in the Bible, whereas a group of nine-year-olds had acquired a sufficient working perspective on history to enable them to answer where George Washington belonged. It is not unusual, however, to find college freshmen to whom the first World War seems as remote as the Civil War, and high school students to whom the depression of the early 1930's is no more real than that of the late 1890's.

Time Is a Relative Concept. Confusions in shorter time units still remain, however, in such concepts as "an hour or two," or "we have just ten minutes to get dressed." Some five-year-olds begin to recognize such units of time as are coincident with the hour or half hour placement of the big hand on the clock. "It is five o'clock" or "It is half past ten" presupposes not only an association between clocks and time of day, but to some extent an ability to read numbers. Most children of four and five, however, who tell time at all do so by more or less accurate guesses made from the position of the hands rather than from reading figures.

Even six- or seven-year-olds have difficulty with "You may play for twenty minutes." Part of this trouble comes from a general human confusion about time. Filled and happy time flies; unfilled and unhappy time drags. Fifteen minutes of play flashes by; fifteen minutes of sitting to think over a misdemeanor seems to last for hours. This is as true of adults as of children.[737]

Many so-called behavior problems result from this relativity. The family sit at dinner with engaging guests; time flies for the adults. The young children, with the conversation over their heads, eat, become bored, and are forced to lighten the boredom by becoming nuisances. Mother calls for dinner; the eight-year-old says, "Just a minute." One more game leads to another, and in fifteen minutes he returns home gaily with the firm conviction that he has been only a minute. To his mother, whose dinner is waiting and whose husband is fussing over the boy's disobedience, these same fifteen minutes seem thirty and she is thoroughly angry. At moments like this, genuine misunderstanding can result. Both boy and mother need to temper their sense of injustice in terms of an understanding of the other's viewpoint, and the boy needs to realize that unless he comes at once when called he is likely to lose track of time with unhappy results all around.

Dawdling, a By-Product of Faulty Time Perception. Dawdling is one of the most acute problems of four- to eight-year-olds. Gesell reminds us that dawdling is found even in two-year-old children and probably represents a normal indifference to social requirements. He says the two-year-old child dawdles "when motivation is low, or at mealtimes when tedious demands are made upon his motor coordination. Dawdling is a form of deliberateness which may have a developmental function without being in any sense a vice or a weakness—a protective kind of negativism or filibustering."[345] He adds that five-year-olds dawdle less with combing and washing and eating, largely because of the added motor skill which a five-year-old possesses as an advantage over the two- or three-year-old.

Part of the difficulty with four- to eight-year-olds lies in the fact that at this age adults are tending to throw more and more of the responsibility for dressing, eating, bathing, and care of personal belongings upon the child. This is as it should be, since development of independence and responsibility are of paramount importance. However, the adults must realize that when the child takes over such duties he will not execute them as neatly or as fast as would the adult. His fingers are more awkward, for one thing. And for another, he lacks a sense of the passing of time.

Consider that the newness of dressing oneself has worn off and it is, therefore, no longer fun. Time drags in the unpleasantness of the task. Things can be lightened up a bit if one plays with one's blocks, or looks out the window, or splashes in the water in the bathroom. If the child has a good appetite for breakfast he may hurry in order to get at the next pleasure. If he has slight appetite, then eating becomes only one more chore, so why hurry? Entrance to school helps many children cut short the morning dawdling because most children like school and do not wish to be late. However, even here, the motive is removed if Mother always gives in and finishes dressing the child so that he gets to school on time anyway. Much of the problem here consists of helping the child to realize that even unpleasant chores can be dealt with best by direct and efficient attack which keeps them from using up too much time. In other words, time, dragged out over dawdling, is gone, and cannot be used for other things. Dressing in competition with an hourglass helps to impress this sense of the passing of time as the sand trickles down. The movement of the hands of a clock also helps, especially if a second hand shows how relentlessly time moves on. Something pleasant happening at the end of the chore tends to lure one through the unpleasant parts, especially if waste of time on the chore obviously cuts out time for the pleasure.

Children Must Learn How to Use Time.   Experiences which give a true appreciation of time are invaluable training. Many children have very little of this sense when they enter school. If they do not have it then, school offers an excellent opportunity to teach it. School, being in a genuine sense the child's job, can begin to develop a feeling of what one does with one's job: one works at a job instead of just fooling around. Thus some children learn to become efficient in their use of job time even though they remain dawdlers everywhere else. The reverse is occasionally true: some children who have a good sense of using time well develop careless work habits at school through bad handling.

What we do not wish to have happen, of course, is a sense of crowding by time, a sense of guilt unless one is at all times working at high speed. Some children, overdriven through the dawdling age, develop a too acute sense of the passing of time and become too ambitious, fretting unless all time is used efficiently. "Work while you work and play while you play" is a good motto because it does not mean high tension nervousness about either one.

Children cannot all be driven at the same speed. Some children show signs of being overdriven at a pace which is too relaxed to get anything but lazy indifference from others. The school teacher's problem is to set a pace which can get efficient work without strain. This inevitably means some adjustments to individual speed of action within any group of children. Parents, dealing with fewer children, can hope to fit the pace better to the child's individual need. Even here, however, it takes a good deal of clear judgment to develop a pace which protects from strain yet which teaches children the value of hard work.

Perceptions of Number. Gesell gives us probably the best analysis of the development of number concepts among young children. He says:

> The basis of counting is similarity. We add like objects. Primitive number concepts are from this point of view traceable to beginning language. Concrete evidence of enumeration begins when, for example, a child points to all the cars that he sees, one after the other, saying 'Car? car?' or 'More car?' as though discovering the genus 'car.' Gradually and very soon after two years he uses the plural form to designate more than one, and the notion of one, as opposed to many, is built up. The notion 'two' likewise usually develops in relation to two objects, but 'three' may first have either a collective or an ordinal connotation.[345]

He points out that a child may be able to match objects with a similar number of objects without having either an ordinal or cardinal number notion.

Gesell found that as early as the preschool years individual differences in number ability appear, some children forming the association between the ordinal or cardinal concepts while other children fail to do so. Ability to repeat the counting sequence, "one, two, three, four," is not to be confused with the ability actually to count objects or to appreciate what numbers mean. Counting objects, "one, two, three, four," with a finger on or pointing to the first, second, third, and fourth object of the series being counted is quite different as a developmental level of performance from merely chattering, "one, two, three, four." However, the child has to have mastery of the recitation of a number sequence before he can combine number recitation with the motor effort of pointing to each separate object as he counts. Gesell[345] found that some children can even count four objects accurately, but if asked "How many are there?" or "Give me four" are quite unable to respond. By five years many children can count ten objects and seem to have a clear sense of what "ten-ness" means.

When number sequences are learned well enough to permit easy counting, simple additions and subtractions of objects which can be seen and handled follow easily. Two blocks laid beside two more are easily put together as four blocks. Some children of five years can add sums up to five and seem to appreciate what this means. At this age experience with numbers of low denomination and conversation about them intrigues some children immensely. It is at this age that a genuine love of numbers and hence of arithmetic can be built if the child is not pushed beyond his depth. The abstraction of "How many are two and two?" is beyond some children until they are six or seven years old. Most children, however, upon entering the first grade possess a working knowledge of at least the simplest number combinations in addition and subtraction. Most entering first graders have no knowledge of the multiplication or division combinations.[142,1011] Knowledge of addition and subtraction combinations increases rapidly in grades 1 to 3 even without formal instruction.[142,999]

Children of nine to eleven can manage numbers beyond 100 in mechanical addition and multiplication, but they cannot genuinely understand them. Even adults, however, have no real comprehension of numbers above 1000 as a rule. Knowledge of the combinations in multiplication and division increases rapidly from grades 3 to 5, probably because these combinations are systematically taught in these grades. Knowledge of these combinations continues to increase, though slowly, from grades 5 to 8 and beyond.[801] One of the most important conclusions drawn from summaries of the available literature on development of arithmetic[137] is that children differ widely at any given age or school grade in the maturity of their development in concepts fundamental to arithmetic. Brueckner[137] is so impressed by this that he urges teachers to organize the teaching of basic number facts so that each pupil may study those facts which present difficulty for him. He says: "This may be done through a plan involving pretests, individual drill material, diagnosis when necessary, and varying the amount of practice according to individual needs."

Development of Fundamental Arithmetical Concepts. An important part of the work of the early elementary school is to give children the "fundamentals" of arithmetic. The technique of addition, subtraction, multiplication, and division occupy much time. It is very difficult to attempt to teach such processes as "add," "subtract or take away," "multiply or two times," "divide or put into two parts" to children who have not already grasped the idea through handling objects. One reason an abacus served mankind so long was that it permitted him to handle simple number combinations in the concrete. Real facility in the handling of numbers can be achieved, of course, only when a wide variety of number combinations is so well memorized that 7×8 is automatically 56, $7 + 8$ automatically 15, $15 - 7$ is automatically 8, $15 \div 3$ is automatically 5, and so on. This involves rote memorizing of the hundreds of combinations. Methods of teaching arithmetic now current in many progressive schools make full use of handling objects as a preliminary to the abstraction of handling numbers. They do very well in motivating arithmetic learning. They often, however, neglect the important drill by which a mastery of number combinations is obtained.

In order to be successful in arithmetic in school, children must have not only number concepts, but also facility with number combinations, and a knowledge of arithmetic vocabulary (*percentage, acre, rectangle,* etc.). Even with this equipment, however, we have a great many failures in arithmetic. Part of the difficulty is that children who can solve arithmetic "problems" in actual life situations cannot solve the too often senseless problems characteristic of many traditional arithmetic textbooks. One of the main reasons for mastering arithmetic in school is that the child may in later life manage his own money adequately, may be able to make accurate measurements, to understand business practices, taxes, and geometric design. We must see that children in school are presented with problems in arithmetic as closely related to real life situations as possible.

From understanding of the meaning of numbers the child moves through the understanding of such concepts as the four fundamental processes of addition, subtraction, multiplication, and division, through percentage and reasoning problems in arithmetic and on, in the later junior high school and in the senior high school, to the stage of development at which algebraic concepts are comprehensible and the handling of other abstractions is possible. Ultimately the extreme abstractions of calculus can be mastered by the higher levels of intelligence.

SUMMARY

Perceptions Can Be Improved through Training.   Children's horizons can be widened by calling their attention to things they have not already observed. A trip through the woods with a person interested in botany calls attention to numberless flowers and plants hitherto unnoticed. A trip through an art museum with a person interested in art focuses attention on numberless aspects of art not previously appreciated. A student of astronomy sees the stars in constellation groupings which escape the attention of another person. Study in any area sharpens one's ability to see, hear, feel, and understand that area. Parent and teacher have an obligation to widen children's areas of perception and awareness.

Teaching can also improve the accuracy of things perceived. Careless observation results in inaccurate reports of situations. Keen and accurate observation of things or of the situations around one, and the ability to make a reliable report of things observed mark the difference between intelligent reaction to the world and continued mediocrity of reaction. Biases and prejudices govern the thinking and reaction of the mediocre observer. Keen and discriminating reaction to the world must be based upon the ability to observe accurately. Children can be taught early in life to observe accurately and to report reliably the world of things around them, at first the simple and obvious things, but, as growth proceeds, more complicated and subtle things and situations. For children who possess a high degree of native intelligence such training in observation can become the basis upon which truly scientific observation and the ability to advance human knowledge develops.

The success of any child in mastering the subject matter of the school is dependent upon many factors, both within the school and its methods, and within the child himself. Among the most important factors within the child is the factor of intelligence.* We have attempted to describe in this section how the child's intelligence is built in the area of his sensations and his perceptions. He can discover many things in his own body and he can develop a

---

* For a summary of 77 studies completed between 1947 and 1950 on the organization of intellectual, moral and other growth in relation to success in high school and college see Hendrickson.[418]

genuinely important sector of his intellect through learning control over his body. Whatever else he learns, however, must come to him through the avenues of his eyes, his ears, his touch, and other sense organs. The handicap of the loss of any sense to the development of intelligence can be seen in the child born blind or deaf.

Intelligence, as we ordinarily find it, is built largely through the use of eyes, ears, touch, taste, and smell. The infant must learn to control his sense organs well enough to make them useful, as we have seen in the description of how he learns to use his eyes. He must then have a gradually expanding but constantly challenging opportunity for experience from which he can feed his mind. Given these experiences through which he can see, hear, touch, taste, and smell a variety of objects and situations, and given ample opportunity to use his own body he will usually proceed satisfactorily in the growth of his intellect. How much he ordinarily learns before he comes to school and what the nature of these learnings is should be understood by every teacher. Only through such understanding can the teacher fit the child's school experience smoothly into the flow of his growth. Only so can she help the slow learner or grower through the experiences he should have had before he entered school. The child's most important learnings in perception of size, shape, texture, distance, and even of time occur before he enters the realm of formal education at all. Important beginnings in understanding of numbers have also taken place in the preschool years. Children learn much which is typically intellectual quite outside the schoolroom.

An important emphasis in all studies of sense perception, as it is of all studies in motor control, is the fact of great individual differences among the children of any given age or school grade. Few investigators into any phase of child development fail to make special comment upon the striking nature of these differences, and to plead for a reduction of mass education which loads teachers with so many children that they cannot hope to adapt the curriculum to individuals. They plead also for the initiative and ingenuity on the part of the teacher which will "take each child *where he is* and lead him where he needs to go," regardless of the size of the class.

EXPERIENCES TO VITALIZE CLASS WORK

1. What would you do to find out if a child who is slow to learn to read:
   a. Has defective eyesight?
   b. Has cerebral dominance characteristic of the left-handed child and is confused in direction of words and lines?
   c. Is immature in form discrimination?
   d. Is too bashful to read before others?

   What would you do to correct each of these?

2. Visit some well run nursery school. What provision did you see for conscious training of sense perceptions? Would you be able to suggest further experiences for the training of perceptions?

3. How should kindergarten materials and experiences for the training of sense perceptions and judgments differ from those of the nursery school? From those of the upper grades?

4. How would you find out if a child who is slow to get started in arithmetic is lacking in basic number concepts? What experiences could you plan for him to remedy this defect? How would you decide whether defective ability to solve problems in arithmetic in the fourth to the eighth grade was due to:

    a. Defective number concepts?
    b. Defective arithmetic vocabulary?
    c. Defective reading ability?

    5. Look up sense perceptions in the current literature (since 1950). What new findings corroborate or refute the material in this chapter?

    6. Look up further material on special defects as well as gifted children, especially in the literature since 1950. What provisions are now being made for the training of such children? Do these provisions seem reasonably adequate in your state?

    7. If you are doing a case study investigate each of the above as it affects "your child."

SELECTED READINGS

Bayley, N.: The Role of Intelligence. Thirteenth Yearbook. Washington, D. C., Department of Supervisors and Directors of Education, National Education Association, 1940.

Blair, A. W., and W. H. Burton: Growth and Development of the Preadolescent. New York, Appleton-Century-Crofts, Inc., 1951, Ch. 5.

Gesell, A., et al.: The First Five Years. New York, Harper & Bros., 1940, Ch. 7.

Gesell, A., et al.: The Child from Five to Ten. New York, Harper & Bros., 1946, pp. 395–399.

Horrocks, J. E.: The Psychology of Adolescence. Boston, Houghton Mifflin Co., 1951, Ch. 7.

Jersild, A. T.: Child Psychology. New York, Prentice-Hall, Inc., 1954, Ch. 13.

Kuhlen, R. G.: The Psychology of Adolescent Development. New York, Harper & Bros., 1952, Ch. 3.

Millard, C. V.: Child Growth and Development in the Elementary School Years. Boston, D. C. Heath & Co., 1951, Ch. 6.

Piaget, J.: The Origins of Intelligence in Children. New York, International Universities Press, 1952.

Thompson, G. G.: Child Psychology. Boston, Houghton Mifflin Co., 1952, Ch. 10.

Zubek, J. P., and P. A. Solberg: Human Development. New York, McGraw-Hill Book Co., 1954, Chs. 7, 8, 9.

CHAPTER 10

Development of Memory;
Imagination; Creative Ability

MEMORY AS AN ASPECT OF INTELLIGENCE

Just when does memory develop in children? This is not an easy question to answer. In a certain way we must consider sheer conditioned responses in the class of memory, since the response is determined by previous experience which leaves its trace in the nervous system. Very young infants show this sort of memory. Even after a few weeks of life and experience a crying infant will become quiet when his mother approaches his crib even though she has not yet made him comfortable. He "remembers" that her presence eventually means relief from distress. Other evidences of such conditioned memory are to be found in the child who, at a year or fifteen months, snatches the tablecloth and pulls it toward him only to have dishes and liquids tumble over him. This usually frightens him enough so that he leaves tablecloths alone for some time thereafter.

To Train or Not to Train the Baby. A deliberate attempt to make the infant remember on the conditioned response basis is recommended in some child training books as a basis for disciplinary control. Such "training" books[302] recommend deliberate "lessons": the six- to twelve-months-old child is to be held on the parent's knee before a table upon which is placed a spoon or other enticing object. If the baby does not spontaneously reach for it, the object is to be banged on the table to make it attractive. Then, as the child reaches for the coveted object, the arm is forcibly withdrawn by the adult accompanied by a firm "No." This is to be repeated until the "No" is sufficient to withdraw the child's hand. Occasionally the recommendation in such training programs is to accompany the "No" with a slap on the back of the hand.*

Such procedures are considered bad practice by nearly all child psychologists. The child should not be tempted to reach, then punished for doing so, since such procedure can only produce confusion in the child's mind. In teaching a child to remember he should be offered as little confusion as possible; the lesson should be simple and clear. Plenty of opportunities to

* Although this book is a 1919 publication, there are still "child trainers" who recommend this procedure.

teach the meaning of the word "No" will present themselves if the adult will wait for the normal course of the child's activities to produce them. In such a case, the adult's "No" represents only forbidden activity, and is not confused by an adult command to reach for an object which is immediately followed by a counter command not to reach for that same object. Some psychologists of sound standing, however, approve the use of slaps on the hand or the building of a conditioned association of "No" with a gentle though firm withdrawal of the child's hand from a forbidden object or even a parental explosion if circumstances warrant. Physical punishment beyond a slap on the hand or side of the hip is frowned upon by current psychologists and psychiatrists almost without exception.* Nearly all psychologists agree that children, even in the first year of life, should begin to learn the meaning of adult-imposed restriction on their behavior.

Babies' Memories Are Short. Memory which is less closely associated with physical comfort or "conditioned" reaction is reported by Bühler,[145] who found that five-months-old infants could remember for a few seconds a smiling face or a game played. Bühler found that children of fifteen to seventeen months could remember for eight minutes; children of twenty-one to twenty-four months could remember for seventeen minutes. The work of other investigators[420] checks with these data closely, for they found in similar experiments that children of nineteen to twenty months remember over a period of fifteen minutes, whereas children of ten to eleven months remember only one minute. It must be understood, of course, that these time intervals refer to specific experimental conditions only. They serve, however, to tell us that babies' memories are very short. Any mother who is separated from her baby discovers that babies of twenty months of age forget even their own mothers after a week of absence and that the mother must become reacquainted when she returns. Because children's memories are, in this sense, so short it is easy to distract their attention from undesirable activities or from something they want but cannot have. Many parents discover this when their children are infants, but fail to appreciate how rapidly memory develops and tend to continue the program of distraction long after it should have been abandoned.

Memory Develops Rapidly The speed with which children of eighteen months begin to acquire vocabulary (see Chapter 11) is testimony to the speed with which memory of the more abstract kind is developing. With the acquisition of words and the ability to use them we find a way of testing the memory of children which we do not have for children of younger age. This memory is of two kinds: immediate memory and longer time memory. We have many evidences of the child's capacity for immediate memory as measured by reproduction of words or numbers repeated immediately after the examiner or as evidenced by the duplication of actions like tapping cubes or marking squares in patterns set by the examiner. Stutsman[916] found that children of eighteen months can repeat single words after the examiner, that

---

* A comprehensive history of methods of discipline and of suggestions for sound discipline in the modern pattern can be found in Langdon and Stout[562] (1952).

children of twenty-four months can repeat five single-syllable words like "Give me the big box." Gesell[345] found children of two years able to repeat a sentence of three to four syllables; children of two and one-half years, six to seven syllables; children of four years, twelve to thirteen syllables (one trial of three); of six and one-half years, sixteen to eighteen syllables. At eleven years children can repeat a sentence of twenty syllables almost without error.[935] The Terman-Merrill Revision of the Simon-Binet Test of Intelligence gives a normal immediate memory span for two digits at two and one-half years, of three at three years, of four at four and one-half years, of five at seven years and of six at ten years.

A number of studies[256] on the earliest memories of older children and adults have been made, showing that occasional correct memories dating from one and one-half to two years have been reported by adolescent children. The average age of first memory for adolescent children seems, however, to be around three and one-half to four years. Unpleasant memories predominate, probably because they are more vivid.* These, we must recall, are conscious memories, those which are available to the conscious mind for recall. Psychoanalysis gives us clear evidence of the deep-lying effect upon adult behavior which is traceable to memories of early childhood or even of infant experiences which have become buried in the unconscious mind.

The Early Elementary School Child's Rote Memory Tempts Us to Poor Teaching. Ability to memorize digits or other "nonsense" material develops rapidly between two and ten years, and at ten is nearly as good as it will be in adulthood. Ability to repeat by rote memory is, in fact, so well developed by school entrance that some systems of education yield to the temptation to exact large quantities of repetition of rote materials, laboring, apparently, under the delusion that what can be repeated is of necessity understood. This is one of the greatest fallacies of so-called education. Almost any child of normal intelligence can be coached to repeat numberless nursery rhymes at two or three years of age. Almost any six- or eight-year-old child can be coached to repeat long and complicated extracts from classical literature or from religious catechisms without more than the vaguest idea of the meaning involved.

It is true, however, that, although not at first understood, such materials, well established during early childhood, often become part of a foundation which comes to the surface easily when needed later in life, when it will be better understood. In other words, basic precepts, established early and well, can serve when needed throughout life. There is defense for this viewpoint in the evidences available that a native language, learned early, may lie in disuse throughout an ensuing lifetime, only to make its appearance when senile decay has erased all later memory acquisitions. The danger of such rote learning comes when children are coached under the wrong con-

---

* The law of effect in learning has long taught that learnings accompanied by pleasant feelings are remembered longer than learnings accompanied by unpleasant feelings. Vivid memories, however, remain longer, whether pleasant or unpleasant, than other memories.

ditions or when lapses in the perfection of learning produce punishment for failures which the child cannot overcome without too great strain. Under such conditions the child comes to hate rather than to love the material thus forced upon him, and comes to resent the school or institution which thus demonstrates its lack of human understanding.

Material which is understood by the child can be memorized with far less effort and with far better emotional feeling. Knowing this, our progressive churches and schools have made every effort to help children through stories, dramatization and other interest-rousing and meaning-clarification devices. Reading preparation in kindergartens is helped by placing printed placards directly on the object (e. g., "T A B L E" placed on the table) thus shortening the process of association between printed symbol and the object itself. Learning the multiplication tables and other fundamental number combinations is done through playing games which use the combinations over and over in fun situations. Learning of the classical poems or speeches or extracts from literature is done through dramatization of the ideas, through class analyses of the meanings, and similar expedients.

Some Pure Memory Work Is Useful. We have in current teaching perhaps made learning too easy. It is quite possible for children to learn multiplication tables, spelling lists, classical quotations by sheer rote memory and without any appreciable nervous strain. In fact, they often appreciate the satisfaction of doing an uphill job of using their memories or their reasoning capacities. Even though we must never abandon the greater ease and understanding which accompany progressive methods of teaching, neither should we entirely lose sight of the fact that memory as such is one of the capacities of intellect which is growing rapidly during the preschool and early school years. It should not be allowed to atrophy from disuse.

Studies of the effect of practice upon both immediate and long time memory are reported in nearly all current texts in educational psychology.[93, 207, 209, 229, 386, 776] There is substantial evidence that the old saying "Practice makes perfect" is based upon a sound foundation and, therefore, that training of memory and intellect, of bodily control, and of social skills does produce effective changes in behavior and is eminently worth doing. The warning which Child Development seems to give repeatedly is that if, in giving such training, our society makes the mistake of offering meaningless material, or of forcing training upon an organism not yet ready for it, the effort is futile or even destructive.

Aids to Memory in School Work. In school the practice of recitations during part of each class hour helps children to review the material read, and hence to remember it better. Studies have proved that review and testing of materials studied helps to fix the memory of the materials, particularly when the reviews and tests are spaced judiciously. Spelling, the fundamental processes in arithmetic, and word recognition in reading call for permanent retention of material which is not in itself meaningful. History and social science, however, call for retention of a different type of material. When, as in spelling, fundamentals of arithmetic, and word recognition, material cannot be made meaningful, permanent and accurate retention can best be assured by a degree of what is called "overlearning," or learning by drill beyond the point where the material can just be recalled accurately.

IMITATION AND IMAGINATION

Imitation in Learning   Much learning of younger children in language and action, and of older children in social practices and attitudes, is due to imitation. Just where the line in learning is to be drawn between imitation, which is a reproduction of other people's behavior, and imagination, which is creative rearrangement of experience in one's own mind, is not a matter of concern to us here since we shall discuss them both without too much differentiation.

Many aspects of body postures and habits; tones of voice, diction and vocabulary; emotional reactions and mental attitudes are imitations of those the child sees or hears about him. Luckily, he copies the good as readily as the bad unless the bad is made more interesting and dramatic than the good. In most families, neighborhoods, and schools, the number of things offered to children as learning patterns which are good and should be copied far outweigh those which are bad and should be avoided. Sometimes it seems hard to convince parents and teachers of this, largely because they take the desirable learnings for granted and tend to see and remember only those pieces of behavior which cause trouble.

Whom Do Children Imitate?   What models children choose to imitate deserves consideration. In general they imitate (1) the models they are exposed to first and most continuously. These are the parents. Teachers, to whom children of school age are exposed one-fourth of their waking time between six and eighteen years of age, are also important models. Each teacher, however, is present in the child's life only one year, or, in high school, five hours a week for one or two years. Parents remain the same from year to year. Thus any given teacher is likely to have less permanent influence than the parents. This is fortunate when the teacher's model is bad, unfortunate if good, especially if the general influence of the parents is bad. It is important that both parents and teachers should set a good example. However, they should not attempt to do this in such detail that their own behavior becomes strained and artificial.

Children also imitate (2) models whom they like. Occasionally a well-loved teacher leaves an impression on a child for life even though he or she is with the child only a year. Children and adolescents tend to imitate each other because they like other children or young people and find them more (3) interesting or (4) more exciting than adults. Any model which is dramatic or exciting attracts attention and is likely to mold children's behavior in some degree. This is one reason they take up slang, which is colorful, or profanity, which is explosive, or "dirty stories," which carry an "exciting" atmosphere. Children also often imitate (5) some older person or child because such a person represents being grown-up, which is in itself interesting. Parents, again have an "inside track" in this type of imitation because a two- to ten-year-old boy's idea of grown-upness is ordinarily his father, and the little girl's idea is her mother.

Adults do not always handle the subject of imitation of behavior with intelligence. It is not wise to single out the neighborhood or the schoolroom bad boy or girl for constant harangue or punishment. It calls too much attention to the poor example. Such a boy or girl should be dealt with as inconspicuously as possible in order to avoid calling the attention of the other children to his or her behavior as a possible model for imitation. Making such a child conspicuous may also suggest to some otherwise bored child a way of stirring up excitement for himself. It may, too, rouse the sympathy and support of children who may jump to his or her defense because they think of such a child as "being picked on."

Another frequent adult mistake is to hold up models for praise to the group. Few children react to such preaching favorably, even though the calling of the group's attention to the praised child would seem, in the light of the above paragraph, to be a good way of getting imitation. The trouble seems to be that children singled out for praise are likely to become intoxicated with it and to become obnoxious to the other children. Then, too, in spite of the fact that modern schools have eliminated, as a rule, the old feud between teacher and pupil, a child who is considered "teacher's pet" is very seldom popular. It is unfair to any child to attach that stigma to him by holding him up as a model to the rest of the group. More than this, the usual implication of "Look at John; why can't you be more like him?" is that there is something the matter with you. This does not tend to rouse favorable emotional tones. Hatred of the model and a determination to avoid anything associated with him is far more likely to result than is a supine reflection of the model's behavior. In fact, any child who reacts positively to a model so held before him is probably only courting adult approval while hiding an inner resentment.

Children should be able to earn praise from adults for behavior which grows out of inner conviction and not merely because they are grovelling to please or to hear themselves held up before other children as models of perfection. Natural praise and blame are essential to good teaching, if we make sure that it is not constant personal praise which singles out any child too often, or constant personal blame which stirs resentment and a sense of being picked on. Every child has something he can and should be praised for. Blame should be quiet and firm, holding the child to the best standard of which *he* is capable, not a standard of which some other child is capable.

What Is Imagination? *Constructive imagination* seems best defined as *that quality of thinking which uses facts to solve present or future problems;* or, perhaps, as that capacity which interprets facts in such a way as to improve present and future living. *Destructive imagination may solve present or future problems in a manner which proves bad either for the individual or for society; or which carries the individual away from the world of facts into a world of wishful fantasy,* thus interfering with efficient living. This includes crime, socially destructive invention, lies, and destructive daydreams or psychotic separation of the psychic life from the real world.

How Much Imagination Is Desirable?   We have heard a good deal in recent years about the dangers of imagination. There are many warnings against retreats into the world of fantasy, about escapes from reality, and about the neuroticism which thus results. So much has been said, in fact, that we have on the one hand many parents and teachers who feel guilty if any child in their care loses his immediate grasp on concrete reality for even a moment. From quite different sources, however, we hear a great deal of criticism of the older traditional discipline and education because it stifles imagination, kills initiative, and chokes creativity. We have, then, on the other hand parents and teachers who seize upon every evidence of fanciful play or conversation as a promising step in fruitful creation, exaggerating the fancy of the child, insisting, for example, upon the reality of Santa Claus long after the child is too mature intellectually to swallow such play as real fact.

How much should children's imaginations be cultivated; how much repressed in favor of an acceptance of cold facts? Good progressive educators seem to have solved the dilemma fairly happily. They recognize imagination as the foundation of all progress; yet they realize that any activity of the imagination which interferes with the orderly and efficient meeting of routine living or with the carrying of ideas into fruitful, productive action is ordinarily to be discouraged. Imagination which leads to constructive action is good; that which interferes with or substitutes for necessary action is bad. The action, to be sure, may be only the telling of an entertaining story to others, or the writing of a play, however pointless, or the creation of an invention, however useless. Pointless plays and useless inventions may be socially futile; but psychologically, they represent a healthier use of imagination than a sheer retreat or fantasy would.

In progressive education we find much use of children's imagination and much encouragement of individuality in style and variety of writing, story-telling, craft production, and other forms of activity. However, even though the more imaginative traditional Mother Goose and fairy tales become part of nearly every child's knowledge of literature (he could never make the Quiz Kids or Information Please without them), the major emphasis today is upon the "here and now" type of story or dramatization. These "here and now" stories deal with the fireman or policeman or similar activity chosen from the near environment for younger children, and with other topics chosen from the wider environment for older children. They are factual and current in the child's experience, and provide him with a wealth of information.

In addition to this, good progressive education builds up scientific information through practical experiences which the child can see and create himself. This serves as a background of fact against which children can check "what they think is" against "what is." Thus, with increasing knowledge, fantastic or impossible ideas tend to fade in favor of creatively possible ideas.

Not only is a background of facts built up as a groundwork for "realistic thinking" in this way, but the child is also given continuous practice in checking ideas against facts, a habit which marks the difference between a "wishful thinker" or impractical visionary and the practical thinker or creative producer.

Education Should Develop Constructive and Discourage Destructive Imagination.   The problem of education becomes, then, the problem of helping children to learn to use their imaginations constructively rather than destructively. This involves acquainting children with as wide a set of scientifically accurate facts as possible. It means training children in the habit of using facts rather than wishes as a basis for thinking. It means training the courageous honesty and foresight which makes lying foolish and shortsighted. It means understanding and guiding children's lives so that they can find the kind of emotional satisfactions in their own real worlds which will keep them living in reality, rather than permitting their real worlds to become so starved or unpleasant that they are forced into the world of fantasy for normal satisfaction. All this involves fine programs (1) in schoolroom teaching of subject matter, (2) in daily schoolroom experiences which make the subject matter live and function in the practical, real lives of the children, and (3) the soundest possible understanding of the needs and experiences of each individual child so that his school, and his out-of-school living, prove emotionally satisfying to him. Teachers and parents should understand signs of wrong uses of imagination and should be trained to turn wrong uses and wrong satisfactions into right uses and right satisfactions.

Studies Showing How Much Children Use Their Imaginations.   Make-believe and other imaginative activities occupy a considerable part of the mental life of nearly all children from three or four to ten or twelve years of age. The easiest device we have for knowing this is observation of children's play and of their speech. A little later than the preschool years some light can be thrown on the content of children's imagination by studies of their dreams and of their expressed wishes. Markey,[627] in a study of the imaginative behavior of very young children, found them participating in imaginative situations at the age of two and one-half years on an average of six and one-half imaginative situations per two and one-half hours. At three and one-half years the number of imaginative situations rose to twenty-six in the same period of time. This is a sharp increase, and marks the beginning of the age at which imaginative play comes to occupy an important part of the child's life. The preschool child shows his imagination in such situations as using a row of blocks for a train, pretending that he is eating sand pies, playing with dolls as if they were real babies, and so on.

Burnham,[149] in a study of young children's language, found a similar jump in use of imagination at around three and one-half to four years of age. At two years to two and one-half years of age children's remarks contained 1.5 per cent of imaginative remarks; at three and one-half to four years the percentage rose to 8.7, some instances being quoted in which the proportion of imaginative remarks was as high as 26 per cent before four years of age.

Imaginative Play Often a Key to Inner Feelings.   Leads into children's emotional problems can often be found in studies of their imaginative play, or their casual conversation, or their dreams. Desires and needs which have been forbidden natural outlet often come out in play or talk or dreams where the child feels free of the censor which forbids the more natural outlet. Most expression of such suppressed or repressed needs is unconscious, the child being quite unaware of what he is revealing. Only trained specialists should attempt to read deeper meanings into children's play or dreams, but much insight into the less deeply hidden emotional needs can be gained from observations of play or translations of dreams.*

Imaginary Companions Part of Preschool Imagination.   Imaginary companions live in the imagination of many preschool children. Children deprived of satisfying companionship with other children of their own age group are likely to substitute for this a child or children who live in the imagination. Even in nursery schools, however, where children have a group of children their own age to play with, imaginary companions are common, several studies showing as high as one-third of such children having imaginary companions. In competition with other children, however, envy of a playmate's baby brother may create in the imaginary companion a baby brother who is lacking, or a parent possessing the envied characteristic of some other child's parent. Boys as well as girls have imaginary companions; extrovertive, popular children have them, as do keenly intelligent children. They are often extremely vivid, so that a child may cry in distress because someone sits in a chair occupied at the moment by the imaginary companion, thus squashing him.

Some people suggest dealing with imaginary companions by "playing up" to them, inviting them to dinner in order to get a stubborn child to eat his own dinner, or laughingly laying the blame for a child's forgetfulness or carelessness upon the imaginary companion. This is bad, since it makes the companion too real. We must remember in dealing with imaginary companions that children often have difficulty in differentiating between real things and imagined things. Adults should not add to this confusion by treating imagined things as if they were real. Children, too, often discover, quite without help, the trick of laying blame on the imaginary companion or of using the companion as an excuse. This habit of "projection"** of blame or negligence upon someone or something else should not be encouraged.

On the other hand, it is not wise to treat these companions as a ridiculous fancy or to punish children for them, since this only drives the companions under cover where they are likely to do real damage. They should always be kept in the open. Only so can we know how important to the child they are, and how much of the child's time and attention they occupy.

Imagination During School Age.   Entrance into school is the period of peak in imaginative play. As Strang puts it: "There seems to be a period, somewhere between five and seven years, while the actual world is no longer

---

* See discussion of projective technique, Chapter 3. See also Bibliography.[407,680,732,864]
** "Projection" is one of the least desirable of the escape mechanisms.

new and strange to them and before they become matter-of-fact, when fairy tales add new delights to living for the imaginative child."[905] As children enter the primary school period they can begin to control imagination for useful purposes such as story-telling and painting on the one hand, or sympathy and understanding on the other.

Sympathy, as based upon the capacity to imagine how other people feel in given situations, develops from four years on through the elementary school years. Genuine understanding of how other people feel, except for the most imaginative people, is based upon some personal experience in the given situation. Sympathy for a wide range of situations is not, therefore, usual until adulthood, where the individual has accumulated a wide range of experiences.

Children of nine to twelve believe in luck, magic, and superstitions—ideas which continue throughout life unless the children are given facts with which to correct these impressions. For example, earlier in their lives they have probably believed in Santa Claus, the Easter bunny, and fairies. As they mature, however, they have been able to replace these ideas with the facts, in many cases preserving the desirable aspects of the former belief in the idea of Santa as the spirit of Christmas and giving, of Easter as a deeply significant reawakening, of fairies as the spirit of adventure and making hard things come true. It is at the elementary school age that facts ordinarily come to replace the more childlike phases of the imagination, and that satisfactions with the gang prove more genuine than satisfactions from daydreams. Belief in luck, magic, and superstitions should give way to facts as the child approaches pubescence.

Imaginary Illness May Start During Early School Age.   Another trait of imagination which should not be encouraged is imaginary illness. Some children have discovered that complaint of pain or refusal to eat causes real anxiety to the parent, or gets sympathy and excuse from work from the teacher. Such an exciting way to get attention, or such an easy escape from an unpleasant task is a great temptation. Adults must be watchful, lest children learn the habit of "cashing in on weakness," since, like projection, this is a destructive practice. Children who tend to do this should be quietly but firmly faced with what they are doing and helped to undertake the disagreeable task instead of running away from it or to learn better ways of bidding for adult attention. Adults must, however, be very sure of what they are doing here, since to ignore a child who is really in pain, or to drive a child to work when he is really ill, especially to imply that he is a liar when he is not, gives rise to a deep sense of outrage and injustice. Any child who is in pain or ill should not be ignored. The only safe rule for the adult is that if there is any doubt whatever about any given stituation the child should be taken at his word. A further suggestion is, that when illness occurs, it should not be made any more dramatic or satisfying than is necessary to keep the sick child comfortable and reasonably happy.

Daydreams.   Daydreams are part of normal development in children. During the elementary school years children are likely to daydream of adventure and conquest through physical feats; in adolescence they are likely to wander about mentally in wealth and luxury or in romantic conquest. These daydreams sometimes become so complicated that they require genuine concentration of attention to follow, in which case the passive fantasy either turns into a form of business-like, uphill thinking, or is abandoned because it bogs down of its own weight.

It is generally agreed among child psychologists that almost every child daydreams to some extent. Abnormality is to be recognized when the fantasies become persistent and symbolic of deeper or hidden wishes and conflicts. It is then that we know the child has escaped into the world of unreality where the events and occurrences of the real world play only an incidental and unimportant role in behavior. The milder forms of systematic fantasy probably serve as a desirable outlet for repressed conflicts which, denied all expression, might become dangerous. However, a decrease in the quality of a child's schoolwork, lagging concentration, wandering attention, particularly in children whose behavior has not had this quality, should be regarded as possible symptoms of a deeper psychologic trouble.

As in every other form of imagination, there is a constructive and a destructive use of daydreams. Most of us have to dream of conquest before we exert the necessary effort to make a conquest real. We must dream of ourselves as more poised, more learned, or more successful before we make the effort to learn social poise, to study, or to improve our jobs. Adolescent daydreams, which picture the young person to himself as a better, finer, more successful person than he is, are often the motive force which leads to the necessary action. Daydreams of the sort which lead to such action are good. However, many daydreams are of the sort that lead to discontent with the world we must face when the dream is over. These are often stimulated by highly romantic movies or novels which picture a path of roses or a degree of luxury impossible for most mortals. Hours spent with such movies and novels are good if they give rest and a momentary fulfillment of ordinary longings for romance and luxury, leaving one rested and willing again to take up the routine of life as it is. They are bad if they deepen discontent, or if they prove so attractive that the individual gives up the struggle to adjust to life as he must meet it, and retreats into the world of fantasy.

We can see tendencies in either direction in young children. The five- or six-year-old child who consistently prefers his imaginary companion to readily available real companions is probably revealing the fact that he cannot "take it" with real children. His imaginary companion is manageable, does as he is told, offers no resistance to the child's domination. Real companions are not so manageable. However, for the average, normally extrovertive or out-going child, real companions are more fun, because they have more ideas. Living with an imaginary companion is satisfying to a child through more than a year or so of time only if he is either a keenly imaginative child who can keep himself endlessly amused with his own ideas, or a deeply frustrated child who cannot find normal happiness in the company of other children. No child who prefers an imaginary companion to a real one can be changed in his preference by scolding or punishment. He can be changed only by being shown how he can gain increasing satisfactions from real children, and this takes a great deal of understanding and patience on the part of the adult as well as some cooperation from the other children who are available.

The Tendency to Exaggerate Facts. Children who exaggerate do so to make an impression. All children do it sometimes, the periods when it is most usual being in the gang stage when there is a great need to appear equal to the gang in strength and possessions, and in the adolescent period when the need takes a slightly different though often even more intense form. Boasting about possessions and accomplishments, either real or imagined, should not be taken too seriously by adults unless it becomes a habit which carries the child too far astray. It is bad when the child indulges in it in the face of taunts and check-ups from his peers, showing that he fails to realize that he is not "getting away with it." It is bad, too, when the boasts about things that are not so become so habitual that the child loses track of what an accurate statement really is. It is bad when it becomes an evidence that the child is failing to impress his peers with real accomplishments and is, therefore, filling the gap with words in place of deeds.

Again, as above, the best weapon to use in correction is not punishment but, rather, help to develop in the child a wholesome pride in his accuracy. Sometimes it helps to make him realize that increasing ostracism from the group is due to his tall stories without deeds to back them up and that a better way is to do the deeds and let someone else tell about them if they rate being told about. Children who are physically handicapped are among those who may find it too hard, or even impossible, to gain normal attention and affection from children of their own age and for whom, therefore, the temptation is great to resort to daydreaming or to false boasts. These children need a special program to teach them how to make life interesting for themselves and for others through the development of other traits than those involved in vigorous physical play.

Children's Lies: a Frequent Problem in Growth of Imagination. Children's lies, as differentiated from mere exaggeration of facts, offer a sufficient problem to the average teacher and parent to be given some discussion here. All children lie sometimes, since a number of types of lies are simply the product of usual developmental patterns. The natural boasting mentioned above belongs in this classification, and occurs in the natural development of bids for attention from one's peers at the gang age or at adolescence. The confusions between fact and fancy which are characteristic of three- to six-year-old children are another type of so-called lie which is the by-product of a stage of development. Many of the preschool child's compromises with the truth are due to his genuine inability to discriminate between what happened and what he imagined as happening. Children of preschool and early school age see many things taking place around them which seem due to magic or fairies. They see someone push a button near a door and flood a room with light. They see hard green apples go into an oven and come out soft and brown.

Without the knowledge of the magic in electricity or the effect of heat, these things seem no less marvelous to a four-year-old than that a fairy should grant any childish wish he may think up. Experience with real things and a widening knowledge of science help the child to discriminate with increasing accuracy between fact and fancy.

Some children lie playfully, watching to see the effect "of the whopper" upon the audience. The fact that other children of equal or of less factual experience sometimes believe these yarns leads children to take a chance on what adult reaction will be. This is especially true in the gang age, and again in adolescence. Not infrequently the adult reaction is (and should be) a laugh rather than a scolding. It is probably wise for the adult to add "You don't expect me to believe *that*, do you?", or some other indication that the yarn is understood as a yarn. Occasionally children begin telling a story based upon truth, only to find themselves captivated by possibilities for embroidering the original fabric. In time they learn the difference between telling a story to amuse people (as they themselves are amused by talking animals, etc.) and reporting a factual situation.

Some children's lies are lies of loyalty to protect a friend in trouble, or to appear noble in assuming blame and punishment to protect another child. This is particularly likely to happen during the gang age. In the long run we wish to develop such loyalty, but children need help to differentiate between when such protection is wise or noble and when another person needs the lesson of being faced with his faults or mistakes.

Somewhat more serious than these are the lies of fear. Many children lie to avoid punishment or to escape the consequences of what they have done. These lies may be rooted in either of two causes: (1) The punishment may be too severe for an average child to bear without attempting to escape; (2) the given child may be too much of a coward to face an ordinary punishment. In the former instance the severity of punishment should be lessened and a more understanding attitude adopted toward the child. In the latter, the child must learn that the consequences of the lie are worse than the original punishment, and thus that facing the truth in the first place pays. In every other possible way such children should be helped to develop the courage to face everyday life situations. In the occasional case in which the child's total nervous constitution makes him retreat from ordinarily difficult situations, the demand of the situation may have to be lightened enough to locate the point at which the child can face the situation without retreat, and the severity gradually increased as he proves able to take the load. Otherwise he may by too severe discipline be driven into exaggerated symptoms of nervousness and withdrawal, or he may be driven into more and more clever evasions.

Some lies which attempt to cover up work not done or to gain a reward show a wide resourcefulness of imagination in their inventiveness. If the work is too hard for the child's ability, or if an overemphasis is put upon stars on the blackboard or honor listings, children cannot help being tempted to gain what is expected of them but what they cannot win honestly. Cheating is often produced in this way. Public rewards should be varied enough to give children of all types of ability a chance at the publicity. If, however, a child's lie is an evasion of a reasonable job or an attempt to gain a reward which he could gain with reasonable work, then the problem becomes one of helping him to understand that such behavior is less satisfactory in the long run than the effort of doing the necessary work would have been.

Some children lie because the adult puts them into a corner and through overpowering suggestion compels them to say what is expected regardless of whether it is so or not. Some children cannot bear to "let" their parents or teacher "down," and even though they can easily take a punishment, they cannot bear to disappoint people. Occasionally an unwise adult by third degree methods extracts a confession which later proves to have been false. There are few ways of damaging children's psychologic lives more severely than this. When in doubt, it is better to let a child get away with a lie than to make him confess falsely.

Probably the worst forms of lies are the lies to gain selfish ends and the lies to get revenge or to tear down someone else. Children who try out a lie or so in order to get what they want usually learn from one or two experiences that it does not pay. If, however, any child sticks persistently to lying for selfish purposes or to get back at other people, he reveals a fundamental defect which should receive the attention of a specialist in children's behavior. If no specialist is available, the parent or teacher must make every effort to analyze why this child must get what he wants at no matter what cost. (1) Is he spoiled and in need of a gradual development of pride in doing work, adjusting to the needs and desires of others, learning "to take it"? If he is spoiled he must be handled firmly though gently since a too brutal hardening process will either break him or send him into a corner with his back against the world, there to develop still more clever devices for getting his own way. (2) If he is so starved for love, or for status that he must lie to gain that for which every child hungers, then every effort must be made to give him what he needs in security and status by honest means within his command. In every case of dishonesty in children, the development of pride in honor is a better way to proceed than to attempt to govern the child by fear of the consequences of dishonor alone.

Genuine understanding of the difference between fact and fancy, between what is and what one wishes to be, between taking an advantage now as against curbing oneself in favor of the future—all this requires a well developed and well disciplined imagination. A sense of honor, self-control, and a vision into the future should remain a clear objective for parents and teachers in the guidance of children's developing imaginations.

CREATIVE ABILITY

What Is Creativity? "Creative ability is usually regarded as a special talent or aptitude which manifests itself late in adolescence or in adulthood and somewhat exclusively among young people and adults who are not quite normal in other respects." Millard,[668, p.175] the author of this statement, goes on to point out that nothing could be further from the truth, that creative ability is present to some degree in nearly all children.

The belief by some misguided persons that "to be creative" is to "be different" or "to express oneself" has led in certain quarters to the assumption that the way to develop a creative capacity is to encourage children to express any and every impulse. Millard calls attention to the fact that (p. 181) "creative ability does not include every uninhibited word or act. . . . Such acts in and by themselves are not necessarily creative, and teachers should be skeptical of the validity of anecdotal data which so characterize every little personality quirk. Deviations in thought and action provide important insights into personality . . . (but) not all such differences in behavior can be called 'creative.' " Huggett and Millard[448] define creativity as follows: "Fundamentally, to create means to endow with meaning a personalized experience. Usually such an activity involves the creation of something new to the individual. . . . A creative act at its best is accompanied by an affective, emotional state."

How Does Creative Action Occur? Creation occurs in the realm of thinking, as well as in art forms. The value of "inspiration" in scientific invention and research, in creative planning for industry or government, and in one's own planning for daily living are known to us as "creative thinking." That such creative production in the deeper realms of thinking comes "out of the clear blue" is an idea with no foundation, according to Walters and O'Hara,[975] who point out that the available evidence shows clearly that (p. 357) "preceding the moment of inspiration there is usually a more or less prolonged preparation, much of which has been devoted to hard work or study. Apparently nothing comes out when the basic ingredients have not been put in, although the organization and form may be truly new and creative." They give four stages of the creative process as follows: (1) preparation, (2) incubation, (3) illumination, and (4) verification. In such creative thinking is seen the value of background and study and of concentration. For significant contribution to any of the art fields, however, this need for a solid background of hard work for knowledge of the works of others, and especially for mastery of the basic techniques of the art involved, seems evident. No composer, writer or painter produces anything enduring without a solid background of technical knowledge and skill. This comes only with long and concentrated work.

Creativity involves also, in addition to the hard work and self-discipline of the master creator, an identification of oneself with the creative activity, the element of self-expression through the medium used, and an ensuing feeling of progress, success, and personal release with resulting peace or happiness. Even in the rudimentary "messing" with finger painting or with clay, or with shop tools in one's basement, there are the facts of self-identification, self-expression, and emotional satisfaction. What seems to be necessary with children is to give them, from early babyhood, opportunities to use toys in ways which *they* initiate (so long, of course, as these ways do not involve destructive or selfish behavior), to build with blocks, to use imagination with a wide variety of "do-with" toys, to express thought and feelings in words or in action, and to feel the satisfaction of such self-expression so long as it is not destructive to others, to property or to their own futures. Thus the child is encouraged early to be independent in his thinking and expression so that his individual personality can find avenues of expression which are his own. Lowenfeld[601] summarizes a discussion of the difference between creativity or self-expression and imitation of the ideas and actions as follows (p. 8):

Self-Expression	contrasted with	*Imitation*
Expression according to child's own level	. . . .	Expression according to strange level
Independent thinking	. . . .	Dependent thinking
Emotional outlet	. . . .	Frustration
Freedom and flexibility	. . . .	Inhibitions and restrictions
Easy adjustments to new situations	. . . .	Getting along with set patterns
Progress, success, happiness	. . . .	Leaning toward others, dependency, stiffness

Thus we see that doing what one is told all the time, or drawing, painting or using any other art form on a copy or imitation basis is to lose the point of the whole performance.

Creative Skills Grow and Develop Through Definite Stages. As with all other skills and abilities, the creative skills and abilities grow and develop through definite stages. Certain basic neural and muscular developmental maturities must be present; certain preliminary stages must be gone through; certain motor, intellectual and imaginative skills must be achieved; certain knowledge and appreciations must be cultivated; certain natural "bents," "interests" or, in exceptional cases, talents must be present. "Training" or "lessons," *per se*, can accomplish nothing without these.

Each art goes through certain preliminary, then later stages of development. Lowenfeld[601] traces development of art through such stages as "disorderly scribbling" (around age two), longitudinal, or controlled scribbling, naming of the scribbling, achievements of form concepts (7 to 9 years), the dawning realism (9 to 11 years), the pseudorealistic or reasoning stage (11 to 13 years), and the period of decision (adolescence). He points out, of course, that these are average ages and that, as in all growth, children pass through these or other stages depending upon talent and opportunity.*

Comparably, children go through rather specific stages of development in music and rhythm (dancing) activities, in clay modeling and sculpture, and in other art areas.**

Suggestions for Parents and Teachers. As was stated above, if creativity in children is to be encouraged, children should have opportunity in babyhood and in early childhood to use toys and other play experiences on an imaginative and free basis. Free play situations, "do-with" toys, and

---

* Lowenfeld: Creative and Mental Growth (1952) gives many details of this development and how to encourage it. He also gives many helpful suggestions to teachers for developing creative ability in schools.

** For discussion of early stages see Rand[756] (1953) and Read[759] (1955). For school-aged children see Millard[668] (1951), Strang[905] (1951), and Guthrie and Powers[386] (1950).

plenty of paper, pencils, crayons, paint, clay, scissors, blocks and imaginative stories offer stimulus to the imagination, training in techniques to the hands, in independent thinking to the mind, and in joy of self-expression to the emotions. If "genius is to burn" in any child it will require opportunity and some encouragement, but no forcing. Many a good potential artist has been ruined by too formal lessons and too long hours of "practicing" too soon in the maturing process.* Millard[668] charges teachers and parents to have unlimited patience, and to be willing to provide time for creative ability. Recognizing the wide individual differences in areas of creativity for each child, he urges that the widest possible variety of areas and of media for expression be made available to children. Lowenfeld[601] is quite specific and says (p. 3ff.), "Don't impose your own images on a child. . . . Never prefer one child's creative work over that of another. . . . Never let a child copy anything." Probably the most important thing to accomplish in creative activity is that it should be enjoyed. Laudeck** points out that the goal of music is enjoyment and few pleasures are more stimulating and rewarding than the close sharing in the creation of music. She urges parents, teachers and children to cast aside inhibitions and to have fun with music. This should be said of all forms of art: Families can enjoy them together on a purely amateur basis with very rewarding results in mutual enjoyment, not only of the art or of the shop work (however rudimentary) but, even more important, of each other.

Training of Creative Capacities Important to General Growth and Adjustment. The importance of training in the expression of emotions and of individuality through creative activity is receiving much attention in the mental hygiene field. Constructive use of leisure time in a world in which working hours are being shortened and in which commercial recreation of a passive type is on the increase becomes of greater and greater importance. "The devil finds work for idle hands to do" is a maxim which leads to an emphasis upon both physical play programs and upon the development of love of music, art, reading, crafts, gardening, and other constructive leisure time activities. These programs have in mind not only the prevention of delinquency, but also the enrichment of living. An important way to heal sick minds is to give hands and intellects something creative to do and to enjoy. Human happiness and purposefulness in living are greatly enriched because of interests and skills which occupy time richly rather than leaving it empty or filled only with cheap movies or noneducational radio or TV programs.

Programs in school which train hands, eyes and ears in arts, crafts, music and dancing are considered helpful not only as creators of good leisure time

---

* Many of the best piano teachers now proceed on the sound psychologic basis of accepting for lessons (with the rarest exceptions of outstanding talent) only children of eight to ten years old because they can then reach sixths on the piano (there is little interesting work written in thirds) and have the maturity level to proceed into fairly serious work. These teachers also refuse to let a child practice for the first year or so unless the teacher is present (thus avoiding the practicing of too many errors), and thereafter upgrade the amount of practice permitted as it becomes evident that the hours put in will be of benefit.

** Laudeck, B.: Children and Music. New York, William Sloan Associates, 1952. This book contains a comprehensive and excellent reference list on creative activity.

activities, but also as mental health devices and as means of training children in concentration and satisfaction in work.

EXPERIENCES TO VITALIZE CLASS WORK

1. Discuss the pros and cons of requiring rote memorizing:
   a. In the primary grades.
   b. In high school.
2. Visit a church school. Are its methods conducive to the development of genuine insight into the principles being taught? Is any provision made for helping the children to live the principles taught?
3. How would you decide whether a poor speller:
   a. Was defective in general memory?
   b. Was more auditory than visual in his type of imagery and therefore less able than average children to remember how words look?
   c. Was unfamiliar with English at home, hence lacking in basic understanding of and familiarity with the words he is trying to spell?
   What could you do about each of these?
4. From the discussion on types of models imitated by children can you make any suggestions for improving the models you saw in action in the last school room (or Sunday school) you visited?
5. Visit a schoolroom or draw on your memory of one and list the things you saw which:
   a. Encourage destructive imagination in the children.
   b. Encourage constructive imagination in the children.
6. How can a teacher use children's creative imagination in order to help them learn rote materials like history dates, number combinations, spelling rules?
7. In view of your understanding of why children lie, how can you educate children to the value of truth?
8. What would you do with a child who gets sick just before the arithmetic period every day? With an adolescent who faints when sent to the principal's office? With a chronic day-dreamer? With an adolescent who romances over movie stars to the neglect of school lessons?
9. From the discussion on creative ability, combined with what you have learned of motor (general bodily and vocal) skills, sketch a program which would teach music and rhythm or art:
   a. In the primary grades.
   b. In the intermediate grades.
   c. In high school.
10. If you are doing a case study, gather material on "your child" about his memory, his imagination, and his creative abilities.

SUGGESTED READINGS

Biber, B., et al.: Child Life in School. New York, E. P. Dutton & Co., 1942.

Biber, B., et al.: Life and Ways of the Seven- to Eight-Year-Old. New York, Basic Books, Inc., 1952, Ch. 9.

Hartley, R. E., et al.: Understanding Children's Play. New York, Columbia University Press, 1952, Chs. 1, 2, 3.

Hurlock, E. B.: Child Psychology. Rev. ed. New York, McGraw-Hill Book Co., 1950, Ch. 10.

Jersild, A. T.: Child Psychology. New York, Prentice-Hall, Inc., 1954, Chs. 15, 16.

Lindsey, H. L.: The Nature and Conditions of Learning. New York, Prentice-Hall, Inc., 1946, Chs. 13–15.

Lowenfeld, V.: Creative and Mental Growth. New York, The Macmillan Co., 1952.

Millard, C. V.: Child Growth and Development in the Elementary School Years. Boston, D. C. Heath & Co., 1951, Ch. 8.

Walters, S. A., and S. K. O'Hara: Persons and Personality. New York, Appleton-Century-Crofts, Inc., 1953, Ch. 13.

CHAPTER 11

Growth of Language, Thinking and Reasoning

DEVELOPMENT OF LANGUAGE

In man language becomes one of the most important implements of intelligence. Some behavioristic psychologists have, in fact, said that all truly human thinking takes place by means of language. This is probably not true, but it indicates something of the importance of language as an expression of and as a means to reasoning. Language is also a primary means of social intercourse, being used not only to relieve people's own feelings or to air their own views, but also to awaken a response in other people and to influence their attitudes and behavior.[109,608,659] Animals have certain means of communication, just as human beings do, through tones of voice and through gestures. But in man verbal expression offers the possibility of transmitting fine shades of meaning and steps of logic which are almost impossible of transmission otherwise.

One of the most important tasks of schools is to train children in the facile understanding and use of their native language. To read quickly and with understanding, to speak fluently and accurately, to write intelligently are goals clearly set as educational objectives in nearly all schools. We cannot truly und erstand the culture and the thinking of any country until we understand its language. The same thing is true of the culture and thinking of one's owncountry. Therefore an understanding of the steps of development in language skills becomes necessary to good teaching. However, when the child enters school, and therefore before he has had any formal teaching from the school, he has made long strides in the development of language. This is in many respects a demonstration of an educational achievement of the first magnitude.

Language an Abstraction of Objects or Situations. We have seen something of how the baby learns about the properties of objects around him, how he learns to react intelligently to the situations which surround him. He does this more and more effectively in the realm of concrete objects and of concrete situations progressively throughout his life. After a few months of such learning in the beginning of his life, however, he begins the next step in "intellectualization," namely, he begins to associate voice sounds with various objects and situations.* Learning to attach meaning to sound takes many forms. Even the very young infant learns to single out and to appreciate his mother's voice from all the other sounds which come to his ears. He learns to associate all the comfort of his mother's care with this sound so that in genuine emergencies her voice and her arms can bring comfort when all else fails. He learns quickly, too, to understand the meaning of crossness in her voice. Babies of a few months react with fear or with hurt feelings to scolding tones in the voice. By slow steps and constant practice they begin to single out from all the tones and words spoken a few words which have definite meaning. The baby of a year is fairly good at reacting to tones of voice, and can react specifically to a dozen or so special words. From this point understanding of language progresses rapidly; the separate words, and later phrases and sentences, are substituted for or symbolize the objects or actions which they represent.

One of the amusing tricks of a nine-months-old baby is to wriggle with anticipation when his cap is put on his head because he knows this means going out. By twelve to eighteen months most children have managed to say the "bye-bye" which indicates going bye-bye, and the word "go" or "out" enters the vocabulary of most children at this time. The tiny infant has no way of indicating that he is thirsty but to cry, with the result that the anxious adult may try out a number of possibilities before arriving at the drink which relieves the child. The acquisition of the ability to say "nuken" or "wawa," if understood by the adult, at once indicates the child's need, but only to the select circle of adults who understand this jargon. Only when the child can say "water" or "drink" can he get results from the public at large.

Most children have acquired an effective working vocabulary to meet immediate life needs by the age of three; and, by the age of five, they have acquired a vocabulary which expresses quite varied shades of meaning and makes oral exchange of fairly complicated thoughts possible. The next stage of abstraction lies ahead, namely the recognition of a set of marks on a page which represent the words he has previously learned to speak. His first abstraction of the object or situation is to use a spoken word to represent it; now he learns words on a printed page as representation of the spoken word. Thus he learns to read. Later he may learn a shorthand symbol as a further representation or abstraction of the written or printed word, or a mathematical or chemical formula as a representation of a very complex situation.

How the Baby Learns the Beginnings of Language. There are two processes involved when a child learns language. (1) He must master the control of breath, larynx, and tongue necessary to speak. (2) He must make the associations between meaning and object or situation which were discussed under sense perceptions and sense judgments in Chapter 9. Language is good only to express meanings. If there are no meanings to express, the child develops no spoken language. We shall see later that restricted general experience is at the root of the difficulty which some children have in master-

---

* This development closely parallels other development in the child, being related to postural control, feeding behavior and dentition. See McCarthy[610] (1952).

ing spoken language as a preliminary to the mastery of reading and composition.

Control of the Mechanisms of Speech. In the first few days of life the infant must learn that air drawn backward over the voice box during crying causes choking. Air must be sent out over the voice box. Even at a month it is possible to understand something in the character of the cry—pain, rage, or just plain exercise. From two months on, experimentation with the vocal mechanism is almost as constant as the movements of arms and legs and head by which the child, during his waking hours, is learning control over his body in general. By four months most infants have fairly well mastered the principles basic to effective use of the vocal mechanism. They blow bubbles, coo, chuckle, gurgle, laugh, constantly experimenting with the use of tongue, larynx, and breath control. This constant use of sounds is called the babble stage of language learning. Through it the infant learns the modifications in tension of vocal cords, tongue, and lips necessary to the formation of each of the sounds. He has command of most of the vowel and a few consonant sounds at four months. By six or seven months he has controlled most of the vowel and consonant sounds and many of the diphthongs and syllables necessary to speech. By eight months he has mastered the foundation sounds from which he can develop the basic language (such as English or French), which he later speaks as his native language.[375] By nine months the babble softens into the rhythm of the speech the child hears around him. Actual words, used disciminatingly, begin to develop at eleven or twelve months when the child's active vocabulary is usually "mama," "dada," and one or two other words.

Development of Vocabulary. *Active vocabulary,* or words which the child can use, develops rapidly from eighteen months on. Smith's[870] studies of increases in vocabulary have been quoted widely, since they were done with great care and, although they have been supplemented, they have not been replaced. She gives the vocabularies of children as follows:

Age (in months)	Number of Words	Gain
8	0	
10	1	1
12 (1 year)	3	2
15	19	16
18 (1½ years)	22	3
21	118	96
24 (2 years)	272	154
36 (3 years)	896	624
48 (4 years)	1,540	644
60 (5 years)	2,072	532
72 (6 years)	2,562	490

The slowness of the development between fifteen and eighteen months is usually explained by the fact that most children are concentrating on the mastery of upright walking at this age and do not seem to have psychologic or physical energy available for increases in language ability. Gesell[345] did not find quite such rapid increases in acquisition of active vocabulary as those reported in the above table. His average at eighteen months was between ten and eleven words. He points out, also, that all children learn words which they seem to forget from time to time. In spite of this, however, from both Gesell's and Smith's studies we see a gain of 500 to 600 words yearly for average children between ages two and six.

There are, of course, marked individual differences in size of vocabulary at every age.[608] Gesell comments upon the wide individual differences in vocabulary apparent as early as eighteen months. In his group of forty children at this age he found a range from four words for one child to "too many words to enumerate" as reported by the mothers of three others. There are also wide individual differences in clearness of enunciation throughout the preschool years, some children speaking clearly even at two years of age, others still speaking so imperfectly as to be very hard to understand at school entrance. Language is essentially a matter of imitation of models. It is important to give children clear models from the beginning by speaking clearly to them rather than yielding to the temptation to talk their own imperfect baby talk back to them.

Increase in vocabulary still continues rapidly after school entrance. Gains reported from grades 3 through 8 vary from 1500 to 3000 words per year, with increases continuing through the high school period at the end of which most studies show an average usable vocabulary of 15,000 to 18,000 words. These increases depend, of course, upon continued expansion of general experience and, particularly, upon the quality of teaching and the range and selection of the child's reading.

Passive vocabulary, or what one understands even though one cannot command the words for active use, always *exceeds active vocabulary* at every stage of development.[608] Even at sixteen weeks an infant will turn his head to the sound of a human voice, and seems to "recognize" his mother or nurse, perhaps smiling delightedly at her approach. By six or seven months he is familiar with a mass of situations and objects, the names of which he begins to recognize. By a year he has a fairly extensive passive vocabulary, which from that time forward continues to develop even more rapidly than his active vocabulary. Many adults, reading magazines and newspapers or listening to the radio, go on expanding passive vocabulary long after their active vocabularies have become static. Listening to the radio or TV is a considerably better aid to increasing of active vocabulary than is reading alone, since it extends the recognition of words beyond seeing and into hearing. One more step is necessary, namely speaking. Words which we recognize the meaning of when read may often spring up to our tongues to be used, but we avoid them because we are not sure of the pronunciation. Radio and TV help this. The final aid, however, is to speak the word until it no longer feels strange on the tongue; only so can it become part of an active vocabulary. Reading of good literature aloud, with a dictionary at hand to check upon pronunciation, is probably the best way to go on expanding active vocabulary throughout life.

Growth of Language Facility.   Words alone do not make speech. It is the type of words used and the groupings of words into sentences which determine true facility. When language responses first put in their appearance the child uses single words to express himself, those words often being repeated several times. As he grows older, more and more words are joined together until ultimately the sentence, first in a structurally incomplete but functionally complete form, puts in its appearance, to be followed by sentences which are both functionally and structurally complete. Smith[870] and McCarthy[609] have both obtained similar figures for the length of sentence in relation to age. According to Smith the child at two years uses 1.7 words on the average to the sentence and at five years 4.6 words per sentence. McCarthy found at the age of eighteen months a mean length of response of 1.2 words, which rises by gradual increments to 4.6 words per response at the age of four years and six months.

Type of Sentence Structure.   At the age of eighteen months simple sentences, consisting of a noun and a verb, have put in their appearance, these being followed somewhat later by simple sentences with a single phrase, then by more complex sentences and compound sentences.* Up to the age of four and a half years, complex and compound sentences constitute only a small proportion of the total number of sentences. Nevertheless it is worthy of note that virtually every form of sentence structure has put in its appearance by the age of five or six years. In the earlier years there are many declarative sentences (which are more frequent than any other at all ages) and many imperative sentences.

The preschool trend toward longer and increasingly complex sentences continues into the school years and on into maturity.[30] Hoppes'[436,437,438] studies of elementary school composition show that in theme writing the simple sentence is the type most frequently used by children in grades 4 to 6, although there is a small, but consistent growth from grade to grade in complex sentences and in compound-complex sentences.** He concludes that help in the use of complex sentences should be given in all grades, and that children below the sixth grade should also be given help in the use of simple sentences. He furnishes, too, a list of suggestions by which elementary school teachers can be helped to estimate progress in language expression: (*a*) increasing length of sentence, (*b*) decreasing ratio of simple to complex and compound sentences from grades 3 to 8, (*c*) marked decrease in run-on sentences beyond the fourth grade, (*d*) decrease in unpleasant repetition of words, (*e*) decline in number of sentences beginning with the pronoun I, and several other suggestions.

Symonds and Daringer[924] in a careful study of sentence structure found that in the fourth grade there are an average of about two errors in every sentence in children's writings, and that this ratio decreases gradually until about the

---

* Gesell[345] (p. 195) says, "Compound and complex sentences, and even sentences with brief subordinate phrases, are rare until along toward three years, but are occasionally heard at two years."

** Other studies[416] corroborate Hoppes' work in showing the peak of use of simple sentences at ages eight to ten (grades 4 and 5) with decreasing use of this form of sentence in favor of increasing use of compound, of complex and of compound-complex sentence from ages ten to fourteen (grades 5 to 9) and throughout the high school period.

eighth or ninth grade, when only about one error per sentence is made. The teacher should, therefore, watch for progress in the reduction of the number of errors per sentence. However, Davis[218] points out the desirability of watching children's progress in terms of correct usages in language, rather than in terms of errors. In her study she found that the number of correct usages increased, and the number of incorrect usages decreased with advancing age, both in absolute numbers and in proportion to the total number of words used. She also found that, as is to be expected, children from upper socio-economic groups, having better language examples at home, make fewer errors than children from lower socio-economic groups. It is encouraging to note, however, that children from the lower socio-economic groups made the greatest improvement in the elimination of errors in the early school years.

Quality of Compositions. The quality of children's compositions improves very slowly from grade to grade.[909] Brueckner[138] points out why this should be so.

> The growth of the ability to write well-organized compositions and letters is a highly complicated process. In the first place, there is involved the gradual development of the oral and written vocabulary. When these are inadequate, the pupil finds difficulty in expressing his ideas, often because of lack of basic experience—he may have no thoughts to express about the topic under consideration. In the second place, there is involved a complex developing physical process (namely, handwriting) that interferes seriously with the expression of ideas in the case of young children. In the third place, there are numerous formalities in style, usage, and grammar that must be borne in mind in expressing ideas. Finally, the pupil must master numerous rules for capitalization and punctuation, which in themselves constitute a real burden.

These mechanics impede fluent expression. One experiment in teaching[839] encouraged young children to dictate stories, poems, or other compositions. Relieved of the necessity of struggling through mechanics, the children "produced charming and meaningful compositions." Many progressive teachers now use this method of encouraging composition. This is an excellent device for helping children to organize and express thoughts on various topics. It should not be used exclusively, however, if children are ever to develop the capacity to write letters or other types of written work. Children need training in the mechanics; teachers need to know how to make the satisfaction of doing one's own writing overbalance the drudgery involved. Studies on the effect of typewriting skill[391] upon the fluency of written composition indicate that typing reduces the physical strain of writing compositions, and facilitates expression, even in the lower grades.

Studies of what use is made of written composition[59,294] show that letter-writing is the writing activity most used by children in the junior and senior high schools, next in order the writing of stories and poems, the keeping of diaries, and the listing of items, the combined total of the last three uses being about equal to letter-writing in frequency. Filling out forms, keeping minutes, and taking notes on what is read outside school are activities confined to only a few children in the junior and senior high schools.

Oral Composition. According to Brueckner,[138] there are few studies available which can give reliable measures of the improvement of the quality of oral composition. These deal with analyses of error rather than with the growth of the quality or richness of oral expression. Several studies[49,59] of the frequency of use of oral speech as distinguished from written composition testify to the far greater use of oral language over written language at every level of development. These studies also show, however, that written composition occupies far more of the language teaching time in nearly all schools than is given to oral composition and expression. The implication is clearly in the direction of a recommendation for greater emphasis upon oral composition.

As in the *studies* of development of all aspects of growth, studies of oral and written composition *reveal tremendous differences of level or development at every chronologic age and every academic grade.* It is a common thing to find in a single class a range in these abilities of as much as six grades or six years of development. It is not unusual to find college students whose language ability ranges as low as the standard for sixth grade. Such a wide range of language ability offers a serious problem to every teacher of English. Some means are now available for estimating the language ability of each student in each of the major branches of language learning.* Some technique of teaching must be developed which can insure progress for each student at his own level.

Specific Uses of Language. Probably the first use of language from the earliest vocalizations is to make known feelings,[608] wants, or needs, and to secure information. "Go bye-bye," "Mine," "Bobby wants a drink," and the persistent "What's that?" "Why?" of the question-asking stage of the three- and four-year-old child are examples. One investigator[115] found that in a single day his three-year-old child asked 376 questions, and that his four-year-old child asked 397. This is probably somewhat high for average children, but gives an idea of why this age is referred to as the question stage. Even at three years language serves the purpose of simple narration, the incidents talked about usually being telescoped into a single simple sentence: "We went downtown," being used to cover all the exciting situations involved. Occasional children of three can enlarge upon this, and some children of four can tell enough of an incident to hold the attention of other children for short periods. Imaginative elements often creep in, possibly as a reflection of the stories being read to children at that age: "Once there was a big engine. It came right up to the door and asked for breakfast."

The most complicated and advanced use of language is to express reasoning: "If I don't wear my mittens I won't get them dirty," or "Where does my dinner go when I eat it?" As the child's experience enlarges, and as his mastery of vocabulary increases, the form of reasoning he can do becomes increasingly complex. He is usually in the fourth or fifth grade before he can, for example, extract the meaning from even fairly simple reasoning problems in arithmetic if they are presented in written form. Somewhat earlier than this he can demonstrate fairly complex reasoning in practical or concrete arithmetical situations if he does not have to struggle with language. Training

* For a comprehensive list of such tests see Jordan[506] (1953).

in the verbalization of reasoning goes on throughout high school and college, and even the keenest adult often struggles to find the particular word or phrase which will express the exact shade of meaning he is trying either to capture for himself or to convey to someone else.

Content of Language.　In content of language we find a predominance of egocentricity in the language of young children.[729] The predominance of the pronouns "I," "me," "mine," so characteristic of the preschool child, continues in the writings and conversation of children of school age. The six-year-old's insistent "Look at me. See me" is familiar to every parent and teacher. However, in proportion to the total number of words used in free conversation there is likely to be a decrease in the proportion of "I's" used throughout elementary school years. *

Speech as a Thermometer of Emotions.　Speech is "the thermometer of emotional reactions."[72] A number of investigations** have shown that in the content of speech of very young children talk is dominantly about things which have emotional content for them. The first word or words of the vocabulary are often interjections or are nouns uttered with an interjectional inflection. Emotionally toned utterances are frequent and are attempts to command, request, threaten, or express desire. This type of response in language decreases as the child gains in socialization and in facility of expression.

Not only what is said by children, but the tone of voice, is important as an indicator of feeling. Children, having not yet learned to conceal their feelings from the world, burst out spontaneously with what they feel. However, there is one stage of language development during which the child's words cannot be taken literally as indicating meaning. For example, many three- or four-year-old children swear with bombastic emphasis, not because they are that angry, but because they have copied a tone of voice from the person from whom they learned the profanity. The tone was exciting and dramatic; it captured the child's attention; he duplicates it, gets an exciting response as a rule from adults, and continues. If he gets no particular excitement out of his own use of the phrases he usually soon forgets them in favor of language which nets more effective social results.

Four- to eight-year-olds characteristically "go tough," largely as an expression of a developing ego.† In dealing with other children, any early primary school child must use fairly obvious means to make his point. In addition to this, bombastic phrases "feel good" not only in the mouth, but as an inflation of one's own sense of security and importance. Therefore, such remarks as "I'll kill you dead!", "I'll chop your head off!", "You dumbbell!" and occasionally phrases even less elegant which include gutter language referring to sex or elimination are common at this age. These, of

* Good case studies and selected conversations of seven- and eight-year-olds can be found in Biber.[90]

** Summarized by McCarthy.[608]

† Aggressiveness in asserting oneself and in dealing with others will be discussed as a desirable phase of personality development in Chapter 13.

course, have been heard; children do not invent such language. If adults stage a complete war on such language, children are likely only to be challenged to increases in toughness as proof, mainly to themselves, that they can hold their own. "Dirty" language is, of course, undesirable at any stage. Probably the best way to deal with this to give the child the proper anatomic and physiologic words for sex and elimination with the understanding that if he wishes to refer to bodily functions he'd better speak correctly. This usually robs this area of language of its punch.

To try to make "a little gentleman" of a child at this age under all circumstances is likely to prove a severe handicap to the child in his gang contacts if the adult is successful; or it may turn out to be a challenge to further toughness if the adult is not successful. Boys, particularly, seem in the average gang to need means of proving themselves unafraid. A few "You dumbbells" or even worse, hurled with good effect may prove useful in gang adjustments. The lesson for children should probably be to learn to differentiate where to use such language and with whom. One does not, for example, call one's parents or grandmother "dumbbell" or "fool."

Even the best homes, however, feel some competition with outside contacts, and find themselves fighting "it ain't" and "he done." Even in good homes a mother may find herself fighting the pattern of ungrammatical slips set up by the father who does not wish to appear effete among his business associates. Or she may try to eliminate a reaction to the father's quite unconscious profanity. The adult should be careful not to nag the child about inaccuracies in language so constantly that he becomes resentful or discouraged in his attempts to seek information and to share his experiences with his family. It is probably better to overlook some bad grammar than to develop a morose and uncommunicative child. Profanity, on the whole, seems easier to deal with. It is quite possible to develop in the child an ability to understand that even though father or a truck driver may so express himself little children may not.

Code Language Popular with Children. Another aspect of language fascinates eight- to ten-year-old children. They love codes and secret languages. "Double talk" characterizes this age as it does also adolescence, when it serves to cement the sense of group solidarity. Any code for letters in which to write secret messages, or any pass word which serves to mark off a separate social group or gang is seized upon avidly. Adults should respect this secrecy, since most of it is innocent. The carefully guarded secret password of one group of nine-year-olds proved upon investigation by worried adults to be "sodium bicarbonate," and of another "Espanoza." Use of codes proves excellent mental exercise, and, as in the Boy Scout signal code, a fine means of training children to alertness.

Correction of Faulty Grammar and Diction. It is useless to attempt to correct a child's bad grammar by telling him he will not be understood. "Me and him didn't have no fun" is quite understandable in spite of its bad grammar. It is more effective with children simply to tell them what is incorrect and what correct. Most effective, however, is exposure to good speech and good reading, since mere rules are monotonous and since good reading and good speech can be made fun.

Bad grammar and diction *per se* must not be confused with certain errors which seem natural in the child's speech development. Nearly all preschool children find confusion in the correct use of pronouns because they hear themselves referred to by a different set of pronouns than they use when referring to themselves. "Me go," "Bobby do" are characteristic two-year substitutes for "I go," or "I do." To nag a two-year-old about such mistakes shows a lack of understanding of how language develops.

Other Language Faults. Certain errors are characteristic of children of elementary school age, the most frequent being errors of punctuation, capitalization, case of pronouns, use of adjectives and adverbs, and use of verbs. Some of these errors persist a long time. Although most children have learned how to begin all sentences with a capital letter in the early elementary grades, nearly everyone, even the college graduate, has trouble knowing when and how to use a semicolon.

Reasons for Language Retardation. If children of two or three years of age are not making real progress in language acquisition they should, if possible, be taken to a specialist for help. There are many reasons why children may not progress normally in the development of their speech. *Deafness* should be the first area of suspicion.* Ten to 20 per cent of school children suffer some defect of hearing.[50,289] Children who cannot hear the model for speech cannot learn to speak through the usual channels. Many of the best public school systems today have special schools for children who are hard of hearing; most states have state schools for the deaf.**

Defects of mouth, larynx, or *tongue* should also be kept in mind; also possible *defects* in the *nerve control* of these organs. Medical examination will reveal such causes if they are present.

Mental retardation is often the cause of retarded language development. The connection between verbal facility and mental superiority and between language retardation and mental dullness seems obvious to most people. However, although all feeble-minded children are slow in learning to talk, not all slow talkers are feeble-minded, as is evidenced here by the many other reasons for slow talking. A good mental test, designed to test general performance rather than verbal performance, should help to provide an accurate estimate of the intelligence of children who do not speak or understand language.

Inadequate or defective model and lack of being talked to will also rob a child of his model for imitation and of a motive for practice. Institutionalized children are conspicuously different in language development from children reared in good homes where there is ample language model. People who lisp, talk

* Gesell[345] (p. 194) says that a child who, at eighteen to twenty-four months, "uses varied well-inflected conversational jargon is unlikely to be significantly handicapped in hearing."

** For a summary of speech and hearing defects in the public schools, with information on how to handle them, see Anderson[31] (1953).

too fast, or stammer are bad models for children in the early stages of language learning. Twins, or children very close together in age, sometimes provide each other with sign language or jargon which delays the acquisition of language.[219,941] Twins, however, seem by nine years of age to have gained enough language ability to overcome the disadvantage of the preschool years. Only children, who have much attention and talking to, develop more rapidly in language than do other children. Many workers agree that the difference in language development between children of the "educated" or professional socio-economic groups and children of the laboring groups is about eight months upon school entrance. This difference is in part a product of the amount and kind of language model these children hear, and in part a difference in basic intelligence. However, in summarizing the literature on the subject Anderson[30] says that we have evidence of a very marked effect of environment upon the development of the language processes in the preschool and early school years.

Children who are exposed to *two or more languages in the learning years* (two to four years) are usually slower in the development of either language than they would be in the development of one language at a time. This is reasonable, since they must learn two or more names for every object and every action. After mastering the fundamental mechanics of each of the languages, however, these bilingual children have the advantage of more than one language and become truly bilingual because they can think in more than one language. The usual recommendation for learning more than one language is to expose very young children to one language only until they have mastered a working foundation in that one (perhaps three or four years of age), then introduce a second language. An occasional psychologist urges the point that too early development of bilingualism prevents the complete conceptualization of objects or situations in either language and, therefore, interferes with complete development in the conceptual or ideational area of intelligence.*

Sometimes retardation in language development is due to *emotional causes*. Too much urging to talk or too much praise or emphasis upon language success may place a too great premium upon learning to talk. Some children, sensing the importance of the accomplishment, become afraid to try. Ridicule, nagging, or any other source of emotional tension concerning speech will prove sufficient to keep certain types of children from talking at all. Some children under such strain stutter. No teacher should ever be guilty of retarding children's language because she ridicules or nags a child or allows other children to do so.

Stuttering. There are two ages at which stuttering is conspicuous. The peak of the stuttering curve comes at about two and one-half to three years of age. This is a time when children have enough vocabulary to discover the joy of communication through words. It is also a time when they are making rapid strides in social development and in the urge to communicate, to attract attention and to tell things. Frequently, however, there are not enough

---

* An excellent summary of the literature on bilingualism can be found in Arsenian[35] (1945). Good case studies can be found in Peck[719] (1953).

words in the vocabulary to permit really clear and facile expression, so the child in his eagerness stutters. Nearly all children between two and one-half and three years, or at the stage of language development which this represents for the average child, stutter some. Many do it so little that we do not notice it as a problem, but many children continue to have considerable trouble for several months. If this stuttering is recognized for what it is, namely, a stage of language learning, and is dealt with in such a way as to increase the child's vocabulary and to develop his confidence that he can find the right words, he will soon overcome it. If, however, he comes to regard it as a serious problem and loses confidence that he can speak freely, he is likely to have serious difficulty in overcoming it. He should never be scolded or nagged or referred to as a stutterer or as someone who cannot talk.

The other peak of stuttering occurs upon school entrance. In this instance the trouble is often nervous strain resulting from the adjustments to new authority, to other children, to the routine of school. The nervous tension created by school entrance may spill over into fingernail biting, a reversion to thumbsucking, a relapse in toilet habits, or, frequently, into stuttering.

Some of the early primary school stuttering is associated with handedness. As was said in Chapter 8, it is never wise to force a child to use his right hand if he is more at ease and more skillful in the use of his left hand.

The flare-up of stuttering upon school entrance usually dies down as the necessary adjustments are made. Teachers should investigate the cause and history of the stuttering of each of their children, and should make every effort to correct any causes which can be corrected through the school. Great care should be taken not to force too timid children to recite or read before the group until they can be helped to develop the necessary self-confidence. Firmness of discipline seems necessary for certain children; but timid children should be handled gently. Stutterers, particularly, need great patience and understanding to help them overcome the difficulty.

About 1 per cent of the school population stutters as a long-continued speech habit. Stuttering is more frequent among mentally retarded than among normal children. It is four to five times as frequent among boys as among girls.* It nearly always begins before or during the earliest school years.

Schools need to understand the language problems of the early primary years better than they now do if trouble is to be avoided, not only in stuttering but also in general emotional adjustment. Witty[1006] states the case clearly when he reminds us that for the average child there has always been some sympathetic adult to interpret his language efforts until the time when he enters school. Upon school entrance each child leaves the warm bath of intimate personal understanding for the more impersonal atmosphere of the school room. The child, then, not only faces the problem of understanding and being understood by persons who are strangers to his home and neigh-

* Girls are superior to boys in language development at all ages and stages of development.[345,668,941]

borhood; he also faces the problem of learning to talk effectively with children of his own age. Witty says:

It becomes apparent, therefore, that the first language problem of the public school is to assist the child to make normal speech contacts with others in his class. This is not a problem which can be solved in the kindergarten or first grade and then forgotten. It is one which recurs each time a student enters a new group, although with increasing experience the time for adjustment decreases. Many schools consistently ignore this need. The difficulty which most adults find in meeting strangers, and in expressing themselves before new audiences, is evidence of our failure in the school. Embarrassment in speech leads easily to other forms of maladjustment. . . .

Accustomed to talking throughout the day (some writers estimate that the average child speaks thirty thousand running words a day before entering public school), the youngster wants and needs to talk about all the new and interesting experiences which are found in school. Consequently his urge to talk is probably increased. Instead we try to channel his language—at least a large part of it—through the written word. It is small wonder that very soon this reading and writing come to be thought of as bars to learning rather than as opportunities.[1006]

READING: PART OF LANGUAGE GROWTH

Reading Is the Major Academic Accomplishment of the Primary Grades. Probably the major all-around accomplishment of the primary grades is the teaching of adjustment to meeting authority, to contacting peers, to facing a routine job every day whether one feels like it or not, and other personal-social adjustments. The primary academic accomplishment of these grades is the teaching of reading. When the child learns to read we know that he has accomplished many preliminary learnings. He has learned mastery over eye muscles; he has developed basic discriminations in form or shape; he has mastered the abstractions of basic language, both in vocabulary and "language sense"; he has learned self-control in a measure, as well as the personal-social adjustments to school mentioned above. In a sense, learning to read is a graduation from "the school of the before-school-learnings."

Readiness to Read. Before children can profit from any given curriculum or method in reading, however, they must be what is known as "ready to read." Reading readiness, like all other readiness (recall Chapter 1), is the product of mental, physical, emotional, and social development.[405] This development is achieved by the normally growing child who has been exposed to normal experiences in the preschool and kindergarten years. On an average over the country the child is generally assumed to be capable of beginning to learn to read at about the time his mental age reaches six and one-half years.

Hollingworth[431] reports that the correlation between reading ability and IQ is $+ .60$ to $+ .90$. Of four children with IQ's over 180 found by her in New York City, every one had learned to read simple matter fluently before or during the third year of life.

Gesell[345] (p. 209) lists maturational indicators for reading as follows:

1. Normal (or corrected) vision.
2. Normal hearing.
3. General mental level of 6 to 6½ years.
4. Good motor coordination, particularly manual control, as evidenced in drawing.

5. Relatively mature personality.
6. Normal use and comprehension of language.
7. Articulation not more than slightly immature.
8. Relatively even development in the various fields of behavior.
9. Interest in, and ability to follow, stories of moderate length.
10. Ability to control attention on set tasks.
11. Ability to adjust to the requirements of schoolroom routine.

Betts[88] points out that confusion of symbols is somewhat typical of normal six-year-old children; and that 80 per cent of six-year-old children are normally farsighted, which means that too much reading is a strain at this age. He has studied reversal tendencies (reading "saw" for "was" etc.) carefully and finds them the normal reaction of an immature child required to read too early. He says some children exhibit this tendency until they are seven and one-half years old. This tendency is particularly strong in left-handed children, who, as we have seen, have a strong tendency to move from right to left in both reading and writing.

Growth in all of these areas which are involved in reading readiness is a natural part of the development of early childhood. That reading involves a test of so many developmental areas, however, is the explanation of why so many children fail to accomplish this important part of the first grade curriculum.

Children vary widely upon entrance to the first grade in their readiness to read. Bennett,[86] in reviewing a summary of the literature on reading disability, presents a table showing seventeen groups of reading disability cases. Boys represent from 60 to 100 per cent of the cases in each group. Difficulty with language as represented in the development of ability to read is only part of a total sex difference in language development in favor of girls.[608]

Variation in teaching methods, in the character of materials offered, and the general procedure in the classroom also has an effect upon how children use what readiness they possess. Children who are mentally able and socially mature can overcome not only handicaps of growth in other areas but also bad teaching methods more readily than can children of lower mental development or of retarded social maturity. It is important that teachers avail themselves of a knowledge of the developmental level of each of their pupils at any stage of learning on any school level. It is imperative that they have such knowledge when trying to teach children to read.

Preparing Children to Read. Streitz[910] reviews the literature on reading readiness and substantiates the findings of Gray's summaries which state that maturation in several areas of growth is basic in determining whether or not a given child is ready to read. She recommends that, while no attention should be given to formal reading instruction in the kindergarten, much can be done to develop reading readiness through listening to stories read to the group, looking at picture books, and engaging in other experiences related to extension of working vocabulary and love of books. There are a number of tests of reading readiness referred to in Streitz' article.*

Streitz reviews an experiment which was set up in the public schools of

* For further tests in this area and for later stages of reading see Jordan[506] (1953).

Cincinnati to deal with 400 children of legal school age but who were developmentally immature and would probably become reading failures. The basis for the program was health, language development, and enrichment of experience. What was done with the health program is suggestive of what can be done. Physical corrections were undertaken in a clinic; a daily program of feeding, rest, fresh air, and exercise was set up. Along with this was a program of special visual education and conversation in the classroom, many excursions, and such experiences as would help tenement children to widen familiarity with plants and animals. No reading was attempted in the first year, but was introduced instead as part of the second year of schooling. Careful checks on health and social adjustment were kept. Streitz reports that "the results seem to indicate that a large proportion of this disadvantage [of mental age] and the apparent immaturity is due to physical conditions and the children's home environment."

Stages of Learning to Read. The Thirty-sixth Yearbook of the National Society for the Study of Education[694] portrays the stages of learning to read as follows: (1) development of reading readiness; (2) accomplishment of word recognition and other fundamental steps leading to the place where the child can engage in continuous, meaningful reading of simple books, can direct his attention with interest and absorption to the content, and has acquired an interest in independent reading; (3) rapid progress in the perfecting of the fundamental skills, habits and attentions necessary to clear comprehension at good speed in both silent and oral reading; (4) extension of personal experience at a rapid rate and the acquisition of increased power, efficiency and excellence in reading; (5) the refinement of reading interests, habits and tastes. Stage 1 is accomplished as a rule in the preschool and kindergarten years; stage 2 in the primary grades; stage 3 in the middle elementary; stage 4 in the upper elementary if the other growth stages have been accomplished; stage 5 is achieved in the junior high school.

One conspicuous point is brought out in reading ability studies. Unless the school has made a special effort to establish homogeneous groupings, there will be found extreme differences in reading ability in all grades. Children in the third grade vary all the way from complete inability to read to genuine maturity in reading habits. Bobbitt[104] studied several thousand senior high school freshmen and found that 4 per cent were unable to score above the third grade level in reading; nearly 25 per cent fell below the sixth grade reading norm. Yet some of these children achieved a level of reading characteristic of college graduates.

Development in Reading Interests. As anyone who has observed children knows, those who are less than five years old love to have stories told or read to them and are delighted with rhymes and jingles. Animal and nature stories, especially those which involve conversation with or by animals, have a strong appeal. Interest in simple here-and-now stories of everyday affairs like the day's routine, the travels of the fire engine or the grocery boy reflect the child's interest in his own routine life and the things in his immediate environment.

With a widening of the child's social and intellectual experiences his horizon of interest widens. As a rule children in the primary grades are still interested mainly in local environment: accounts of toys and games, of pets (conversational animals who live a family life or go on adventures still dominate in popularity) and homes and parents, and, reflecting the great new interest of their lives, the affairs of the school. This range of interest includes holiday stories around any given holiday time. Dramatizations of stories read for holiday celebrations help to clarify and fix knowledge, e. g., the landing of the Pilgrims. Any stories of other children like themselves, who live as they do, are of great interest. Interest in Indians develops here, partly because most children have owned an Indian suit or visited some part of the country which is noted for an Indian incident. Interest in less dramatic or primitive groups is, however, delayed as a rule until later.

As we saw in Chapter 6, interest in "funnies" begins almost as soon as children can read. Some clever primary teachers are competing with this interest by using other parts of the newspapers as a means of increasing vocabulary. The headlines and large print are brought to the classroom and the children pick out the words they know. This appeals to their feeling of being grown up and doing as their parents do. It proves a good means of practice in word identification and is an excellent background for interest in current events in the later grades.

Pupils of the middle grades want to branch out in their interests. They want to take trips into the world of other nations, to explore habits and ways of living different from their own. They have a concern with why things are as they are, with how things work, where milk and other food and clothes come from. Most of them love fairy tales of one sort or another. However, as a rule, boys are more interested in the whys and hows, and girls in the fairy stories. Celestine[173] found that realistic animal stories are a dominant interest of nine-year-olds, at which time stories of children of other lands also compel interest. Boys of this age are interested in adventure stories like the Boy Scout Series; girls like stories of home and school life. Action, adventure, excitement, and mystery as well as realism, suspense, humor-mischief, stories of adventure and bravery, of sports, airplanes and other inventions are reported by Lazar[567] as of great interest to children in grades 4-A to 6-A inclusive. Speed of silent reading develops rapidly enough from the age of seven or eight to twelve or fourteen that this interest in a wide variety of stories can be used to fix habits of love of reading for the later years. More voluntary reading is done between ages nine and fourteen than at any other age, as we shall see below. We should not allow this habit to fade.

As children move into the upper elementary grades and junior high school, interest in stories of adventure like the Pony Express continues to increase for boys. Stories of how and why things work as they do, such as stories of invention and of informational material, make a strong appeal to them too. Fiction reaches a high point of interest for girls at around twelve years of age, at which time stories of adventure and accounts of people become popular. Both boys and girls like stories of boarding school life, perhaps as a reflection of their own half-felt desire to escape what appear to them as the restrictions of home life. From twelve to fifteen years the child's interest in a broader environment is reflected in interest in history and biography. Adventure still occupies an important place. Boys lean toward newspapers and current events, sports, and hobby literature. Girls read fiction and movie magazines, with a preference for the sensational and for impossible situations of wealth or romance.

Interests at all levels are conspicuous for variety. They change clearly from one level of development to the next, but the interests of one level merge into those of the next, and vary with sex, mental age, background of experience, availability of interesting reading material, and home influence. Unless children are given guidance they adopt narrow interests in reading and fail to enlarge their experiences through reading. On the other hand, with guidance they may expand reading interest rapidly, thus expanding their life experience as much as it is possible to expand it through reading. Much depends on the teaching methods used and the material made available. "Each teacher faces both the opportunity and the obligation of studying the interests of her pupils and of utilizing and stimulating them in appropriate directions."[372]

Recommendations for Reading Curriculum. Unfortunately, reading curricula in the past have been organized largely in terms of activities assumed to be desirable for children at the various grade levels. This practice has been emphasized repeatedly in recent literature as inadequate. Such factors as the physical, mental, emotional, and social maturity of the learner should be considered. Gesell[347, p. 379], says: "There is no simple method of learning or teaching reading. There are multiple methods—visual, auditory, manual and phonetic—which should be used freely and variously and separately and in combination to suit the fluid psychology of the school-beginner, and to do justice to the individual differences which prevail among all school-beginners."* Until recently all introductory reading matter has been based upon content which is of interest to five- and six-year-olds, but which is trivial to the eight-year-old who still needs primer material, and impossible to the adult who may be trying to learn to read.

There should be created a wide variety of interest material both at the beginning and at the more advanced levels of reading in order to stimulate reading among those upper elementary children who need practice in reading but who reject the content of most of the "readers" offered them. Wide use of well-selected resource material helps in this. One of the greatest problems of psychologic clinics or of special reading teachers is to find adequate practice material on the second or even on the fifth grade level, the content of which will interest the extroverted seek-the-gang boys and girls who, because of their deep interest in the gang, give too little attention to practice in reading. There is an abundance of the imaginative story-book materials which interest the introvertive children who already love reading and get much practice in

---

* An excellent summary of many of the almost countless studies on methods for teaching reading (Guthrie and Powers,[386] 1950) points out that children differ widely in their reactions to different methods of teaching reading.

it. Popular Mechanics and similar magazines captivate the extrovertive or out-going boy who can read at a fairly advanced level. But until he can read at that level he is likely to find little of interest in most of the reading material available to him.

A word is needed here about older children who find themselves in the fourth or sixth grade with a reading level equal to the second or third grade. Such children can read easily and with satisfaction the rare books which are written in the size of print and difficulty of the vocabulary appropriate to their second or third grade level of ability and which have a content challenging to the interests of the older child. Given enough of these books, gradually stepped up in difficulty, these children will get the necessary practice in reading which will improve their level. Even more important, they will find themselves liking to read. Unfortunately, however, few teachers or school librarians understand this. Such children, sent to ask for books on their reading level, usually return saying, "The teacher said I shouldn't read those books. She said I ought to be ashamed reading baby books. She said I ought to be reading fourth grade (or sixth grade) books." This mistake is not often made in public municipal libraries in the larger cities where specially trained children's librarians are available. These libraries usually place interest in reading at a premium. They, therefore, search carefully for any book which seems to stimulate the interest of a given child, regardless of its "grade" level. Once they are sure of the reading interest of such a child these librarians encourage trying something a little harder saying, "I'm sure you'll like it. It's a good story." Teachers should adopt more of this philosophy.

It seems apparent that the problem of the primary grades is to teach the skill of reading and to arouse interest in independent reading; of the middle grades it is to provide a wide range of materials of different ability levels and extensive interest content compatible with the interests of children of these ages. The junior and senior high school years are critical in the maintenance of interest in reading. Loss of interest in reading at these ages may be, and probably is, in part due to the intense interest in social activities characteristic of adolescents, and in part to the inroads upon reading time made by radio, movies, television and other commercialized recreations. It is doubtless also due to teaching failures, especially in junior and senior high school English classes where the kind of reading material offered is often lacking in interest.

DEVELOPMENT OF THINKING AND REASONING

Thinking and reasoning are generally assumed to be the crowning achievements of intelligence. The ability to utilize experience in the drawing of practical or theoretic conclusions, and to solve problems, as we have seen earlier, requires, first, a background of sensation and sense perception. For the highest types of reasoning a genuine facility with objects and a wide background of experience are necessary; and for certain types of higher reasoning language mastery is also required. So much background is needed, in fact, that many writers claim that children are incapable of reasoning before seven years of age; others say before twelve years. Much is written in prose and poetry about the age of reasoning, and many primitive and civilized ceremonies center around the assumption that children come into reasoning power and the capacity for making important decisions for themselves with the onset of adolescence.

If, however, we define reasoning as including all reactions involving choice, or all activity used in problem solving, or all logical thinking, we must understand that these capacities do not spring rapidly into being at any age. They are in the process of development from infancy. Neither can we accept the idea that some people are born to reason and others not to. Within the limits of general intellectual capacity the ability to reason can be developed—to higher perfection, of course, in the gifted of intellect, less highly in the subnormal. Through training in sensory judgments, through widening horizons of experience, through the development in the technique of decision making, and through experience in solving one's own problems, whatever reasoning capacity any given person possesses can be brought to an optimal level. If, however, the groundwork is not laid in general development, and if training in the actual processes of thinking is not given, whatever native capacity there is cannot function at its best.

What Reasoning Is.   Perhaps we can best understand what is meant by giving children opportunities to use whatever capacities they possess if we analyze briefly what is involved in reasoning. Any thinking involving an analysis of *cause and effect* relationships may be classified as reasoning. This does not, of course, mean such conditioned associations as muscle jerk responses to bells which are rung. It does mean, however, any intellectual process which marshals facts or experiences into orderly sequences. Such a comment as "Mother, why does the drinking fountain choke?" made by a three-year-old who thought the fountain was coughing because it gurgled, shows an association between choking and coughing, and an application of this knowledge to a concrete, present situation. Another three-year-old observed that a person who had gray eyes must be old. One two-and-one-half year old had hurt her neck. A playful older child suggested that she blow on it to relieve the smarting. She replied, "I can't. It's behind." In a less verbal way we see a two-year-old relating cause and effect when, in running with harness dangling, the harness is caught in a snag. He stops, tugs, discovers the cause, backs up, and releases the harness.

Whenever two variables vary together, people are likely to say that one causes the other. Because of faulty training, many adults attribute the causal relationship to the wrong variable or ignore the possibility of a third agent causing both. For example, seeing a high percentage of feeble-mindedness in the slums, they may assume that the slums cause the feeble-mindedness, thus ignoring the fact that people of less intelligence tend to be unable to care for themselves on a higher socio-economic level and therefore gravitate to slums. We observe the same faulty reasoning in a four-year-old who sees trees waving as the wind blows and concludes, "Trees waving make the wind blow." Constant training in accurate analysis of cause and effect relations is, as it should be, a major concern of schools. Science courses carry a particular responsibility for this training. But homes and preschools should also recognize this thinking process in its beginnings, and plan a definite program which will give accurate knowledge and real practice in such thinking.

Generalization and *deduction* are parts of another important type of reasoning, the same in some ways as relating cause and effect, but involving wider conclusions and an ability to apply principles when needed. Although children seem somewhat slow in accumulating a wide enough background of experience from which to draw general conclusions, we see the process in action in four-year-olds in the following instance: At a school which promotes children into kindergarten on their fifth birthdays John, age four, said to Carroll, also age four, "I'm five." Carroll replied, "No, you're not. If you were you wouldn't be in this school."

We also see it when Eddie, age three, says to Ralph, age four, "When I'm five I'll be older than you"; whereupon Ralph answers, "No. Next Christmas you'll be four, and next Christmas I'll be five. I'll always be older than you."

However, among young children, as among adults, we see many false conclusions. One five-year-old thought standing in the rain would make him grow because it makes plants grow. Another thought men were filled with sawdust because dolls were. Charlotte, age four, was overheard saying one day, "My birthday will come when it snows." A few days later the teacher said, "Look, children, it's snowing." Charlotte said, "Then, when I get home I'll have a birthday."

A practical difficulty met by school teachers in teaching generalizations is to get children to apply names accurately. One kindergarten teacher, in trying to teach the concept of squareness and roundness, always presented blue squares and red circles. She found several of the children associating the two together, thinking that all squares were blue and all circles red. We find some children, and adults, too, concluding that all people of a particular nationality are fine people because the only one they know is fine, and that all people of another national extraction are bad because one person they know of that extraction is bad. Such jumping to conclusions is extremely faulty reasoning. Children must be taught to delay judgment a reasonable length of time, or to hold judgments in suspense ready for change if further experience proves the first judgment wrong.

Problem solving is the form of thinking most generally agreed upon as a type of reasoning. Any use of past experience, of presently available tools, of skills and habits to solve a practical or a theoretic problem is the form of thinking which differentiates man from the animals. It is in this area that children can be seen to reason most clearly. The year-old child, pulling the table cloth toward him to get something, is using cause and effect to solve a present problem. Bobby, age three, who wants to go down the slide backward as he has seen other children do, finds that he cannot turn himself around on the top step. So he descends, turns himself around, and manages to ascend the steps backward in order to be in position at the top. He has solved a problem. Such problems are not solved in words; they are solved in action. Use of language as a tool in reasoning and problem solving is one of the last uses made, as has been said earlier. It is because children do not ordinarily solve problems in words, and because they do not generalize readily or apply principles concretely, that many people discredit their reasoning power.

Not every writer accepts these simple action solutions of problems as examples of reasoning, reserving the term "reasoning" for solutions of problems involving abstractions. Piaget[731] analyzes different kinds of reasoning as they are related to each other and as they develop in children. Only gradually, he feels, does the child broaden his intellectual horizons so that he has background for greater abstractions and more complex forms of reasoning. Around age seven, Piaget believes, the child becomes more deductive in his thinking, develops more rigor, becomes more objective, and from this age onward his thinking becomes more like that of an adult. Piaget concludes that up to the age of seven the child shows no evidence of logical reasoning in this thinking. From seven to eleven or twelve the child's reasoning is based largely upon direct observation. Not until eleven or twelve does he become able to make assumptions which he does not necessarily believe, or which are more abstract.

Long and Welch[599, 600] found that children were less and less able to solve problems as the abstractness of the situation increased. These writers found that the capacity to handle abstractness developed gradually with age, rather than as suddenly as Piaget implies. It would appear from most of the studies that even young children have some basis for generalization, and that, as Thompson[941] summarizes the situation (p. 234): "reasoning ability improves gradually with increasing perception and concept formation." Gesell[345] comments that although the five-year-old's capacity for reasoning is similar in kind to the reasoning of adults, it is primitive indeed when we lay it beside the five-year-old's facility with language, which is highly advanced as a civilized accomplishment.

We can see, then, that although the reasoning of children seems the same in form as that of adults, it differs in being simple and primitive.

What This Means in Dealing with Children. It matters a good deal in practical dealing with children whether we believe them capable of some reasoning, or whether, believing them to be incapable, we assume that they can learn only by physically conditioned responses. If we believe the latter, we tend to make discipline physical, immediate, and concrete. If, however, we believe that children do reason, no matter how primitively, we tend to teach by natural consequences, by pointing out sequences of events, and by helping children to draw conclusions and to solve their own problems.

General recommendations in child training parallel the findings in child development research. Discipline for children less than two years of age, it is generally recommended, should be concrete, quickly following the situation needing discipline, and not accompanied by too much talking. After two, however, as the child acquires language facility and some reasoning capacity, the recommendations are in the direction of less and less physical or concrete punishment, more and more in the direction of "consequences of action" and helping children to discover for themselves the results of good or bad behavior, talking or "reasoning" coming to have a place. During the two- to five-year period parents and educators are urged to make increasing use of concrete situations as a basis for generalization, and to increase constantly the situations in which the child is encouraged to meet issues and solve problems for himself. Simple verbalization helps. Such sequences as: come in from play, wash, eat, for example, must be repeated over a long time before a child will form the automatic habit. He will "get the idea" and form the habit much faster if he is helped by having it pointed out that "we wash after playing so that we can have clean hands when we eat."

Although a program of "natural-consequences-of-the-act" is recommended, care must be taken to see that no child is forced to make decisions or solve problems which are too complex or in which the consequences of a mistake are too serious. If this happens, he may become discouraged or frightened away from decisions and independent problem solving. Even for the six- to twelve-year-old child much learning is not a consciously thought-out process. It is, rather, a casual by-product of concrete experience, an incidental activity in a world of factual living. Although the elementary school age is above all a period of rapid learning, most learning still takes place through conditioning, through chance observations, through the random experimentation which we call "trial and error," and through imitation of others. Only the more "intellectual" children learn before adolescence by intention to learn rather than by chance or by adult motivation. In spite of this, however, all authorities agree that children of upper elementary school age show rapid progress in capacity to generalize and to make deductions. They become increasingly able to draw conclusions from fewer and less concrete situations than are necessary in teaching preschool and primary, or lower elementary school children. They learn fairly rapidly how to apply rules to specific situations, and they become more skillful in solving problems in the mind as contrasted to the necessity for solving them in concrete reality as younger children must.

Reasoning Capacity Continues to Grow Well into Adulthood. A careful analysis of the available data leads to the conclusion that mental growth, especially growth of the power to reason, continues to the end of the 'teens, or, under stimulating conditions, even longer.[442]

Brooks, in a summary of the literature on growth of intellect from fifteen to twenty-two years, says:

The best available evidence on the intellectual development of young people from fifteen to twenty-two leads us to place great emphasis upon the stimulus value of the environment which surrounds them. . . . Critical, constructive, creative thinking in setting up educational programs for youth in the 'teens and early twenties may be expected to yield important intellectual and social benefits.[126]

Largely because of increasing experience and better reasoning power, an individual at twenty-five or thirty has more mental ability than he had at twenty; he reasons better on complex problems; he manages himself and his affairs more efficiently; he adjusts to increased complexity in his life situation.

Similarly, if growth is not cut off, the man of thirty-five or forty manages his affairs better than the man of thirty.

Individual Differences. We must recall individual differences here again. We have not only the children whose general mental level is low and hence who cannot learn intellectual material; we have also among children of the same general IQ level a fairly wide range of memory capacity and ability to understand. Some seem "mechanical minded," being capable in the area of handling things; some seem "verbal minded," having better ability with words than with things; some seem dominantly "social-minded," having their greatest ability in responsiveness to people and in clear judgment about themselves as people. The typically feeble-minded child, however, is low in all intellectual capacities, having short attention span, poor understanding of factual or of personal relationships, poor auto-criticism, and is limited in his use of general experience. Gifted children, on the other hand, are facile in all these areas.[16,933]

EXPERIENCES TO VITALIZE CLASS WORK

1. Visit a 1-A grade. Select some child who is retarded in language development. What is responsible for his difficulty? Outline a practical plan for helping him if you were his teacher.

2. Visit an upper elementary grade. What language experiences are the children having? Would you judge these experiences to be didactic and meaningless, or alive and meaningful? Is there any plan for individualizing instruction? If not, could you make a practical one?

3. Do you feel that your own reading interests, and the amount of reading you did, slumped from the junior high school through the senior high school? How usual do you feel your own experience to be? How adequate are your own speed and comprehension in reading? What, if anything, should you do about them?

4. Do you have any plan for extending your own active vocabulary? For improving your own diction and use of grammar? What would you consider the advantages of such improvement?

5. Are the elementary and secondary schools which you know encouraging or discouraging reasoning power in children? What has progressive education contributed to the improvement of the teaching of reasoning?

6. How can a parent help a child to reason accurately? Did the discipline your parents used on you improve or discourage your reasoning capacity? Where and how did you develop such reasoning capacity as you have?

7. If you are doing a case study, evaluate "your child" in language and in reasoning capacity. Evaluate also his environment in relation to these two capacities.

SELECTED READINGS

Biber, B., et al.: Life and Ways of the Seven- to Eight-Year-Old. New York, Basic Books, Inc., 1952, Ch. 3.

Carmichael, L. (editor): Manual of Child Psychology. New York, John Wiley & Sons, Inc., 1946, Ch. 10 by D. McCarthy on Language Development in Children.

Gesell, A., et al.: The Child from Five to Ten. New York, Harper & Bros., 1946, pp. 395–399.

Gesell, A., et al.: The First Five Years of Life. New York, Harper & Bros., 1940, Ch. 8.

Jersild, A. T.: Child Psychology. 4th ed. New York, Prentice-Hall, Inc., 1954, Ch. 12 and pp. 516–520.

Strickland, R. G.: The Language Arts in the Elementary School. Boston, D. C. Heath & Co., 1951.

Thompson, G. G.: Child Psychology. Boston, Houghton Mifflin Co., 1952, Chs. 9, 12.

Walters, S. A., and S. K. O'Hara: Persons and Personality. New York, Appleton-Century-Crofts, Inc., 1953, Ch. 13.

CHAPTER 12

Social and Personality

Development—(GENERAL PERSONALITY TRENDS)

PERSONALITY, WHAT IT IS AND HOW IT HAS BEEN STUDIED

Children grow socially as they grow physically, from year to year developing greater complexity of social behavior, greater skills in getting along with people, and greater self-control. As in the discussion of every other type of growth, we must realize that, although we discuss stages or steps in this growth, it would be a serious mistake to assume that these steps proceed in the same order or during the same years of age for all children. Social and personality development is an orderly process in each child, but it does not follow the same precise pattern from child to child. We have already discussed "fast" growers and "slow" growers as children whose growth is faster or slower than the average. In physical and in mental growth we see all kinds of variation in tempo of growth and hence in physical and mental maturity of children of any given age or of any school grade level. These differences are equally wide in social growth. They are probably even wider in personality development which is, if we can judge from the evidence now available, even more responsive to the amount and quality of experience to which the individual has been exposed.

What Personality Is.   The ordinary lay person's conception of personality as that which makes one popular with people is not the psychologist's conception. The psychologist thinks also of the dominating, destructive attitudes of a gangster, or the blank emptiness of an idiot as making up part of the complex of feelings, attitudes, and behavior which is personality. Landis[561],[p. 73] says that "personality is a composite of hereditary factors and developmental influences, of genes, and of social experience." Sandiford[806] defines an individual's personality as "what he really is; it is the state of being a person." He warns, however, that to consider only those aspects of personality which are evident in observable, or overt, behavior, is to miss an important part of it, since that part which is known only to the individual himself is important. One may be and feel many things which, as a controlled or "civilized" person, one does not show to the world in one's behavior.

Lay people are likely to say, "Oh, he (or she) has so *much* personality." The psychologist will answer that every person has "much personality," since every person has a complex of traits, attitudes, and characteristics. When these make up an "ineffectual" personality we have what the lay person means by "little" or "no personality." Every person has great depths of feelings and attitudes which do not appear evident to the lay observer, but which motivate behavior and in exceedingly important ways determine the type of personality reaction peculiar to each individual. This substructure, called the "subconscious" (see Chapter 3) by psychologists, is present in all people and plays a vitally important role in behavior reaction. It determines the quality of personality reaction. In the study of personality, then, it is the quality of personality rather than the quantity with which we are concerned. We shall be concerned here with personality as the complex of feelings, attitudes, and behavior which makes each one of us the unique person that he is.

How Personality and Social Growth Have Been Studied. There is a substantial body of research material on studies of personality and social growth. Many of these studies are based upon direct observation of the behavior of children who were placed in controlled experimental situations and detailed stenographic records of behavior taken. Others depend upon ratings of traits or behavior on check lists carefully worked out to cover the total range of possible behavior. These ratings may be made by especially trained experimenters, or by teachers who know the children well, often by both; they involve ratings of children in free play or work situations.* Other studies[940] are based upon stenographic reports of everything a given child does or says in given half-hour or longer intervals. An analysis of these records may be used to classify social contacts, play activities, content of conversation, and the like. Some workers, notably the psychoanalytic group, feel that overt, or observable behavior of children does not tell enough of the story of emotional reaction or inner feeling in social situations.

The present trend in studies of social behavior and personality growth seems to be in the direction of attempts to understand the total personality structure and function as a background for specific behavior reactions, and in the direction of studies of the total interaction between individuals and groups or between the individual and the total situation, both past and present, in which he finds himself at the moment of any given behavior.

One of the most widely used current methods for the study of social behavior in relation to the total personality is the study of children's emotions and attitudes through the "projective method," which was discussed in Chapter 3.

---

* Authors are not agreed as to how accurate such ratings are in portraying real personality.[782]

The Rorschach ink blots,[24,305] in which ink blots are presented and the subject is asked to say what they resemble, offer a promising way of getting at the inner content of mind and personality. The Children's Apperception Test,[686] based upon animal characters, has also been widely used in the study of development of personality.* The projective technique, Rorschach and apperception methods, however, are laboratory devices. They do not give us the child in critical action in everyday situations where he deals with his routines, his toys, or his playmates.

In summarizing present available research on social and personality growth, Murphy[684] concludes that, although in agricultural experiments one may try out different soils for growing different plants, children are more subtle; in fact, they are so complicated that a generation of intensive research has failed to produce definite laws of the soil-rain-sun level of simplicity. As for defining laws regarding the kind of social behavior to expect from different types of children, under different conditions, we have as yet made only a beginning.

Exactly how personality develops as a product of the interaction between the inner impulses and needs of the individual and the play of his environment upon him needs much study. We do not yet know how parental influence can be made to stand against gang influence, or when it should. We do not know as much as we should about how to produce or to control aggressiveness, or how much of it is desirable at the various stages of development. We are only beginning to understand the influence of physical vigor upon personality functioning, or the effect of the various grades of intellect. We have made good beginnings in investigations into the effect of cultural or community demands upon personal and social development, and in the effect of routine demands, and of creative opportunity upon the unfolding of native capacity.

CAN PERSONALITY BE CHANGED?

Some Experimental Evidence.   One of the current emphases in the study of personality is whether or not personality patterns change as individuals grow and develop; or, if change occurs, how much change there can be, what produces change and in what direction the change takes place. Again we see in the literature the old heredity-environment controversy; and as in other answers to this riddle, we see both nature and nurture at work.

Landis[561] says (p. 73): "Personality is dynamic, a growing entity. Physiologically it is vested with the capacity for maturation. Except as mutilated by environment, physical traits follow their predestined course from childhood to maturity. Psychologically, it is plastic, capable of an infinite number of modifications by external stimuli. Sociologically, it is dependent on the

* For a comprehensive discussion of so-called "tests" of personality see Thompson[941] (1952).

group to provide the patterns of development, for human nature is a group product."

One study of detailed life histories of twenty-five college-trained women[787] would indicate that, although some personality traits in any given person change as the individual passes through certain kinds of experiences, each personality preserves a central stability, a central core or focus or "center of gravity" which does not change. Some personalities are far more flexible than others, and change radically under radical changes of environment; others have a "granite-like" quality which withstands the impact even of the most radical changes of environment. But all personalities have a "center of gravity" which lends stability to the personality in the sense that it preserves a balance of traits within each personality. You are who you are, in other words, because of the unique quality and balance of your own particular personality.*

In spite of this individuality of organization of personality which tends to endure throughout life, individual traits do change. Personality is more fluid, or subject to change through influence of the environment than is physique or even intelligence. The center of gravity, or core around which organization of traits takes place, is made up of a set of habits and attitudes which are essentially fixed early in life, but which may be added to and modified by the experience of the individual. The greater inflexibility of the older personality is probably due to a larger and more fixed core of personal habits and attitudes, which, like any habit, no matter how fixed, can be changed if sufficient emotional shock or continuous and strong enough pressure is brought to bear upon it.

However, it would be disastrous to jump quickly from this to the conclusion that we can, by enough nagging or punishment, change people, particularly adults, to suit our liking. The very stability of a central core of personality around which habits and attitudes achieve a working balance in any given personality proves to be the reason we cannot, or should not try to make over basic traits in any personality unless we have the help of highly trained specialists.** To change any basic trait without due regard for the other traits, habits, and attitudes which balance this trait may be to invite disaster through a serious disturbance in the total personality balance.

However, the training and forming of the personality of young children is quite another matter. There are many studies which show the influence of

* Allport[11] refers to this quality of organization in the personality when he says: "Psychologically considered the important fact about personality is its relatively enduring and unique organization." And again: "In addition to separateness and uniqueness a human being displays *psychological* individuality, an amazingly complex organization comprising his distinctive habits of thought and expression, his attitudes, trait and interests, and his own peculiar philosophy of life."

Landis[561] says (p. 77): "There are core patterns (in the personality) which give the life of the individual consistency."

** Psychiatrists are the specialists who should be consulted if a basic change in any given personality seems required for a reasonably good working adjustment to life situations.

environment and training upon the formation of young personalities.* Apparently, while the core of stability or "the integration center" is still in the early stages of formation, much in the way of change or moulding is possible without disturbance to the general balance. Even so, it is not wise to force any child into a preconceived pattern. Even very young children seem to have a certain physiologic and psychologic constitution which can be forced only so far from its original pattern without producing stresses and strains which shatter the mechanism. Parents and teachers must learn to read signs which indicate that any given child is under undesirable strain. They must understand certain needs which must be met in every child before his growth can be smooth and healthy. They must recognize that they cannot force any child into a pattern for which he has no original talent or capacity, nor can they without disaster long deprive him of expressions and outlets which are necessary for normal growth.

An Example of How Change Can Be Effected.   We have some help in what can be done to change personality reaction around the central core in the work of Jack,[464] who studied the dominant behavior of individual children in groups. Jack's study, being one of the first to investigate experimental modification of personality reactions, is widely known. She selected a group of four-year-old children in the Iowa Child Welfare Research Laboratories, pairing each child serially with ten others and observing on a carefully worked out scale how much each child dominated or was dominated by the others in the experimental situation. She discovered that the chief difference between the ascendant and the nonascendant child was a difference in the degree of self-confidence each felt in the given situation. Proceeding on this, Dr. Jack trained each nonascendant child in three different things which the other children did not know, such as assembling a mosaic of blocks or learning to know a story book. Armed with these skills the nonascendant children were again paired with each of the ten children of the original test situation. Only one child (and he had a serious speech defect) failed to increase his ascendancy score decidedly. These children did not always succeed in dominating originally strongly dominating children, but they greatly increased

* Some children show marked variations of behavior from situation to situation or from time to time, whereas other children show more continuity.[255]

Each baby exhibits a characteristic set of personality traits that change little with age. Personality differences are apparent at birth.

"The understanding of any behavior in relation to the whole personality, then, depends upon an understanding of the child's status, as far as general outgoing social responses is concerned, then the range of behavior which he shows in different situations, dominant trends and dynamics of variation within the range. It may be repeated here that probably the range of behavior, dominant trends, and particular forms of variation shown by a given child depend upon the influence from both his immediate and his general cultural setting, interacting with the constitutional characteristics he himself brings to his culture.

"Prediction of a child's behavior in a new situation would depend upon accurate analysis of this situation, in relation to his own range of possibilities and the dynamics of response to variations in his subjective relation to situations, or their value for him. Seen geometrically, any one aspect of behavior or trait is a point of intersection of different lines of influence, and the interaction of these different influences with the situation determine the point at which this intersection occurs."[678]

their attempts to do so. Their increase in attempts to dominate and their successes in doing so were greater in directing activities of other children than in maintaining property rights, which probably indicates that the training effects were specific.

Implications for Parents and Teachers. The indication from this study to parents and teachers is that children can, through specific training, be helped to gain self-confidence at least in some areas. This in turn can be utilized by the children to improve their leadership possibilities with other children. It is good schoolroom practice to encourage the less prominent children to be the best passers-of-papers or cleaners-up. But most teachers use in such capacity only those children discovered to be already good in something. Much more than is ordinarily done can be done to train the less prominent and less skilled children in some special capacity which will be useful to the group and which will give them status in the group.

Page[714] corroborated Jack's study with young children, finding that ascendant behavior is subject to training, and that the effects of training are cumulative. Apparently a child, once finding some confidence with other children in one skill or ability, is encouraged to try others, and can be led on into more and more ascendant behavior. We see, then, that children are benefited socially when they learn specific skills which are useful in building self-confidence and prestige with other children. It is not wise as a playground teacher, for example, to force the shy and unskillful boy into a baseball game, where his lack of skill only makes a nuisance of him with the result that the group avoids him still further. Much better is a plan which takes the child off in private and teaches him to throw, catch, hit, and run until he can take a desired place in the game. If he is hopeless as a ball player, he may become a good marble shooter, swimmer and diver, track man, singer in the glee club, or the accompanist for the glee club.

Jack's and Page's experiments show, too, that ascendance is not a static part of the personality, but that it varies from situation to situation. Children differ in leadership or dominance qualities at least somewhat in terms of the skills they possess in the natural world of childhood and which they acquired without special teaching with an eye to making them leaders. As a result, their leadership-followership position is ordinarily determined by the successful use of these "natural" skills measured in terms of the skills and interests of the particular group of children with whom they find themselves working or playing. If we accept the implications of these studies, we shall have to change the present *laissez faire* policy of most schools and playgrounds which assumes that children learn social lessions in free group play without teaching or supervision. The best democracy should function so as to "cash in" on all of its leadership. That probably means that no one person has all the answers all the time, but rather that, depending upon the situation and the activity, the leadership of any group should pass from person to person in order to give the person possessing the greatest skill or knowledge at the time and about the situation an opportunity to lead. Too many schools fall into the practice of letting one or two children run a given class for all activities and from year to year. Too little effort is expended in developing qualities and offering opportunities which will spread leadership.

Adult leadership in child play groups, however, must not be allowed to revert to the old idea of planning for the group all of its activities, and then "bossing" the children into the plan. It means, rather, preserving all the advantages to children's growth of the present *laissez faire* policy which lets them work things out as far as possible for themselves, but having the adult leader take a somewhat more active interest in helping individual children to develop skills and qualities which will give them the necessary self-confidence to go ahead in a group.

How a Sense of Failure Can Be Modified. Another study of importance which shows the possibility of changing a personality reaction is that of Updegraff and Keister,[964] in which they demonstrated that children's reaction to failure can be changed favorably. They selected by means of special tests children who showed undesirable or immature reactions to failure. Immature responses were "giving up," requesting help more than half the time, destructive behavior, more than two rationalizations in the test situation, exaggerated responses. These children were subjected to training periods in which (1) tasks presented were graded in difficulty so that the child's first experiences were successful and the later ones were within the possibility of success but required increasing effort and perseverance, and (2) tasks were so chosen that the child could see his progress and previous successes. Children so trained showed "remarkable improvement." They ceased to sulk and cry; interest and effort increased significantly; dependence on adults decreased; violently emotional behavior was eliminated.

This experiment followed the lines recommended by the best clinicians. Children who react badly to failure must be helped to see that crying, destruction, and other emotional behavior does not help. The only good way to show them this is not to punish them for such behavior, but rather to teach them how to get better results. This involves going back to the level of performance where success is possible, that is, "taking the child where he is," and teaching him through increasingly difficult successes how to persevere and win, "leading him where you want him to go." This is an especially effective technique for teaching constructive attack upon problems when children are young and their habits of approaching things are in the making.

Dominance or Submissiveness Is Less Educable as the Child Grows Older. There are indications that the older the child the less subject he is to training in such group techniques. The reason for this may be that as the years go by and as he has increasing experience in being dominated by others, he accumulates increasing conviction that he is a nonascendant person, and an increasing lack of self-confidence. Then, too, as the years go by, competition for a place in the group becomes harder because the other children are accumulating keener and keener skills, not only in the sports or songs or other activities, but also in actual social awareness of what to expect from people and how to get along with them. It becomes increasingly difficult for the nonpracticed child to catch up to the point where he can compete on favorable terms with the practiced children. Dominance or submission seem to be fairly fixed personality traits by the time the individual reaches young adulthood.

Like many traits, the dominance pattern varies with the situation, some people being dominant at home but thoroughly dominated at work, or vice versa. In general, adolescents from higher socio-economic levels are found to be more dominant than those from lower socio-economic levels. As with younger children, adolescents who tend toward dominant behavior have a larger repertory of skills and abilities than do the nondominant; children who have exceptionally good bodily skills tend to be especially dominant.*

Thus, although the emotional disorganization and ego deflation attendant upon failure can be changed in young children (Updegraff and Keister), and although the dominance position in a group can also be changed in young children (Jack and Page), our evidence indicates that such changes are harder to effect in older children and young adults in whom the personality seems to be more structuralized** and the ego level more static.

Changes Can, However, Be Made Even at Adolescence.   Such changes are not hopeless for adolescents, however, as is indicated by experiments at the Institute for Juvenile Research in Chicago. There, maladjusted young people or young people needing help to improve their relationships to their school or community groups were given special training in skills (bodily, creative, and social) in summer camps. Camps were used because in them young people have a twenty-four-hour exposure to the new situation and close personal contact with the counselors who give them the training. This demonstrates what is probably the most effective possibility of making personality changes for older children. That constructive group experience, especially in camping situations, can effectively modify aggressive behavior in preadolescent and adolescent children has also been clearly demonstrated by Redl and Wineman[763] in Detroit.

The results of these two experiments indicate that adolescent and pre-adolescent children can be helped greatly to develop more effective reactions in their school and neighborhood situations. There seems some definite hope that these changes are effective as a start toward accumulative improvement such as that found by Page in the dominance studies with younger children. As we learn more about how to do it in schools, camps, settlements, and recreation centers we may find that much more in the way of character and person-

---

* Girls majoring in physical education at the University of Wisconsin center as a group near the 90 percentile of dominance in Bernreuter Personality scores. This seems to be general among young people especially skilled in body control. This probably does not mean that physical training produces dominance, but rather that, as Maslow[633] found, the naturally dominant feel free and can express themselves well through bodily action. Doubtless there is an interaction between the two factors, the naturally (or early-acquired) dominant children being free to express themselves in bodily movement, getting practice, becoming more skillful, and more self-confident, and so on around the circle.

** A term rather generally used to indicate that the personality moves from the generalized, nebulous, vague reactions of infants toward a more definite form of reaction to specific stimuli. (See Lewin.[587])

ality education is possible even with older children and young adults than has generally been supposed.

Life Itself Sometimes Changes Personality Through Crises. Roberts and Fleming[787] found that peripheral traits in personality, and occasionally even core traits, were sometimes changed even in adults by such life crises as loss of a beloved person, the birth of a child, the sharp impact of quick success, and other similar situations. We have a tendency to protect children from trouble, struggle and the tragedies which we know to be stunting to their growth. Yet struggle and adversity sometimes strengthen personality. Murphy says:

> It seems to be a matter of common observation that some persons grow better—at least at times—under very adverse conditions, getting anything but what they ask for and rejected by those whom they want. Even more commonly it seems true that personality development along healthy lines is furthered by having a multitude of both friends and enemies, a loyal inner circle upon whom one can rely, and an outer world offering a stimulus to competition and often opposition. There are probably individual differences in this as in everything else in social behavior, and a great need for research at this point is evident.[684]

The lesson to be learned from this is that overprotection of children may seriously stunt their personality growth.[585] Only by facing and coping with difficult situations can children develop the strength with which to meet hard and unpleasant things. A life made up only of pleasure and ease cannot possibly develop poise in the face of trouble, a mature and well-balanced life philosophy. Until one has met difficulty successfully one cannot know the thrill of success after up-hill work. Too often progressive educators and super-conscientious parents protect children from effort with the result that they cannot work, and from failure with the result that they have no sense of proportion about their own capacity for meeting failure. The Updegraff-Keister experiment gives us the key as to how to help children meet failure without being destroyed by it.

Effect of Maturation on Personality Development. Personality structure is, as we see, exceedingly complex.[434,561,668,941] Many biologic factors influence it, as do many environmental or life-experience factors. Another set of studies than those we have been discussing center around the factor of maturation, or inner growth as an influence in determining personality. Maturation and learning experiments in social skills, at least for young children, corroborate other maturation experiments. Among these, Jersild and Fite[475] studied two groups of children, one group who had attended nursery school for one or two years, the other group entering nursery school for the first time. This study was done in New York City where social experiences for preschool children are limited unless the children are in a nursery school. On a sample of the number of social contacts of each group at the beginning of the nursery school year studied, the experienced children spent almost twice as much of their time in social contacts as did the beginning group. By the end of the year, however, the groups were almost exactly equal in social contacts. These figures are in terms only of the number of social contacts and do not give us light on the quality of the contacts. Jersild,[475] in summarizing literature on social contacts as affected by increasing age, reports that there is throughout the preadolescent period a steady increase in size of group and complexity of teamwork with increase in age.

Social Contacts Also Important in Modifying Personality. These and similar studies would imply that in social learnings, as in motor and language learnings, maturation is probably a factor of greater importance than training. However, we must pause to speculate here as to whether we should trust maturation to produce social growth if children were not subjected to social experiences.

Children whose social contacts are too long delayed probably do not suffer too much when they make their initial contacts with children whose social skills are as inadequate as their own. There is no sense of stigma, and everybody can be awkward together. When, however, the initial contacts come at the age of strong awareness of other children's reactions (six or seven years up), children who find themselves novices in competition with skillful children are very likely to develop a sense of inferiority and a feeling of discouragement at ever being able to accomplish the necessary learnings. Their awkwardness and their mistakes stand out in sharp contrast to the smoothness of the other children. Instead of quickly progressing through the first unskillful stages, they often withdraw, tending to develop the "sour grapes" attitude that they "don't really like to be sociable anyway." Such children may retreat into the world of reading if their reading skills are good enough, or into solitary fantasies where they find themselves more successful than in the world of reality.

As in the learning of academics, it is probably not wise in our present cultural situation to delay the first stumblings in social learning beyond the age at which most children are acquiring ease. This is one reason why nursery school attendance is valuable to children of three to five years of age who do not have an opportunity to contact other children in fairly free relationships. It explains why experienced kindergarten and early elementary teachers should do everything possible to help shy or awkward or boisterous and aggressive children to make adequate social adjustments before the pattern of retreat or of unhappy social relationship becomes fixed, and before the social skills of the great mass of children progress too far toward perfection thus offering a more and more hopeless competition for the unskilled child. It explains why the many exclusive boarding schools fail to put polish on an awkward girl or boy, since in such schools the general level of social skill is often too high for any but very skillful children. Sororities and fraternities at college are successful as social polishers only if the young person being polished is far enough along in social development and the acquisition of social skills to benefit from the extra practice and somewhat more advanced pattern. They fail whenever the awkwardness and lack of skill of the neophyte is too far below the general standard and, therefore, results only in hopelessness and increasing self-consciousness.

Effect of Cultural Pattern upon Social and Personality Development. How important the influence of cultural pattern is upon social and personality growth can be seen in the work of Mead,* who observed the development of character and personality in a number of primitive tribes. She reported that the development even of such so-called "sex traits" as greater aggressiveness on the part of the male and of submissiveness on the part of the female were apparently a product of the culture more than of the innate sexing. This is somewhat at variance with the work of certain biologists who have observed changes in aggressiveness or submissiveness with removal or implantation of testicular or of ovarian tissue in animals, the testicular tissue seeming to increase aggressiveness, the ovarian tissue seeming to increase submissiveness. Mead observed among Arapesh men a cooperativeness, gentleness, unaggressiveness, and solicitousness which were characteristic also of their women. On the other hand she observed among Mundugumur women the violent, aggressive, competitive, and hostile behavior characteristic of their men. Our idea of sex roles was reversed among the Tchambuli men and women. In this tribe the women were powerful and did the fishing and making of the most important articles of trade; the men engaged in artistic, nonutilitarian activities. Their women were practical and efficient, and adopted an attitude of tolerance toward the men, who were timid, sensitive, dependent, and graceful. Any person of either sex who differed from the established pattern of behavior for each sex in any of these tribes was considered a sexual deviant. Mead concluded that such standardized personality differences as are found between the sexes are the product of the cultural patterns and expectations in which the individual matures.

The important thing to consider in discussing the impact of the culture upon the development of the individual is not so much the exact pattern of behavior set by the group, but rather the relation between these patterns and the possible achievement of them by the individual. For example, as we saw in Chapter 5, the early days of American development placed great emphasis upon the large-framed, muscular and aggressive man. So fixed was this as the pattern for boys that hypersensitive boys who loved beauty and hated fighting were in the unhappy position of complete inability to achieve status in the eyes of the group and as a result were unable to marry any but masterful women who found fulfillment in the control of a mate instead of in the feminine pattern of leaning on one. As a result such a boy often lived a miserable life. In eighteenth century Europe, however, a "gentleman" could dress in elaborate velvets and laces and sniff his snuff with a dainty curve of the little finger. These patterns vary in marked form from period to period. But they also exist within any period, differing from family to family.**

* Mead[637] and many other cultural anthropologists[282, 434, 633, 659, 989] have contributed to these ideas, many of the publications having appeared since 1950.

** "Woe betide the child if he does not 'act like a two-year-old' (with proper enthusiasm for large-muscle and aggressive activities), or like a Middletowner, or like a son of Eli, or like a member of the Harriman family. Presumably the task of the educator is to become discriminating regarding the times when normative pressure is useful to a growing organism, as compared with the times it arouses conflict and distorted social patterns."[684]

"In our culture, both the personal-value, conflict-with-reality emphasis, and the ego-social ambivalence appear as primary determinants of the behavior of small children, and are probably responsible for the deep demand for the attention of adults and the early

Personality a Product of the Interplay of Factors.   In spite of the emphasis, then, which some studies place upon maturation as a dominant factor in personality and social development it seems evident, as we have seen, that learning factors are of great importance, too. Personality and social development, like every type of development, is dependent upon an interplay between the natural "type" or original endowment of the person, and the learning experiences he has. Let us take, for example, the social development of a fifteen-months-old child who has a special language capacity and great interest in people, but who cannot yet walk. His social behavior will be quite different from that of the fifteen-months-old child who can run about freely and, therefore, gives much attention to things, but who cannot talk at all, and therefore gets little from language contacts with people. The ten-year-old boy who has the average boy's longings to be with a gang will get quite different things from the gang in the way of personality development if he is large physically and skillful in coordinations than he will if he is under-size physically. The sexually mature thirteen-year-old girl who is mentally keen will have quite a different set of social experiences and will react to them quite differently than will the sexually mature girl of thirteen who is feeble-minded but pretty.

We have, too, a good deal of evidence that the personality traits of children sometimes change markedly when they move from one neighborhood to another where school and gang contacts are markedly different. Apparently the impact of the gang and the neighborhood upon the developing personality is sufficient to modify behavior. For example, children who are moved from a group where they are young and fairly inadequate in contrast to the contact group sometimes assume positions of leadership when placed in groups as young or younger than they are. This does not imply that the child is changed innately, but rather that what is called out of him in the way of behavior is changed.

Components of a Healthy Personality.   Something has been said in other places in this book about goals of growth. Here we wish to review briefly some of the goals for personality development as outlined in two outstanding discussions of the subject. As an antidote to a current feeling that a healthy personality suffers no conflicts or maladjustments, Thompson[941] says (p. 183):

> Normal adjustment is a relative thing. Every child suffers some anxiety, displays some behavior that is unacceptable to others, fails to reach some goals that are extremely important to him, and experiences some periods of what he calls unhappiness. However, the child whose psychological adjustment can be considered within normal range 'bounces back' from these disappointments and depressions. He continues to orient his

---

prominence of egocentric behavior. It is surely superfluous to point out that any planning for the social education of children must be done in the light of these considerations: first, the intimate interdependence of any one aspect of personality and all the rest of the person; second, the shaping of the boundaries of the personality, both its habits and the deepest emotional mechanisms, by the culture in which it grows, within the limits of the organism; third, the flexible response of young individuals to different situations within a culture, in terms of the meaning of those situations to them."[685]

behavior toward goals that promise to satisfy his needs, and he adjusts his goal-setting to the social demands of his culture.

The Midcentury White House Conference on Children and Youth[665,1001] lists the components of a healthy personality as follows:

1. A sense of trust—that sure feeling that everything is all right.
2. A sense of autonomy—that strong feeling.
3. A sense of initiative—that more clean-cut feeling: my plans and my ideas.
4. A sense of accomplishment—that feeling of importance: I can do.
5. A sense of identity—that new–old feeling: Who am I really?
6. A sense of intimacy—I am one with others and I care for others.
7. A parental sense—interest in producing and caring for children of one's own.
8. A sense of integrity—ability to accept the life cycle and the people involved in it.

SOME STAGES OR PATTERNS OF SOCIAL GROWTH

Let us turn now to what studies show to be some of the stages or patterns by which children in our culture grow or develop, recalling always that these stages are only in part the product of innate inner growth forces; they are also the product of the impact of our particular American culture upon the average American child.[222] We can understand children better as we meet them in school or informal education if we know something about the steps by which they develop their sense-of-self as contrasted with things or with the total social group; if we learn something about the development of their individuality as expressed by their attempts to stand as individuals against the impact of the social group, namely, about their aggressiveness or their conflict with the social group; and if we learn something about the manner in which they develop cooperativeness with the social group, namely, about cooperation, friendship, sympathy, respect for property rights, and other so-called "moral behavior."

Individual Differences Must Not Be Forgotten. In considering these stages of development we must not lose sight of the vast individual differences which occur in personality reaction to situations. Some children are naturally "in-going" or thoughtful, imaginative, and daydreamy; others are naturally "outgoing," aggressive in attack upon things and people, easily stimulated to action by objects and situations outside themselves. Some cling to the protected area of dependence upon adults; others seek every opportunity to do things for themselves. One child, kept in a limited educational environment will, nevertheless, find things to do; another, even in a rich educational environment, will seem to miss most of the opportunities. One child, faced with a new baby in the family, will fight desperately for his place in the center of the household; another child will welcome the freedom to do as he pleases so long as he does not get in the way. One child, placed in school and faced with reading and number work, seizes upon this as a way to exercise his inner capacities and to win status; another cannot give up the world of vigorous physical play, finding the challenge of the intellectual world colorless indeed; still another will cling to his world of fantasy, managing to escape the insistence of the schoolroom world.

Children differ, too, in the way they express themselves. One child, delighted with the touch of fur at a few months, may touch, shiver, crow his delight, look around at the adults to share his pleasure with him; another child may touch, touch again, and continue to explore the new sensation, absorbed in the reaction itself and giving little open expression to his emotion. Expressions of sympathy differ widely even in the preschool years. One child may promptly cry himself when he sees another cry; another child may attempt to smother the sufferer with hugs and kisses, only adding to the confusion and unhappiness of the victim; still another may run for adult help; while still another may start an intelligent probing to locate the cause of the difficulty. Even quite young children differ in the way they fight; some snatch and hit, others simply cry in impotent rage; a few use subtle methods of distraction and persuasion; an occasional child will drop the matter and wait for a more opportune moment for revenge.

Then, too, fundamental urges expressed at one level of development may prove a source of constant discipline, whereas expression of the same urge at another level may prove a source of great satisfaction. For example, keenly alert and inquisitive children who constantly explore the environment and exhaust the experimental possibilities of everything which comes to hand are the worst type of nuisance in their preschool years and are likely to receive constant discipline and restriction. This same faculty, properly guided and properly understood, may win steady acclaim in school because of the child's eagerness to learn, his ingenuity and resourcefulness in exploring the world about him. In adulthood, his refusal to drop a thing until he has explored its every possibility may make him a famous inventor or explorer.

How the Sense of Self Develops. Much of a child's development of selfhood, of standards of behavior and of his patterns of feeling grow through his "absorbing" of the "atmosphere" around him. Just how this takes place is a matter subject to question, but we know that much of the process is due to identification of the child's self with the people who are close to him.

Tiny babies do not seem to know where their own bodies leave off and the crib or toy begins. We see them biting a toe and looking puzzled because it "feels," whereas biting a rattle produces feeling only in tongue or mouth and in the fingers which hold it. In the same way, tiny babies seem to draw no clear line between themselves as ego structures or persons and the people around them. They cannot mark off where their own ego stops and that of someone else begins. Therefore, the influence of other people as closely identified with themselves as the mother or father or other close attendants is especially marked. What mother and father are, he himself is. What mother and father say is right; he has no judgment apart from theirs. His mother and father, the source of food and protection, the source of knowledge, and his alter-ego, are objects of supreme interest and influence in the life of the infant. They *are* his ego, the first extension of himself.[347]*

---

* For further material on the development of the ego see Chapter 14. See also Bibliography.[109, 857, 864, 989, 1010]

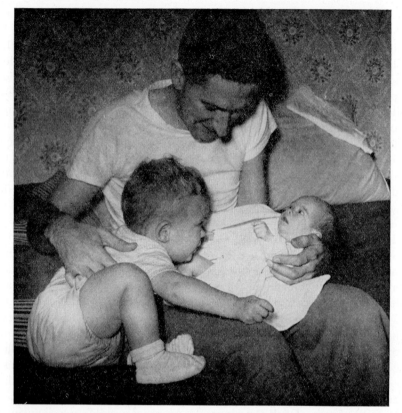

Fig. 42. Father, as well as mother, is important to the development of the sense of self.

Having identified himself with his mother and father or nurse, the pre-school child's circle of interest spreads to include other members of his family and friends who come frequently into his experience. What they think and feel and do he must think and feel and do. As Piaget[727] points out, even when the child is three or four years old he assumes that others see the world as he does. One of the chief lessons the child learns from contact with other children in nursery school or kindergarten or in free play is that other children have mothers and fathers, too, that they think and feel, too; but that they think and feel and live as individuals, as separate entities, the same in many ways as the child himself, yet also different in many ways. It is the young child's tendency to identify himself with the world about him which makes him love stories of animals who keep house and think thoughts and have conversations, just as he does.

In the sense that he identifies himself with his family in the early years of his life he is helpless against their influence. He has too little awareness of himself as a person, too little experience separate from theirs to question their opinions or to have a judgment of his own. He may, and usually does, fight hard for what he wants; but he has no self-criticism apart from their judgment of him, no sense of rightness and wrongness apart from theirs.

Even his language reflects his absorption of the personal ideas and standards around him. Such words as "good," "bad," "pretty," "ugly," "funny," have for the young child only meanings reflected from other people. "Good" means that one complies with routines, tastes and standards of the people around one. "Bad" means that one does not so comply, or that one hurts others or interferes with others. That one might differ with these ideas, having any ideas of one's own (any separate ego), is not possible to the nebulous self of a very young child.

Thus we can see how much of the child's selfhood is created by the people around him. This fact is important to people who adopt children. Since most adults have not developed flexibility as part of the core of their own personalities, they do not adapt readily to intimate family living with children who reflect standards and attitudes substantially different from their own. Older children have a selfhood which is the product of the people and experiences they have lived with. Few adoptions of children over ten years of age prove to be happy experiences for both the children and the foster parents. Success in such adoptions requires unusual adaptability on the part of both child and parents and a maximum of similarity in tastes and standards. For smooth family living foster parents should either adopt very young children or assure themselves that the tastes and standards of an older child's previous home or homes are compatible with their own.

As he enters school the child encounters another, less close source of identification in his teacher. In so far as she follows the pattern of his home he has no reason to question the universality of the rights and wrongs, the feelings and prejudices, and the actions of his world. In so far as she differs from his home he must face decision, and with it growing self-judgment. His ego, then, is forced to withdraw from the universally evident; is compelled to set itself up as judge. Thus he more clearly defines himself, marks out the beginnings of self-criticism, begins to question the universal rightness of the home pattern, and probably begins to reject certain opinions of his parents. "But teacher says it is so-and-so," or "John's father says it is done this way" are familiar to the ears of parents of six-year-olds.

By adolescence the sense of clear-cut individuality, of self-criticism, or independent capacity for judgment is usually at a freshly acquired peak. Therefore, the tendency to question everyone else's judgment, especially the judgment of the earliest patterns (the parents) is great. The new-found self-independence overweighs for a time the feeling of identification with any group other than the close feeling of unity with other adolescents. The natural outcome is unreasonable rejection of any judgment but that of one's peers, a storming against adult authority, a railing against old-fashioned conservatism. This sharp insistence upon the autonomy of one's own judgment may be a necessary part of the bolstering which the adolescent needs before he can break away at all from his childlike dependence upon the judgment of others. Only when he has convinced himself that he is no longer afraid can he have the courage and clear-headedness to weigh intelligently his own judgment against the wisdom of the race, the church, or his parents.

Development of the Sense of Failure or Success: an Important Part of the Sense of Self. Sound judgment about one's own successes or failures is an essential part of a healthy adult personality. Little children have none of it. A baby is delighted with himself when others are delighted with him. He is crestfallen when scolded. He tends to do whatever will bring the reward of approval and tends to avoid anything which results in disapproval.[222] He has no sense of success or failure within himself but will behave in any manner which will please the adult closest to him. By three or four years of age, however, children have set up a sufficient standard of what is expected of them to use it as a gauge of success or failure. They have also discovered a sense of success in controlling their own bodies or the world of things and people about them, and have developed a sense of frustration or failure when they fail in these controls. They give evidences of these feelings of success and failure since, by the time they are three years old, success will cause them to change from passive to active behavior, whereas failure makes them appear dejected. A nursery school child who has just succeeded in going down the slide in the school yard for the first time will throw back his head to crow with delight, then burst into activity, usually repeating the stunt, though sometimes simply jumping up and down or running around excitedly. Failure to keep one's bed dry if parents are putting pressure on one to do so usually produces a "deflated" dejection, although such a failure may drive a certain type of child to noisy behavior as a cover-up.

The child must feel a challenge, however, before he reacts to success or failure. Tasks which are too simple in the mind of a child do not raise his ego feelings or reflect in his behavior when he succeeds, largely, it seems, because he considers them "baby stuff" and not worthy of pride. Similarly, tasks which are too far beyond him do not, as a rule, deflate him when he fails because he does not expect himself to succeed. It is, therefore, important that parents and teachers set a level of expectation for each child which will be within possible accomplishment, yet which will challenge effort. To expect too much may drive sensitive children either to a frenzy of effort or to sodden despair. Luckily, the average child, being not too sensitive, does not gear his aspiration level too far beyond reasonable effort, and develops an indifference to impossible adult standards, thus becoming "behavior problems" in the minds of the parents or teachers who set the impossible standard.

In adult life one's effectiveness lies in how well one accomplishes what one is best able to do. Society expects the best we have. Therefore, society's measurement of success is couched in terms of what people do in relation to what they are able to do. Happiness is determined in an important way by whether one feels oneself a success or a failure. Many people fail either because they aspire to things they cannot do or because they do not aspire to do what they are able to do. The relationship between what one aspires to do, what one does, and how one feels about it determines whether or not one is successful and happy.[316] Although everyone differs in his aspiration level for different things (thinking it important to be good at business but feeling no urge to succeed in family life, for example), the general level of aspiration in relation to general level of accomplishment can be observed. Some people carry an aspiration level in general which either keeps them constantly failing in their own eyes, or which makes "impractical idealists" of them. Other people "have their feet on the ground," keeping their aspiration level constantly checked against their accomplishments, yet far enough in advance of accomplishment to keep progressing in accomplishment. Others carry very low aspiration levels, "lacking ambition," and placidly "getting nowhere."

People react differently when they realize that their accomplishment has fallen short of their aspiration. Some try to do better; some become discouraged and give up; some dream of success, or make excuses or use other forms of psychologic escape; some combine these.[369,826] The best reaction to failure to reach one's goal is either to do better, or, if the goal is set so high that good effort cannot reach it, to change the goal.

In early childhood the aspiration level is easily influenced, and the habit of expecting nothing at all, or too much, or just enough of oneself is in the making. Indications from current studies are that by late adolescence the relationship between one's goal ambitions and the tempo of one's effort to achieve them is fairly well set. Frank's study[316] seems quite definite in indicating that this relationship between what one expects of oneself and what one does is set as a relatively permanent personality characteristic fairly early in life.

We should teach children to evaluate themselves and their accomplishments in terms of goals which are high enough to stimulate constant growth, yet low enough to permit success with reasonable effort. By so doing we help them to lay a basic cornerstone for mental health. Circumstance, however, helps to mould this aspiration level, even when parents or teachers expect the right amount from each child. One dull child (80 IQ) whose parents were thoroughly aware of his ability and who, therefore, were very conscientious about not making him feel that they expected more than he could do, nevertheless went to pieces from a sense of failure in schoolwork. The key to his situation was four brothers and sisters with IQ's ranging from 120 to 150, whose academic accomplishments were so obvious that, even though the entire family conspired to keep such accomplishment in the background, the dull child knew he was not up to the family pattern. One of the strong arguments in favor of homogeneous groupings in schools is to keep dull children from an aspiration level set by inevitable competition with brighter children, and which, therefore, is too high for them. Similarly, homogeneous groupings keep brighter children from setting an aspiration level which is too low for their own good or the good of society. Competition of bright children with bright children as a rule keeps aspiration levels for these children where they should be. Homogeneous groupings, of course, set up competition between groups, setting the "bright" group off from the "dumb" group.

The Effect of Competition upon Aspiration and Success. Competition with other children which sets aspiration levels for individual children in terms of the accomplishments of other children near them seems a unique product of our Western culture, as well as of certain European and Asiatic cultures. Studies of Hopi Indian children[36] show that they are not concerned about getting ahead as our children are. When placed in a situation where they are expected to be motivated by being first or by being ahead of someone else, they fail the teacher miserably because self-depreciation is good form and obvious desire to appear better than other people is bad form among the Hopi. In contrast to this the Lynds[603] found in Middletown that ambition outran ability in a considerable proportion of a midwestern American town's population. There is a definite pattern in our culture by which parents and teachers get as much school work out of children as possible. The difference between progressive education and the older education is not that we try to get less work out of the children, but that progressive education tries to do it so pleasantly that the children will learn to like getting as much as possible out of themselves not only in school but in life afterward.

Granted, however, that our objective in education is to teach children to expect great things of themselves, or at least, to expect the best possible of themselves, we might turn to some of the current studies on how best to do this.

Effect of Praise and Blame.　Early studies done in 1916[354] indicated that reproof of children motivates them to learn more effectively than praise does. This was in line with the "spare the rod and spoil the child" philosophy current in formal education and in parental attitudes of the 1890's and early 1900's. In other studies[974] done in the late 1920's it was found, however, that the degree of effectiveness of reproof depends upon the kind used. Reproof administered in private, for example, was more effective than reproof administered in public. Ridicule and sarcasm, particularly when used in public, resulted in a sharp drop in learning. One study on high school seniors[120] showed that sarcasm used in public caused 6.2 per cent of the students to do better, 29 per cent to remain the same, but 64.5 per cent to do worse. Sarcasm in private was somewhat more effective, but still caused many children to do worse. Reprimand used on junior high school or college students was less than effective when used in public (causing 46 per cent to do worse) but when used in private caused 83 per cent to do better. Public ridicule caused 64 per cent to do worse, whereas public commendation caused 91 per cent to do better.

The findings of these earlier studies, which indicated that certain forms of reproof disturbed children badly and that commendation, particularly in public, was on the whole an effective means of motivating learning, led to more careful work on the effects of praise and blame. The well established Law of Effect was formulated by Thorndike* and has deeply influenced home and school practice with children. According to this law of learning, people learn faster and retain longer anything which is pleasant; they avoid or soon forget anything which is annoying. For some years the philosophy governing child training was, "Always praise a child to get him to learn; do not punish or reprimand him"; "Always say do; never say don't." Child psychologists adopted this principle widely. Progressive parents and teachers

* As reported in many current educational psychology texts.[93a, 207, 210, 229, 386, 766]

felt that they must never reprimand a child, but must always use a "positive" approach.

Still more current studies[176, 307] reveal that, although praise is in the long run more effective than reproof, a judicious combination of both is better than either used alone. Either used alone is, in turn, better than ignoring the child's effort. We might grade the effectiveness of adult procedure with children somewhat as follows:

Ridicule or sarcasm (especially in public)—handicaps learning.
Ignoring child's effort—discouraging, or, at best, ineffectual.
Reproof (particularly if administered in private)—somewhat effective.
Praise (for genuine effort)—somewhat more effective.
Praise for good effort combined with reproof (especially when accompanied by constructive suggestion)—most effective of all methods.
A judicious adjustment of any method to individual children—absolutely necessary.

Effect on Motivation of Knowing the Results of Effort. One further principle of motivation has been established beyond doubt. There is no disagreement among a number of studies* that children learn better when they know what the result of their work is than when they are left in doubt. This should speak loudly to teachers who throw children's papers in the waste basket and to parents who do not trouble to follow through on tasks they ask children to do. We should not leave children who are learning a new skill or job in doubt as to whether the task they have done is satisfactory or unsatisfactory.

EXPERIENCES TO VITALIZE CLASS WORK

1. Observe the personality of some child, preferably one whom you know fairly well. If you are doing a case study use "your child." List his outstanding traits, both desirable and undesirable. What traits need further development? Which ones need curbing? What would you regard as this child's "center of gravity" traits; which ones are peripheral? Should this have anything to do with your recommendations for change?

2. Visit a playground or other free play situation. Which children lead the group? Which are never leaders? Does leadership change from activity to activity? What personal qualities or skills made the leaders successful in leadership? Can you make suggestions for developing the nonleaders? Do you notice changes in position of leadership or followership as the group changes in personnel?

3. Find some child who hangs around the fringes of a baseball, marble, or other skill game. Take him (or her) aside for a few short periods of quiet practice in this skill. The practices should be spaced over several days. Do you see a change in his ascendant behavior as he returns to the group?

4. Do you recall from your own childhood a change in your own outlook on life when you changed from failure to success in schoolwork, or in games, or in helping with household chores, etc.? Can you remember other dramatic incidents which changed basic habits and attitudes for you? Did you make any basic changes in yourself as you came into the period of "self-awareness" in adolescence? How hard did you find it to reeducate a habit of years? How did you finally succeed in doing so?

5. Set up, if possible, a brief learning experiment (learning accurate throwing of a dart, learning some game or academic skill, etc.). Study the effect of praise, of blame, and of praise-blame-instructions-for-improvement combination.

6. Look up current literature (since 1950) for material on projective methods, both as they are used in research and as they are used in therapeutic work with children. Present your findings to the class.

* See Bibliography.[288, 717, 923]

7. Look up personality development in adolescence in the current literature (since 1950) and present your findings to the class.

SELECTED READINGS

Biber, B., et al.: Life and Ways of the Seven- to Eight-Year-Old. New York, Basic Books, Inc., 1952, Ch. 4.

Harsh, C. M., and H. G. Schrickel: Personality Development and Assessment. New York, Ronald Press, 1950, Chs. 14–17.

Honigmann, J. J.: Culture and Personality. New York, Harper & Bros., 1954, Chs. 8–12.

Klopfer, B.: Personality Diagnosis in Childhood. A chapter in Lewis et al.: Modern Trends in Child Psychiatry. New York, International Universities Press, 1945, pp. 89–104.

Kuhlen, R. G.: The Psychology of Adolescent Development. New York, Harper & Bros., 1952, Ch. 4.

Landis, P. H.: Adolescence and Youth. Rev. ed. New York, McGraw-Hill Book Co., 1952, Chs. 5–7.

Martin, W. E., and C. B. Stendler: Child Development. New York, Harcourt, Brace & Co., 1953, Ch. 7.

Thompson, G. G.: Child Psychology. Boston, Houghton Mifflin Co., 1952, Chs. 5, 12, 14.

Witmer, H., and R. Kotinsky (editors): Personality in the Making: Fact Finding Report of Midcentury White House Conference on Children and Youth. New York, Harper & Bros., 1953.

CHAPTER 13

Social and Personality Development—
(CONFLICT AND AGGRESSION; COOPERATION
AND FRIENDSHIP)

DEVELOPMENT OF INDIVIDUALITY AS EXPRESSED IN
CONFLICT AND AGGRESSION

A number of studies of children's social behavior center around observations of children's aggressiveness. This is fairly easy to understand, since it is when the child fights or teases or disobeys or is jealous that he is troublesome. "The wheel that squeaks gets the grease" seems true here, since troublesome behavior notoriously gets more attention, even among research workers, than does cooperative behavior or just ordinary routine behavior.

Definitions of Aggressiveness Differ. Murphy[684] and associates define aggressiveness as "all forms of insistent response to obstacles socially imposed between children and their goals." This indicates that children are not aggressive just for the sake of aggressiveness, but rather that aggressive behavior appears only when something happens to keep a child from achieving some goal. The use of the words "socially imposed" suggests that the thwarting must be imposed by people, either adults or children. Other psychologists usually include under aggressive behavior that which results when a child displays anger or other aggressive behavior if crossed by things as well as if crossed by people, e.g., if the child cannot succeed in getting the pieces of a puzzle together and he throws it on the floor as a consequence. It is also defined as failure to obey commands, to relinquish toys or materials, or to discontinue activity that someone else tries to interrupt; responding with retaliative measures to pushing or hitting or other physical stimuli; crying or saying, "No"; or any situation in which the child himself proves the stimulus for resistance or acquiescence.

The various studies of aggressive behavior are based sometimes upon one of these definitions, sometimes upon another. We shall assume that aggressive behavior includes all the phases of behavior defined above.

Theories Explaining What Causes Aggressiveness. There are several different theories used in explaining aggressiveness in children. One is that displays of anger or jealousy or disobedience are primarily attention-getters. Since such unsocial or asocial means of getting notice are considered bad, the method of dealing with such displays is to repress or to ignore them, and to teach the child better means of gaining attention.

Another theory about aggression is that it is one of the basic instincts and must have a way of expressing itself. When it appears, then, it must not be repressed, since repression of basic impulses is dangerous, but it must be redirected. The idea is, for example, that one should not repress anger; one should redirect it. "One must not fight against other people; one must fight with and for them or for some worthy cause." In this general idea of aggressiveness we see an implication that certain aggressions are necessary as a balance in personality development. The baby, completely dominated by the adult, must develop and display aggressive behavior in order to nourish his growing ego, so that he may become a person apart from the persons who absorb him.[42,43] Therefore, aggressiveness is welcomed by proponents of this school as a healthy sign of a developing personality. According to this school of thinking it should not be repressed, but rather should be carefully nourished. The less sane advocates of this school have produced some extremely disagreeable children. The saner advocates agree that aggressiveness must not be allowed to run rampant, but must be disciplined into socially acceptable channels, "canalized," in other words, into socially acceptable patterns of behavior.

One branch of the "express-it-rather-than-repress-it" school assumes that aggression is called out only when the child is frustrated or interfered with. Some of the advocates of this school imply that situations which cross the child should be avoided; in other words, that the child must never be crossed. Others imply that such situations should and must be allowed to occur, since all of life disciplines us and the child must learn early how to adapt himself in a socially acceptable manner to thwarting.

Another way of regarding this "well-of-agression-in-the-personality-which-must-be-expressed" is to regard as imperative the necessity for planned outlets for aggressiveness. The idea is that if the child does not express his aggressiveness he will turn it in upon himself, developing into a masochist, a person who enjoys inflicting pain upon himself or having it inflicted on him by others. As a substitute for hitting people, then, we should give him opportunities for rough play, a punching bag to hit, nails to "swat," and the like. At the present writing this method of providing opportunities for the expression of aggressions offers a happy compromise between the "children-should-be-seen-and-not-heard" school and the "let-them-do-as-they-please" school.

Research Findings. Research on this subject has given us some helpful insights to guide our treatment of the overaggressive behavior which so often troubles parents and teachers. One group of investigators[362] found aggressiveness to be primarily an expression of such physical factors as fatigue or hunger, or of such psychologic factors as wanting something which is forbidden or which is too hard to get. They recommend that when a child behaves badly, we should find out what is the matter with him or what unreasonable circumstance has occurred to rouse him. If we follow the lead given to us by these researches we shall learn to look for some physical condition such as hunger or impending illness as an explanation of tantrums. Or we shall try to find out how much the child was aggravated by circumstances before we punish him as "being a bad child." If he is behaving badly because he wants something he cannot reasonably have, he must be helped to develop desires for things he can have and to give up other desires.

Another group of investigators* has emphasized the inner or instinctive reactions of the child. Their work has called to our attention the emotional or instinctive forces which may drive a child to explode whether the thwarting circumstance seems to the observer to warrant his explosion or not. They have helped us particularly in cases where children seem to explode with what appears to the adult a totally inadequate aggravating cause. Hidden emotional blockings or conflicts often drive children to what appears on the surface as quite unreasonable or inexplainable behavior. Punishment of such behavior is harmful because it only further frustrates the child and adds to his internal turmoil. Nothing but understanding and a strightening out of inner conflicts and emotional longings can correct aggressive behavior which stems from such causes.

Murphy[684] has found that children who are more aggressive tend also to be more sympathetic toward other children. Hattwick[411] found that there is a high correlation between aggressiveness and feelings of insecurity, aggressiveness being especially acute in children who come from homes where they feel rejected by their parents. Caille[155] found that children who are most resistant to adults are also in general the children who are most acquiescent to adults. These are all indications of the relationship between inner passivity or repression and aggressiveness, and between inner longings and explosive behavior.

Caille[155] found that even though children are as aggressive with adults as with children, they actually resist other children more frequently than they do adults. In spite of the popular idea that boys are more resistant than girls, Caille found only a slightly (even this was statistically unreliable) higher resistance among boys, at least of preschool age. Jersild and Markey[480] and Dawe[223] found, however, a corroboration of the lay belief that boys are more aggressive than girls. They found, even in the preschool age, that boys fight somewhat more than girls do, and that, in general, boys fight more with boys, girls with girls than do boys fight with girls and vice versa. This is corroborated by Goodenough,[362] who found boys more resistant than girls at every preschool age.

Most of the studies agree that negativism or resistant behavior is a behavior pattern which is subject to modification by training unless the resistance is the consequence of inner emotional conflicts or longings. In this case only removal of the conflicts or provision for fulfilling the longings will change the behavior.

Two Types of Aggression.   We may be able to differentiate between

---

* The psychoanalysts.[8, 680, 857, 864, 1010] See also Dollard[250] and Jersild[475] for complete discussions of frustration and aggression.

the behavior which we should try to modify by discipline and that which we must correct from within if we recognize two forms of aggression in children: (1) that displayed by children because of self-confidence; and (2) that which arises because of feelings of insecurity, the children behaving aggressively because they feel unwanted and must strike back at the world, or because they must dominate younger children or any situation possible in order to restore the balance of self-respect, or because they carry a deep sense of frustration which explodes beyond their control.

Children who display the former kind of aggression can be expected to develop mature patterns of behavior in dealings with adults since they are capable of acting with discrimination, obeying when it seems wise to do so, disobeying only when they feel they must to gain their point. Children who display the type of aggressiveness due to feelings of insecurity act from blind inner necessity and, therefore, do not develop the discriminations which make more mature behavior possible unless they can be made to feel more secure.

Aggressive Behavior Normal and Desirable in Children. Most writers in the field of child development have concluded that in our culture, in the United States at least, a certain amount of aggressive behavior against both adults and children is a normal part of early social development and has a definite place in the acquisition of independence in the adolescent years. Most nursery school teachers and observers of young children feel that a child who never fights is a child who lacks normally active contacts with other children or who is emotionally immature or maladjusted. Judging whether or not the child is normally mature and normally self-confident depends upon his age and developmental level, upon the group with which he plays or works in school, and upon the particular situation in which he does his fighting or the losing of his temper. The type of punching and pushing which a four-year-old uses in defense of his toys would not, for example, be the type we should expect from a nine-year-old. In a group of mild children, easily dominated, a normally aggressive child would quarrel or explode seldom; whereas, in a more aggressive group he would do so frequently.

We saw in Chapter 3 that, like other emotions, anger changes, both in the stimulus to anger and in the manner of expression, as the child grows. We saw that arousal to anger and explosiveness of expression are characteristics of the emotional patterns of infants and young children. We saw also, however, that in the course of normal development we learn to leave these "childish things" behind and to become more self-controlled, more able to adjust inner emotional tensions to socially acceptable patterns.

Our Culture Demands Certain Forms of Aggressive Behavior. One must learn in our competitive culture to "stand up for one's rights," not "let other people run over one." Fathers, particularly, urge sons to "fight your own battles." These lessons are being learned rapidly in the school years, but not without confusion to adult and child alike. We expect children to become increasingly free of dependence upon adults, to grow into a capacity to "take it" without whimpering, to move forward in spite of obstacles (to fight aggressively for success). Yet, when they refuse to knuckle under when punished, we regard it as stubbornness, forgetting that this same trait is "courage" on the playground. When they fight by any method they can command to win their own way, we are worried over disobedience. The problem for adults is to understand which traits to encourage and when. The problem for children is to learn what to fight for, when to fight for it, against whom, and by what methods.

Learning Approved Methods for Fighting.   General progress in fighting according to socially approved technique means moving along the scale from hurting, snatching at the cost of others, carrying a chip on one's shoulder, toward the type of aggression so highly approved in our present society, namely, having enough self-confidence to get what one wants (so long as this does not deprive others), participating freely and in the capacity of leadership in groups, gaining professional or vocational prominence, and fighting to defend oneself or others. Children characteristically suffer confusion because they are urged to hit back if struck, but are themselves hit (spanked) for hitting when angry or when fighting for something they want. They are urged to "get ahead," but severely disciplined if they cheat to do it; they are constantly urged to beat others in grades at school and in sports, but are promptly checked if they boast of their own successes, or even if they sacrifice other values to achieve them. Even in beating other children to the honor roll, they are disciplined if they try to keep other children from getting there ahead of them. Learning to "fight right," meaning "within the rules," is one of the most complicated learnings our culture imposes upon children.

Gradually, however, they do learn the rules; but much experience and many years of time are required. Children who lack experience between three and six are likely to enter school on the three-year level of hitting and snatching for material possessions. It will not take most such children three years to "catch up," but it will take a little time and a good deal of patience on the part of the teacher.

Patterns of Aggressive Behavior Determined by Cultural Impacts. Whatever these patterns of growth and the ages at which they appear in our culture, we must realize that both patterns and age of appearance are not the product of inner development *per se*, but are the result of the impact of our culture upon the child. We have two- to three-year-old negativism because we put children of this age under such pressures as eating for themselves, toileting regularly and with increasing independence, learning not to snatch or throw or cry when thwarted. We get "ten-year delinquency" at the stage where we emphasize a next step in respect for property rights and further learnings in self-control, promptness, consideration for others, and "socialized" behavior with peers. In our culture, for example, taking other people's things is a laughable baby trick at two years, a mistake at four or five, but a crime at ten years. In some social cultures taking everything one can is socially approved behavior so long as one is not caught. Society must, of course, impose restrictions upon primitive behavior. We are not pleading a case for the removal of restrictions. But a good teacher or parent must understand that every child at some stage in this interplay between his impulses and society's restrictions will break down into "naughty" behavior. Our task is to know when such behavior is simply evidence of an as yet incomplete learning, when it is evidence of confused attitudes which need basic retraining, or when it is the reflection of deep inner conflicts which need skilled professional help.

By adolescence most children have pretty well mastered the knowledge of what to fight for, when, against whom, and by what methods. The adolescent's problem is to apply this knowledge to himself. He still has desire, as do many adults, to fight for the wrong kind of recognition or possessions; he still suffers from immaturity in self-control, has childish habits to overcome.

DEVELOPMENT OF COOPERATION AND FRIENDSHIP IN EARLY CHILDHOOD AND PREADOLESCENCE

Three Kinds of Personal Relationship.   The child's development in capacity to make friends outside the family is ordinarily regarded as one of the most important aspects of his social development. Some people live fairly satisfactory lives in social communities with few, if any, friends, but they are the exception rather than the rule. Other people claim hundreds of "friends" who are really only acquaintances or playmates, few, if any, of whom can stand the test of tragedy or serious demand upon the relationship. The ideal in our American culture seems to be the capacity to "meet any man at his own level" or "to win friends and influence people." This involves three different types of relationship to people. One type of relationship is involved in the superficial social techniques of what to say and do at teas or receptions and how to "sell" in the business world. Another type consists of maintaining smooth relationships with the people at the office or in the school dormitory or adult club, getting along with people whether we like them or not, because they are where we have to meet them or work with them frequently. A third type of relationship consists of those intimate harmonizings of person with person which close friendship and family living require. The finest of our American ideals implies mastery of all three types of social relationships.

Children must learn something of social "*skills*" as such, something of ease and poise, along with reasonable self-confidence if they are to master the first type of personal relationship. "Smooth" business or social manner eases the way for casual social relationships, or for good selling or business contacts. Knowing what to do with one's hands and feet, how to introduce people, how to order lunch and eat it, how to talk smoothly and convincingly about nothing in particular or about "the product" or "the company" are all invaluable. These skills and "manners" are grounded most securely if learned early. Four-year-olds who have learned not to smack lips or gobble food are not likely to forget in a critical deal over a luncheon table in adulthood. (As was pointed out earlier, it is not implied here that young children should have "perfect manners"; to expect this is to produce severe strains in children.)

Smooth voice, free flow of good grammar and diction, ease in introductions and casual conversation come through patterns set for the child by parents and friends, and, on certain occasions, by teachers; they are achieved through early and relentless practice. Consideration for the comfort, the desires, and most of all for the ego of others comes through exposure to such consideration in childhood or through unremitting self-discipline and close observation of the reactions of others in later childhood and adulthood. Some people who missed these "cultural" advantages in childhood learn through grim determination in a college dormitory or through conscientious practice based upon books of etiquette. Poor habits of grammar learned and practiced in childhood may be lost through relentless practice in adolescence or early adulthood, but in crises the old habits may spring up and trick one, even after years of later practice.

The second type of personal relationship can also be acquired later in childhood, though it is based even more upon early childhood beginnings. To keep one's temper day after day in the face of irritating traits displayed by fraternity brothers, or the other people in the office, requires self-control. To keep one's personal grievances to oneself requires the knowledge that only friends and family care about such things, plus the self-control to keep one's tongue and to smile when grouchy. To work whether one feels inspired or not, to carry one's share, to "make good" without snatching authority from others, to take or to give orders effectively—all this depends in most people upon basic habits and attitudes built through childhood. School teachers, church workers, and others who supervise the work and play of children have constant opportunities to teach them to *live and work and play skillfully and effectively with whatever group propinquity provides*. "Being a good sport" carries a clear set of concepts and patterns of behavior in the minds of most elementary and secondary school children.

Intimate friendship and family living, the third type of personal relationship, test the deepest facets of the personality. Here one cannot cloak impulses and desires, habits, and basic attitudes. In time, close living and close friendship reveal what one is. In a certain sense the only preparation for this type of personal relationship is the laying of sound foundations in the personality structure. In another sense, however, friendship and successful family living can be learned; for, even though the relationships involved test what one is, a certain "art" of friendship and love can be acquired. In this sense, fine friendship and wholesome love can make one over, enriching and disciplining habits, attitudes and feelings, and thus developing the "art" of love and friendship. There is something more to friendship and love than being a person; one must know how to find and win other persons who will respond to one's real self, and, ideally, each person should become a richer, more useful and happy personality because of friendship and love experiences.

Even elementary school children learn something of this art of revealing themselves to others, and of responding to others on a friendship basis. Kindergarten and preschool children learn less consciously, but deep layers of the friendship and family-life relationship are being laid nevertheless in the first years of life. How much one concedes to the people one loves, or demands of them; whether one "goes to war" in the open about differences of opinion and desire or disciplines one's resentments, loyalty, or self-centeredness; whether one is generous or selfish, cheerfully accepting or glumly resistant—these are all attitudes and practices in intimate living caught as patterns from the intimate living one knows best in childhood. Family attitudes, viz., what men are like and what they expect of or concede to women, what women are like and what they expect of or concede to men, whose work is what, who manages money or dominates the relationship, what parental duties, responsibilities or privileges are—these are absorbed early and throughout childhood from one's own parents and immediate relatives.

However, even in these more intimate relationships much is learned on the way through life. Each friend loved happily or unhappily teaches most people something. Next to parents perhaps the most influential person in making one's personality is one's mate.[312] Next to families and beloved teachers or informal education leaders, children probably learn most, socially and personally, from their friends.

Some Research Findings on Cooperative Behavior and Friendship among Preschool Children: Social Behavior in Infants. Many studies have been done to give us knowledge of the typically "social" or "personal-reaction" development of children. One of the earliest was that of Bühler[144] who found in work with infants that a beginning of "social relations" was made in the second or third month when children began to respond discriminatingly to their mothers. She found them "socially blind" to other infants, however, until they were four months old. Later studies refer to personal-social development earlier than this, however. Gesell[345] observes that at four weeks the average child fixes a transient gaze upon a face bent over him, reflecting his awareness of the face by a slight change of expression. He responds in a comparable manner to the human voice, is soothed when picked up, and thus shows what can probably be referred to as "security" if handled in a calm and assured manner. These are the beginnings of social-personal development. Gesell feels that by four months, the average child gives clear evidence of recognizing his mother or the person who tends him most often, since he smiles when she approaches, but looks soberly at a stranger. Bridges[119] in a careful study reports that social interest in other children grows slowly up to nine months, but rapidly after that.*

Gesell[345] gives us a clear picture of the genuine self-sufficiency of the infant and young preschool child. Absorbed with acquisition of control over his own body and with adjustment to simple daily routines, the young infant has scant attention or energy left for adjustment to people. By the age of a year, however, compared with three-, six-, or nine-months-old infants, the child has acquired what Gesell calls "a high degree of social reciprocity." He has acquired considerable social status in the family, not infrequently at the very

---

* The deep effect of these early "identifications of the self" with the mother, and later with the father, should be recalled here from Chapters 3 and 12. See also Ribble[781] and other psychoanalysts.

center of the group. He "plays the galleries" by repeating tricks which rate a laugh, pleasing himself thereby as much as he does his audience. Some early primary school children are in this stage. But the baby has no genuine sense of self-identity or of self-criticism. He is merely pleased with his performance because he is pleased with the total social situation in which others are pleased. However, the six-year-old child who may be behaving in a babyish manner has sufficient self-identity so that, with help, he can soon develop more mature social purposes than playing the galleries. Remnants of bids for the center of the social stage, however, appear here and there throughout the elementary and secondary school years, being particularly evident as a by-product of the more acute self-awareness characteristic of early adolescence.

Further Research Findings: Social Behavior in the Preschool Years. At eighteen months of age children have a sense of "me" and "mine," both words being frequent in speech at this time. The run-about child is in his own way as self-absorbed as the infant. The world offers endless possibilities for exploration and new experience. This makes discipline problems since much of what he gets into is and should be forbidden. Thus at times he finds people an annoyance and a hindrance to his will. He does, however, interrupt his activities as a rule to "notice" newcomers, either adults or children, and, even though he seems to be little aware of them, may cry if they leave.

Some nursery schools and most day nurseries accept children of one and one-half years to two years of age. Even with a number of them together, however, there is nothing which resembles group cohesiveness. Children in the earliest stage of group social development spend most of their time in *solitary play*. Teachers of two-year-olds should expect very little, if any, group co-operation.

Very young children play beside other children, rather than with them, a form of play referred to as *parallel play*. In this each child plays pretty much by himself, yet enjoys his play more, has more ideas about it because of occasional interchange of ideas between the children, and stays with it longer than he does when by himself. Even at this age and under these conditions of play the children influence each other somewhat. A bad "snatcher" may create more conflicts, a cry-baby may stimulate more emotional scenes than would be natural to the average child. On the other hand, a cooperative child with a fairly strong personality may influence the other children favorably. Friendship as such scarcely exists since almost any child will do as well as any other child to play with. Kindergarten and first-grade teachers must learn to recognize this type of play among their less experienced pupils. Unless children have a certain amount of exposure to other children, they cannot grow through the various stages of social development. Inexperienced kindergarten children usually spend much of their first year passing through this parallel play stage and the other stages characteristic of preschool children. Solitary play, which is characteristic of infancy and early preschool years, and which is preserved as a habit when opportunity for group social growth is lacking through two or three years, may be very hard to overcome.

The teacher should welcome even so immature a form of social behavior as parallel play if it indicates that the given child is moving forward a step from infancy. Our job is to know what steps to expect, and to guide children through these steps as rapidly as they can absorb the necessary learnings characteristic of each step.

Three-year-old children, though still self-absorbed, are, if given proper opportunity to play with other children, increasingly aware of others. In spite of the fact that solitary and parallel play are still dominant, socialization proceeds in the form of learning to take turns at swing or slide, and in the elementary sharing of toys. At four years children exposed to other children become aware of themselves as belonging to a group. In nursery school they can be heard to ask, "Is this what the children do here?" thus showing their awareness of themselves as children in contrast to adults and their growing identification of themselves with other children.* Whereas a two-year-old is seldom successful in eliciting a desired response from other children, a four-year-old often succeeds, and shows such a wide repertory of social responses as reaction to the distress of others, making requests for assistance from other children, making suggestions for dramatic play, and utilizing a variety of techniques of acceptance, refusal, evasion or transformation of the situation. Murphy[685] sketches development of social expression as, first, a tendency to help others only when it is convenient or when it does not interfere with plans, and only later, the development of a tendency to stop what one is doing in order to help another. Expressions of sympathy from young children are rudimentary, and vary from child to child, some children simply staring at another in distress, occasional children putting an arm around the sufferer saying, "Does it hurt?" or "What are you crying for?"** Some preschool children even progress far enough to show kindness to newcomers in a group, or to defend the rights of younger children.

The Transition Period between Preschool and Gang.   It seems in the nature of four- to eight- or ten-year-olds to show contradictory social traits. They fight their best friends and most beloved brothers and sisters more than they fight other children, probably because they spend more time with these children and therefore "run afoul" of each other's self-absorptions and selfishnesses more often. The most aggressive children are often the most sympathetic when anyone else is hurt or in trouble. However, Murphy[685] found that children who showed outstandingly sympathetic behavior sometimes displayed exceedingly unsympathetic or even cruel behavior. This is true of girls as well as boys.

During this four- to eight- or ten-year period the child moves forward from solitary and parallel play into genuine group play. Highly organized group activity becomes characteristic of the gang age, which is usually set at anywhere from eight or ten years of age through pubescence. As a transition before this we find children playing in *shifting groups*, a form of play in which

---

* An excellent discussion of these preschool social growth stages can be found in Gesell et al.[345] and in Rand et al.[756]

** Bridges[119] gives an excellent account of this.

group activity goes on but the form of organization is so loose that any individual child may abandon the group for his own activities without disturbing the project. Highly popular projects at this age are keeping store, playing show, or playing school. Child A and B may say, "Let's play store." They build the store, but meanwhile child C or D may join, lay a few blocks, or decide to make vegetables or other produce out of clay. Child E may elect himself delivery boy—long before there are any customers or produce. Child A may wander off to ride his wagon a while, yet the project goes on. In these shifting groups much can be learned which prepares children for the more highly organized play of the gang age. Yet, as they should be, lessons are geared so low that neither children nor project suffers if any child grows tired of group adjustment and withdraws to the peace of solitary play while he rests. Such leadership as exists in these shifting group projects is likely to be unstable in the sense that it passes from one child to another without any particular upheaval, and the child who leads most often today may gradually give way to another who leads most often three months from now. However, teachers of young children have often observed that a certain group cohesiveness may center in one given child, so that when that child leaves or is absent such group spirit as existed dissolves and the children who had participated in the group return to play as individuals again.

Research on Cooperation among School-Aged Children. Among the earliest and best known studies of social behavior of gang age children is the work of Father Furfey[329] of the Catholic University. He studied groups of boys as early as 1926 and created the concept of "developmental age," comparable to the "mental age" or "height age." This developmental age is "a type of maturity, uncorrelated with mental age, which shows itself in changing play preferences, in a changing reaction toward authority, and, in general, in constantly maturing behavior patterns."[329] This measure of the social maturity of children has come into fairly general use for both boys and girls although Furfey's work was with boys only.

The groups into which girls organize themselves are often referred to as cliques, whereas the boys' groups are referred to as gangs.* Among elementary school girls cliques are less well organized and have less well defined purposes and less outstanding leaders than boys' gangs. Brown[129] says that girls organize as frequently as boys, but on less conspicuous bases, with the result that boys' clubs or gangs have been much more frequently studied. One study, reported by Brown, of 965 high school girls showed that 77.5 per cent of them belonged to some form of unsponsored club or group.

Furfey[329] divides the age range from six to sixteen years into three periods. They are

... the *individualistic period, the gang age,* and *adolescence.*** The latter two are sharply separated by the phenomenon of puberty. The former two are separated by a less well defined transition period occurring on the average somewhere around ten or eleven. Each of the groups mentioned has its own psychological characteristics.

* Both gangs and cliques are frequently referred to in current writings as "peer groups."
** Italics ours.

We have referred to his individualistic period above and extended it to include the earlier stages before six of solitary play, parallel play, and shifting-group play. It was Furfey's work which first set the lower limits of the gang age at eight to ten years. According to him, boys of eight are not found in clubs unless they are definitely accelerated in developmental age, whereas a high proportion of twelve-year-olds belong to some kind of club. Similarly, he says about team games that it is impossible to organize a baseball team of eight-year-olds because everyone wants to pitch, whereas at twelve baseball teams or clubs are entirely possible because the right fielder will take a vicarious pleasure in the exploits of his pitching ace.

Characteristics of Group Play During the Gang Age. Furfey considers the gang age a sharp contrast to the individualistic period because it is distinguished by three phenomena: (1) the separation of the sexes in play, (2) interest in clubs, and (3) enthusiasm for team games in which the team, and not the individual, wins or loses.

Brown[129] observes that up to around eight years the play group often includes both boys and girls, especially if the girls are active in body movement or imagination. At least 92 per cent of the group of 168 boys studied by Furfey played with girls when they were six years old; even at age ten the percentage was still as high as 83; but at twelve the percentage of boys who would play with girls had sharply dropped to 20. It should be noted here, however, that although boys and girls usually prefer to play separately from eight to twelve years of age, they *can* be polite to each other in coeducational play and school situations. The "double-standard" begins to assert itself at eleven with teasing, bantering and jealous competition between the sexes. Campbell,[158] in reporting observations on children of ages five to seventeen who belonged to recreation clubs, found that "there is at first an undifferentiated social relationship with the opposite sex until about the age of eight years, then a rising preference for children of the same sex, until puberty, when heterosexual feelings (feelings of attraction to the opposite sex) begin gradually to develop."

Interest in clubs (Furfey's second characteristic of the gang period), and enthusiasm for team games in which the team, not the individual, wins or loses (his third characteristic) are accepted by most writers as characteristic of group play during the upper elementary and early secondary school periods. Brown[129] points out that after eight years of age there develops an interest in the organization itself rather than in the activity. Clubs with pass words, initiations and an attitude of exclusiveness or "You can't belong" become frequent. "The Dirty Dozen," "Three Musketeers," "Jones Street Gang" are typical names. Settlements and play groups find special interest clubs easy to form. "The Adventure Club," "The Hobby Club" are typical. These clubs sometimes take on bizarre forms.

Influence of Gang Play upon Personality. The influence of the gang or play group on the formation of personality is clearly recognized by most writers on the subject. Brown[129] says that no other group except the family itself is of such fundamental importance in the social development of the child as the play group. Here the child acquires another type of "we" feeling. Cooperation is learned as common interests are developed and common activities carried out by the group. He adds that formerly the gang was explained on the basis of gregariousness. Now it is probably better understood, not as a response to a child's need for being in the midst of a group, but rather as a means of wider self-expression, a place to develop leadership, and an opportunity to make normal social contacts.

Thrasher,[946] after investigating 1313 Chicago city gangs, arrives at a conclusion almost diametrically opposite to the conventional theory which assumes that gangs are a spontaneous result of a gregarious impulse. Instead of gangs being natural or inevitable, he concludes that they are the products of social deterioration and disintegration in communities. This principle he believes to be true at least for the closely knit groups that he included in the "gang" category. He adds that gangs start on a diffuse basis, becoming solidified through continued association of the members with each other. If the solidified gang persists, it either conforms to the standards of adult society and becomes a club or conventionalized gang, or it defies society as a criminal gang. In either case it deeply influences the character of the gang members. We must remember that Thrasher's study was made in a large city with many slum areas. Furfey,[329] working in a different type of environment, finds that gangs tend to dissolve after puberty at which time, although they do exist, they exercise less influence upon the boy's life.

Hollingworth[430] found that gifted children (IQ above 180) often do not have a gang experience because there are too few children near their ages who prove to be congenial to them. Terman[933] gives convincing evidence, however, that gifted children are above average in social skills. They simply have such a wide variety of interests that they spend a great deal of time with things and ideas, whereas less gifted children spend most of their time with people.

It is generally agreed among writers in child development that children learn invaluable life lessons in group activities. Murphy and associates say:

> The young child or the adolescent 'finds himself' in the group. It is in the group that one realizes oneself as a personality. It is impossible to find out what there is inside of an organism except by stimulating it; and in order to find out anything really profound about it, one has to give it varied social stimulation, intensive and prolonged. At the end of the process, the individual may quite literally be a new person, for better or for worse. It is likely that for this reason there is a considerable amount of sense in Jung's contention that the personality is never completed, but goes on building itself forever, as long as the world and the organism interact, that is, as long as life is maintained. There is even greater sense, we believe, in Burrow's contention that groups can liberate what is socially meaningful in the person and give it direction and a chance for self-development much better than any individual can. . . . We believe that not only momentary behaviors, but many deep springs of child personality, are liberated in group situations. The individual 'finds himself' because others find him.[684]

Competition Rather than Cooperation Is Often Encouraged by Adults During the Gang Age.   The effect upon children's personalities of experiences of conflict or competition and of cooperation and friendship within the gang, or found elsewhere at the gang age, deserves some further comment.

Even though the gang is primarily a teacher of cooperation, the gang age is a period in which children either naturally or by copy from our American cultural pattern indulge in competition in speed, strength, endurance, and fortitude. In the classroom they can easily be led into competition for first place in arithmetic or other academic subjects. Competition is in fact so widely used as a motive for effort among children at home, in school, and in informal educational groups that we should review any justification for it offered by the literature. Murphy and associates[684] review a number of studies on the effect of group competition and individual rivalry upon effort and learning. In the studies reviewed, whether in this country or Austria, with preschool children or grade school, high school or college the results are the same. Competition and rivalry produce results in effort and in speed of accomplishment.* However, there are individual differences in responsiveness. Some children show a strong desire to excel, some remain calm and fairly indifferent to competition, still others are frustrated and disturbed by it. Some studies show boys responding more vigorously than girls; some indicate that elementary and high school children respond to competition more than preschool children. Even among preschool children there seem to be differences, the two-year-olds, according to Leuba[579] merely looking on and failing to get the idea, the three- and four-year-olds responding to rivalry from children next older than themselves, the five-year-olds showing genuine rivalry-dominance patterns like those of elementary school children.

Experimentally, then, we can say little against competition and rivalry as methods to be used in motivating children. The widespread opposition to competition as a motivation for children has risen, not from grounds that it does not work, but rather from grounds of philosophy. Many people feel that schools and informal educational agencies like churches, camps and settlements should not further develop an impulse which so dominates our present American culture but which, they feel, is not conducive to the best welfare of either individuals or of humanity. Aggression, domination, and rivalry are not part of the religious or moral teaching in most religious philosophies. Yet they flourish in our business and social world. The people who are struggling to motivate children from some other source are doubtless struggling to break the hold that everyday motives have over our behavior.

Three Types of Competition or Conflict May Characterize Groups. Brown[129] points out that conflict in gangs or clubs is of three types: (1) rivalry among group members for recognition within the group itself, (2) conflict between the group and rival groups (this can be both constructive and destructive), and (3) conflict between a group of children and the organized agencies of society. Some of these teach lessons in cooperation; some prove disastrous to the child's personality development.

In the first type, competition within the group itself, Anderson[28] found even young children using commands, threats, or force to gain their objectives. This is not very well integrated or socially mature behavior, since integrative behavior means some yielding to another, the finding of a com-

* See Bibliography.[373, 579, 973, 1021]

mon purpose among differences of opinion, and cooperation. Anderson found in 1030 paired types of behavior which he studied among young children that dominating behavior calls out either domination or submission from the other child but not integrative, or socially desirable, behavior. In contrast to this, however, integrative behavior on the part of one child tended to call out integrative behavior from the other. The conclusion drawn is that the type of companionship in play groups should be of major concern to parents and teachers. Although the authors know of no studies of this kind among older groups Brown[129] quotes case studies which indicate that domination by a gang leader may force submission from the rest of the gang outwardly, but actually creates counter dominance in the other children and is, therefore, not socially healthy as a technique. Adult leaders can often help children to develop more satisfactory group techniques than the lower form of competition between members.

Conflict of the second type, between the group and other groups, serves to solidify the group within itself and proves, therefore, healthy for the spirit of any specific group. This is a universal social phenomenon. War with another nation wipes out differences of race and creed within the nations at war, fanning loyalty to the country into a clear flame. Group leaders of children, teachers, settlement workers, scout leaders, church leaders all recognize this principle when they set up competition with other groups, trying, of course, to keep the rivalry on a friendly and sportsmanlike basis.

The third type of conflict, that between a group and society, should be of concern to every adult worker with children. Outright defiance of law by a preadolescent or adolescent gang, or flouting of social convention by a group of adolescents, can prove serious in its consequences. Much of such conflict represents a basically wholesome impulse, viz., the child's general attempt to stand on his own feet. Difficulty arises when this impulse "gets off the track" because unwise adults have insisted upon over-rigorous supervision or because environmental background has failed to provide adequate habits of sound recreation and emotional outlet. Much bad group behavior has rather simple beginnings in "swiping" apples for fun, smoking a cigarette on the "sly," and accidental or careless destruction of property. Trouble flares up when adults treat such episodes as the beginning of a career of crime, punishing too severely, ostracizing too completely, producing too much excitement and sense of defiance. Children should be helped to find excitement in more wholesome directions, may perhaps need to be told that many children go through such stages only to discover that it is much more fun to get excitement and adult attention in more grown up and satisfactory ways. This does not, of course, mean that such behavior should be neglected or condoned; rather, it should not be allowed to become a focus for adult-child conflict and antagonism. Adults represent law and order to children. Encouraged to hate adults and to try to evade or outwit them, children are by this fact encouraged to hate law and to try to evade it or to outwit its authorities. Adequate provision of wholesome recreation is also an imperative in solving delinquency problems, as is the provision of community facilities to deal with maladjusted children during the early stages of maladjustment. Better parental supervision and more adequate law enforcement (concerning, for example, serving liquor to minors) are also vital.[414]

Factors Which May Produce Conflict or Cooperation. The *age range of children* in a group affects conflict or cooperation in the group. Confusion and conflict result if children of different ages are put into a program which does not allow a wide choice of activity and adequate equipment for play or work. In schools or on playgrounds where activities are scheduled or space limited, wide age ranges create confusion and conflict. The general experience of school people corroborates this since they try to group children by age and ability rather than in groups representing wide ranges of age and ability. Most camp, settlement, and playground workers find that four- and five-year-olds do not mix well with ten- and twelve-year-olds, nor do preadolescents mix well with postadolescents.

The effect of *large or small groupings* depends a good deal upon the child. Some children are confused and unable to get into effective action in groups of more than two or three. These children seek always to avoid the larger gangs and to find one or two special friends. Other children seem to function best in larger groups, playing most happily in groups of eight or ten to eighteen or twenty, and working best in groups of twenty-five to forty.

An important factor in determining whether any given child reacts favorably or unfavorably to any given group is *the capacities and interests* of that child and *of the majority of the group*. An extremely active child who prefers large-muscle play may find himself ostracized and "a bad boy" in a gentler group of children who prefer small muscle activities. A child who does not like music and has no ability with it may find himself a misfit in a group of children most of whom love the music period and therefore spend considerable time with it.

A good deal also depends upon the *patterns of behavior and feeling in the group*. Some groups are dominantly gentle and sympathetic, stopping play to attend to an injured member. Most gang-age groups are sarcastic and intolerant of "cry-babies," thus helping a too soft child to become somewhat more robust in the face of pain. Some groups place a great premium upon defiance of adults, calling anyone who complies with adult authority a "sissy." Other groups, although not timid, accept cooperation with adult authority as a matter of course.

To what extent the *quantity and variety of equipment* promotes or retards socialization seems still a matter of dispute. Some studies report that more equipment stimulates the children to more action and hence more contacts with each other. Other studies report that less equipment makes the children more dependent upon each other, thereby stimulating social contacts. The differences are probably due to a lack of agreement on basic setup. It seems reasonable that groups of children on crowded playgrounds devoid of equipment or in bare gymnasiums might be greatly stimulated to socialization by introduction of a ball or two. On the other hand, playgrounds and schoolrooms heavily loaded with swings, slides, clay, easels and paints and other equipment which stimulate children to busy themselves by themselves, may find that removal of some of these will stimulate group activities more. Doubtless the answer to the effect of equipment upon conflict or cooperation within any given group lies in what the equipment is as well as in how much there is of it.

The *quality of adult leadership* is also important[588, 761] to the determination of conflict or cooperation within the group, some leaders being gifted in ability to stimulate cooperative behavior, others thinking they are thus gifted because they can dominate the situation by force or the implication of force in such a way that they keep the children quiet. Some leaders seem by their very presence to stir up conflict of the undesirable sort.

In nursery school studies we have some evidence on the best number of children to have in a group, the best age range, the amount of space, kinds of equipment which are desirable, types of personality most to be desired in teachers, and best adult technique for handling children in order to get a maximum of cooperation and a minimum of conflict. The evidence on pre-school groups is not yet extensive enough, however, to be conclusive on any of these points. We have a good deal of evidence about these matters for children of school age. The great difficulty in making use of what we know lies in our inability so to finance public education or public recreation as to make possible the size of the groups, the use of materials, the plant and space, and the hiring of teachers of the type we know to be best for the development of children. Public school groups in large cities are almost always too large. Materials and equipment in most rural areas and villages as well as in larger cities are almost always too limited.

Fortunately, the Urge to Cooperation Is as Innate as the Urge to Competition. Just as conflict and competition seem inherent in the nature of gangs, so also does cooperation. This is encouraging to the teacher or group worker, since it is the basis for constructive development through group activity. As we have seen above, it is, in fact, partly through conflict that the nature of cooperation is made clear to children. There is, however, also an element of pure spontaneity in much of the cooperation children give each other. They imitate each other as early as fifteen or eighteen months of age. They play in a loose group, in parallel or independent but nevertheless imitative play, as early as two years. In fact, this liking to play near another child, doing what he is doing, even though each child does it independently, is a preferred form of play for many two- and early three-year-olds. Children of three to five love to look at things together, or to hear a story together. They begin to like certain specific companions for the sheer sake of companionship. Around four they play in the shifting group formation, even though no adult urges them to, or even sets the stage for such play. By five or six years, if children have had an opportunity to play with other children, rather closely woven play of an organized group develops, again with no urging from adults. From eight or ten years to adolescence most children find gangs or cliques quite apart from adult urging and often in defiance of adult discouragement. Furfey,[329] who, as we have seen, knows boys well, says that the average gang, like the average individual, is more good than bad, though he warns us that gang standards are not to be measured in terms of adult standards. Adolescents find each other also in spite of adult discouragement. This all comes about quite spontaneously, the urge to be with others and to cooperate with them seeming thoroughly natural.

The Highest Type of Cooperation, However, Is Not Innate. Cooperation of a high type, however, does not spring full blown into mature existence. It must be learned. But it must not be forced. Many parents and teachers are overanxious about "getting along nicely with one's little playmates." During the stage of parallel and shifting group play children wander off into their own pursuits in a manner which might be regarded by the not too understanding adult as discourtesy to each other. Contacts at this stage, usually ages two to four or five, are typically brief and somewhat egocentric. In the shifting group and in the early stages of more closely organized group activity (usually from five to ten or twelve years of age) young egos are strong and not too well controlled; social techniques are amateurish and full of rough edges. Quarreling is frequent and often violent. Children should not, of course, be allowed to hurt each other seriously, but they should be left free of adult interference in order to work out their techniques of getting along together. Wise adult guidance and some help in seeing that opportunities in space and equipment are available will help to speed the process; continued adult interference can only stifle it.

The usual and desirable developmental picture is one of increasing self-control on the part of individual children, of increasingly smooth social or play techniques, and of an emergence at adolescence or early adulthood of higher forms of cooperation. The adolescent should continue to learn better and better how "to take it" in group activity, should develop an improved self-control, and should gain further insight into the needs and wishes of others.

What Makes a Child Choose the Friends Who Make Up His Gang or Clique? As in the studies of preschool friendships we see also in the friendships of the gang age a tendency for children of similar chronologic ages to form more friendships than do children of different ages. This, of course, seems obvious, since children of similar chronologic age are, as a whole, of similar mental and developmental age. However, where children differ from the average for their age in mental or developmental age, we find them choosing friends from among children of a similar mental or developmental level, rather than from among children of the same chronologic age.[716] Superior children choose other superior children of the same age or average children who are older. Retarded children choose other retarded children of the same age, or younger children. Children gravitate toward similarities in height and weight, developmental age, scholarship, extroversion, and physical achievement.

Leadership in Gangs. Leadership in gangs or highly organized play groups is affected by age, social status, intelligence and school marks, since the children of obvious ability and prestige seem to sustain the role of leadership.[684,452] Hollingworth[430] in studying extremely superior children found that such children were not chosen as leaders by average children as often as were moderately superior children. Apparently a too brilliant child has too little in common with other children to be chosen for leadership by them. However, throughout childhood and adolescence, leaders are usually above the average intelligence of the group led.[452] Leaders seem to be physically healthier and psychologically more extroverted than average children.[452] Two studies[28,733] agree that the child who attempts to lead by domination is a less strong leader than the child who leads through understanding, skill, and the use of the cooperating principle. Children who are genuine leaders must have some self-discipline, some grasp of abstraction and recognition of social ideals, some awareness of other personalities, ability to pursue objectives consistently and to subordinate immediate to more remote goals. These are seldom developed before the age of nine or ten, so that full-fledged leaders are seldom found among children younger than this. Certainly, some of the important lessons to be learned in the gang are self-control, how to get along with other people by developing sympathy, tolerance and understanding to replace the boisterousness, loud language, bullying, and bidding for attention which characterize the six- to eight-year-old child. Fortunately, the influence of the gang in the development of a personality adequate to meet adult demands is fully recognized by most parents, particularly fathers, and by most teachers.

Some Children Spend Too Much Time in Gangs or Group Play. We have, in our culture, a general feeling that the child from six or eight to puberty who does not "socialize" or seek a group of peers is somehow a problem child. The child who likes to spend considerable time by himself, reading, building, or otherwise entertaining himself is likely to be considered a social deviate, a child who is somehow failing to grow normally. Although there is little doubt that good adult adjustment to the business and social world as we know it depends heavily upon skills with people, and although we can see clearly as we watch child growth that many of the most valuable of the lessons of how to get along with people are learned through gang or clique experience, it seems evident that too much social participation in play is just as unwholesome as too little. Witty, in discussing his extensive studies, says:

> These data suggest that certain sociologists and educators should revise or abandon their pleas for indiscriminate sociability. One frequently hears that the nonsocial child is a misfit, that wholesome growth is consummated only through numerous and varied social contacts. It seems, from the data presented in this study, that one should not encourage indiscriminate sociability if one desires the most wholesome development of the growing child. It appears to be the kind of social contacts made, not the number, which should be of great concern to the person charged with the guidance of children.[1005]

Furfey reminds us that not all children of any given chronologic age are of the same developmental age. Some of them do not fit into available groups of peers, and this produces a whole set of problems for such children. Any child who dislikes sports or is not skillful in them or who lacks courage, or is sensitive may be ostracized by the only available group of peers. This may produce bitterness in the child who feels from parents or teachers that he has somehow failed them in failing to find popularity in a peer group. Such children sometimes suffer deep feelings of inferiority and may become moody, may retreat into fantasies or other undesirable emotional behavior. As we saw above, many gifted, charming-to-know children fail to find congenial companionship in the available peer groups. The more fortunate of the non-gang children, however, usually find one or two congenial friends, and in these friendships have not only companionship and freedom from loneliness, but also an opportunity to learn many of the lessons of give and take, of sympathy, self-control, and tolerance which serve them well in adulthood. Some of the too successful "gang" children find in gang activities so much satisfaction that they develop no other academic or creative interests, and, therefore, remain in the gang stage of social development for the rest of their lives. Such people are those who know no recreation apart from night club, movie, or ball game, who have few inner resources, no greater command of the techniques for getting along with people than are characteristic of gang-age children. Apparently, in socializing with the gang during the gang age, the motto of "enough but not too much" seems to apply.

Fitting the Child to the Group. Association with the "right" gang is often a problem to parents and teachers. It is well known that gangs made up of a majority of wrong-standard children will do many destructive things which any of the individual children would not have thought to do alone, thus setting a bad pattern for individual children, or often getting otherwise harmless children into real trouble. It is equally true that a gang made up of a strong majority of "right-minded" children can prove a thoroughly wholesome influence on "wrong-minded" children. Parents and teachers, therefore, often attempt to do considerable shifting of children from one group to another, not only to remove an individual child from a bad group to a good one, but, often, to get him into any group at all which will accept him.

Just how much we should shift a child from one group to another in an attempt to find the group in which he will function most easily is open to question. Some parents keep shifting a child from school to school in an attempt to find some group of children or some teacher who will "understand" him. This only encourages such a child to think that all the adjustment between himself and a group should come from the group and none from him, or that a school situation can be found which will exactly fit him as he is. Even though every clinician and worker with children knows that sometimes the type of group or school is not one to which a given child should be asked to adjust, he also knows that to ask no adjustment on the part of the child to group or school is to allow him to get an entirely false idea of what to expect from life. Every child, in order to benefit from a group or a school, needs to feel at least somewhat equal to the situation, to feel some hope of achieving status on the basis of his own capacities. A hopeless situation means inevitable defeat and discouragement, both of which are destructive to personal and social growth. Children should be moved out of a too hopeless, too discouraging situation. However, there seems an evident necessity for workers with children to discover ways of giving children ample confidence in any reasonable situation, partly because we cannot always change children from one group or school to another, partly because we cannot always change group situations to fit the needs and capacities of every child in a group, and partly because life in his adult years will ask much from him in the way of adjusting to situations as he finds them.

DEVELOPMENT OF COOPERATION AND FRIENDSHIP IN ADOLESCENCE

Children Carry Certain Residua from Gang Age into Adolescence. Even though in some socio-economic groups gangs persist after puberty, the end of the gang age is marked by adolescence, according to Furfey, as we have seen. As boy-girl interests emerge, in most socio-economic groups the gang gives way to a "crowd" which is made up of couples, or, in early adolescence, of boys and girls who pal around as a group without as yet pairing off with "a steady."

During infancy and childhood home, school, church and gang have developed and clarified the child's ideas of himself as a person and of his status or role with other people. We cannot, therefore, deal intelligently with young people in junior and senior high school unless we have some understanding of what has gone before in their lives and what they have gotten out of their previous experiences.

Characteristic Changes Occur.   One of the most characteristic changes which occur as children pass from the gang age into adolescence is a change in interests and activities. Play interests, as defined by baseball, marbles, and other activities which boys share with boys, and girls share with girls, all wane somewhat in favor of party activities and other means of being together in boy-girl groups.[572] When the adolescent does play team games, as he still frequently does, he plays them "in a somewhat more critical spirit."[329] He wants organized team competition, coaches, uniforms, and equipment. The vacant lot no longer satisfies him. Since girls mature physically earlier than boys, Stolz and associates[898] found girls taking the lead in instituting social dancing and in arranging parties attended by boys and girls together. Some of the boys allowed themselves to be taught to dance, though it was not until a year or so later when they were biologically mature that they became really interested in participating. During the transition period many of the boys simply hung around the dancing and watched.

Tastes and Characteristics Preferred in Peers.   Tryon[958] made a careful study in Oakland, California, of the characteristics which 200 pubescent and adolescent children considered desirable in each other and which is worth summarizing at some length. What boys expected or liked and what girls looked for as desirable differed so much that they are cited separately. What is considered ideal in the seventh grade differs from what is considered ideal in the ninth and in the twelfth grades; therefore, these are cited separately.

Seventh grade boys admire in other boys: expertness in organized games, readiness to take daring chances, ingenuity in leading or directing games. Activity of any sort is high in choice of qualities to be admired; aggressiveness, boisterousness and a rough and ready appearance are definitely preferred to submissiveness, reserve or tidiness. Their idea of a happy person is a noisy, raucous type.

Seventh grade girls consider desirable that behavior which represents the standards held by their mothers and their women teachers: the demure, prim, ladylike, docile prototypes. They admire pretty, friendly, popular, tidy girls who are sedate, submissive, and nonaggressive. They are only mildly interested in organized games. They like a happy, humorous person who has a sedate kind of emotional buoyancy. Tomboy girls who are daring and jocular are accepted by the group, but are not especially liked or admired, just as the gentle, pleasant, lovable boys are accepted but not emulated by the boys.

Ninth grade boys still admire physical skills, courage, strength, and agressiveness, but somewhat less; and unkemptness has become highly unpopular. (This is encouraging to the parent who feels that the seventh grade boy will *never* wash himself.) Boisterousness and showing off have become "childish" in the mind of the ninth grade boy, and a too high energy output in the classroom is likely to condemn one as a nuisance. Either conforming with or defying adult commands is a matter of slight significance. Social ease and poise, personableness and likableness share honors in popularity with physical skill, strength, and aggressiveness.

Ninth grade girls shift the emphasis from their seventh grade admiration for ladylike conformity with adult standards to being a good sport and attractive to boys. It is interesting to note that the girls admired most in the seventh grade for their ladylike qualities were not the same ones who, two years later, were the ideal of the group for their social attractiveness. In the ninth grade "peer culture" is forcing girls to be socially active in a hail-fellow-well-met way, having many friends, and being "popular" in large groups.

Twelfth grade boys still maintain a high regard for skill in athletics. An outstanding athlete needs, apparently, to have little else to retain a position of great popularity. However, a mediocre athlete can win a place for himself if he is good-looking, tall, grown-up, and mature. Popularity with girls can be achieved with such traits as appearance and easy social manners, and with an ability to do smooth social dancing. A socially poised, or mature, boy with high academic standing is popular; "brains" and intellectual achievement minus the social skills are not admired. The boys in the twelfth grade of this study probably express the ideal of twelfth grade boys in the country at large when they set as their ideal a boy who must be both honest and capable in anything he undertakes.

In this study *twelfth grade girls* expressed as their ideal the girl who had accepted and achieved her feminine role, the well-groomed, pretty girl. According to this study, the "feminine" girl may be of several types, but she must have enough ability in physical activity to be able to do something with boys besides dancing. She may win at the twosome games sometimes, but she will not usually be popular if she gives the impression that she can win all the time. The twelfth grade girl who wishes to be popular must in any case dress in good taste and be stylish according to the standards of the girls in her group.

An Individual Adolescent's Social Success Depends upon General Development and Training. All of these standards will, of course, vary from community to community, but in general they show the development of young people's ideas of themselves and their standards for friendship. How these young people accept each other and discover the best ways to manage their friendships and personal relationships is dependent upon their general background of self-control, their training in consideration for the needs and wishes of others, their own individual conception of the masculine or feminine roles in life, and their general level of psychosexual development.

Friendships and personal relationships in adolescence take on an emotional tone which probably reflects the sexual development so important at this age. At the same time that the adolescent declares his independence of adult standards and controls, he is actually very dependent upon conformity with his peer group. His keenest interest, once adolescence is well established, is in boy-girl friendships. This accompanies rapid progress in his psychosexual development, so we shall turn in the next chapter to a review of this aspect of growth.

EXPERIENCES TO VITALIZE CLASS WORK

1. a. Observe a group of preschool children. What evidences of conflict do you find? What types of cooperation are in evidence? What part does any adult who is present play in either type of behavior?

b. Do the same for a group between six and twelve years of age.

c. Same for a group fifteen to eighteen years of age.

2. Select some child who is a problem because of too aggressive behavior. Find out as much as you can about what situations call out this behavior. Find out as much as you can about the satisfactions and frustrations of the child's present living. Also his life in earlier years. Can you explain his behavior? What, if anything, can or should be done about it?

3. Select some child who is a leader and outstandingly popular with both adults and children. Observe him in the classroom and in free play. Is his popularity based on sound work and cooperation or is it a product of charming bids for attention? What can you find out as the causes of his present behavior and personality?

4. Observe a group of junior high school boys, a group of junior high school girls, one of senior boys in high school and one of senior girls. Do you find that their general ideas of what they consider desirable in themselves and in each other correspond to those outlined in this chapter?

5. Recall your own childhood (or, if you are doing a case study, do this for "your child"). Can you trace the steps of your own social and personality development? What do you think you can do now to further improve your social adjustment?

SELECTED READINGS

Blair, A. W., and W. H. Burton: Growth and Development of the Preadolescent. New York, Appleton-Century-Crofts, Inc., 1951, Chs. 2, 3.

Dollard, J., et al.: Frustration and Aggression. New Haven, Yale University Press, 1939.

Garrison, K. C.: Growth and Development. New York, Longmans, Green & Co., 1952, Ch. 15.

Jersild, A. T.: Child Psychology. New York, Prentice-Hall, Inc., 1954, Chs. 8, 11.

Landis, P. H.: Adolescence and Youth. Rev. ed. New York, McGraw-Hill Book Co., 1952, Chs. 7, 12.

Thompson, G. G.: Child Psychology. Boston, Houghton Mifflin Co., 1952, Ch. 11.

Walters, S. A., and S. K. O'Hara: Persons and Personality. New York, Appleton-Century-Crofts, Inc., 1953, Ch. 19.

CHAPTER 14

Social and Personality Development—
(MORAL JUDGMENT AND PSYCHO-SEXUAL DEVELOPMENT)

DEVELOPMENT OF MORAL JUDGMENT

Moral Judgment a By-Product of Many Other Learnings.   A large part of that mature balance of judgment which sees individual rights in clear perspective with the rights of others, which sees the relationship of one's own present behavior to one's own future well-being, is called moral judgment. It is made up of all those self-controls, awareness of self, skill and insight into others, reactions to the authority of parents, of church or of cultural mores which we have been discussing. The child gradually accepts group codes; his ability to adjust his own selfish, impulsive behavior to these restrictions grows as his conscience grows. Moral behavior is in many senses a by-product of his general social experience.

As we have seen in the development of the self, the child's first conception of what is *right* or *wrong* is simply that which his parents permit or forbid. He is governed in early childhood by what Piaget[730] refers to as *moral realism* in which the world is exactly what it seems to be; there are no points of view; there is no relativity; things are black or white, wrong or right. As nearly as the young child sees, parents know everything; therefore, what they say or think is right *is* right. Children judge behavior quite objectively and not at all in terms of motive or circumstance. Punishment should be meted out, according to the conception of the primary school child, in terms of the amount of damage done rather than in terms of possible mitigating circumstances. Authority is absolute.

Learning to Fit Rules to Circumstances.   Only with time, experience, and a great deal of adult help does the child take the next step in development of moral judgment. Gradually, according to Piaget[730] he learns that rules are not objectively real, but that they are made by people, and can be modified to fit circumstance. One child, for example, was sternly taught to come home at once from school. He accepted this rule as absolute, and one day ran home through a heavy rain, splashing mud on his clothes. He was punished for his lack of judgment in not waiting at school until the rain was over. He was thoroughly bewildered at the punishment, since the only factor which governed his behavior was adherence to a rule which he considered absolute. It is only in a more mature stage of development that the child can

388

see the flexibility of authority situations in terms of the "greater" good which lies behind most rules. Only in the more mature stage can the child see that the rightness of an act lies in carrying out the spirit rather than the letter of the ruling.

Understanding Justice as Different from Blind Application of Rules. Only in a fairly mature stage of development, according to Piaget, is moral judgment "tempered by considerations of equity." In the preliminary stage the child learns to adjust the rule to the spirit of the rule; he sees rules in terms of their use to people, but all people are absolutely equal. Only in the later stage does he grasp the concessions necessary to fulfill real justice: the lame boy can be given a handicap in running; you don't push girls around in "pump, pump, pull-away"; you don't strike children who wear glasses.

Lerner,[577] in a study of American children of somewhat more privileged socio-economic status than Piaget's selection of Swiss children, found a general check with Piaget's findings, and made one valuable addition. He reports that children from eight to twelve are governed by a double basis for morality. It is, for example, worse to lie to your father than to your mother, not only "because he can punish harder," but also because "your mother is sweeter" or "understands you better." The child in such an instance is governed not only by the fear of punishment but also by the desire not to "let mother down."

While Learning to Adapt Rules Children Often Come into Conflict with Adult Standards. Murphy,[684] in reviewing studies on this subject, concludes that the step from absolute acceptance of objective rules to the modification of rules or codes in terms of the people involved is not a simple step. Children do not assimilate the moral rules which are handed down from one generation to another as ready-made principles. Each child must "rework" these principles into something which he can integrate into his own life, in terms of his own individual needs and his own identification with and respect for the other people in his environment. For this reason Murphy states that many moral judgments of children of elementary school age are often in violent conflict with those of their parents or even of the whole cultural group around them. This is because the children have not made the rules thoroughly their own. Preschool and primary school children have a limited capacity to extend their identification with or interest in other people. Their moral judgments are, therefore, largely in terms of the world as seen through their own eyes, or in terms of the prestige and authority of their parents, or later, other adults. As the child's capacity to identify himself with others and to be interested in others grows, his capacity to judge situations on the wider basis develops. He becomes less dependent upon adult authority, and in time even less dependent upon the majority rule of his peers; he develops the capacity to "judge" situations for himself.

The Balance between Selfishness and Moral Behavior. In specific terms, the child learns about morals or the group mores as, for example, he learns about honesty, which includes honesty in property, money, time, truth telling, and so forth, or as he learns about the rights and privileges of others, viz., as he learns self-control and consideration for others. He must learn this self-control and consideration for others through learning that in the long run he has a happier time living with others if he curbs himself in favor of the welfare of others. Practically, of course, there is a limit to self-sacrifice in favor of others, since the person who fails to preserve his health and to protect himself sufficiently to keep a balanced frame of mind, soon ends his usefulness to society. Gradually children must develop a fine sense of balance between what is due oneself and what one owes to others. Sexual morality is grounded upon these other moralities, viz., upon self-control and a fine sense of consideration for others. It also involves a sense of proportion which can postpone immediate pleasure for the sake of a greater future fulfillment.

Step by step children must develop control enough over their primitive or selfish impulses to enable them to live considerately in a group. Repression of desirable emotions and urges, or impossible restriction of any basic urge is not what is meant here. The lesson to be learned is a direction of emotional energy along channels which prove socially useful rather than socially destructive. One of the necessary parts of development of self-contol is learning to "resist temptation." Children do not learn this by being protected from all temptation; they learn it only by facing increasingly strong temptations successfully. Personal pride in the development of a social and ethical responsibility to others seems to be one way of combining the egotistic and the altruistic impulses. Practice in generosity, in sharing work under circumstances which are fun, praise, and a building of a sound reputation for being a dependable person are all effective.

Development of Conscience.   Basic to all this is a development of what the psychoanalysts call the super-ego.* In popular language this is conscience, or self-censorship. The child's experience, to be sound, must be such that he learns not only to avoid clashes with adult or group authority but so to censor his own behavior that he behaves from inner standards and not simply to "get by" or not to "get caught." At first, of course, as we have seen from Piaget's work, he behaves from outer standard and fixed rules which are made by others. Only as he matures does he develop that inner standard which fits *him* and is integrated into *his* life philosophy.

Jones[504] says that the limits to which one's conscience can be made to function in making intricate and subtle distinctions are probably dependent at least in some measure on native endowment. There may even be certain prepotent impulses which influence the kind of conscience which an individual develops. But, within certain very broad limits, children and adults acquire their consciences by reacting to the stimulation which such environmental factors as home and friends, church and school, afford.

As we saw in Chapter 3, the child is at first aware only of his own body and of his inner, instinctive needs. As his sensory mechanism develops and his awareness increases he comes gradually into possession of the inhibitions

---

* Mahler[623] (p. 44) quotes Freud as follows: "Freud described three parts of the total personality; First the *id*, which furnishes the instinctual energy generated by the biological processes of the organism and which is entirely unconscious, secondly, the *ego*, which develops through differentiation and higher organization from the id, and which consists of conscious and unconscious parts, and third, the *super ego*, which represents in the total personality the mores and standards of the parents and our cultural society."

and controls which "watch over"* the instincts. Out of this set of inhibitions and controls there comes in time to be an inner censorship or conscience which is dependent at first entirely on the standards and ethics which the parents represent and which they hold for their child. As the child branches out beyond his home he encounters the approval and disapproval of the teacher and of other children and their families. As his standards of behavior and how he feels about his standards are influenced by others his conscience is affected. Thus, throughout the years of childhood the conscience develops, becoming, if development is normal, a more and more effective instrument for the guidance of behavior into socially constructive channels, and a more effective censor of undesirable and destructive behavior.

Conscience governs behavior in ways which do not always operate through the conscious mind. Many of the impressions, feelings and beliefs which ultimately determine how one behaves in a given situation lie deep within unconscious layers of the mind. A feeling of guilt may often be an uneasiness which the individual cannot explain because the reasons for it are not easily accessible to the conscious mind. In other words, people often behave in a way which at the moment seems quite satisfactory to the conscious mind, only to discover that they are afterward gnawed at by a sense of guilt which they cannot understand. The reason is that the real censors of behavior are deep-lying inner forces, laid in largely during early childhood, and grounded in feeling rather than in intellect.** It becomes extremely important, then, that the child should have throughout childhood a desirable grounding in the affectional security and the effective discipline which make for desirable development of the conscience, both at the conscious and at the unconscious levels.†

Development of Tolerance.   Awareness of social problems *per se* is a matter of being able to think and feel past the people *I* know personally.

* Mahler's term.[623]

** Bartemeier, L., a psychoanalyst, said during a series of lectures at the Merrill-Palmer School, Detroit, in 1946: "The ego, which is always in contact with the outside world, must take into account what is going on in the environment. It has to meet the demands of reality, such as 'You must obey Mother because she will spank you if you don't.' But it also has to meet the inner demands of the super-ego while at the same time reacting to the pressures from the id which says, 'Go ahead and do it.' The ego has three masters in life: the environment, or the life outside; the conscience; and the id. The better the ego manages this triangle the better the balance of personality. To get this balance one should give the child an optimum of satisfaction on the one hand and an optimum of frustration on the other. The key is to be aware of which situations the child can, with reasonable effort, handle for himself and of which ones we must protect him from. Give the maximum of work that the child can take with success, and also a maximum amount of frustration that he can take without too great reaction. The first period of life must be complete protection and spoiling. [see also Ribble[781]]; but as the child becomes able, he must be encouraged to do things for himself, and he must be gradually exposed to things that he fears or that frustrate him."

† Hacker and Geleerd,[389] in a careful study of a number of case histories from a school which handles disturbed adolescents, found that adolescent disturbances can be handled with better results and with a more favorable prognosis when treated with firm authority, rather than with an atmosphere of unlimited freedom. "The *id* impulses are tremendously intensified in adolescence. The superego, though existent, is inoperative, which results in increased anxiety. The behavior problems of adolescents can be understood as defense mechanisms against anxiety or as acting out because of anxiety. Granting of unlimited freedom leaves the adolescent unprotected in the throes of anxiety, induced by his instinctual urges, and is actually experienced by the patient as increased danger."

Prejudices can arise, and reflect the attitudes and words and voice tones of the people around the child.* A three-year-old is still struggling to grasp the fact that other children in the same social group as himself are people, having parents, homes, interests, and feelings like himself. By six or seven the child from across the railroad tracks will be thought of in the terms set by the attitudes of parents and other adults. At eight or ten, however, the child may discover for himself that the child from a different social group is a good person to know, and thus widen his social tolerance in spite of adult pattern. School is another means of developing tolerance. There he learns, for example, that little Dutch children wear wooden shoes and live beside canals with windmills. One of them was noble and stopped up a dike with his hand. Such specifics make a groundwork for tolerance. Tolerance as an abstract principle, not just speaking kindly and thinking kindly of this national group or that socio-economic class, but as a general principle comes only later, if at all. Like all abstract learnings, however, it comes most clearly to the children who have a sound foundation of repeated specific instances. This, as well as the elementary school children's omnivorous appetite for new facts, is a reason for including the stories of children from other lands now widely taught at the elementary school level.

Home, School and Other Agencies Should Cooperate in Development of Standards. The school in some instances may compete with the home in the formation of standards, as may the standards of the child's play group. Movies, radio, television, and scout troops all play a part, and, in recent years, an increasingly important part, in the formation of the child's moral pattern. Brown in his *Sociology of Childhood*[129] considers that the demands of competitive outside forces are making basic cooperation within the family increasingly difficult. He suggests fighting these outside forces by encouraging reading aloud in the family in the evenings, family parties to the movies, sharing radio programs, and especially sharing household duties and responsibilities together.

Unless confusion of standards is to result, however, home, school, and community must not fight each other in this matter. They must get together, each learning what the other is doing and each, if necessary, conceding points in training to the other. It is not always possible, of course, to reach an agreement. Some homes in any school district will find that they differ basically from some standard of behavior set by the school, such, for example, as amount of home work required and what the child's attitude toward it should be. The school wants the homework done; the parents think school hours should be enough for anything the school should require. Such deadlocks are hard to break; meanwhile the child's attitude about his responsi-

---

* Reimann,[764] after surveying recent (to 1951) sociologic and psychologic studies o prejudice in children, found that very little is really known about how children acquire or resolve prejudices. However, one recent book (Trager and Yarrow,[955] 1952) reports a study in which 15 Philadelphia kindergarten, first and second grade teachers in 5 schools participated. They concluded that "the children learned attitudes consistent with the experimental social atmosphere which they experienced" in the study.

bility to work may suffer. We must do what we can to solve such conflicts for the sake of clarity and effective integration of attitudes for the child.

Bases for Moral Growth.   Basic to good moral growth are: (1) As good physical health as possible. Children who are strong as a rule have more courage to stand on their own feet and to resist temptation. They remain as free as possible of bitterness and revenge motives. (2) Emotional security, a sense of being loved and wanted, of companionship and sharing. In this atmosphere the child learns to "love thy neighbor" because he is himself loved; he has no need to compensate for a sense of isolation, no need of bitterness or a revenge motive which so often lies at the root of delinquency. (3) Adequate occupation and avenues for the expression of adventure and excitement along wholesome lines so that he is not driven to being "bad" for excitement or freedom from boredom. (4) Continued discipline in self-control so that he becomes able in increasing measure to curb childish impulses. A warning is needed here that he should not be forced into repressions of natural activities, or be expected to achieve adult control in childhood. This must be an increasing achievement throughout the childhood period. (5) Continually widening social horizons so that he gains a constantly increasing ability to know, to tolerate, to sympathize, to understand, and, therefore, genuinely to consider the rights and privileges of other people. (6) The inspiration (usually provided by religious training) to desire the right strongly enough to find sincere satisfaction in doing it.

Beginnings in Moral Growth Can Be Made Early.   These developments must be gradual. But even in early infancy a beginning can be made. Even an infant should not be allowed to force others to dance unnecessary attendance upon his whims, since even an infant must begin to realize that the world does not revolve around his wishes and needs.

During the preschool period the child should learn to take much of the burden of his own care, feeding himself, waiting on himself at the toilet, caring for his own playthings. He should also have made a real beginning in doing things for others, little errands for the family, picking up the newspapers or other helpful household duties, thus realizing that he has some responsibility for the happiness and welfare of the family group. In social contacts he should have learned not to snatch toys or strike other children "because they don't like it any better than he would if they did it to him." Taking turns teaches the rights of all. Hearing about other children's mothers and daddies, other children's lives and interests broadens sympathy and understanding. All these experiences break into his "moral realism" and compel a widening of his conceptions and identifications to include others.

Gesell[345] says that five-year-old children are sometimes aware of deceit or cheating by others, and may begin to try out such deceptions for themselves. He warns that, depending upon how these instances of behavior are handled, the child begins to form favorable or unfavorable ideas of honesty. The child naturally continues to use such methods if they are considered cute or if they are made profitable. If they are condemned and found unprofitable, he abandons them unless his life is too boresome or his emotional needs such that even strong treatment only encourages the wrong behavior.

Entrance to School Teaches Much. Upon entering school, children undertake a job which in many ways resembles the work they must do as adults. Definite beginnings in a sense of responsibility should have been made at home. Whether or not they have been made, the child in school must begin to take responsibility if his development is to be normal. His attitude toward work as such, his sense of the worthwhileness of effort, as well as his sharing of school property, his sharing of teacher's time and attention, and his learning to "team" up with his peers are all in the making from the day he enters school. The school age, too, is a period of learning how to accept defeat in games like a sportsman; of learning how to react to failure as a challenge to greater effort; of learning not to cheat in work or play; and of expanding group participation and shared responsibilities. Although most of these lessons are continuing throughout the school years, the first three years in school usually determine the child's attitude toward school and the job of school for the rest of his school life, and often his attitude toward work for the rest of his work life. There are, of course, instances in which children have failed completely to fit the school's idea of responsibility yet have made brilliant successes of their work lives (Edison was supposedly one), but these are the exception rather than the rule. Every effort should be made in the early grades to help children develop a sense of responsibility to work.

Schools Also Influence Standards of Honesty. A by-product of the attitude of reasonable willingness to do a job which must be done whether you like it or not is the development of honesty in relation to work. False systems of merits and demerits often teach children to work only for artificial ends, or even to achieve an end-result by dishonest means. Hartshorne and May,[409] in carefully controlled experiments, found that from 35 to 60 per cent of the children studied were dishonest in their schoolwork, the percentage of dishonesty increasing with the importance of the assignment and the pressure of examinations leading to marks on report cards.

These authors also found, in a study of responsibility and service of school-aged children to their groups or local communities, that the friends a child goes with, his classroom code, the nature of school adjustment, and the example of his parents are definitely related to children's sense of responsibility and their tendencies to be of service. Age, intelligence, sex, and emotional conditions, however, have little to do with such tendencies. Therefore, we see that schools, homes, and associates contribute the determining factors in development of moral standards.

Ways to Aid Moral Growth During School Years. Hartshorne and May, as a result of their studies, say that the teaching of cooperation, charity, and self-control requires (1) careful planning of situations to which these activities are the natural and successful response, (2) provision for building a group morale which supports the desirable mode of conduct, and (3) increasing complexity and difficulty of situations in order that general principles may emerge and be brought into play for the guidance of conduct and the integration of behavior.[409]

Parents and teachers can encourage neighborhood and school projects which make it possible for children to work in groups for the good of all. Clever principals of "tough" schools have long realized the efficacy of turning the group energy toward rebuilding playgrounds, draining neighboring swamps, cleaning up alleys around the school, and in other ways taking responsibility for the appearance and usefulness of school, school grounds, and immediate neighborhood.

Respect for Property an Important Lesson in Early School Years. Sharing of responsibility for property used by all is an excellent lesson not only in responsibility but also in respect for property. One "moral" lesson which every child of early elementary age (six to ten) seems to have to learn is not to "steal." Scarcely any child of this age fails to have at least one experience in taking something which does not belong to him. This is so frequent at age six that Gesell[347] in describing honesty in six-year-old children says (p. 420): "His needs are strong. Sense of the limits of ownership is weak. Thus he takes what he sees and wants, regardless of who owns it." At seven, Gesell describes as typical behavior (p. 420): "Takes home school pencils and school erasers." At eight: "Child *needs* what he wants. If not provided for may take money, which is now meaningful in terms of what it will buy." Apparently at least one experience in taking what does not belong to them in the primary school years is necessary to teach all but a small minority of children the requisite self-control in the face of temptation.

This "stealing" is most often in the form of taking money from the parental purse. Children see their parents shop, exchanging the magic coins for things desired. Children are usually given occasional coins with which to effect the exchange for coveted objects. These coins come from the family purse. The occasion almost inevitably arises when the child, more than half aware that he should not, takes a coin or several coins from this seemingly inexhaustible source. He usually sneaks behind people's backs in doing this because he has usually been forbidden the amount that he desires. Often, however, the taking is purely an impulsive response to an unexpected chance to do it. As a rule these coins burn the child's pocket because he realizes that they should not be there. In this case, they are spent at the first opportunity for chance objects rather than for something long coveted.

Probably the most effective way to deal with this is to explain where the family money comes from, that there is only so much of it, that it must go for food, clothes, rent, and the like, that, although mother and father seem to have no end to what they spend, most of what they spend is for the family. Therefore, no one in the family is free to take money for special things unless everybody understands; otherwise there may not be enough money for necessary things. Most children do not know these simple facts about family finance. The first misappropriation of money may be the time to teach them.

Calling the child a thief, and announcing that he cannot now be trusted is the last thing that should happen. Children's reputations for honest dealing should be carefully created and consistently maintained. This does not mean that a gullible adult should let a child "put anything over." It does mean, however, that the quickest way to make a thief of a child is to give him that reputation so that he will conclude that he "may as well have the gain as the name."

This stealing from the family purse is in many ways the same as stealing chalk from school. The purse belongs to everyone, and, therefore, not to anyone specifically in the child's mind; the chalk and other school property is no one's because it is everyone's. Lessons in "mine" and "thine" learned so painstakingly in the preschool period are not effective when property held in common is concerned. An understanding that property owned or used by everyone belongs to everyone, rather than to no one, is a definite next step in learning about property rights. Some people never learn it, as is evidenced by careless use of public parks, school property, and city streets. Protection of property held or used in common, and respect for it as shown by caring for it as if it were one's own, is a rather advanced stage of "property morality."

The first stealing offenses of children from five to ten should be regarded as "mistakes." "It was there. It was not yours. You made a mistake and took it. We'll return it"; or, "we'll pay for it." This should not be done, however, with money lightly given by an adult to the child, but with money from the child's allowance or from money which he earns. Some children need second or third offenses in order to clarify the fact that even though the object is very tempting, one's hand does *not* reach out for it. To make a shy child go through the process of returning an object to the clerk of the store, if that is where the object was taken, may be to subject him to a too painful emotional experience.

Most children whose growth of conscience is progressing satisfactorily learn that the pain of a guilty conscience is too sharp to be agreeable. The memory of it simply checks any future temptation. Such children have an adequate, occasionally a too burdensome, super-ego or conscience. Other children are more "hard-boiled." They need pain from external situations because the pain of conscience is inadequate to prove a future check. These children should "face the music" of returning things. A rare child needs to replace something before his classmates; but such public discipline is almost without exception unwise, and the teacher who protects a child from public censure, making it possible for him to restore the property or rectify his error in private, often wins a loyal friend. Real understanding of a child's situation under such circumstances usually seals a pact between the child and such an adult—a pact which serves to strengthen moral behavior for that child for the rest of his life.

Continued stealing, of course, requires special attention since it indicates that something is basically wrong. It is only the first two or three offenses that can be considered in the category of learning lessons about property. The great majority of children need only two or three repetitions of property-rights lessons in order to learn the necessary judgment and control. Offenses repeated through a long period of time indicate either that the development of conscience is defective, or that more basic lessons in self-control are needed, or that the stealing is satisfying some deep emotional need. Particularly in the latter case professional help is needed, and should be sought whenever such help is available.

Strength of Temptation Differs for Different Children.   Any adult who wishes to help children in these early elementary-age experiences with learning about property rights must realize that temptation differs for different children in the same situation, or for the same child in different situations. If the adult himself is to demonstrate what we have discussed earlier as mature moral judgment, then he must deal with children in terms of the circumstance, the strength of the temptation and the child's motive.

For example, there is evidence that the temptation to steal is greater for underprivileged children on the one hand because they have less, and is greater for overprivileged children, on the other hand, because they are spoiled and have developed less strength of self-control than have middle-class children.

It is more difficult for children of underprivileged homes to learn property rights than for children of average homes. Because of the lack of individual towels, drawer space, playthings, even clothing, the child has little opportunity to get a clear-cut conception of "mine" and "thine." Every child must learn this sense of possession, and must learn the difficult lesson of keeping his hands off those things which belong to others. But circumstance makes the lesson much harder for underprivileged children. Schools have an obligation to the underprivileged child to sharpen his sense of "mine" and "thine," to develop the feeling of personal property owned and cherished by each of us—"the book I use this year," "the pencil which is mine," etc.

Overprivileged children are also handicapped in learning about property rights because: (1) They have so many things that the value of any one thing remains at a minimum. When possessions are abundant the keen feeling of cherishing any given thing may remain undeveloped. Therefore loss or damage carries no genuine pain to some wealthy children because replacement is too easy. Like the underprivileged child, but from another cause, the privileged child finds it difficult to develop the sense of guilt which should be felt when one damages or appropriates the possessions of another.

(2) Privileged children have so many things, and are likely to be waited upon and indulged so much that they do not develop self-control. Self-control is necessary if one is to keep one's hands off something which belongs to another, no matter how much one may want it for oneself. When there are few lessons in self-control and few opportunities to exert genuine effort anywhere in one's life, the ability to resist temptation remains undeveloped. Most private schools dealing with overprivileged children find it necessary to emphasize the importance of caring for property and to give definite training in effort and self-control so that these children will be able to resist the urge to appropriate what does not belong to them.

(3) Some stealing on the part of overprivileged children, especially the stealing of automobiles by adolescent boys, can be traced to another factor inherent in the lives and training of these children. Overprivileged children have an exciting, gratified life. They have many planned surprises, extravagant gifts, much concentrated excitement and fun. For some of these children the appetite for excitement becomes overdeveloped, while, at the same time, the means of arousing excitement become exhausted. Fortunately, many parents and teachers of privileged children recognize this danger, and manage to build self-control and respect for property and law, while at the same time they contrive to distribute the thrills so that the appetite will not become abnormal nor the possibility of fulfillment impossible as the years pass.

Causes of Stealing Are Varied.   Occasional children steal because of dire physical need, as the diabetic child steals sugar. Occasional children steal because they are taught to or expected to. Some steal to gain attention or fame, as did one child who became famous as the best thief of mentholatum balm in a large city. Such children need to find fame, or status, and excitement in more wholesome ways. Some children steal, as we have said above, to fulfill deep-lying emotional needs[414, 557, 902] or because of unfortunate emotional conditionings which accompany stealing. They may steal to revenge themselves on parents or companions or because of buried conflicts and tensions that are relieved by the act. Such children should have the help of specially trained guidance workers. Most children steal, however, to gratify desires; they are too weak to resist, or too spoiled to think they *should* resist anything they see that they want.

Learning about Truth. Another Important Lesson of Early School Years. Just as children must learn "mine" and "thine" in property rights as a step in mastering clear notions about our group mores concerning material possessions, so must they lay foundations for consistent truth telling. Children lie for a variety of reasons. One, in the preschool years, is that children of this age confuse real and imagined situations. Many of the preschool child's compromises with the truth are due to his genuine inability to discriminate between what happened and what he imagined as happening. (See the discussion on development of imagination, Ch. 10.) Many children lie because, although truth is more obvious than falsehood, they observe that adults and other children sometimes lie. When parents consciously or unconsciously lie to others or to the child they can expect him to follow their example. Lying is a natural sequence of stealing or other misbehavior. Many children lie to avoid punishment, especially if punishments given are oversevere. Parents and teachers, when discovering a child doing this, should evaluate the severity of the punishments they are using with him. If the punishment is too severe, it should be modified. If, however, it is found to be reasonable, the child may need to learn more courage. Occasional children simply stumble by chance upon the possibility of lying rather than telling the truth. Every child requires certain experiences with untruth in order to clarify his ideas of what truth is and why one clings to it. Probably no school-age child escapes some sort of experiment with truthtelling.

CHAPEL SERVICE

December 14, 1960

Organ Prelude

Call to Worship

*Hymn 117 — "Hark! The Herald Angels Sing"

Scripture — Matthew 11:2-11

Prayer

Meditation — "The Great Divide"
　　　　　　Rev. Arthur R. Hall
　　　　　　Central Presbyterian Church
　　　　　　Louisville, Kentucky

*Hymn 114 — "Lift Up Your Heads"

Benediction — Organ Amen

Organ Postlude

As in children's experiments with property rights, it is important to deal wisely with experiments in truthtelling. Jumping too quickly into accusations of "You're lying—now I can never trust your word again," leaves as serious consequences as the accusation "thief." Nothing promotes lying faster than to feel that one has no reputation for truth. However, standards for truthtelling must be maintained. The child must appreciate the seriousness of lies, and must have it understood that truth alone is expected from him.

Teasing and Bullying. Teasing and bullying is another type of behavior characteristic of many children in the elementary school age which must be dealt with wisely if the moral development of such children is to be desirable. Preschool children often whine or tease their parents to gain some end. Adults should see that such teasing and whining profits the child nothing, and should, whenever possible, give him whatever he asks for nicely. Among school age children teasing and bullying of other children may result from the example of adults or peers. Occasionally it is due to illness or fatigue which "sour" the child's disposition. Often it is simply the danger signal of idleness. Much of what seems to be cruelty to animals, or to other children, for example, may simply be curiosity or experimentation with things or with standards when more constructive occupation is lacking. Bullying may also be due to jealousy, or may serve as a compensation for feelings of inferiority. In any case, a child who persistently "picks on" or bullies younger or weaker children needs special attention from guidance experts.

Effect of Adult Moralizing. Many adults attempt to deal with stealing, lying, cruelty, and bullying by constant moralizing. They read no story to the child without pointing out the moral. "Good" children, they moralize, win rewards; "bad" children suffer awful consequences. Some children learn to hate stories and reading because no story is left a good tale in itself, but must be used by the overconscientious adult as a moral. Other children as a result of this treatment become compulsive in their incessant self-questioning as to whether they did right or wrong, were good or bad. Occasional children worry themselves into a serious emotional state because they react with too conscientious self-questioning and an overacute sense of guilt. Most healthy children, however, learn to disregard such moralizing by negative adaptation. It is like the ticking of a clock, and they become so accustomed to hearing it that they do not hear it. In any case, moralizing when overdone has negative or harmful consequences.

The problem seems to be to teach children a sense of honor within themselves without fear of police or outside forces, yet to avoid the instilling of superstitious fears or a superconscientious overanalysis of every item of their own behavior. Good religious training helps children to accomplish this. However, "hell-fire and damnation" doctrines usually either captivate aggressive children (who give full play to such ideas in imagination, yet change their behavior very little) or worry sensitive children into nervous or unstable emotional behavior. The real objectives for the teaching of morality are (1) to help children find the richness of sharing, of "loving thy neighbor," and (2) to bring about "peace within" which comes from "the good life," to teach, in other words, that "imperfection is uncomfortable in the face of perfection." *

Development of Moral Judgment in Adolescence. Children from nine to twelve years of age can make excellent progress in reasoning, sympathy, esthetic sense, tolerant love, and true morality.[191, 442, 561, 624, 941] They can learn to regard the truth, to be fair, to understand justice in more than elementary ways. With adolescence all of these concepts come to have deeper meaning as the abstractions behind most rules and principles come to be understood, and as awakened interest in other people enriches the child's feeling for the rights and feelings of others. The normally developing adolescent assumes increasing responsibility for himself, for his school job, and for participating in his school and community activities. Even though in many communities school programs, extracurricular activities, and increased social interests take the time of the adolescent to an extent that leads many parents to assume all household responsibilities in order to free the child, the need for an adolescent to be aware of his responsibilities to his home should somehow be met. Responsibility for the selection and care of his own clothing, for taking even a small part in the preparation of food and in dishwashing, for assuming the care of his own room seems the minimum if he is to realize anything of what he owes to his family for his maintenance and school tuition. Instead of coming to assume that the world owes him a living, he must somehow learn to "earn" his living, if only by doing well the school job for which his parents continue to support him. The average adolescent's need to think for himself, and therefore, to break from parental domination, too often becomes confused with the assumption that he owes his parents nothing. When this happens, he frequently feels that he has a right to do as he pleases, being quite lacking in any realization of or appreciation for the fact that as long as his parents pay his bills they have some right to dictate his behavior. Failure to appreciate this shows immaturity in "moral judgment."

For modern city-bred children moral maturing becomes complicated by certain of our present cultural impacts. Landis expresses this as follows:[561, p. 141]

The experience of collecting and reading more than a thousand autobiographies of college students, mostly freshmen, and of watching the course of life on a college campus has developed a *conviction that the youth of today has faced more moral alternatives by the time he is twenty years of age than his grandparents faced in a lifetime.*

Three influences create conditions that underlie problems of moral choice and make them of preeminent concern in the experience of the adolescent:

1. Movement is so prominent in our society that most young folk leave the neighborhood and family group early in life.

2. Change has been so rapid in all phases of experience that well-defined moral standards no longer exist; parents are often so uncertain in matters of the rightness ond wrongness of specific acts that their teaching of moral precepts often either is neglected or lacks positiveness.

3. Many adolescent-youth groups exist in our society in which the codes of the new generation hold sway, there being relatively little chaperonage by adult codes.

Each of these conditions is in a very real sense modern and primarily a product of city life. These three influences—mobility, change, and self-sufficient youth groups—are the external circumstances that bear most directly upon problems of moral choice.

* For an excellent discussion of religious development see Cruze.[209]

Even under these circumstances, however, adolescence should normally be a period of rapid expansion in ability to cooperate smoothly with others, in appreciation of justice and fair play, and in loyalty to associates and to "the rules of the game." Self-improvement is usually rapid, and much of its direction is toward finer and more idealized thoughts and behavior. There is, typically, in adolescence a great blossoming of idealism, a desire to reform the world, and often willingness to expend great energy in self-sacrifice. The tragedy of our contemporary situation is that this idealism and energy have outside of war had so little outlet in action. It is little wonder that so much of this idealism and energy, denied constructive outlet, either remains penned up in the young people, there to find expression only in daydreams about movie stardom, or bursts out in socially destructive crime.

PSYCHO-SEXUAL DEVELOPMENT: THE EROTIC ASPECTS OF HUMAN RELATIONSHIPS

Sexual Morality an Important Part of Total Morality.   One of the sharpest concerns of adults about the "moral" behavior of adolescents is that over sex behavior. This is rightly a matter of concern, since learning to handle the newly awakened sex impulses offers adolescents themselves one of their major problems. What these new longings mean, how to express, and how to control them occupies much of the attention and energy of many adolescents. There are marked individual differences in this, however, as we shall see later.

Since sexual morality is a matter of concern not only to single persons but to partners in any sexual act, and since sexual acts under certain circumstances involve not only production of offspring but the whole structure of family life, society rightly considers sexual morality an important part of total morality. We cannot, however, understand the development of an adequate sexual morality until we understand something of the development of sex itself. Sexual development has two aspects—physical and psychologic. Because these two are inextricably interwoven in the individual we have come to speak of psycho-sexual development. Reference to the chapter on physical growth will review the strictly physical aspects of sex. We turn now to the more psychologic aspects of that development.

Psycho-Sexual Development Begins in Infancy.   At one time the child was considered to be "innocent" of sex or sexual urges until adolescence, at which period in his life the development of his sexual anatomy, being rapid and clearly evident, led writers to suppose that this was the birth of sex. The work of psychoanalysts,[272,680,857,864,1010] however, has led to the conception of infant "sexuality," and has clarified our understanding of the development of sex. We now know that sex feelings and sex attitudes, although greatly stimulated in adolescence, actually have their roots back in the earliest months of life. With this awareness, our attitude toward sex education has changed. Children are no longer "protected" from sex information, kept "pure" by the lies of stork or doctor's bag as the source of babies, and otherwise led to repress all curiosity about sexual and eliminative functions. Freud found that such suppression in early childhood often led to neuroses in later life. Sex and elimination need to be dealt with frankly throughout life as natural parts of the life process. Correct names for genital organs and eliminative processes should be taught as naturally as correct names for anything else in life. Evidences of infant sexuality, like curiosity about the child's own body or the bodies of the opposite sex, manipulation of his genital organs (indulged in by nearly all children at some time or other*), interest in his own eliminative products, should all be dealt with frankly and honestly.

Sexuality in Infancy and Preschool Years. The child's interest in his own body increases rapidly from six to twelve months[420] and is a by-product of general curiosity, increasing skill in use of hands, and the birth of self-awareness. This was discussed in Chapter 8. Between twelve and twenty-four months the child in our American culture usually has a great deal of attention paid to toilet training. This was discussed earlier. For a more complete discussion see Rand et al.[756]

With great emphasis during these years upon self-care, of which dressing and undressing are important parts, many children find it fun to undress and run about free of clothing. One study[243] has given us insight into the age at which children in our culture develop attitudes toward the body. In a group of superior preschool children the investigator found that young children showed the same attitude toward the body undressed as dressed, although in some cases they showed an emotional attitude toward the body. The younger the child the less interested in bodies he was. Hence we see that young children lack self-consciousness about nudity. They become "modest" only in the later preschool years. Modesty must, of course, be taught, since without it older children run counter to the group mores and into trouble. But to attach shame to the naked body, to ingrain attitudes of horror and "nastiness" is to lay a foundation for inhibition and repression which bodes ill for successful marriage. Occasional boys who have been badly handled under such childhood circumstances become the sexual perverts who get sexual pleasure from exhibition of the penis.

Sexuality in Elementary School Years. Nearly all children between five and ten encounter some episode or episodes of sex play.[347,558,997] Investigation of each other's bodies, handling of each other's genital organs, playing "father and mother" or the child's clumsy attempt to imitate the adult

---

* Meagher, J. F.[638] after an exhaustive study of masturbation says: "Infantile masturbation is practically universal; in adolescents, it is the rule with boys, and is very common in girls; . . ." . . . "Sympathy and encouragement are great aids to the patient, whereas an antagonistic attitude, censure, and punishment are usually harmful."

Horrocks[442] says (p. 203): "Misguided adults tell children that masturbation will stunt their growth, make it impossible ever to adjust to married life, undermine their will, or involve some other severe penalty. Categorically such statements are false and their psychological effects may be vicious." There is much clinical evidence that such treatment of a child or young person leads to feelings of guilt and sometimes to serious psychologic maladjustment, and that this in turn increases the temptation and drive toward masturbation.

Landis et al.[558] report that 54 per cent of the women they studied reported having masturbated at some time in their lives, and they found no differences between the normal and the psychotic women in the number who had masturbated. For further figures see Kinsey.[529,530]

sexual embrace are almost inevitable, unless the child is so overprotected that he meets no other children. Even though a boy has had careful sex education at home and hence knows what his little sister looks like, he has a curiosity to discover if all girls are the same. Or children, in an urge to play adult, not only play other aspects of adult housekeeping, but the father-mother game, too. "Hospital" is always a favorite game; playing that a baby is being born is a natural enlargement on the idea. Children must, of course, learn not to play these particular games, and should be helped to participate in other kinds of play. But we must be careful not to deal with such situations in a way which will cause the child to be shamed, to feel ostracized, or "nasty," since when these feelings result children may be enticed into continuation of such play for excitement and defiance. If this is not the result, we may find that we have inhibited impulses which will be necessary to the enrichment of marriage. Parents often worry acutely about these episodes, thinking that the child must be displaying precocious and therefore dangerous sexual development. They have often heard, too, that masturbation or other sexual behavior in childhood will lead to insanity. There is no evidence whatever that any sexual experience in childhood in itself causes insanity.[553] There is evidence, however, that sexual episodes in childhood sometimes lead to such unfortunate treatment by adults that the resulting repressions and emotional conflicts produce insanity. Sane treatment by adults is imperative if unfortunate results are to be avoided.

Children who persist in sex play after the initial experiences with it, like children who steal after the natural lessons have been taught, evidence by this fact that they need special help in straightening out attitudes toward sex and toward the adult world in general. This is particularly true of children who have sneaky or "dirty" atittudes. However, the great majority of children soon forget sexual episodes if their parents "keep their heads" and deal quietly and frankly with the reasons why such behavior is undesirable while at the same time giving any sex information which the child seems to need at the moment. It is possible, of course, to be too frank, or to be fearful that one is not telling the child enough. Too much of the wrong kind of frankness about sex from misguided parents often lends an abnormal emphasis to the topic which reflects in the child's continued preoccupation with it.

Farm children have an easy and natural opportunity to learn about sex and to accept the naturalness of the eliminative processes, since they are exposed to animals and have the responsibility of caring for animals in all fundamental life processes. City children are less fortunate. Summers on farms or possession of such pets as are possible in cities help. Wholesome experiences with animal reproduction do much to keep children's attitudes healthy.

Apart from the sexual experiences which many children have with each other there are the rarer episodes precipitated upon children by adults or older children. Some older child, or more often, some perverted adult may subject a child to sex attack or enticement. Either boys or girls may be the subjects of such experiences, particularly in underprivileged neighborhoods where crowding is great and where the dregs of humanity tend to drift. Any child in any neighborhood may, however, have such an experience, either in the city or the country. Although these are, fortunately, rare, they are of such importance to the child's later development when they do occur that we cannot neglect them here.

Far more important than the experience itself is the way in which it is handled when it becomes known. Even in instances of cruel and thoroughly frightening attack proper handling can bring the child through with a minimum of psychologic scar. Landis,[558] in a careful study of sex development, says that making a trauma or permanent psychologic wound of early sex attack or experience is disastrous. Overwarning or anxiety to prevent such accident or experience is still worse. Usually such experiences occur without knowledge of the parent and without trauma to the child then or later in sex life. Children can survive severe psychologic experiences, and, if the episode is handled wisely, may even be stronger and saner because of the philosophy developed through the experience. Just as a child who has a serious physical illness or accident needs a doctor's care, so can a child who experiences such severe psychologic situations as those involved in sexual attack be helped through the care of a psychologist or psychiatrist.

Gang Age Experiences Can Contribute Much to Moral Judgment in Sex. The gang age has a certain function to perform in sex development. Children need to learn that ugliness and sordidness exist in sex, as they do in the other moral areas of lying, stealing and profanity. But they need to learn, too, that each individual must build his moral concepts upon a satisfactory basis in spite of this. Occasional experiences with the uglier sides of life can and should be utilized to give the child a sound sense of the realities, so that later, when he no longer has his parents and teachers to lean on, he can face whatever is necessary. Immunity to "wrongdoing" seems for most human beings to be developed only through exposure to temptation and through conquest of it. The person who is "pure" because he has been so protected that he knows nothing of temptation must go through life continually protected if he is to remain "pure." The person who really knows how to meet temptation and who can trust his strength is the person who has tested that strength.

Whatever the child's experience with sex, his adolescent and adult life can be normal and fulfilling only under one condition. He must *not* grow up with the feeling that sex and everything connected with it are nasty and dangerous. Many misguided adults make of sex a dangerous dragon which lies in wait to destroy the child. The "we can trust you, but we can't trust your sex impulses" attitude may either fascinate the child or throw him into a panic of fear. The bogy feeling about sex makes of it a demon apart from the child and beyond his control. No child should feel sex to be greater than he is; he should know always that, hard as the struggle may be, *he* can always be the master of what is, after all, only one of his impulses. He must realize to the full extent of his attitudes and feelings that sex under the proper conditions is one of life's greatest fulfillments. He must know this, and have the life-long training in self-control, the life-long development of deep consideration for others which will make it possible to take *his* sex at the time and under the circumstances which will fulfill rather than destroy his life.

Sexuality in Adolescence. The rapid development of sexual organs, the appearance of secondary sexual characteristics, and the interest in the opposite sex which follows these phenomena reveal the "sexual awakening" of adolescence. As we have said, these evidences of sexuality at adolescence are so marked that, until recently, they have been considered the beginning of sexuality. We now know that the sexual phenomena of adolescence are only a step in a long sequence; they have been preceded by many important physical and psychologic growth phenomena which bear directly upon the nature and direction of sexual development at adolescence.

Marked Individual Differences Characterize Adolescent Sexuality. We cannot deal intelligently with adolescent sexuality, however, unless we understand the wide differences in age of development and in intensity of sexual impulses. The range of age of biologic maturation has been discussed in Chapter 7. We have an equally wide range of intensity of sexual impulses. Some people have very intense sexual urges; others have little drive in this direction. The scatter along a normal probability curve characteristic of other capacities is applicable here. Most people cluster around a middle tendency, having fairly strong sexual impulses yet finding control of sexual behavior not too difficult.

The average girl menstruates at about thirteen and one-half years of age. The average boy matures at about fourteen and one-half or fifteen years of age. Some boys and girls mature two to three years earlier than this. These youngsters may have a somewhat fuller sex impulse than average children.* Whether or not they do, we can assume at least an average sex impulse which strikes them at an earlier age when their social experience, intellectual maturity, self-control and other aspects of moral development are less than those of children who mature at the average age.

Thus we can see several types of young persons emerging here, each with a somewhat different problem in control of sex impulses. One type is the young person of rather late biologic maturing, with adequate early training in self-control, with rich sublimatory interests, and varied social outlets. For him chastity is no problem. If the young person is of a second type, namely, a person of early (and, therefore, as a rule full) biologic maturing, and if he possesses also rich sublimations, excellent self-control and wide social outlets with the accompanying self-confidence which these things mean, chastity is possible, although it is in some cases a pressing problem. But if he is of a third type, namely, the early-matured, not too well self-disciplined young person, especially if he is a person for whom social and emotional gratifications in other directions are lacking, chastity is, if not impossible, at least a completely absorbing problem.**

---

* The point is generally accepted clinically but has not as yet been established by child development studies.

** For current statistics on the frequency and intensity of the problem see Kinsey,[529, 530] Landis,[558] Rockwood and Ford,[793] Seward.[836]

Counselors must differentiate among these types of young people if they are to be of genuine help. To the first type, sex *per se*, being only a slight problem and often of not too much interest, "frank" talks about sex problems seem, if not embarrassing, certainly of slight interest, or even irrelevant. To the second type, sex information and some viewpoints on how to utilize wholesome work and recreation to keep sex problems at a minimum are helpful, but great emphasis upon the subject is unnecessary, or may even prove the extra stimulant which makes their problems really acute.

There is, unfortunately, also the third type, namely, the highly sexed, not too self-controlled young people who think sex, talk sex, act sex in such a way that they find any other subject uninteresting, any other activity "tame" and babyish. These young people are a problem to themselves, and not infrequently a menace to their peers. They are the ones who start circles of sex talk or even of sexual activity. They are the ones who often tip the balance for the second type, from wholesome preoccupation with varied activity to unwholesome preoccupation with sex ideas and activities. These young people need fearless frankness and strong inspirational guidance. Threats of venereal disease or illegitimate pregnancies are futile. There is usually no venereal disease in these circles of young people, although for boys the prostitute problem may be a real one, and they are far too self-confident about their knowledge of contraceptives to think there is any possible danger from this source. It often helps them to learn from authentic sources that no known contraceptive is "sure" and at the same time safe for the delicate tissues of the genital systems. The only reasonably sure and safe contraceptive must be prescribed and fitted by a reliable physician for the particular person who uses it.[300,900,966]

Skillful guidance people find that the most constructive approach to such young people is to help them to see the difference between the physical expression of spiritual or psychologic union and mere gratification of physical sex tensions. The one is richly fulfilling if it can take place under conditions which make for physical comfort and complete psychologic assurance. The other, mere release of physical tensions, soon becomes a drug which creates its own increasing tensions until, in time, even the physical tension cannot be released. Nothing is more pathetic than a person who has played with the physical aspects of sex until he has worked himself into a state where orgasm becomes impossible, tumescence cannot be released, and the physical and psychologic preoccupation with sexual tension makes a nervous wreck of him.

Most young people who play around with the physical thrills of sex divorced from psychologic meaning (viz., a deep and enduring affection) do one of two things. They come to be disgusted with it and abandon it as meaningless and empty, in which case they rob themselves of any possible success in either the physical or the psychologic aspects of marriage. Or they become so preoccupied with physical tensions and releases that they place themselves in time in the position where tensions can no longer be released— with consequent nervous disaster. Most young people of good family and training cannot long play with physical sex alone. The girl who gives her body without love has been deeply conditioned in most cultures of the western world; in time it occurs to her that this is what is meant by prostitution, and she gives it up. Girls who have had this experience need careful and constructive help if they are to "pull out" of such experience and make good wives and mothers.* The boy who encourages girls to such behavior, but who is well-conditioned through good sex education, usually soon discovers that sex snatched in the back seat of an automobile or under a bush in the park does not really relieve physical tensions satisfactorily, nor does it provide the thrill that he really wants. Experimentations in physical sex alone seldom last long for well-trained young people.

Sexual expression within the confines of love is quite a different situation. Many guidance people feel that much of the sexual experience of young people outside the bonds of marriage is grounded in the rationalization, or perhaps the reality, that the partners love each other. A very high percentage of the premarital sexual experience of girls occurs with the boys they are engaged to and firmly believe they will marry. Under these conditions there is no sense of prostitution, but only the guilt feeling of "sin" or the dread of pregnancy.

In many instances, however, this guilt feeling or this dread proves sufficient to spoil the complete surrender and relaxation necessary to genuinely fulfilling sexual embrace, with the result that a considerable proportion of these seriously-in-love young couples give up the practice.** If they give it up with an understanding of the reasons why it is not completely fulfilling, or of why it may even leave highly keyed, ungratified tensions in its wake, they usually modify petting practices and occupy their time together in such a way as to avoid sex tension. In the end these young people may experience a complete and fulfilling marriage. If, however, the young couple give it up under the delusion that because they do not find complete gratification they "are not made for each other," one of two things happens. Either they break their engagement, leaving the girl no longer a virgin and with all the problems our culture has conditioned young people to feel over this situation, often causing disaster when her eventual husband finds it out. Or they marry from a sense of guilt. If they do this, there are certain cases in which the original love asserts itself and the earlier unfortunate conditionings built around the physical sex experience break down, resulting eventually in a complete and satisfying marriage. In many cases, however, the earlier unfortunate conditionings persist, and the marriage is a failure.

SEX EDUCATION

General Principles.　　The sexual aspect of morality assumes such importance that much has been written about how children should be educated in this particular aspect of their lives. It is generally conceded, as we have

---

* See Bibliography.[274, 275, 809] All of these books are extremely helpful to adults who work with such young people.

** One of |the most helpful pamphlets available is Banning, Margaret Culkin, "The Case for Chastity" published and distributed by The Reader's Digest, August, 1937.

seen throughout this book, that such important feelings and attitudes as those concerned with sex are molded at home by parents in a more permanent and deeply rooted manner than can be achieved by any other person or agency in the child's life. In discussing psycho-sexual development we have referred to methods by which adults should meet the various aspects of psycho-sexual development, particularly when the child's developing sexuality reaches the surface in overt behavior which comes to adult attention. We have warned against shock or disgust as an adult reaction and against leaving the child with a sense of guilt, horror, disgust, or fear of sex. Continuing self-control, widening sublimatory or socially acceptable expressions for sexual thoughts and feelings, and increasing understanding of what sex is and how it functions are constructive measures to be achieved. All lessons in self-control (without blocking or repression), all growing consideration for others and development of other aspects of moral judgment contribute to sound sex education.

Children should acquire factual knowledge about sex as they have need for it. Proper names for eliminative products, for genital organs, and for the sexual act, for menstruation, and other sexual realities should be given soon enough to protect children against using "gutter language" or other false substitutes. One of the chief reasons for this is that scientific names are free of the attitudes of nastiness or sneaking which inevitably accompany the "gutter" names. Adolescent children should have some concrete knowledge of the anatomy and physiology of the sexual mechanism of their own sex and of the opposite sex. Without such basic facts the young person is handicapped in his social and emotional experiences, being far more likely to make mistakes through ignorance than through knowledge. We must remember, however, that possession of factual knowledge is only a minor part of an adequate sex education; proper attitudes and wholesome feelings about this realm of life are vastly more important than facts alone. The ideal, of course, is possession of both facts and well-educated feelings.

Sex Education of Preschool Children.   We have already discussed the necessity for dealing with the usual evidences of sexuality in infants and young children in such a manner that harmful feelings do not result. Infants should not continue to manipulate genitals as their interests and manual skills widen beyond their own bodies. If adequate routines and ample play materials are available, exploration of one's own body tends to slip into the background of attention and interest. Questions about where babies come from are natural if a new baby appears in the family or neighborhood, or may stem from a normally inquiring mind that wants to know, "Where did I come from?" These questions deserve an honest answer in simple language.* Intelligent preschool children nearly always ask at some time, "What is the difference between boys and girls?" This is a perfectly natural question in a world where people are divided into two obvious groups which dress differ-

---

* The Child Study Association, 221 W. 57th St., New York City, and The American Social Hygiene Association, 50 W. 50th St., New York City, have pamphlets which help parents to answer sex questions for children of all ages. See also Chesser[180] and Swift.[921]

ently, do different jobs and must be spoken to differently. (Note any three-year-old's difficulty with "him," "her," "he," "she," "Mr.," "Mrs.," "Yes, Ma'am," "Yes, Sir.") These, and any other questions should be answered without embarrassment, and with complete honesty. Otherwise they will assume an aura of "different-from-other-questions," with the result that children will wonder and think about them far more than they do questions not singled out by their parents as embarrassing and worth evasive answers. Answered quietly and adequately, they slip into the category of answered questions which can be forgotten about for the time being.

Psychoanalysts have assured us that children accurately informed about basic facts of sex have no need to indulge in fantasies about the origin and birth of babies, or about the relation of their parents in the sex caress. Only children who are deprived of such knowledge indulge in persistent fantasies centered around sex.

These questions about origin of babies and differences between boys and girls are, however, only an expression of the child's need to know facts. Far more basic to the child's psychologic well-being, as we have said, are the attitudes toward sex which he should already have developed. By five years of age the child should have survived infantile masturbation, leaving it behind in the natural course of his development. He should have established regular and acceptable habits of elimination and should have developed satisfactory attitudes toward elimination and eliminative products. He should have accepted and adjusted satisfactorily to younger siblings in his family, having learned to share the love and attention of his parents.

Questions Which Should Be Answered for School-Age Children. With entrance to school the child inevitably meets other children with all the differences in sex practices and attitudes which any group of children represent. A child with a sound sex education up to this point is not only not likely to be swung aside into undesirable practices and attitudes, but may prove a wholesome influence to other children less fortunate than he is.

Most writers think that by the time children enter school they should have adequate words for the eliminative processes, should know the true origin of babies, and should be familiar with the differences between boys and girls. Adolescents should understand the facts of menstruation and of nocturnal emissions, the physiology of stimulation to tumescence in both boys and girls, differences in male and female sexual reactions, and other "basic facts."

The School's Responsibility in Sex Education. How much and what kind of sex education (meaning, usually, the limited conception of sex education which deals with facts and knowledge) the high school or college should undertake is a question subject to debate. Even though curiosity about the origin of babies and the anatomic differences between boys and girls is pretty general before six years of age,* most writers, as we have said, recognize a "latency" period preceding adolescence. Instruction in the physi-

---

* Landis says that this interest is not very intense, and places the first real curiosity about sex between six and nine years of age, with a latency period from nine to eleven, and renewed curiosity at the onset of adolescence.[558]

ology and anatomy of sex occurs in biology or zoology classes in elementary and junior high schools, but the lessons seldom mention the human animal. Schools, as a rule, have assumed that the answers to younger children's questions about sex have been given, or should be given, at home. One thing that can be said for the widespread parent education movement of the past thirty years is that parents now are fairly generally conscious of the need for answering children's questions about sex truthfully and as accurately as possible. School teachers should be similarly equipped to answer simple questions about sex, and should make every effort to follow whatever attitude about the answering of sex questions is dominant in the immediate community. Nothing but confusion can result to children who receive one set of answers in school and a completely (and violently defended) different set at home. Until the majority of parents in any given community are prepared to "follow along" with modern ideas on sex education the school should move slowly.

Sex Education in Junior and Senior High Schools. The generally recognized renewal of interest in sex which occurs with the onset of adolescence has led many educators to argue as to whether or not the public high school can afford not to give accurate information as a preventive of false information obtained from less reliable sources and with less desirable emotional tone.

Most educators now recognize that the least important part of sex education is the imparting of the facts of anatomy and physiology. The really important part of sex education, they concede, is the fixing of attitudes, habits, and emotional patterns; and they realize that this must of necessity occur in the homes and neighborhoods in which young people have spent their early childhood. Although schools can make little impression upon these fundamental attitudes and emotional reactions, educators are coming to feel that schools have a responsibility to do what they can. There seems little disagreement with the belief that, rather than leave children uninformed, as numberless homes still do in spite of the parent education movement, the schools should undertake the task.

Programs in homemaking skills and in marriage and family living are fairly general for girls, while a number of schools include boys in such courses. Courses in psychology or personality development are also common in high schools. Sex education is sometimes taught as a part of these, or as units in hygiene taught by the biology teacher, the school nurse or doctor. In some schools it is taught by any subject-matter teacher who has the right life philosophy and the right rapport with the young people.

Basic to good attitudes and feelings about sex is the acceptance of one's own sex role. What does one think and feel as a girl (or a boy); what does it mean to be a wife and mother (or a husband and father); what is it to be a woman (or a man) in the world of work, of friendship, of civic government? How does one behave with boys if one is a girl, or with girls if one is a boy? What do boys expect of girls? What do girls expect of boys?

One's ideas of what it means to be a woman are gained largely from one's mother and from one's father's attitudes toward and reactions to women. One's ideas of what it means to be a man are gained largely from one's father and from one's mother's attitudes toward and reactions to men. Teachers, especially high school teachers, can and do have an influence upon these concepts of sex role. Important to this education in attitude are concepts and feelings about what controls should be placed on impulsive behavior in favor of the future; how one regards the responsibilities and benefits of marriage and of parenthood; and the multitude of other attitudes and practices basic to boy-girl relationships and to one's role in society as a boy or a girl. These can be influenced by good teachers and should be the real basis for a "sex education" program. Discussion of the anatomy and physiology of human sex is helpful, of course, and should be undertaken wherever the sentiment and understanding of the community permit.*

It is imperative, however, to face the fact that not all teachers, no matter what their scientific training, are emotionally and philosophically equipped to undertake such teaching. Presented in the wrong way, "sex education" can result in serious damage to attitudes and feelings. Only emotionally sound and sexually well-balanced people should be permitted to teach the subject of sex and marriage. There is considerable dispute as to whether these courses should be taught to freshmen or to seniors, to boys and girls separately, or to mixed groups. Numerous experiments are under way which should eventually help us to know how, when, to whom, and by whom such courses should be taught, if at all in our public schools. In most communities parents have been in entire sympathy with such attempts on the part of the schools, especially in cases where the school has kept parents informed through the Parent-Teachers Association or Parents' Club, or better, asked the advice of parents as to how to proceed.**

PSYCHO-SEXUAL DEVELOPMENT: WIDER PERSONAL RELATIONSHIPS

Closely bound up with the sexual aspects of psycho-sexual development are the more humanitarian impulses of love in its wider sense. There are innumerable personal contacts throughout the life of the child other than the more narrowly sexual or erotic relationships. These wider relationships enrich his sex relationships and are, in turn, influenced by his sex experiences. Combined with the individual's sex experiences they make up his love behavior in its widest sense. Genuine maturity in psycho-sexual development lies in the capacity to choose a mate wisely, to woo and win this mate, to establish an adequate and satisfactory sexual and psychologic marriage relationship, and to accept and rear children. Much of this as well as of the capacity to love friends and people in general is the product of growth in

* Helpful are such books as Corner,[202, 203] Foster,[311] Landis,[559] McHose,[617] and Smart and Smart.[867]

** For an excellent discussion of sex education in schools see Bibliography.[177] For a discussion of homemaking programs in schools see Home, School and Community Experiences in the Homemaking Program, Vocational Division Bulletin No. 252, Home Economics Series No. 29, U. S. Department of Health, Education and Welfare, 1953.

love capacity in its widest sense. Let us, then, trace the development of this wider aspect of love.

Infants Essentially Limited in Capacity to Love.   As has been implied before, a newborn baby knows little about love. People as such do not exist for him. His awareness of life consists largely of consciousness of himself, particularly of his physical self.[475, 623, 756, 781] When he is well-fed, exercised, clean, and comfortable, he is content. As was shown earlier in this chapter, he gradually becomes aware of other people and learns to accept those who take care of him. In this sense he has learned to love another person than himself, and he may show his love by permitting only the favored person to wait on him and by rewarding that care with a smile or with cooing sounds. There are some adults who have not progressed beyond this stage, whose entire conception of love is to allow people to wait on them, and who have no more sense of responsibility to other people than to pay them with a smile or a physical caress.

Babies should be thus loved and thus served. We have ample evidence[272, 440, 561, 747, 781] that being loved and wanted, or being secure in the love of one's family in infancy and early childhood, is essential to adequate personality development. As has been emphasized before, the child must not only be loved, he must be disciplined as well.* Healthy babies, loved and cared for, will have a sound foundation laid for adequate adult love relationships. Sickly, unwanted or neglected babies usually develop a preponderance of negative emotional feelings and thus develop cravings or resentments which color adult love relationships unfavorably.

The Scope of Love Broadens in the Preschool and Primary School Years.   Children of two or three years have usually passed the stage of selfishness described above and have broadened their conception of love so that they do not demand unlimited service. They should have learned to care for some of their own needs and to perform some degree of service for some one else. They should have made a real beginning in feeling responsible to the family group, in developing ability and willingness to do everything possible in feeding themselves, in keeping their toys in order and in doing occasional errands for other members of the family. They should have broadened personal affection to include not only the mother or nurse who gives physical care but also other members of the family[607] and other persons whom

---

* Mahler[623] (p. 47) says: "In the course of the educational process, the emotional relationship between the parents and the child must be such that the child should feel neither disappointed at not getting compensatory love, nor ought he to feel too sure of getting love irrespective of his behavior. If a child feels unloved, he will soon feel cheated, he will not find it worth while to renounce his ways of repressing objectionable wishes. He will only suppress his egoistic cravings because of physical inability to get his own way. He will not renounce his pleasurable ways of aggression, will not bestow love on other people, but will use up his entire love energy in self-love. Such a child will remain egoistic and resentful. He has no reason for altruism."

Again (p. 53): "Educability is conditioned by a normal though not excessive fear of loss of love, and by a normal though not excessive fear of punishment. If both are excessive, a condition results that clinical psychiatry classifies in the group of primary behavior disorder of the conduct type, and that in the psychoanalytic nomenclature would be called neurotic waywardness or delinquency."

they meet often and who, therefore, become familiar to them. Preference is usually shown, of course, for those persons who provide the best amusement or the greatest amount of praise, as well as for those who give the greatest number of presents. One could scarcely expect a three-year-old child not to be swayed by such advantages. Tragedy may result, however, for the adult who can love only persons who minister to his physical needs, who flatter and praise constantly or who pay the highest material price in the giving of presents. Mates chosen on such a basis are seldom successful; friends chosen on such a plane are likely to be similarly limited in the conception of love, and, therefore, not very satisfactory in the long run.

In the nursery school age, as we have seen, love and conflict often occur together.[323, 347] For example, we can see two children, both good friends yet in conflict over a tricycle. Each will be clinging to the coveted object, each crying, each puzzled at the resistance from the other, each of them clinging to the tricycle with one hand, but patting the crying friend sympathetically with the other hand. Here, each child has progressed far enough in love growth to feel concern at the unhappiness of the other; yet each is still egocentric enough to be blind to the fact that he is causing that unhappiness. Many husbands and wives, full grown chronologically, are only this old in love development, since they live thus concerned at the unhappiness of the other, yet thus blind.

Another far more important foundation for adequate adult love relationships is being laid in the preschool age. The boy's early relationship with his mother sets deeply his later emotional reaction to women. Loved wisely by his mother, a boy can accept fully the love of a wife in later years. Loved wisely by his father, he can develop a clear masculine pattern for his own behavior as a husband and father in adult life. So it is with a girl; in the love of her father she can accept the love of a member of the opposite sex; in the love of her mother she can develop the pattern for her own behavior as a wife and mother in adult life. Loved unwisely by his mother, the boy may either become unwholesomely attached to her in such a way that he can never step beyond his preschool dependence upon her; or, if his personality is strong enough, he may break away in spite of her. He will be lucky if he accomplishes the break without a bitterness which leaves him forever suspicious and fearful of the love of women. The analogy is the same for a girl and her father. If his love is too possessive and jealous, or if their relationship becomes so completely fulfilling for the girl that she cannot later accept a less indulgent and pampering love from men, she will almost certainly remain unmarried or fail in marriage.

It is in the later preschool period and again in adolescence that the psychoanalytic school attributes considerable importance to the fact of the boy's attachment to his mother and the girl's attachment to her father. However, very closely associated with the period of intense preference for the parent of the opposite sex there is also a period in which the child needs to identify himself with the parent of the same sex. The little boy, for example, imitates his father at around three years, the age at which he is normally intensely attached to his mother. Ultimately, the child finds it necessary in his emotional development to incorporate both the father and the mother into his growing ego structure.[60, 440]

Gesell,[347] in a careful objective observation of many children over a long time, offers some corroboration of psychoanalytic theories. He found that the mother is usually the favored parent at three years of age and does not mention a difference in sexes of children in this regard. However, at three and one-half years girls may propose to the father saying, "I love you." He found that at four years some children say they hate their fathers, especially if his being at home cuts them off from mother. He found also at four great pride in the mother: the child boasts about her away from home and quotes her as an authority. The mother seems to be the center of the child's world at five: he (or she) likes to help her, to be near her. Boys may talk of marrying mother. Relations with the father are smooth, pleasant, and undisturbed; some children will now for the first time, according to Gesell, accept ministrations by the father when the mother is ill; excursions with the father are enjoyed; the child is fond and proud of the father and may obey him better than the mother. When the child is six years old, the mother is no longer the center of his world, though the child is very sensitive to the mother's moods, emotions, and tensions; there are contrary responses to the mother in which the child may say he loves her, then says he hates her; is unwilling to accept help which he needs from the mother; is rude and argumentative toward her. He both fears and admires the father more than the mother, obeys him better, is not rude or resistant toward him; is hurt by a cross word from him. By seven, however, the child is again in harmony with the mother, is easier for her to discipline, is proud and self-conscious about her in public, though there are still occasional strong battles of will between mother and child. At seven some children, especially boys, "worship" the father, think he is wonderful, have long confidential talks with him. Girls are more sensitive to any reprimand from the father and may be jealous of his attention to the mother. At eight, the child shows strong physical and verbal expressions of admiration and affection for the mother, tries to live up to what she expects of him, may be jealous of the mother and father when they are together. The relationship with the father is less intense, but smoother than with the mother. There are less ardent expressions of affection, and smoother obedience. By nine the child, being busy and self-centered, has smoother relations with his mother, provided she treats him with respect for his increased maturity; this is also true of the relationship with the father if he respects the new maturity. Boys at this age sometimes enter into a new relationship with the father in which many interests are shared.

Gang Experiences Contribute. As we have seen, too, the gang teaches lessons that force consideration of others. Group loyalties gradually force a child to curb his most self-centered impulses in favor of group welfare; otherwise he is ostracized, a fate which no normally growing child can endure. Gang lessons are usually quite objective and impersonal. Faults are discussed openly; discipline is prompt and relentless. Black eyes and bloody noses are all part of the experience for boys. Coldly turned backs and cruel words serve to whip girls into line. These lessons are more open and more cruel than the lessons which can be taught in the family where parents and older siblings are too fond of the child thus to discipline him. It is fortunate that most children have a strong urge to play with peer groups, since in many instances, if their urge were less strong, they would never tolerate the cold wind of objective discipline but would retreat to the warm bath of parental indulgence and understanding.

Another aspect of the gang age which is of importance to psychologic development is the so-called "sex antagonism" characteristic of the period. As we have seen in Chapter 13, there is an "instinctive" gang interest and liking for groups separated according to sex at this age. The psychoanalysts refer to this as the "latency," or quiescent period in psycho-sexual development. Viewed against the rapid fixing of love attitudes in the preschool period, and, again, against the rapid development of the adolescent and early adult period, it is, indeed a latency period. The analysts' use of the term "latent" does not mean, however, that sexual interest is nil at this state, but rather that it continues to exist, though in a less obviously growing form.* People interested in coeducation in the United States are convinced that sex antagonism is not so active as to make it impossible to educate mixed groups in the elementary years. Most of our public schools assume the ability of boys and girls to work smoothly together sitting in the same room without even being separated on two sides of the room. Although the typical elementary school pattern in this country is one of mixed groups in the classroom, the rule outside on the playground is separation into separate sex groups for play. After kindergarten or primary grades the toilet rooms are separated, and, in a few large cities where a large foreign population keeps European traditions and attitudes alive, playgrounds are separated, boys and girls using separate entrances to the building and separate locker spaces in the halls. A few eastern public school systems have separate high schools for boys and girls. Many private schools, even in the United States, separate the sexes in all grades above the kindergarten or primary. Many private junior and senior high schools, and many private colleges believe that during the emotional awakening of puberty and adolescence it is imperative to keep the sexes separate in order "to get any work done." Our large public high schools and universities offer testimony for either side of the argument, depending upon the particular school and its atmosphere, and upon certain groups of young people in any school regardless of general school atmosphere.

Even when the gangs are clearly separated into own-sexed groups we find a certain clearly expressed awareness of the opposite sex throughout the latency period. A group of boys, for example, will seem to remain absorbed in baseball or football when a group of girls, or a particular girl attractive to a particular boy, goes by. The typical behavior, however, is a little louder yelling, a few "side-show" activities, definitely designed to attract the atten-

* Interest in and curiosity about sex is common in the elementary school period.[558, 827, 997]

tion of the girls. Similarly, the girls switch their skirts a little more, raise voices, giggle, and give clear evidence of their "reactivity" to the boys. Teasing between the sexes is a common bug-bear of the elementary school teacher or the parent of six- to twelve-year-old children. Calling names, pulling hair, silly rhymes, putting names together on sidewalk or walls are common practices which show that sex awareness is not dead during the gang age.

The Early Adolescent Period: Hero Worship. From twelve or fifteen years of age through the next two or three years there is, as we have seen, a time when, if the child is developing normally, he shifts from the less impersonal relationships of the gang to more intense personal relationships. Love becomes a much more emotionally personal thing. Hero worship occurs, often with such complete devotion that the child's personality undergoes important changes in the direction of imitation of the hero. If the hero, real or fictitious, is a good model, the changes are for the better. Habits of personal cleanliness, good attitudes toward work, and real progress toward preparation for vocation or profession may result from the emotional impetus afforded by the desire to emulate a hero. If the model is desirable parents would do well to curb a natural tendency to jealousy and to regard this experience as one more step in the growth process.

Much of the hero worship of this period is an attempt by the young person to grasp a concrete picture of the personality he dreams of for himself. His worship of the hero is, in many instances, only a worship of that which he hopes for or longs for in himself. He sees in the older person of his own sex a picture which clarifies what he thinks, at least at the time, he needs to fulfill in himself. If he has been deprived of material possessions he tends to select the affluence, or the romantic love-attractiveness of a movie or TV star. On the other hand, every adolescent feels himself deprived in some area because he lacks what the movies and TV offer, and in that sense movie and TV heroes and heroines are the heroes of most pubescent children. The average young person, however, soon finds a more realistic idea of what can be expected from life, and gives up any real resentment that he cannot have such extravagant riches or attention as the movies and TV seem to promise.

Adults should guard against jumping to conclusions about what it is that the child "sees" in the hero, since what he really struggles to achieve through the hero may not be at all evident on the surface. Therefore, even when the chosen hero seems all bad to the adult, the wise adult will attempt genuinely to understand what freedom, or what adventure, or what nobility the hero represents *in the child's eyes.* This is extremely important, since we can be of no use to the young person in guiding him to a fulfillment of himself along socially acceptable lines unless we know how the world looks to him, and what he is trying to achieve in his early adolescent striving to fulfill himself as a person and as a sex member (man or woman).

The Early Adolescent Period: Intense Friendships. Another aspect of early adolescent development is the tendency toward intense friendships with other members of one's own sex. The child seems in a sense to return to the beginning of the love cycle at which his chief concern was with himself. In this instance, however, he has progressed beyond self love to the extent that he is capable of loving some one other than himself, but he chooses some one most like himself; namely, a member of his own sex. Murphy and associates say,

The meaning of intense love-friendships and crushes for adolescents is not yet entirely clear; they may reflect both the projection of the child's need for affection and the sublimation of growing emotions that in another culture might have more immediate sexual expression.[684]

There is some scientific evidence and a good deal of clinical opinion to the effect that crushes between adolescent girls or between adolescent boys are most characteristic of groups which have little contact with the opposite sex. However, it is thought of by most scientific writers in the field as a normal part of the psycho-sexual development which lasts a shorter or longer time and which assumes a greater or lesser intensity depending upon the particular young person involved. Psychoanalysts and many psychiatrists are inclined to regard the crush, or homosexual aspect of psycho-sexual development, as fulfilling an important role in the child's love development.

Sullivan* (p. 20) explains something of how this can be in the following sequence:

Around the age of eight and one-half or nine and one-half to twelve, in this culture, there comes what I once called the quiet miracle of preadolescence. . . .

I say 'miracle' of preadolescence because now for the first time from birth, we might say even from conception, there is a movement from what we might, after traditional usage, call egocentricity, toward a fully social state. . . .

When the satisfaction or the security of another person becomes as significant to one as is one's own satisfaction or security, then the state of love exists. So far as I know, under no other circumstances is a state of love present, regardless of the popular usage of the word. . . .

This state of affectional rapport—generically love—ordinarily occurs under restricted circumstances. In the beginning many factors must be present. Some of these may be called obvious likeness, parallel impulse, parallel physical development. These make for situations in which boys feel at ease with boys rather than with girls. This feeling of species identity or identification influences the feeling involved in the preadolescent change. The appearance of the capacity to love ordinarily first involves a member of one's own sex. The boy finds a chum who is a boy, the girl finds a chum who is a girl. . . .

As soon as one finds that all this vast autistic and somewhat validated structure to which one refers as one's mind, one's thoughts, one's personality, is really open to some comparing of notes, to some checking and counter-checking, one begins to feel human in a sense in which one has not previously felt human. One becomes more fully human in that one begins to appreciate the common humanity of people—there comes a new sympathy for the other fellow, whether he be present to the senses or mediated by rumors in the geography, or the like. In other words, the feeling of humanity is one of the aspects of the expansion of personality which comes in preadolescence.

Crushes are particularly likely to occur in camps,[967] most of which separate the sexes, and all of which, except the family camp, separate the young people from the familiar settings, routines and particularly from the personnel of their family. Even though the adolescent is in the throes of establishing him-

* Dr. Harry Stack Sullivan, Psychiatry (Journal of the Biology and the Pathology of Interpersonal Relations), No. 1, v. 3, Feb., 1940. Excerpts from Lecture II, "The Human Organism and Its Necessary Environment."

self as a grown person, he still misses the security of familiar family routines. He is especially prone to attach himself to some family substitute, particularly if there is available a counselor or older camper who will not only serve as a family substitute but also combines the qualities, spoken of above, which represent the child's dream of himself. Crushes in camps grow not only out of loneliness for familiar surroundings but also out of the continued intimacy of twenty-four-hour-a-day living with the other campers.

Like any other life experience, these intense friendships may, of course, result in harm to the participants. However, they may, and usually do, result in constructive growth. When the young person passes too quickly into the later adolescent or heterosexual stage he may find himself lacking an appreciation of friendship with members of his own sex. Men who pass too quickly through the friendships-with-one's-own-sex stage may, later, learn how to meet other men in business, and may find social friendships with other men because of business contacts. The usual sequence for "boy-crazy" girls, however, is early marriage and a career in homemaking. The typical life pattern of the married woman limits her activity and her energy to her home and her children in such a way that, unless she has learned early to make and keep women friends, she is likely to find herself lonely, unable to pick up club or community contacts, unable to win and hold the friends who give companionship aside from her husband and children. The boy, then, who passes quickly through the homosexual into the "girl-crazy" stage may learn later, when he has settled down to one girl, how to meet men and win friends among them. The too quickly "boy-crazy" girl, however, finds it more difficult to fill the gap in her life later. More than this, the boy or girl who ties all of the newly awakened emotion of adolescence into boy-girl relationships, thus finding all of his or her companionship, sharing and fun with members of the opposite sex often finds that becoming tied down to one member is dull, monotonous, or even impossible. This is not a good background for marriage. We see, then, that valuable lessons can be learned in the intense-friendship period of development.

The Difference between a Wholesome and an Unwholesome Crush. Camp counselors and high school guidance teachers should learn to recognize the difference between an unwholesome and a wholesome crush. If the identification of the child with another member of his own sex teaches him to control his own selfish desires and impulses in favor of those of another; if the relationship widens his interests, teaches him better personal habits, improves his personality, then the relationship is doubtless wholesome. Most young adolescents must do some stumbling and "nose-bumping" in the process of learning how to manage a close, emotional friendship. An almost universal tendency at first is to wish to possess the beloved person exclusively. There is nearly always a certain amount of "if you 'go with' anyone else you can't 'go with' me," a certain jealousy of any friend who is likely to compete. In general this tendency is unwholesome, since it tends to restrict rather than to widen the interests and the love relationships or friendships of both partners to the relationship.

Most young people have to experience this possessive relationship once or twice in order to find that it does not work as a principle upon which to build friendship. If they *do* learn this principle, then the relationship can be considered profitable. If they fail to learn it, but continue to flit from one intense, possessive friendship to another, then some constructive help must be given. Most adults, in dealing with such intense friendships, simply condemn them as "abnormal," shaming the participants, or attacking the qualities of the beloved person in an attempt to bully the young person out of the friendship. Only for spineless young people do these methods work. If the young person has any fine quality of loyalty such adult bullying only places him on the defensive and makes him protect his friend. It often compels him to rationalize qualities which do not exist but which, stated in the friends' defense, appear now to exist, thereby strengthening the love. Another result of adult bullying is to intensify the young person's determination to declare his independence of adult judgment, thus forcing him to cling to the forbidden friendship by way of proving his right to do so long after the natural sequence of events would have weakened or dissolved the tie.

One constructive approach is to help the young person to see that if he and his friend limit their activities, their friendships and their experiences to each other, the time will come when they will no longer be interesting to each other. Thus the keen edge of their enthusiasm for each other will inevitably be dulled. The best way to remain keenly interesting to each other is to do some things at least with other people, to widen activities and interests. This should mean that Betty goes on with the school paper even though her close friend Susie has no ability in that direction; Bob goes on with his model airplanes while his friend John plays football. Most young people understand this idea once it is presented to them, and are willing to "sacrifice" the time of the friend to his or her previously pursued activities in order to keep the glow of the friendship intact. Such an approach usually succeeds, and in the correction of the intensive exclusiveness of the relationship, the more wholesome aspects of friendship often develop. When this results the young people not only learn an invaluable lesson about human relationships, viz., that one can hold love only by freeing it, but they often save a valued friendship which might, and probably would, otherwise soon wear thin.

Some clinicians judge the wholesomeness or unwholesomeness of such friendships purely on the basis of physical expressions of affection. This is an unsound basis for judgment. Some of the most possessive, restricting, unwholesome psychologic relationships exist quite apart from any but superficial physical expressions. Occasionally the reverse is true, and a rather intense sexual expression may exist within the framework of a quite sound psychologic relationship. On the whole, sexual possession of the friend leads to or accompanies an attempt to possess the friend psychologically. In this case there is jealousy of the friend's other interests and loyalties. In adolescent crushes, then, there is a high correlation between physical sexual expression and warping of psychologic relationships. In general, but not always, the criterion of physical sexual expression as a measure of unsoundness in close friendships is a good one.

However, we must clearly differentiate between rather innocent though somewhat passionate embraces, and actual sexual activity which involves a full adult orgasm. Nearly all normally growing personalities feel a desire to express sincere, idealistic affection by some physical means. Holding hands, walking with arms about one another, even fairly intense kisses remain for most young people in the realm of expression of friendship rather than in the realm of erotic sexual excitation. An overexcited or oversuspicious adult may create by the wrong approach a sexual consciousness in the young person which does not naturally exist. It is hard for fully matured, fully experienced adults to remember that young people, at least those of average sexing, have not yet had the experience which leads casual caresses into tumescence and craving for sexual completion. Young people usually do not react to passing embraces with an arousal of the complete sexual mechanism. Highly sexed young people, of course, sometimes do so react. However, highly sexed young persons, given a normal exposure to members of the opposite sex, do not remain long in the early adolescent, or homosexual, stage of psycho-sexual development. They do not, therefore, give us much anxiety in the homosexual field.

It is true, of course, that some people develop physical practices in the homosexual stage which fix their sexual expression at this level, making sexual satisfaction improbable on the heterosexual level. Such studies as those of Davis,[220] Exener,[285] and Landis[558] indicate that although intense emotional relationships are common between girls, overt homosexual physical practices are a fairly rare experience for girls, being a more common experience for young adolescent boys. This is probably because girls are more severely conditioned from childhood to avoid overt sexual experiences. Most of the literature on mature sexual functioning indicates that most boys escape from these experiences undamaged, entering adult heterosexual experiences quite normally. Unless the individual is predisposed constitutionally to the homoerotic pattern, his normal growth pattern carries him through these experiences and into normal adulthood quite unscathed.

The chief damage which comes from overt homoerotic practices seems to come from the "guilt complex" which may result from the young person's feeling of guilt in connection with the practices, or from unwise handling of a situation when discovered by adults. If the young person comes to doubt the "normality" of his masculinity the result may prove disastrous, since the seed of such doubt may grow into wrong emotional conditionings around the sexual function, thus arresting development and blocking normal adult functioning. Wisely handled, such experiences for most young people need not leave disaster in their wake. It cannot be too strongly urged here that teachers, parents and guidance people turn the handling of such aspects of psycho-sexual development over to experts specially trained to handle them.

The Later Adolescent's Progress toward Maturing.   It is evident from the above that an important step in the maturing process of later adolescence is accomplished when the young person has a fairly wide experience in boy-girl relationships. Through this experience, the transition from the homosexual period takes place and a basis for adequate mate selection is laid. Young people normally pass through the homosexual into the heterosexual periods of psycho-sexual development as the biologic functioning of the sexual mechanism becomes sufficiently established to induce interest in mating. The chronologic age at which this occurs varies from eleven or twelve to eighteen or nineteen years for girls (about one to two years, as a rule, after the menarche), and from twelve or thirteen to nineteen or twenty for boys.

A great deal of concentration upon boy-girl relationships is an accepted and desirable part of our cultural pattern for adolescent young people. Since we permit (or even force) them to choose their own mates we must make it possible for them to do enough "shopping around" to make the wisest possible choice. It is only in our modern Western culture and, very recently, in China and India that we have permitted young people to make so serious a choice for themselves. Centuries of tradition dictated that parents knew better what was necessary for a good mate than young people could possibly know. More than this, families who knew each other, often for generations, chose knowingly. Today, we not only permit young people to make their own choices, but we permit them to do so from among young people whose families, whose backgrounds, whose early experiences and habits, whose tastes and abilities and attitudes are almost entirely unknown. Rapid changes of neighborhoods, extensive contacts in high schools and colleges made up of thousands, highly mobile means of transportation all widen the marriage market, exposing our young people to a bewildering choice which would test the wisdom of the oldest and most experienced person. For the first time in history we are asking young people to take a life responsibility with which we have never trusted them in the past.

It is slight wonder that parents feel anxious about the experiences of their young people, knowing how important are the choices and the involvements of boy-girl behavior through this after-sexual-maturity-and-before-marriage period. Yet the peer-culture of these young people, the dictates of the "modern" procedure, exposes them to wide contacts with the opposite sex under conditions which take them away not only from the chaperonage of parents but, through the automobile, easily away from the deterring effect of any people who know them. The anonymity which the automobile gives today's young people places upon them a heavier responsibility for self-control than has been placed upon sexually mature young people in recorded history. On the whole, they seem to be managing this responsibility extremely well.

EXPERIENCES TO VITALIZE CLASS WORK

1. Observe a group of gang-age children, or recall your own childhood gang or clique. What moral judgments and ethical attitudes do you see being learned or did you learn through this period? How were these lessons effected?

2. Recall some episode of stealing in your life. What made you do it? How was it handled? What was the result for you? Do the same with some lie you told as a child.

3. Discuss what elementary schools can or should do in developing moral judgments and ethical attitudes.

4. Recall some young adolescent whom you know well. Does he have heroes? Who are they? What effect do they have upon his behavior? If the effect is bad, what would you do if you were his parent?

5. Outline what would seem to you to be a workable plan for counseling high school students on whatever personal problems you consider to be the province of the high school.

6. Trace your own psycho-sexual development or that of some young person you know well. Can you recognize the progressive steps by which you acquired important personal and social attitudes? What kind of sexual experiences did you have? What kind of sex education? What do you need now in attitudes and self-controls in order to complete your growth into a sound adulthood?

SELECTED READINGS

Banning, M. C.: The Case for Chastity. The Reader's Digest, August 1937. Reprint.

Blair, A. W., and W. H. Burton: Growth and Development of the Preadolescent. New York, Appleton-Century-Crofts, Inc., 1951, Ch. 2.

Cruze, W. W.: Adolescent Psychology and Development. New York, Ronald Press, 1953, Ch. 9.

Healy, W., and A. Bronner: Delinquency as a Mode of Adjustment. Chapter 67 in Kuhlen and Thompson: Psychological Studies of Human Development. New York, Appleton-Century-Crofts, Inc., 1952.

Horrocks, J. E.: The Psychology of Adolescence. Boston, Houghton Mifflin Co., 1951, Ch. 6.

Jersild, A. T.: Child Psychology. Rev. ed. New York, Prentice-Hall, Inc., 1954, Ch. 9.

Landis, P. H.: Adolescence and Youth: The Process of Maturing. Rev. ed. New York, McGraw-Hill Book Co., 1952, Chs. 8–11.

Malm, M., and O. G. Jamison: Adolescence. New York, McGraw-Hill Book Co., 1952, Ch. 6.

Thompson, G. G.: Child Psychology. Boston, Houghton Mifflin Co., 1952, Ch. 13.

CHAPTER 15

A Summary of Growth Achievements

The Demands of Life.   When the school years are over and the young person must meet life, he will, as we said in Chapter 1, have to be prepared for certain tests of his previous growth and development. He will have to be economically independent; he will have to make a social adjustment to the people with whom he works and lives and who live in his community; he will have to function as a citizen of his community and of the world; he will have to adjust to marriage or to the lack of it; and he will have to live successfully with himself and with his place in life. In other words, he will have to have an adequate life philosophy.

   What It Takes.   If he is to do these things successfully he must have acquired through his growth period:

1. Adequate physical health and vigor.
2. Well-formed habits of feeding, sleeping, exercising, and health protection.
3. Sufficient command of bodily skills to:
   (a) Insure exercise enough to keep well,
   (b) Utilize his body for efficient work and restful play,
   (c) Encourage general self-control through bodily control.
4. A satisfactory appearance and manner.
5. A well-developed intellect, a good background of facts and ideas, and good habits of clear thinking; adequate diction and vocabulary and the ability to express himself well.
6. A progressive weaning from childish behavior and from excessive dependence upon others.
7. A widening range of interests and creative outlets.
8. Increasingly adequate social skills; ever-widening insights; tolerance and understanding; genuine consideration for others.
9. A well-balanced moral and ethical code of behavior and the ability to live up to it.

Let us review some of the steps by which this growth comes about. We shall assume a good heredity and adequate prenatal and obstetric care.

   From Birth to One Year.   'A newborn baby is of no use and is the world's biggest nuisance. . . . If his training program is right he ceases to be a nuisance and becomes a joy."* Sleeping, eating, and exercising are the major business

* From a lecture by William Blatz given at Utah State College, July, 1939.

of the infant, because rapid physical growth is the order of the day for him. Not only does he grow rapidly in length and weight, his internal organs also develop rapidly. About eight teeth erupt and permanent teeth begin to be laid in during the first year. Foods which differ from milk in flavor and consistency are introduced, although vegetables and meats must be sieved or scraped. Spoon and cup supplement and gradually replace breast and bottle feeding, thus beginning the adjustment to new conditions as well as starting the weaning from too close attachment to the mother and to one's own babyhood. Two naps a day remain in the schedule, as do more frequent feedings than will occur later. This rapid growth and the laying in of teeth necessitate special attention to growth-stimulating foods, activity and rest. Limited ability to fight disease requires reasonable protection from bacteria; limited ability to adapt to wide ranges of temperature make it important to guard him against temperature changes.

Helplessness is to be expected in an infant. He is not supposed to carry any responsibility, to care for himself in any capacity except to exert the effort of sucking when food is presented to his lips. Yet, within a few days of birth he has accomplished much in the realm of learning and mental growth, and within the first year he has probably learned more new things than he will learn in any other year of his life. From an undifferentiated uncontrolled mass of movements characteristic of the newborn, the year-old child will have learned the postural controls and will have developed the muscular strength for standing alone and, soon to follow, for independent walking. He will have learned to see, to hear, and to touch, and will have blended these learnings into eye-ear, eye-hand, and hand-mouth coordinations. Through these he will translate much of the world about him into intelligible meaning and will have gained some useful command of the things which come within his reach. He will understand a considerable amount of language and will have begun to speak two or three meaningful words. He will have begun to make decisions and to solve problems which lead to more complex reasoning. He will have discovered people and already will have developed fundamental personality reactions to them. He will, in his own way, have discovered the beginning of authority, reactions to success and to failure, the satisfaction of work to accomplish results, the pleasure of the struggle which leads to achievement.*

Erikson[282]** states that the first year of life is the crucial time for the establishment of the first component of a healthy personality, namely, *the sense of*

---

* For further discussion see Bibliography.[756,781,886]

** In Chapter 3 the concept of developmental tasks was discussed and a summary of the tasks as listed by Havighurst was given for each major developmental level. Erikson has developed his own version of critical learnings which must be accomplished (or of problems which must be solved) for each developmental level if personality growth is to proceed smoothly. If these problems are solved successfully the child develops vigor and confidence for the next stage of growth. Erikson describes these problems as conflicts of feeling and desire which appear in a new form with each shift in experience and environment. However, each type of problem appears in its most critical form at a particular stage of development; if it is well solved at that stage it forms the basis for progress to the next stage; if not solved it continues to exist as an unsolved problem in the personality.

trust. As the infant finds his needs for food, cleanliness, and comfort met by his mother he comes to feel that his needs will be met when they arise. As he begins to bring his own body under control he feels a growing confidence that he can adapt his movements to achieve his goals. As he plays peekaboo he sees something disappear and return, disappear and return again; thus he grasps the fact that things continue to exist even though he does not see them, and hence that there is order and stability in the universe. At six to nine months the struggle to trust or to mistrust the world comes to a climax as the child comes to realize that he and his environment are things apart. The mother, if she loves him and is sensitive to his needs, helps him to develop trust, not only in her, but in his other surroundings, and, especially in himself. Erikson says that development of this sense of trust is not only the first, but the most important component of a healthy personality.

Later Infancy and Early Preschool. Between one and three years of age physical growth proceeds somewhat less rapidly, though changes in bodily proportion and development in the neuromuscular system permit the rapid acquisition of balance and skill which characterizes the child who is learning or has learned to walk and run about. At three years the child has all of his deciduous teeth and is laying in many of the permanent teeth. Because of his slower rate of growth and absorption in his growing abilities and in his environment, his appetite may decrease temporarily. His food, which is no longer puréed, comes to include nearly everything eaten by the family except highly seasoned, rich, or very coarse foods. This is an important time for extending food likes and for establishing good food habits. At this time most children join the family at meals and thus become much more a part of family life and routine. They usually require a supplementary cracker and milk or fruit juice between meals. One nap a day, usually in the afternoon, now suffices if night rest is long enough.

In mental growth the spectacular achievements of this period are in the acquisition of rapidly increasing controls over general bodily skills and hand controls, the tremendous explorations into "what, why, and what for?" about all the familiar things and events in the immediate environment. Rapid expansion of both understanding and use of language also occurs. Adequate playthings to encourage vigorous bodily play as well as to develop manual skills and to train sense perceptions are important.

Although the year-old child does not appear to be aware enough of routines to resist them, the eighteen-months-old child is likely to do so.

At eighteen months the child is a nonconformist, not because of a propensity to rebel but because his stock of perceptual differentiations and embryonic conceptions is so small and so precarious that he clings to his mental possessions as he clings to his mother or to an object in his hand. For him sudden changes are precipices. He avoids them by lying down, by backing away, by running off to hide, by screaming, struggling or beating the air.[346]

This, added to the other aspects of developing personal aggressiveness and confused sense perceptions and judgments, produces the negativism or temper tantrums which characterize this period. If routines are more rigorously imposed than the child's readiness can adjust to, food strikes are a frequent manifestation of this negativism, as is also resistance to toilet procedures. Learning to control this resistance or temper is one of the most important accomplishments of this period since it represents real beginnings in self-control and cooperation with others.

Even though he resists routines and changes, the two- and three-year-old child is advancing rapidly in his understanding of and cooperation with health habits and in his conformance with the domestic conventions of dressing, bathing, eating, etc. Control of elimination should move toward perfection during these years.

It is, too, a period of rapidly expanding awareness of other people as separate from oneself. However, the child of this age animates inanimate objects and carries on long conversations with himself as if one of him were talking to another, and thus gives evidence that separation of self from others is still not complete. He has imaginary companions from three years on, and in other ways around three years seems to carry other personalities around within himself as not quite separate from himself. His interests widen beyond himself and his immediate toys and his affection spreads from his mother to include other members of his immediate family.

Erikson[282] says that from twelve to fifteen months through the next two years much of the child's energy will center around asserting that he is a human being with a mind and will of his own. Thus he develops a *sense of autonomy*, the feeling that he is an independent human being even though he still needs and is able to use the help of others. He develops this sense of autonomy through the constant exploring of objects around him, the constant insistence that he be allowed to do things (or at least try to do things) for himself, that he be permitted to make such choices as he is able to make, and through learning that in spite of temper outbursts he can accept and tolerate restrictions where necessary. This is, as can be seen in the behavior of two- and three-year-olds, a struggle between his need for help and his urge to independence. The favorable solution of this problem, Erikson says, is self-control without loss of self-esteem. An unfavorable outcome results in a lasting sense of doubt about others and about himself.

The Later Preschool and Kindergarten Period. Between three and five or six years the child's physical growth rate is slower than at any time between infancy and pubescence. The knock knees and pronation which characterize many younger children now tend to disappear. Appetite is still not keen. The child eats regular meals with the family, needing only to have his meat cut to bite size and his bread spread with butter. He will usually still need midmorning and midafternoon supplementary food. He should continue an afternoon rest even though he may not sleep. Toilet control should become complete during these years.

All motor skills progress rapidly toward perfection during this period. Self care activities like feeding, dressing and undressing, care at the toilet, washing, and picking up toys progress as a by-product of the improved physical skills and as a definite beginning in the business of carrying one's own load in life. Cutting, pasting, "drawing" and "painting," block building and other creative activities are begun. Interest in hearing and in telling stories develops. Accuracy in sense judgments approaches perfection; appreciation of the meaning of numbers is begun, and some accuracy in the understanding of the shorter time units is developed. Eagerness to meet new things and new experiences is in full swing and leads to rapid expansion of factual knowledge and of language. Reasoning and problem solving become more adequate in direct proportion to the opportunity the child has to reason and to solve the simple problems of his daily living.

The child is now conscious of how he looks and is unhappy if he is conspicuously different from other children. He gives many evidences of conforming to social demands, and is willing or even eager to run simple errands, to help with drying the silverware, dusting or setting the family table. He constantly asks, "Is this the right way?" "Am I doing it right?" His eagerness to please and to follow the "right way" is so constant that a marked persistence of behavior problems at this age is suggestive of faulty functioning in some area of his growth.

Contacts with people, especially with other children, should widen during this period so that elementary lessons of give and take may be learned as a preparation for the social adjustments which school will require. Weaning from too great dependence upon the mother or other members of the family should be well under way. When he meets other children we can know that his behavior is immature for his age if he creates disorder, interferes with the work or play of other children, leads them into mischief, frequently pushes or pulls them, complains of them to adults for his own gain, avoids friendly advances from other children, or in other ways shows a concentration of interest upon his own wishes and impulses. It is at this age that beginnings of cooperative behavior should be made. Adults can help the child to get along with others with a minimum of conflict, to substitute verbal methods for fighting and snatching, not to be a crybaby when hurt or crossed but rather to develop courage in the face of pain or disappointment.

In less privileged economic groups, children of this age or even younger have frequently made adjustments of self-care, ease and familiarity with a wider variety of adults, and even the care of younger children. Such children can often make change up to a dollar, can drive a rather sharp exchange bargain, and are sometimes almost entirely responsible for household affairs while parents are absent at work. Whether the child is economically privileged or underprivileged the preschool period sets certain attitudes and emotional habits, especially those which concern home standards, so that they are fixed, or only slightly modified, thereafter.[*]

Erikson,[282] continuing his discussion of the problems which must be solved at the various ages, says that the child of four or five, having become sure for the time being at least that he is a person in his own right, now wants to find out what he can *do*. He closely observes the activities of the adults around him (particularly of his mother and father, but also of the milkman and truck driver) and tries to imitate their behavior. Thus, with the enlarging horizons

[*] For further discussion see Bibliography.[756,347]

as he enters kindergarten and as he widens his experiences beyond the immediate neighborhood, this period becomes one of enterprise and imagination, and of joyous, creative play. As was seen in earlier chapters, this is a period when conscience begins to function as an inner censor of his behavior. Erikson says that the problem to be worked out at this stage of development is to experience the use of one's own will without too much sense of guilt about one's actions. The fortunate outcome of this period is a sound *sense of initiative* guided and modified by conscience.

Erikson feels that if the first three stages of personality development (the sense of trust, of autonomy, and of initiative) are achieved satisfactorily and if, with them, are developed caution, self-control and conscience, progress through the later stages is fairly well assured.

The Childhood or Early Elementary School Period. The childhood cycle, which closely approximates the elementary school age, begins with the appearance of the sixth-year molars and lasts until the onset of pubescence. This is ordinarily from five or six to ten or eleven years of age.

During this age the child consolidates his previous learnings and carries forward earlier growth accomplishments. Slow, steady physical growth is the rule. Many underlying changes preliminary to pubescence take place, but spectacular adjustments do not command the attention of the adults as they did earlier and will again in pubescence.

This age is no time, however, to relax on health supervision of children. The need for careful protection of health and for recognition and correction, in so far as possible, of physical defects in the early elementary years is indicated.[428a] In a study of the physical status of a group of army selectees examined and disqualified for military service, Ciocco and associates[185] found that the great majority of the men who were disqualified because of eye, ear, or dental defects had shown some indication of these defects in their early elementary years. Of those rejected many had been in their early years below par physically as indicated by underweight, fair or poor nutrition or posture. Good health care during the early school years should be good insurance for the future. There is a sharp peak in communicable disease in elementary years. The common cold still appears frequently.[69]

The early elementary school period is one in which children are more "on their own" in physical routines, and one in which correct food, rest, and elimination habits should be functioning without close adult supervision. Not only should good habits of physical hygiene be developed, but children should also learn the reasons for these habits. By the end of the elementary school period the child should not only be efficient in self-care; he should also be able to follow simple precautions against colds, and against spreading infectious diseases recklessly; when ill he should be accustomed to following orders of a physician without bribery by his parents; he should be aware of any shortcomings of his body and reasonably responsible for doing something to meet them, e. g., not running if the defect is a bad heart, not eating sugar if it is diabetes.

Entrance to school tests the adequacy of the previous physical as well as psychologic development, since it demands physical strength, a reasonable resistance to colds and other diseases, the ability to leave home and mother, the ability to concentrate for at least short periods of time, adjustment to an authority other than the parents, a capacity to be with other children without fear on the one hand or intoxication on the other. It requires reliability in toilet habits, independence in dressing (at least for outer garments), ability to understand and to speak language, sufficiently developed sense perceptions to warrant success in school subjects.

School is the child's business—his job. The attitudes he takes toward this job will determine much of his early success or failure with it. The attitudes he learns from it will be of great importance to his attitudes toward work, toward responsibility, toward himself, and toward life in general in later years.

Erikson's[282] fourth stage, which begins around six years of age and extends over the next five or six years, has as its achievement objective the *sense of industry*, or, as Witmer and Kotinsky[1001] have chosen to refer to it, a *sense of duty and accomplishment*. As was said above, in certain underprivileged groups children learn this before they are six years of age. Learning how to do things and to do them well is an important aspect of this stage of personality development. School, of course, becomes (or should become) an instrument of basic importance in this development.

Upon entrance to school and in participation in gang activities many children for the first time meet standards of moral and ethical behavior which differ from those of the parental home. Some of these are good and serve to widen the child's horizon of acceptable behavior, and hence his tolerance. Some are bad and he must develop an immunity to these as he does to new germs he meets at this time.

Boys, particularly, resent nagging and oversupervision, even though dependence upon the home is still great during this age. Food and shelter are rarely obtained away from home; the security and sweetness of parental protection and love are still very attractive—the boisterous boy still likes to be tucked into bed at night with a bedtime story, and often with his favorite doll or toy animal. However, increasing independence from adults is not only desirable, but imperative, since the child of this age who associates with adults to the exclusion of peers becomes dependent, shy with children, and too amenable to adult and child authority. Deprived of adequate opportunity to learn adjustment to peers he may even become whiny, sulky, and subject to inferiority feelings.

Particularly evident during the elementary school years is the abundance of energy which makes "roughnecks" of these children. Their movements are vigorous, their voices loud. For boys there is great emphasis upon "being a regular guy"; shirts are hanging out, sox rumpled, and hair is mussed as evidences that one is not a "sissy." One understanding mother who had an older son said of her younger nine-year-old: "Now you can't get him into the bathroom. Wait five or six years and you won't be able to get him out of it." Both girls and boys fight as they develop an aggressiveness which seems at a premium in our American conception of "looking out for oneself." They have a great need for activity, both physical and mental. Control over the body proceeds rapidly as the child practices physical skills by the hour. Control over the mind is also challenging, and most children enjoy the feeling of having learned new and difficult things. Reading, writing, arithmetic, playing games, controlling muscles, learning to get on with peers are the preoccupations of the early elementary school child. Children of this age show an eagerness to extend horizons intellectually as well as physically. They are alert to learn about everything near themselves, and are willing to be carried into a grasp of world affairs. They love to dramatize the history of the Pilgrims, of Indians, of the Civil War, and to celebrate Washington's Birthday. They can work for months on a transportation project and love to visit the creamery or other sources of food and everyday things. In a real way this is simply an extension of the constant what-where-why curiosity of the preschool child.

This is a desirable time to utilize the alertness and eagerness of the child for the development of hobbies and interests which will serve to enrich his life in later as well as in the present years. Interest in woodwork, collecting, arts and crafts, and dramatics can be stimulated easily. In fact, the years from nine to twelve are the ones of greatest range of play and hobby activities and interests. Objective criticism and a sense of responsibility can be developed because of this eager interest in work.

The child's natural desire to learn is perhaps the reason we exact so much learning from our early elementary school children.

We expect the child from five to eleven to learn, apart from the school curriculum, more about the social customs of our world than at any other age. We expect him to learn the principles of honesty, private property, courtesy, thoughtfulness, tidiness, cleanliness, and others.*

Standards in these things are often set by the adult at a higher level for the child than the adult expects of himself or maintains. The development of conscience and of moral standards moves forward rapidly. This emphasis upon standards by adults sometimes combines with the child's natural urge to do the right thing and produces a heavy emotional burden for the child. Some children become overconscientious and are weighed down with a sense of futility and failure. In spite of all these demands, however, most children adapt well to the increasing need to adjust themselves to the world about them.

In spite of this desire to learn, however, the boisterousness, noise and clumsy haste of these children make fifth- to seventh-graders the hardest groups in the school to keep in some order and to move forward in a smooth academic sequence. This is a time, fortunately, when the gang impulse is strong, and group solidarity can be used to move a class in a group even though individual competitiveness also characterizes this age. Although the gang interest helps the teacher in providing a sense of solidarity it places another handicap on school work in addition to its encouragement of boister-

* From a lecture by Dr. William Blatz, given at Utah State College, July, 1939.

ousness. It fosters the naturally silly behavior which characterizes this age. Poking, tripping, practical jokes for boys, incessant giggling for girls can try the teacher's or the parent's patience to the breaking point.

Aside from the mistakes with property rights discussed under stealing in Chapter 14, and those with truth-telling discussed in Chapters 10 and 14, there are two types of behavior problems which characterize this age. Teachers and parents are aware of the one type, namely, aggressive boisterousness and silliness, inattention, carelessness, disorder, disobedience and disrespect, truancy, and failure in school. The clinician is aware of the other type, namely, shyness, daydreaming, passive failure to cooperate, nervousness and hurt feelings, fears, and other retreats from activity. These are all symptoms of incomplete learnings, of schedules which provide too little activity or demand too much, of school courses which bore children or which produce tension and anxiety, of emotional instability or physical inadequacy or discomfort, lack of emotional security either present or past, or some other situation which is not conducive to normal growth.*

The Junior and Senior High School Age. The outstanding phenomenon of these years is the onset of pubescence with the rapid biologic maturation of the body and the changes in social and personal interests which accompany this. The rapid physical growth of early pubescence places great demands upon the child. This is a period of accentuated physical differences between early and late maturers. It is also a "time of physiological learning,"[847] a time when bodily functions are becoming stabilized. These facts should be taken into consideration in planning physical and psychologic programs for young people of this age.

Complete adult height is achieved during the pubescent and postpubescent years, and the eruption of permanent teeth is completed except for the wisdom teeth. The pubescent child's appetite is either voracious or he becomes "picky" about food and he is likely to begin a habit of between-meals munching which may lead into a bad cycle. Candy bars after school dull the appetite for dinner. Another snack by bedtime, combined with a later bed hour than should be allowed in a period of such rapid growth, results in heavy fatigue in the morning and no appetite for breakfast. Soda fountain snacks, an ill-chosen lunch at the school cafeteria and further snacks after school may set up a cycle in which the child gets a preponderance of sweets with too little of the substantial growth-promoting foods. Health habits during this period should receive careful attention both at home and at school, since even the most carefully trained child may appear to forget all he knows about self-care at this time.

Early adolescence is ordinarily a period of good health. However, the adolescent who develops poor health practices may find that rapid growth, combined with rapidly increased school and social demands, may make him a prey to tuberculosis. That this happens fairly often is indicated by the relatively high incidence of tuberculosis among adolescents. Periodic health examinations are important now, as they were during the earlier years of

* For further discussion see Bibliography.[93,668,905]

childhood. Not only is it necessary to watch carefully for evidences of inadequate food and rest and of too great academic and social strains; it is also excellent preventive mental hygiene to help young people to understand and adjust to the growth phenomena peculiar to this period. Appearance of secondary sexual characteristics is often a source of anxiety and conflict. The question, "Am I normal?" occupies far more of the early adolescent's attention and emotional energy than is generally supposed.[442, 518, 561, 696, 1016] These psychologic as well as physical situations in young adolescents should receive attention from physicians and guidance personnel at regular intervals. The imperative necessity for adequate sex education is, of course, obvious.

Intellectually, the adolescent experiences a steady widening and deepening of capacity to think and reason. If home and school offer adequate stimulation there is a growing sense of current events and world affairs. There is a dawning awareness of the fact that soon he must not only know about the world but will also be required to meet life as an independent adult. Although schoolwork often suffers because of the young person's concentration on his social and personal problems, there is frequently a sense of being born intellectually. New ideas become fascinating; the unending scope of the "not-yet-known" stretches out ahead and urges the student into eager pursuit of knowledge. Children who have been indifferent to schoolwork sometimes become seriously devoted to the exploration of new academic fields. Occasionally, of course, this newly acquired student attitude is merely a cover-up for a feeling of failure in social contacts.

In our culture adolescents are expected to achieve at least three major steps in growth. (1) They must complete the weaning from dependence upon parental authority and protection and learn to think and act as mature, rational adults. (2) They must effect the transition from gang interests to adequate heterosexual adjustment. In most lives this eventuates in marriage and establishment of families. (3) They must adjust to their own capacities and limitations; they must learn to accept and use their capacities, to accept, or whenever possible to change, their liabilities. They must take over the responsibility for making themselves the best possible and the most useful possible persons without at the same time losing their sense of proportion about the size or importance of any single individual in the scheme of ultimate existence.

Erikson[282] expresses this another way when he calls attention to one of the problems of pubescent and adolescent growth as the establishment of a *sense of identity* through which the young person comes to clarify who he is and what his role in society is to be. Erikson points out that this sense of identity is the person's only safeguard against the lawlessness of his biologic drives on the one hand and the autocracy of his overweening conscience on the other. After the sense of identity is formed it then becomes possible for the young person to develop a *sense of intimacy*. This sense of intimacy must come about in his feelings for persons of the same sex as well as in his feelings for the opposite sex and for himself. As he becomes sure of himself, he can then seek and express closer relationships in friendship, love, and inspiration.

The young adolescent usually senses all of these obligations at least vaguely. He longs for freedom from adult authority, yet he dreads the responsibilities of adult living. He looks forward eagerly at one moment, yet he looks back longingly to the security and freedom of childhood at another moment. This explains some of his inconsistencies, since he is clean and "prinked up" to the point of silliness one day but slovenly and dirty the next. He works feverishly for a time, then relapses into childhood's comfortable laziness. He is businesslike and dependable, cooperative and eager one time, yet rude, uncooperative and defiant the next. He gives every evidence of his ambivalent feelings about growing up, and he shows clearly his state of confusion about his changing feelings, his temporary organic incoordination and instability, his eagerness to measure up to adult expectations, his conflicting fear that he may not do so, and his contrary inner need to defy authority.

Adjustment to the newly intensified sex feelings which follow soon after the appearance of secondary sexual characteristics absorbs much energy and thought, often competing strongly with schoolwork. How well the young person adjusts to moods, distractions and temptations will, of course, depend upon his previous habits of self-control, of responsibility, of consideration for others, and of seeing the future consequences of present behavior. However, glandular changes, rapid physical development, sharpened social awareness, and society's emphasis upon popularity with the opposite sex may provide a situation which outweighs even good previous training. Self-consciousness, shyness, feelings of insecurity which were dormant but never previously evident may be thrown into action, with the result that previously felt inadequacies are sharpened and a confused inability to understand and control the newly strengthened sex impulse produces uncontrolled and socially undesirable behavior. The young person may, at least in the early stages of adolescence, display an inability to measure up to the many new and exacting demands which parents, schoolwork, and society lay upon him. Conflicts and confusions which were present in earlier childhood are often revived in adolescence. All of his previous physical and psychologic strengths and weaknesses, habits, skills and attitudes are likely to be called into action. If previous training has not been good, disastrous behavior is more likely to result. However, good school training may combine with a basically sound constitution in the young person to avoid trouble even when previous habits and outlooks have been faulty. Last-minute gestures in the direction of control by parents seldom produce anything but sharpened antagonism and exaggerated defiance.

In our demand that the adolescent display adult judgments and responsibility we should recall that in our particular culture we keep young people in school, unmarried, and economically dependent upon their parents for some years after they are physically ready to reproduce the species. The situation was different in primitive cultures and, until the present generation, in oriental cultures, and even in our own culture until the past two generations. Young people, even before adolescence, were apprenticed to a trade so that they were established in lifework early. This, plus a tradition of generous dowries, made early marriage not only possible, but the custom. Young people grew up together, families knew each other well; parents either gave advice about mate selection or chose the mate outright. Choice of mate was not the "shot in the dark" that it so often is today. There are still a few sociologic cultures in the world in which parents or tradition determine life-work and launch the young person in it early, in which codes of social behavior are fixed and require no special judgment, in which mate selection is done for one and marriage immediately follows or even precedes biologic maturity. In these cultures confusion for the young person is at a minimum, and the problem of adolescence consists mainly of curbing individual desires in favor of an acceptance of whatever destiny is selected for one.

Our young people have a tradition of free occupational choice among bewildering possibilities. We have the tradition, and in a genuine sense the reality, of free choice of mate. This frequently takes place under conditions where possible mates are new acquaintances and their families and backgrounds are unknown. Any advice from parents or oldsters is likely to be regarded as interference. This throws a heavy burden of wisdom of choice upon the young person. His problem is complicated by the economic and educational necessity for delay of marriage for several years after the sex urge is mature and ready for function. This leaves our adolescents with the important problems of vocational choice and mate selection, while at the same time they are economically dependent upon their parents, thus necessitating submission to parental authority with consequent delay in decision-making.

Our high divorce rate testifies to the number of mistakes that are made in mate selection. High labor turnover among young people who go to work early and delay in decision about professional choice for those who can afford professional training testify to the difficulty of making adequate vocational choices. Our high rate of neuroses and psychoses testifies to the difficulty of acquiring balanced and satisfactory personal philosophies. Yet, the great majority of young people live through a fairly smooth adolescence, make fairly wise vocational and mate choices, and in due time develop a fairly workable philosophy of life.

Professional workers with children and their families must continue to learn as much as possible about how to promote desirable growth. Research is accumulating rapidly enough that an alert guidance worker cannot afford to lean on past knowledge any more than physicians can afford not to keep up with medical advances. School personnel have a particular obligation to practice the best that is known since they are the one group who join public health officials in reaching all of the children in any given community.

CASE STUDIES

The following case studies, one of a preadolescent boy, the other of an adolescent girl, may serve to make concrete our review of growth. Each is a typical, normal child whose good adjustment in the present stage of growth is the natural product of good inheritance, a good family who were interested in his development, and satisfactory growth in infancy and early childhood. Each had occasional difficulties of adjustment, but a sound attitude toward these on the part of parents and teachers brought the child through each incident to satisfactory readjustment. Each child has been at average in some phases of growth and different from the average in other phases. Each, in other words, has had his ups and downs but each has grown on the whole very satisfactorily.

CASE STUDY—A PREADOLESCENT

Ted at ten and one-half years can be considered a typical preadolescent. He is full of energy, which he uses in all kinds of muscular activities, and which sometimes gets him into conflict with adults because of his exuberant spirits and boisterousness. He scorns girls and considers cleaning up at mealtime a nuisance.

Ted is the youngest of a family of three children. He was born at a time when his father, a professional man, was having financial difficulties and the family was forced to live on a marginal level. In order to supplement the family income Ted's mother went back to teaching as soon as he entered nursery school.

Ted has always been well, except for an occasional children's disease and colds. He has grown in height and weight at a rate similar to that of most boys. His bone growth, however, has been slower than that of most children of his age which indicates that he is "growing" faster than he is "growing up" as measured by the maturation of bone. While there has been no measure of his muscle development, in light of his motor ability his muscle development could be considered good. He has always been skillful in the use of his large and small muscles, and at present he is adept at ping pong and dodge ball, and can manipulate a jig saw admirably. Like many preadolescents he uses these skills to attract attention to himself.

Ted's physical habits have been fairly good. His appetite has been excellent and he has learned to like a fairly wide variety of foods. In his preschool years he expressed his dislikes freely. At ten and one-half years he still carries a little "hangover" from earlier food attitudes since, although he says he likes a food, he nevertheless gives innumerable excuses for not eating it. Fundamentally he still has some food dislikes, but has become more skillful in covering them up.

Ted has developed mentally more rapidly than he has physically. He has consistently ranked as superior with especially good ability in reasoning and memory. His progress in school has been somewhat uneven, not because of limited capacity but because of periods of lack of application. Those periods have been part of a total picture of unruly behavior which resulted from faulty discipline. During his preschool and early school years Ted missed his mother's companionship and close guidance. Out of school hours he was under the care of a series of maids and his behavior got out of hand because of the lack of consistent and firm yet understanding guidance.

Ted, when he applies himself to a task, has always been a good, enthusiastic worker. He will work, for example, a long time with the jig saw and do a good job of which he is justly proud to the point of being boastful. Occasionally when he is unsuccessful he makes excuses, but for the most part he is a very good sport about failure. Ted is primarily interested in physical activities. Swimming time in school is his favorite school period. The academic subjects such as reading and arithmetic are less appealing to him. They are something to hurry through in order to pass on to the more intriguing things of life.

His behavior in nursery school as well as in elementary school showed that he could be an "angel" or a distinct nuisance. When situations and surroundings were new and strange, as for example at the beginning of his nursery school experience and again during the early months of elementary school, Ted was the "model" boy, cooperating and being a quiet member of the group. When he began to feel at home he cast aside all inhibitions and became obstreperous. He behaved in this way because he was fundamentally shy. However, he has always had a great urge to be accepted by peers, hence "loses his head" once his shyness has worn off.

About two years ago, after much forbearance on the part of his family, his brother and sister assumed the responsibility of helping Ted to grow up in his behavior. Earlier these two siblings, who were eleven and nine years older respectively, were no help to him. In fact, they made only two more older people to nag him and create confusion in his discipline. As Ted approached eight years of age, however, his hero worship of these older siblings led them to take an interest in him. They were unusually fine young people and their influence soon became a real force in shaping Ted's behavior into more satisfactory patterns. At about this time the financial condition of the family improved with consequent release of emotional tensions.

The family during all of Ted's life has lived in a good residential neighborhood but unfortunately the children nearby have been either younger or older than Ted. Thus he has had little opportunity to practice social skills with peers outside of school. Even in school his progress has been slow because of his undisciplined behavior and he has been in trouble frequently with both children and teachers. It is not surprising, therefore, that Ted is still a little slow in making friends and in becoming one of a group. He continues to carry a pattern of approach to social groups similar to the one he showed upon entrance to nursery school, kindergarten and the first grade. When he enters a new social group he becomes a quiet observer for a time. As he begins to feel at home he becomes more and more active and tries to tell the other children what to do. His overtures are not always successful and when the other children calmly ignore his efforts he becomes more and more boisterous. His wealth of ideas and his ready wit make it possible for him to get the attention of others by arousing their curiosity and to become a ringleader in practical jokes such as putting salt and pepper in somebody else's milk. Whether his many ideas and abounding energy are used in constructive activities depends to a great extent upon skillful guidance by the adults present.

Thus we see that Ted is a healthy, attractive, somewhat shy boy with a winsome smile and many fine qualities although he is often in difficulty with both peers and adults. In spite of this he quickly wins popularity among adults with his ready smile, his wit and humor, his intelligence and his ability to converse easily. With boys (he has no interest in girls) his popularity is won more slowly, but his skills and his wealth of ideas are in time an opening wedge into the gang. He has much to learn but is progressing rapidly. He is acquiring techniques that will help him to get along with people; he is learning when to be serious and when to be silly; he is gradually learning that others have rights and privileges; that a boy can be neat at mealtime without being considered a sissy. He is accumulating habits and attitudes, values and standards which will be very useful to him later in adolescence and maturity.

CASE STUDY—AN ADOLESCENT

Jane at eighteen is an attractive, intelligent girl who knows where she wants to go and is determined to get there. It is hard to believe that at three she was the shy, insecure child who came with her twin to nursery school. These two children had a difficult start in life. Both parents having died, the children had lived in five different boarding homes before they became a part of a family that gave them love and security. In this new environment Jane soon lost her apprehensiveness and settled down to growing. She has been a robust child from her early years. With the exception of an appendectomy and pneumonia during her adolescence, she has had nothing more serious than an occasional cold to interfere with her physical growth. In addition to what appears to be a sound physical constitution she has had good habits of eating and sleeping which were established by her foster family at an early age. Jane fortunately was the kind of child who took to regularity easily. A habit was quickly set and easily became a permanent part of her life. A good appetite, a good family diet and fine parental attitudes combined to give her an interest in food and a liking for a wide variety of foods. Her few dislikes have persisted from the preschool years. Consistency and texture of foods have been more important to her than flavors. Even at eighteen she still leaves the crusts of bread because she dislikes the "feel" of them.

Jane has been a fast grower. She has been tall for her age with broad shoulders and a good physique. At eighteen she is 5 feet 9½ inches. At times she may have longed to be petite for she has always tended to like little girls. During adolescence, like most girls, she has wanted to be slim. She has watched her weight carefully and has refused to eat certain foods she liked in an attempt to lose weight. During her early school years she had had some trouble with her teeth and later upon hearing that "cokes" and candy were bad for teeth she stoically gave them up. This was only one evidence of her strong determination.

She has a fine intelligence and has always made excellent progress in school. Entrance to school presented no difficulty to Jane. Even as early as school entrance she could care for herself and her twin as well. By the time the girls had reached the sixth grade they were sent to separate schools for two years because Jane tended to dominate her sister, who needed to learn to be on her own. While in intermediate school Jane was put on hall duty. This was unfortunate because it accentuated her desire to be the center of attention. The natural interest in self which all children have was stronger in Jane than in many others. Some of her peers helped her none too gently to become aware of this trait and an understanding counselor soon sensed the situation and promoted her to another duty in which she was less conspicuous.

Her scholastic achievement was consistently high and finally she was graduated from high school in the top 5 per cent of her class of 500 boys and girls. Her intellectual interests have been broad. She reads the National Geographic and Readers' Digest regularly. In high school she attended a club in which international affairs were discussed and was on the staff of the school paper for which she did much of the art work. She has been especially interested in design and looks forward to making that her profession.

During the summer before entering college she worked in a department store where her alertness, independence, and perserverance won her the admiration of her employer and an offer for work during the Christmas holidays. She saved enough from her earnings to buy all her clothes for college. Spending her money wisely was nothing new for Jane. She had long been a good manager because her wise and understanding family had given her previous experience in selecting her own clothes. While Jane had never been given a set allowance, nor was she "on a budget," she had learned the value of money and had acquired the ability to buy wisely by living in a family where value had been learned through living.

While Jane was the dominant twin, her sister made friends more easily. From early childhood Jane had the frequent experience of seeing her sister chosen while she was left behind. In spite of this she has always been devoted to her sister and has never been jealous when she was not included. She has always been eager to have friends, has great interest in knowing people and learning all about them and is inclined to champion the under-dog. When the interest in boys developed in adolescence she became wholeheartedly absorbed and for a time devoted all of her energies to this new interest. However, she has never been as popular with the boys as her sister, probably because of her critical attitude toward the boys she dates and her appalling bluntness. She is learning, however, to be tactful and to keep her critical comments to herself. Characteristic of most adolescents, Jane desires above everything else to be one of a group. To be left out is a bitter experience. She also has the fear, common to many young people, that she may not marry. To her marriage is the most important goal to be achieved.

Jane at eighteen is a charming girl who still is interested primarily in herself, but who has a staunch loyalty and affection for her family. She is extremely curious about people and things, has a particular interest which will lead to a vocation, has achieved considerable independence and has an inner drive that will carry her over many an obstacle. She is well on her way to meeting the tests of life demanded of a mature person. She was indeed fortunate to grow up in a family with a sound philosophy of life, where the children had the security of understanding and love combined with sound discipline and ample opportunity to "try their wings."

EXPERIENCES TO VITALIZE CLASS WORK

1. If you are not doing a case study, observe the same child whom you observed in Chapter 1. In the light of what you now know, get relevant history and background as a basis for determining his physical, mental, and emotional status. Make suggestions for adapting his school and outside-of-school programs to meet his needs.

2. If you are not doing a case study, write a biogaphical sketch of some young adult whom you know well. Trace patterns of growth and the influences which molded them.

3. Make specific suggestions for changes in schedule, curriculum and methods of teaching which would make it possible to utilize better our present knowledge of child development in:

    a. Kindergarten and early elementary grades.

    b. Upper elementary or intermediate grades.

    c. High schools.

4. Go through this book and review the particular contributions of the home to the growth and well-being of children.

SELECTED READINGS

Biber, B., et al.: The Life and Ways of the Seven- and Eight-Year-Old. New York, Basic Books, Inc., 1952, Chs. 11, 12.

Erikson, H. E.: The Child and Society. New York, W. W. Norton & Co., 1950, Ch. 7.

Havighurst, R.: Human Development and Education. New York, Longmans, Green & Co., 1953.

Horrocks, J. E.: The Psychology of Adolescence. Boston, Houghton Mifflin Co., 1951, Ch. 16.

Landis, P. H.: Adolescence and Youth. Rev. ed. New York, McGraw-Hill Book Co., 1952, Chs. 17–21.

Spock, B.: The Common Sense Book of Baby and Child Care. New York, Duell, Sloan & Pearce, 1946.

Strang, R.: Introduction to Child Study. Rev. ed. New York, The Macmillan Co., 1951, Chs. 9-12.

Witmer, H. L., and R. Kotinsky: Personality in the Making: The Fact-Finding Report of the Midcentury White House Conference on Children and Youth. New York, Harper & Bros., 1952, Ch. 1.

LIST OF FILMS AND FILM STRIPS

The following films and film strips may be useful with this text. The list is arranged topically to conform in order with the topics of the chapters. The subject matter of some chapters is not covered by this list because at the present time there are no appropriate films for those areas.

It is suggested that films be previewed and an introduction be given to the class before the showing for the purpose of guiding the students' observation of the material shown in the film.

The distributors of the films are listed. However, films frequently may be obtained from local libraries or borrowed from universities with large film libraries, as noted in the Preface.

He Acts His Age. (McGraw-Hill) 13 min.
  Typical behavior of children at ages 1 to 15 years.
Principles of Development. (McGraw-Hill) 17 min.
  Fundamentals of growth and change from early infancy through childhood.
  Demonstrates basic principles of growth and development.
Heredity and Environment. (Coronet) 11 min.
  Gives the full meaning of heredity, which gives an individual certain basic capabilities, and of environment, which helps determine the extent and direction of the use of these capacities.
The Endocrine System. (Encyclopedia Britannica Films) 11 min.
  Nature and function of endocrines; animated diagrams.
First as a Child. (Southern Educational Film Production Service for Virginia Department of Health and U. S. Children's Bureau) 20 min.
  Story of a crippled boy who receives treatment and resumes an active part in his home and community.
First Steps. (United Nations) 11 min.
  Camp as a place where children learn to walk again.
Children's Emotions. (McGraw-Hill) 22 min.
  Discusses the major emotions of childhood: curiosity, fear, anger, jealousy and joy—what they are like and how they can be affected by teaching.
Toward Emotional Maturity. (McGraw-Hill) 11 min.
  A girl makes a rational decision on the basis of what she has learned in school and from her own experience about emotions.
Age of Turmoil. (McGraw-Hill) 20 min.
  Characteristic adolescent changes including changing relationships with parents and peers from ages 13 to 15 years.

Food for Freddy. (Canadian Film Institute)*
>Showing healthy nine-year-old Freddy's food experiences at home and at school. Detailed film presentation of Canada's guide to good eating.

Child Care and Development. (McGraw-Hill) 17 min.
>The habits of daily care that ensure a happy, healthy child.

Your Children's Sleep. (British Information Service) 23 min.
>Analyzes a child's difficulties in going from active play to sleep and explains the role which dreams play in the child's developing mind. Gives some good suggestions for helping children to relax and accept sleep.

Preface To A Life. (University of Wisconsin-Castle) 29 min.
>An excellent film on influence of parental dreams for the child.

Your Children and You. (British Information Service) 30 min.
>The period of child rearing from birth to school age.

Parents Are People Too. (McGraw-Hill)*
>Teen-agers earn adult standing with their parents by showing that they are dependable, can handle responsibility and can see their parents' viewpoint as well as their own.

Let's Teach Better Nutrition. *Film Strip*. (Department of Nutrition, Harvard School of Public Health) 35 min.
>Demonstration of the way a school community may develop a nutrition education program.

The School That Learned To Eat. (General Mills) 20 min.
>Nutrition education around the school lunch.

Teacher Observations of School Children. *Film strip with 33¹/₃ rpm. record.* (Metropolitan Life)
>How to observe children for signs of physical health and illness.

A Child Went Forth. (Brandon Films) 20 min.
>Story of a child at a progressive camp. Idea of freedom within sensible bounds is developed. Suggests potentialities of a camp situation in contributing to a child's total growth.

Developing Your Character. (Coronet) 11 min.
>Home and community influences on the development of character.

Lambertville Story. (Paramount Pictures) 20 min.
>Story of a community effort to establish a Saturday night teen-age recreation center.

Human Reproduction. (McGraw-Hill) 22 min.
>Structure and functions of both male and female reproductive organs, and how fertilization takes place. Explains menstruation. Animated diagrams.

Physical Aspects of Puberty. (Adolescent Film Series, McGraw-Hill) 19 min.
>Basic facts of physical development for boys and girls done mostly in animated drawings.

Meeting the Needs of Adolescents. (McGraw-Hill) 19 min.
>Physical and psychologic needs of adolescents; how parents can help to prepare for these and future needs.

* No time listed at time of going to press.

Life with Baby. (March of Time) 18 min.
   Gesell's work with infants. The classic on infant growth and development; largely the achievement of motor controls.
Social Development. (McGraw-Hill) 17 min.
   Social behavior at different age levels and the reasons underlying the changes in behavior patterns as the child develops.
From Sociable Six to Noisy Nine. (McGraw-Hill) 22 min.
   A wealth of information about the age levels dealt with.
Shyness. (McGraw-Hill) 23 min.
   Shows three shy children and how the most typical of these was helped to become an active member of a group.
Developing Friendships (Coronet). 11 min.
   Explores individual differences in capacity for friendliness and helps young people understand the meaning of friendship.
Social-Sex Attitudes in Adolescence. (McGraw-Hill) 22 min.
   The growing understanding of the meaning of sex in the teen-ager.
Marriage Is a Partnership. (Coronet) 16 min.
   A positive approach to the realities of marriage.
Marriage Today. (McGraw-Hill) 22 min.
   Physical and psychologic companionship for two or three couples of differing personalities.

DISTRIBUTORS OF FILMS LISTED ABOVE

Brandon Films, Inc., 200 W. 57th St., New York 19, N.Y.

British Information Service, 30 Rockefeller Plaza, New York 29, N.Y.

Canadian Film Institute: Contemporary Films, Inc., 13 E. 37th St., New York 16, N.Y.

Castle Films: United World Film, Inc., 1445 Park Ave., New York 29, N.Y.

Coronet Films, Coronet Building, Chicago 1, Ill.

Encyclopedia Britannica Films, 1150 Wilmette Ave., Wilmette, Ill.

General Mills, Inc., 400 2nd Ave., Minneapolis 1, Minn.

Harvard School of Public Health, Department of Nutrition, 695 Huntington Ave., Boston 15, Mass.

McGraw-Hill Book Co., Text-Film Department, 330 W. 42nd St., New York 18, N.Y.

March of Time Forum Films, 369 Lexington Ave., New York 17, N.Y.

Metropolitan Life Insurance Co., 1 Madison Ave., New York 10, N.Y., or 600 Stockton St., San Francisco 20, Calif.

Southern Educational Film Production Services for Virginia State Department of Health: Film Program Services. On loan from all state health departments.

Paramount Pictures: Teaching Film Custodians, Inc., 25 W. 43rd St., New York, N.Y.

United Nations: Films and Visual Information Division, United Nations, New York, N.Y.

BIBLIOGRAPHY

1. Abbott, M.: Choosing the movie. Educ. Method. *13:* 89–94, 1933.
2. Abel, J. M., and N. F. Joffe: Cultural backgrounds of female puberty. Am. J. Psychotherapy *4:* 90–113, 1950.
3. Abernethy, M. E.: Relationships between Mental and Physical Growth. Monogr. 1 (7). Washington, D. C., Society for Research in Child Development, National Research Council, 1936.
4. Ackerman, N. W.: Dynamic patterns in group therapy. Psychiatry *7:* 341–348, 1944.
5. Addison, V. E., et al.: Effect of amount and kind of protein in breakfasts on blood-sugar levels. J. Am. Dietet. A. *29:* 674–677, 1953.
6. Alcock, A. T.: Quoted in: War strain in children. Brit. M. J., Jan. 25, 1941.
7. Aldrich, C. A., and M. M. Aldrich: Babies Are Human Beings. New York, The Macmillan Co., 1938.
8. Allen, F.: Psychotherapy with Children. New York, W. W. Norton & Co., 1942.
9. Allen, F. H., and G. H. J. Pearson: The emotions of the physically handicapped child. Brit. J. M. Psychol. *8:* 212–235, 1928.
10. Allers, O.: Personal communication in Terry, T. L.: Retrolental Fibroplasia. In Advances in Pediatrics, Vol. III. New York, Interscience Publishers, Inc., 1948.
11. Allport, G. W.: Personality: A Psychological Interpretation. New York, Henry Holt & Co., 1937.
12. Almquist, H. J.: Nutritional Applications of the Amino Acids. In Greenberg, D. M.: Amino Acids and Proteins: Theory, Methods, Applications. Springfield, Ill., Charles C Thomas, 1951.
13. Alschuler, R. H., and L. W. Hattwick: Painting and Personality: A Study of Young Children. Chicago, University of Chicago Press, 1947, Vols. 1, 2.
14. Altland, J. K., and B. E. Brush: Goiter prevention in Michigan; results of 30 years' voluntary use of iodized salt. J. Michigan M. Soc. *51:* 985–989, 1952.
15. Amen, E. W.: Individual differences in apperceptive reaction: A study of the response of pre-school children to pictures. Genet. Psychol. Monogr. *23:* 319–385, 1941.
16. American Association for Gifted Children: The Gifted Child. Boston, D. C. Heath & Co., 1951.
17. American Camping Magazine (all issues). American Camping Association, 343 Dearborn St., Chicago, Ill.
18. American Council on Education: Helping Teachers Understand Children. American Council on Education, 744 Jackson Pl. N. W., Washington, D. C., 1945.
19. American Council on Education: School Buildings and Equipment *3* (8). Washington, D. C., 1939.
20. American Medical Association Council on Foods: Iodized salt and goiter, an iodine deficiency disease. J. A. M. A. *29:* 1691, 1932.
21. American Youth Commission: Youth-Serving Organizations. Washington, D. C., American Youth Commission, American Council on Education, 1937.
22. Ames, L. B.: Bilaterality. J. Genet. Psychol. *75:* 45–50, 1949.
23. Ames, L. B.: Development of sense of time in the young child. J. Genet. Psychol. *68:* 97–125, 1946.
24. Ames, L. B., J. Learned, R. W. Métraux, and R. N. Walker: Child Rorschach Responses: Developmental Trends from Two to Ten Years. New York, Paul B. Hoeber, Inc., 1952.
25. Anastasi, A.: Differential Psychology. New York, The Macmillan Co., 1937.
26. Anastasi, A.: Psychological Testing. New York, The Macmillan Co., 1954.
27. Anastasi, A., and J. Foley: An analysis of spontaneous drawings by children in different cultures. J. Appl. Psychol. *20:* 689–726, 1936.
28. Anderson, H. H.: Domination and integration in the social behavior of young children in an experimental play situation. Proceedings: Second Biennial Meeting, Society for Research in Child Development, 1936, pp. 27–29.
29. Anderson, H. H.: Experimental study of dominative and integrative behavior in children of preschool age. J. Social Psychol. *8:* 335–345, 1937.
30. Anderson, J. E.: The Development of Spoken Language. In Thirty-Eighth Yearbook, National Society for the Study of Education. Bloomington, Ill., Public School Publishing Co., 1939, pp. 211–224.
31. Anderson, V. A.: Improving the Child's Speech. New York, Oxford University Press, 1953.
32. Arbuthnot, M. H.: Transitions in discipline. Childhood Education *15:* 101–107, 1938.

33. Arey, L. B.: The degree of normal menstrual irregularity. Am. J. Obst. & Gynec. *37:* 13–29, 1939.
34. Arnold, F. A., et al.: Effect of fluoridated public water supplies on dental caries prevalence. Seventh year of Grand Rapids-Muskegon study. Pub. Health Rep. *68:* 141–148, 1953.
35. Arsenian, S.: Bilingualism in the post-war world. Psychol. Bull. *42:* 65–86, 1945.
36. Asch, S. E.: Personality Development of Hopi Children. Unpublished data in Murphy, et al.: Experimental Social Psychology. Rev. ed. New York, Harper & Bros., 1937, pp. 443 ff.
37. Ashley-Montagu, M. F.: Adolescent Sterility: A Study in the Comparative Physiology of the Infecundity of the Adolescent Organism in Mammals and Man. Springfield, Ill., Charles C Thomas, 1946.
38. Association for Childhood Education: Growth through School Living. Washington, D. C., Association for Childhood Education, 1940.
39. Association for Childhood Education International: Using What We Know For Children in the School, the Home, the Community. Washington, D. C., Association for Childhood Education International, 1951.
40. Atkinson, R. K.: A motor efficiency study of eight thousand New York City high school boys. Am. Phys. Educ. Rev. *29:* 56–59, 1924.
41. Atkinson, R. K.: A study of athletic ability of high school girls. Am. Phys. Educ. Rev. *30:* 389–399, 1925.
42. Ausubel, D. P.: Ego Development and the Personality Disorders. New York, Grune & Stratton, 1952.
43. Ausubel, D. P.: Negativism as a phase of ego development. Am. J. Orthopsychiat. *20:* 796–805, 1950.
44. Averill, L. A.: Adolescence: a Study in the Teen Years. Boston, Houghton Mifflin Co., 1936.
45. Baber, R.: Marriage and the Family. New York, McGraw-Hill Book Co., 1939.
46. Baden, C. S.: Modern Tendencies in World Religion. New York, The Macmillan Co., 1933.
47. Bailey, E. W., A. Laton, and E. L. Bishop: Studying Children in School. 2nd ed. New York, McGraw-Hill Book Co., 1939.
48. Bain, W. E.: Parents Look at Modern Education. New York, D. Appleton-Century Co., 1935.
49. Baker, E.: A social basis for the teaching of elementary English language. Elem. Sch. J. *30:* 27–33.
50. Baker, H. J.: Introduction to Exceptional Children. Rev. ed. New York, The Macmillan Co., 1953.
51. Baker, H. J.: A study of juvenile theft. J. Educ. Res. *20:* 81–87, 1929.
52. Baker, K. H.: Radio listening and socio-economic status. Psychol. Record *1:* 99–144, 1937.
53. Baker, R. G., et al.: The Psychological Ecology of a Small Town. In Dennis, W. (editor): Readings in Child Psychology. New York, Prentice-Hall, Inc., 1951.
54. Bakwin, H., and R. M. Bakwin: The Clinical Management of Behavior Disorders in Children. Philadelphia, W. B. Saunders Co., 1953.
55. Baldwin, A. L.: An analysis of some aspects of feeding behavior. J. Genet. Psychol. *66:* 221–232, 1945.
56. Banning, M. C.: The Case for Chastity. Reader's Digest, (Aug.) 1937.
57. Barker, R. G., J. S. Kounin, and H. F. Wright: Child Behavior and Development. New York, McGraw-Hill Book Co., 1943.
58. Barker, R. G., in collaboration with B. A. Wright, L. Meyerson and M. R. Gonick: Adjustment to Physical Handicap and Illness: A Survey of the Social Psychology of Physique and Disability. Bull. 55, Rev. Social Science Research Council. 230 Park Ave., New York, 1953.
59. Barnes, R.: The Uses of Written Language by Junior High School Pupils. Unpublished thesis for Master's degree, University of Minnesota, Minneapolis.
60. Bartemeier, L.: A series of lectures given at the Merrill-Palmer School, 1945–46.
61. Baruch, D.: Aggression during doll play in a preschool. Am. J. Orthopsychiat. *11:* 252–260, 1941.
62. Baruch, D.: Parents and Children Go to School. Chicago, Scott, Foresman & Co., 1939.
63. Baruch, D.: Therapeutic procedures as part of the educative process. J. Consult. Psychol. *4:* 165–175, 1940.
64. Bates, S.: Your Town and Your Child. University of Iowa Publications *1019* (Dec.), 1938.
65. Bathurst, J. E.: A study in sympathy and resistance (negativism) among children. Psych. Bull. *30:* 625–626, 1933.
66. Bauer, I. L.: Attitudes of children with rheumatic fever. J. Pediat. *40:* 796–806, 1952.
67. Baxter, B., et al.: Elementary Education. Boston, D. C. Heath & Co., 1952.
68. Bayer, L. M.: A psychosomatic view of the soma. Stanford M. Bull. *3:* 93–97, 1945.
69. Bayer, L. M., and M. M. Snyder: Illness experience of a group of normal children. Child Development *21:* 93–120, 1950.
70. Bayley, N.: The California Scale of Motor Development. University of California Syllabus Series 259: 1936.
71. Bayley, N.: Factors Influencing the Growth of Intelligence in Young Children. In Thirty-Ninth Yearbook, National Society for the Study of Education. Bloomington, Ill., Public School Publishing Co., 1940. pp. 49–79.
72. Bayley, N.: Mental Growth in Children. In Thirty-ninth Yearbook, National Society for the Study of Education. Bloomington, Ill., Public School Publishing Co., 1940.

73. Bayley, N.: The Role of Intelligence: Mental Health in the Classroom. In Thirteenth Yearbook, Department Superintendent & Directors of Instruction. Washington, D. C., National Education Association, 1940.

74. Bayley, N.: Size and body build of adolescents in relation to rate of skeletal maturing. Child Development *14:* 51–90, 1943.

75. Bayley, N.: Skeletal maturing in adolescence as a basis for determining percentage of completed growth. Child Development *14:* 5–46, 1943.

76. Bayley, N.: Studies in the Development of Young Children. Berkeley, University of California Press, 1940.

77. Bayley, N., and L. M. Bayer: The assessment of somatic androgyny. Am. J. Phys. Anthropol. 4ns: 433–461, 1946.

78. Bayley, N., and A. Espenschade: Motor development from birth to maturity. Rev. Educ. Research *11*: 562–572, 1941.

79. Bayley, N., and S. R. Pinneau: Tables for predicting adult height from skeletal age: Revised for use with the Greulich-Pyle hand standards. J. Pediat. *40:* 423–441, 1952.

80. Bayley, N., and R. Tuddenham: Adolescent Changes in Build. In Forty-Third Yearbook, National Society for the Study of Education. Chicago, Ill., National Society for the Study of Education, Department of Education, University of Chicago, 1944.

81. Beach, F. A.: Hormones and Behavior. New York, Paul B. Hoeber, Inc., 1948.

82. Beck, S. J.: Rorschach's Test. II: A Variety of Personality Pictures. New York, Grune & Stratton, 1945.

83. Bell, H. M.: Youth Tell Their Story. Washington, D. C., American Council on Education, 1938.

84. Benedict, A., and A. Franklin: Your Best Friends Are Your Children: A Guide to Enjoying Parenthood. New York, Appleton-Century-Crofts, 1952.

85. Benezet, L. P.: The story of an experiment. J. Nat'l. Educ. Assoc. *24:* 241–244, 301–303, 1935.

86. Bennett, C. C.: An Inquiry into the Genesis of Poor Reading. Teachers College Contrib. Educ. No. 755. New York, Teachers College, Columbia University, 1938.

87. Bernhardt, K. S., and R. Herbert: A further study of vitamin B deficiency and learning with rats. J. Comp. Psychol. *24:* 263–267, 1937.

88. Betts, E. A.: Foundations of Reading Instruction, with Emphasis on Differentiated Guidance. New York, American Book Co., 1946.

89. Biber, B.: Children's Drawings: From Lines to Pictures. New York, Bureau of Educational Experiments, 1934.

90. Biber, B., et al.: Life and Ways of the Seven- to Eight-Year-Old. New York, Basic Books, Inc., 1952.

91. Bibliographies on physical and mental development: Reviews of Educational Research *3* (2): (Apr.) 1933; *6* (1): (Feb.) 1936; *9* (1): (Feb.) 1939.

92. Binning, G.: "Peace be on thy house": The effect of emotional tensions on the development and growth of children, based on a study of 800 Saskatoon school children. Health—Canada's National Health Magazine, March-April 1948.

93. Blair, A. W., and W. H. Burton: Growth and Development of the Preadolescent. New York, Appleton-Century-Crofts, 1951.

94. Blair, G. M., et al.: Educational Psychology. New York, The Macmillan Co., 1954.

95. Blanton, A. W.: The Child of the Texas One-Teacher School. Bull. No. 3613, Bur. of Research in Soc. Sci. Study No. 17, Austin, Texas, 1936.

96. Blanton, S. M.: Mental and nervous changes in children of Volkschule of Trier, Germany. Ment. Hyg. *3:* 343 ff., 1919.

97. Blattner, R.: Comments on current literature: Rheumatic fever. J. Pediat. *42:* 129–131, 1953.

98. Blatz, W. E., K. D. Allin, and D. A. Millichamp: A Study of Laughter in the Nursery School Child. University of Toronto Studies in Child Development, Ser. No. 7. Toronto, University of Toronto, 1936.

99. Blau, A.: The Master Hand. Am. Orthopsychiat. Research Monogr. Series, 1945.

100. Blewett, G. W. and C. Schuck: A comparison of the food consumption of men and women college students. J. Am. Dietet. A. *26:* 525–528, 1950.

101. Blonsky, P. P.: Das einzige Kind in seinem ersten Schuljahr. Ztschr. f. p"dagog. Psychol., *31:* 84–97, 1930.

102. Blos, P.: The Adolescent Personality. New York, D. Appleton-Century Co., 1941.

103. Boas, F.: The tempo of growth of fraternities. Proc. Nat. Acad. Sc. *21:* 413–418, 1935.

104. Bobbitt, F.: The Wider Vision. The New Wonder World. 5th ed., Vol. xi. Chicago, G. L. Shuman & Co., 1939.

105. Bochner, R., and F. Halpern: Clinical Application of the Rorschach Test. Rev. ed. New York, Grune & Stratton, 1945.

106. Bodman, F. H.: War conditions and the mental health of the child. Brit. M. J. II: 486–488, 1941.

107. Bonar, H. S.: High school pupils list their anxieties. School Rev. *50:* 512–515, 1942.

108. Bookwalter, K. W.: Grip strength norms for males. Research Quart. *21:* 249–273, 1950.

109. Bossard, J. H. S.: The Sociology of Child Development. New York, Harper & Bros., 1948.

110. Bower, P.: The Relation of Physical, Mental and Personality Factors to Popularity in Adolescent Boys. Doctor's Dissertation, University of California, 1940, Berkeley, University of California

Library. Reported in Jones, H. E.: Development of Physical Abilities. The Forty-Third Yearbook of National Society for Study of Education. Part I. Adolescence. pp. 100–122. Department of Education, University of Chicago, Chicago, Ill., 1944.

111. Boyd, J. D.: Clinical appraisal of growth in children. J. Pediat. *18:* 289–299, 1941.

112. Boys' Clubs of America, Inc.: Boys' Clubs: A National Movement. New York, 1937.

113. Brackett, C. W.: Laughing and Crying of Preschool Children. Child Devel. Monogr. No. 14: p. 91, 1934.

114. Brain, W. R.: Speech and handedness. Lancet *249:* 837–842, 1945.

115. Brandenburg, J., and C. C. Brandenburg: Language development during the fourth year. Pedagog. Semin. *26:* 27–40, 1919.

116. Brazelton, T. B., et al.: Emotional aspects of rheumatic fever in children. J. Pediat. *43:* 339–358, 1953.

117. Bridges, K. K. B.: Emotional development in early infancy. Child Development *3:* 324–334, 1932.

118. Bridges, K. K. B.: The Social and Emotional Development of the Preschool Child. London, George Routledge & Sons, Ltd., 1931.

119. Bridges, K. K. B.: A study of social development in early infancy. Child Development *4:* 33–49, 1933.

120. Briggs, T. H.: Praise and censure as incentives. School and Society *26:* 596–598, 1927.

121. British Association for the Advancement of Science: Report of Eighty-Third Meeting, Birmingham, Eng. pp. 268–300. London, John Murray, 1914.

122. British Medical Association: Report of the Committee on Nutrition. London, British Medical Association, 1950.

123. Broadbent, B. H.: The face of the normal child. Angle Orthodontist *7:* 183–208, 1937.

124. Broadbent, B. H.: Ontogenic development of occlusion. Angle Orthodontist *11:* 223–241, 1941

125. Bromley, D. D., and F. H. Britten: Youth and Sex. New York, Harper & Bros., 1938.

126. Brooks, F. D.: Intellectual Development from Fifteen to Twenty-two. Growth and Development. The Basis for Educational Programs. Progressive Education Association, New York, 1936, pp. 105–111.

127. Browe, J. H., and H. B. Pierce: A survey of nutritional status among school children and their response to nutrient therapy. Milbank Mem. Fund Quart. *28:* 223–237, 1950.

128. Brown, F. J.: Knowledge of results as an incentive in schoolroom practice. J. Educ. Psychol. *23:* 532–552, 1932.

129. Brown, F. J.: Sociology of Childhood. New York, Prentice-Hall, Inc., 1939.

130. Brown, G. D.: The development of diabetic children, with special reference to mental and personality comparisons. Child Development *9:* 175–183, 1938.

131. Brown, G. D., and W. H. Thompson: The diabetic child. Am. J. Dis. Child. *59:* 238–254, 1940.

132. Brozek, J., et al.: A study of personality of normal young men maintained on restricted intakes of vitamins of the B complex. Psychosom. Med. *8:* 98–109, 1946.

133. Bruch, H.: Obesity in childhood and personality development. Am. J. Orthopsychiat. *11:* 467–474, 1941.

134. Bruch, H.: Obesity in children: III. Physiologic and psychologic aspects of the food intake of obese children. Am. J. Dis. Child. *59:* 739–781, 1940.

135. Bruch, H.: Obesity in relation to puberty. J. Pediat. *19:* 365–375, 1941.

136. Bruch, H., and G. Touraine: Obesity in childhood: V. The family frame of obese children. Psychosom. Med. *2:* 141–206, 1940.

137. Brueckner, L. J.: The Development of Ability in Arithmetic. In Thirty-Eighth Yearbook, National Society for Study of Education. Bloomington, Ill., Public School Publishing Co., 1939.

138. Brueckner, L. J.: Language: the Development of Oral and Written Composition. Child Development and the Curriculum. In Thirty-Eighth Yearbook, National Society for Study of Education. Bloomington, Ill., Public School Publishing Co., 1939.

139. Brueckner, L. J., et al.: The Changing Elementary School. New York. Inor Publishing Co., 1940.

140. Brumbaugh, F. N.: Stimuli Which Cause Laughter in Children. Ph.D. dissertation, New York University, 1939.

141. Brunschwig, L.: A Study of Some Personality Aspects of Deaf Children. New York, Teachers College, Columbia University, 1936.

141a. Buckingham, B. R.: New Data on the Typography of Textbooks. Thirtieth Yearbook, National Society for Study of Education. Part II, pp. 93–125. Bloomington, Ill., Public School Publishing Co., 1931.

142. Buckingham, B. R., and J. MacLatchy: The Number Ability of Children When They Enter the First Grade. In Twenty-Ninth Yearbook, National Society for the Study of Education. Bloomington, Ill., Public School Publishing Co., 1930.

143. Buehl, C. C., and S. I. Pyle: The use of age at first appearance of three ossification centers in determining the skeletal status of children. J. Pediat. *21:* 335–342, 1942.

144. Bühler, C.: Die ersten sozialen Verhaltungsweisen des Kindes. Quel u. Stud. z. Jugkd. *5:* 1–102, 1927. (Translated and summarized in Handbook of Child Psychology. Rev. ed. Worcester, Mass., Clark University Press, 1933.)

145. Bühler, C.: From Birth to Maturity: An Outline of the Psychological Development of the Child. London, Kegan Paul, Trench, Trubner & Co., Ltd., 1935.
146. Burchard, E. M. L., and H. R. Myklebust: A comparison of congenital and adventitious deafness with respect to its effect on intelligence, personality and social maturity. Part II: Social maturity. American Annals of the Deaf *87:* 241–250, 1942.
147. Burgemeister, B. B., and L. H. Blum: Intellectual evaluation of a group of cerebral palsied children. Nerv. Child *8:* 177–180, 1949.
148. Burnham, H. A., E. G. Jones and H. D. Redford: Boys Will Be Men. Rev. ed. Philadelphia, J. B. Lippincott Co., 1949.
149. Burnham, M. P.: Imaginative Behavior of Young Children as Revealed in Their Language. Unpublished Ph.D. thesis, Teachers College, Columbia University. Cited in Jersild, A. T.: Child Psychology. New York, Prentice-Hall, 1940.
150. Buros, O. K.: The Fourth Mental Measurements Yearbook. Highland Park, N. Y., Gryphon Press, 1953.
151. Burton, W.: The Guidance of Learning Activities. 2nd ed. New York, Appleton-Century-Crofts, Inc., 1952.
152. Buseman, A.: Siblings and ability in school. (Title trans. from the German.) Ztschr. f. Kinderforsch. *35:* 509–516, 1929.
153. Butterworth, J. E., and H. A. Dawson: The Modern Rural School. New York, McGraw-Hill Book Co., 1952.
154. Caille, A.: Left-handedness as an educational problem. Am. J. Clin. Meth. *66:* 2.
155. Caille, R. K.: Resistant Behavior of Preschool Children. Child Development Monograph 11. New York, Teachers College, Columbia University, 1933.
156. Caldwell, O., and B. Wellman: Characteristics of school leaders. J. Educ. Research *14:* 1–13, 1926.
157. Callahan, J. W.: Television in School, College and Community. New York, McGraw-Hill Book Co., 1953.
158. Campbell, E. H.: Social-sex development of children. Genet. Psychol. Monogr. *21:* 461–552, 1939.
159. Canadian Council on Nutrition: A Dietary Standard for Canada Approved by The Canadian Council on Nutrition. Bull. 2, Canadian Council on Nutrition, 1950.
160. Cannon, P. R.: Importance of Proteins in Resistance to Infection. In Implications of Nutrition and Public Health in the Postwar Period. Proceedings of Conference, Children's Fund of Michigan, Detroit, 1944.
161. Cannon, W. B.: Bodily Changes in Pain, Hunger, Fear and Rage. Rev. ed. New York, D. Appleton-Century Co., 1939.
162. Cannon, W. B.: Digestion and Health. New York, W. W. Norton & Co., 1936.
163. Cannon, W. B.: The Wisdom of the Body. New York, W. W. Norton & Co., 1939.
164. Cantril, H., and G. Allport: The Psychology of Radio. New York, Harper & Bros., 1935.
165. Carey, T. F.: The Relation of Physical Growth to Developmental Age in Boys. Washington, D. C., Catholic University of America, 1935.
166. Carmichael, L.: The Onset and Early Development of Behavior. In Carmichael, et al.: Manual of Child Psychology. New York, John Wiley & Sons, Inc., 1946.
167. Carmichael, L., et al.: Manual of Child Psychology. 2nd ed. New York, John Wiley & Sons, Inc., 1946. (Rev. ed. 1954.)
168. Carpenter, A.: Strength, power and "femininity" as factors influencing the athletic performance of college women. Res. Quart. Am. Phys. Educ. Assoc. *9:* 120–127, 1938.
169. Carr, L. J.: Delinquency Control. Rev. ed. New York, Harper & Bros., 1950.
170. Carrel, A.: Man the Unknown. New York, Harper & Bros., 1935.
171. Carr-Saunders, A. M., H. Mannheim, and E. C. Rhodes: Young Offenders: An Inquiry into Juvenile Delinquency. London, Cambridge University Press (New York, The Macmillan Co.), 1944.
172. Cavan, R. S., et al.: Personality Problems in Old Age. Chicago, Science Research Associates, 1949.
173. Celestine, Sister M.: A Survey of Literature on the Reading Interests of Children of the Elementary Grades. Educ. Research Bull. of Catholic Union *5* (2-3), 1930.
174. Chalmers, A. K.: Preliminary notes of an inquiry into the physique of Glasgow schoolchildren. J. Roy. San. Inst. *26:* 903, 1904–1905.
175. Charters, W. W.: Motion Pictures and Youth. New York, The Macmillan Co., 1933.
176. Chase, L. E.: Motivation of Young Children: An Experimental Study of the Influence of Certain Types of External Incentives upon the Performance of a Task. University of Iowa Studies, Child Welfare, *5* (3): 1932.
177. Chase, W. L.: The school's responsibility to the home and the child in sex education. J. Social Hyg. *25:* 321–329, 1939.
178. Chase, W. P.: Color vision in infants. J. Exper. Psychol. *20:* 203–222, 1937.
179. Chenoweth, L. B., and T. K. Selkirk: School Health Problems. 4th ed. New York, Appleton-Century-Crofts, Inc., 1953.
180. Chesser, E., and Z. Dawe: The Practice of Sex Education. A Plain Guide for Parents and Teachers. London, Hutchinson, 1946.

181. Child Development Abstracts and Bibliography. Child Development Publications of The Society for Research in Child Development, Inc. 1341 Euclid, University of Illinois, Champaign, Illinois.

182. Children's Center for Infants and Preschool Children. Second Annual Report, The Judge Baker Foundation, Boston, 1944.

183. Chow, B. F.: Sequelae to the administration of vitamin B_{12} to humans. J. Nutrition 43: 323–343, 1951.

184. Christie, A.: Prevalence and distribution of ossification centers in the newborn infant. Am. J. Dis. Child. 77: 355–361, 1949.

185. Ciocco, A., et al.: Child health and selective service physical standards. Pub. Health Rep. 56: 2365–2375, 1941.

186. Clark, C. C.: Sound Motion Pictures as an Aid in Classroom Teaching. Unpublished doctor's thesis, New York University, 1932.

187. Cleghorn, R. A.: Endocrine Influence on Personality and Behavior. In the Biology of Mental Health and Disease. The Twenty-Seventh Annual Conference of the Milbank Memorial Fund. New York, Paul B. Hoeber, Inc., 1952.

188. Clemmons, A. M., and H. Williams: Motivating adolescents to optimum growth with the Wetzel Grid. J. Home Econ. 44: 192–194, 1954.

189. Cohen, F. J.: Children In Trouble: An Experiment in Institutional Child Care. New York, W. W. Norton & Co., 1952.

190. Colby, M. G., and J. B. Robertson: Genetic studies in abstraction. J. Comp. Psychol. 33: 385–401, 1942.

191. Cole, L.: Psychology of Adolescence. 4th ed. New York, Farrar & Rinehart, 1954.

192. Collins, L. B., and V. S. Blanchard: A Modern Physical Education for Boys and Girls. New York, A. S. Barnes & Co., 1940.

193. Committee of Seven: Teaching of Linear Measure, Square Measure, and Time: Results of Experiments and Recommendations for Curricular Placement. Winnetka, Ill., Winnetka Educational Press, 1938.

194. Conard, E. N.: The growth of manuscript writing. Childhood Educ. 11: 170–174, 1935.

195. Cook, D., and S. Rahbek: Educational Film Catalogue. New York, H. W. Wilson Co., 1939 and ensuing years.

196. Cook, L.: Community Backgrounds of Education. New York, McGraw-Hill Book Co., 1938.

197. Cooley, H.: Vision in Television: The Origins and Potentialities of Educational Television. New York, Channel Press, 1952.

198. Coon, C. M.: Family food consumption studies. Pub. Health Rep. 67: 788–796, 1952.

199. Cooperative Study of Secondary School Standards: Evaluative Criteria, Washington, D. C., 1940.

200. Cooperman, N. R.: The relationship of adolescent menstruation to body temperature and sterility. Am. J. Obst. & Gynec. 57: 701–710, 1949.

201. Cornelius, E. T., Jr.: Language Teaching. New York, Thomas Y. Crowell & Co., 1954.

202. Corner, G. W.: Attaining Manhood: A Doctor Talks to Boys about Sex. Rev. ed. New York, Harper & Bros., 1952.

203. Corner, G. W.: Attaining Womanhood: A Doctor Talks to Girls about Sex. Rev. ed. New York, Harper & Bros., 1952.

204. Cox, G. J.: Fluorine and Dental Caries. In a Survey of the Literature of Dental Caries. Food and Nutrition Board, National Research Council Publ. 225. Washington, D. C., National Academy of Sciences, National Research Council, 1952.

205. Cox, G. J.: Oral Environment. In A Survey of the Literature of Dental Caries. Food and Nutrition Board, National Research Council Publ. 225. Washington, D. C., National Academy of Sciences, National Research Council, 1952.

206. Cozens, F. W., H. S. Cubberly, and N. P. Neilson: Achievement Scales in Physical Education Activities for Secondary School Girls and College Women. New York, A. S. Barnes & Co., 1937.

207. Cronbach, L. J.: Educational Psychology. New York, Harcourt, Brace & Co., 1954.

208. Cruickshank, W. M., and J. E. Dolphin: The emotional needs of crippled and non-crippled children. J. Exceptl. Child. 16: 33–40, 1949.

209. Cruze, W. W.: Adolescent Psychology and Development. New York, Ronald Press, 1953.

210. Cummings, W. D., and B. Fagin: Principles of Educational Psychology. New York, Ronald Press, 1954.

211. Curtis, E. A., and C. L. Nemzek: The relation of certain unsettled home conditions to academic success of high school pupils. J. Social Psychol. 9: 419–435, 1938.

212. Cutts, N. E., and N. Moseley: Better Home Discipline. New York, Appleton-Century-Crofts, 1952.

213. Daum, K., et al.: Effect of various types of breakfast on physiologic response. J. Am. Dietet. A. 26: 503–509, 1950.

214. Davenport, C. B.: The growth of the human foot. Am. J. Phys. Anthropol. 17: 167–211, 1932.

215. Davis, A., and J. Dollard: Children of Bondage: The Personal Development of Negro Youth in the Urban South. Washington, D. C., American Council on Education, 1940.

216. Davis, C. M.: Feeding After the First Year. In I. McQuarrie (editor): Brennemann's Practice of Pediatrics. Vol. I. Hagerstown, Md., W. F. Prior Co., Inc., 1948.

217. Davis, C. M.: Self-selection of diet by newly weaned infants. Am. J. Dis. Child. *36:* 651–679, 1928.

218. Davis, E. A.: Accuracy vs. error as a criterion in children's speech. J. Educ. Psychol. *30:* 365–371, 1939.

219. Davis, E. A.: The Development of Linguistic Skills in Twins, Singletons with Siblings, and Only Children from Five to Ten Years. University of Minnesota Institute for Child Welfare Monogr. 14. Minneapolis, University of Minnesota Press, 1937.

220. Davis, K. B.: Factors in the Sex Life of Twenty-two Hundred Women. New York, Harper & Bros., 1929.

221. Davis, R. A., A. M. Vance, and H. Taylor: The teaching problems of 1,075 public school teachers. J. Exper. Psychol. *9:* 41–60, 1940.

222. Davis, W. A., and R. J. Havighurst: Father of the Man. Boston, Houghton Mifflin Co., 1947.

223. Dawe, H. C.: An analysis of two hundred quarrels of preschool children. Child Development *5:* 139–157, 1934.

224. Day, R. and M. S. Haines: Intelligence quotient of children recovered from erythroblastosis fetalis since the introduction of exchange transfusion. Pediatrics *13:* 333–338, 1954.

225. Dean, H. T., et al.: Studies on mass control of dental caries through fluoridation of the public water supply. Pub. Health Rep. *65:* 1403–1408, 1950.

226. Dearborne, E., and J. Rothney: Predicting the Child's Development. Cambridge, Mass., Science-Arts Publishers, 1941.

227. Dearborne, E., et al.: Data on the Growth of Public School Children. Monogr. III (1). Washington, D. C., Society for Research on Child Development, National Research Council, 1938.

228. de Castro, J.: The Geography of Hunger. Boston, Little, Brown & Co., 1952.

229. Deese, J.: The Psychology of Learning. New York, McGraw-Hill Book Co., 1952.

230. De Haas, J. H., and J. H. Posthuma: Nederlandsche kinderen in Japansche interneerings kampen op Java. Nederl. tijdschr. v. geneesk. *90:* 1530–1541, 1946.

231. de Jongh, T. W., E. H. Cluver, and E. Jokl: The principle of physical performance grids. Manpower *I:* 10–38, 1942.

232. Dennis, W.: Infant development under conditions of restricted practice and of minimum social stimulation. Genet. Psychol. Monogr. *23:* 143–189,1941.

233. Dennis, W.: Infant reaction to restraint: An evaluation of Watson's theory. Tr. New York Acad. Sc. *2:* 202–218, 1940.

234. Dennis, W.: Laterality of function in early infancy under controlled environmental conditions. Child Development *6:* 242–252, 1935.

235. Dennis, W. (editor): Readings in Child Psychology. New York, Prentice-Hall, Inc., 1951.

236. Department of Nutrition, Harvard School of Public Health: Goals—for Nutrition Education for Elementary and Secondary Schools. New York, The Nutritional Foundation, Inc., 1947.

237. Despert, J. L.: A method for study of personality reactions in preschool age children by means of the analysis of their play. Am. J. Psychol. *9:* 17–29, 1940.

238. Despert, J. L.: Play Analysis in Research and Therapy. In Lewis, et al.: Modern Trends in Child Psychiatry. New York, International Universities Press, 1945.

239. Despert, J. L.: Preliminary Report on Children's Reactions to the War, Including a Survey of the Literature. New York, Josiah Macy, Jr. Foundation, 1942.

240. Despert, J. L.: Sleep in preschool children: Preliminary study. Nerv. Child *8:* 8–27, 1949.

241. Deutsch, A.: Our Rejected Children. Boston, Little, Brown & Co., 1950.

242. Dewey, R., and W. J. Humber: The Development of Human Behavior. New York, The Macmillan Co., 1951.

243. Dillon, M. S.: A Study of Preschool Children. (Unpublished.) Reported in Murphy, et al.: Experimental Social Psychology. New York, Harper & Bros., 1937, p. 426.

244. Dimock, H. S.: A research in adolescence. I: Pubescence and physical growth. Child Development *6:* 176–195, 1935.

245. Dimock, H. S.: Rediscovering the Adolescent. New York, Association Press, 1937.

246. Disher, D. R.: The reactions of newborn infants to chemical stimuli administered nasally. Ohio State University Studies, Contributions to Education *12:* 1–53, 1934.

247. Dockeray, F. C., and C. Rice: Responses of Newborn Infants to Pain Stimulation. Ohio State University Studies, Contrib. Psychol. *12:* 82–93, 1934.

248. Doll, E. A.: The Feeble-Minded Child. In Carmichael, L., et al.: Manual of Child Psychology. New York, John Wiley & Sons, Inc., 1946.

249. Doll, E. A.: Psychological Moments in Reading. Bull. No. 15, Clinical Reading Association of State Teachers' College, Glassboro, N. J., 1945.

250. Dollard, J. L., et al.: Frustration and Aggression. New Haven, Conn., Yale University Press, 1939.

251. Dorfman, R. I.: Biochemistry of Androgens. In Pincus, G., and Thimann, K. V.: The Hormones: Physiology, Chemistry and Applications, Vol. 1. New York, Academic Press, 1948.

252. Downes, J.: Social and environmental factors in illness. Milbank Mem. Fund Quart. *26:* 366–385, 1948.

253. Draper, G., C. W. Dupertuis and J. L. Caugey: Human Constitution in Clinical Medicine. New York, Paul B. Hoeber, Inc., 1944.

254. Dreizen, S., et al.: The effect of milk supplements on the growth of children with nutritive failure. I: Height and weight changes. Growth *14:* 189–211, 1950.

255. Driscoll, G. P.: The Developmental Status of the Preschool Child as a Prognosis of Future Development. Child Devel. Monogr. 13. New York, Teachers College, Columbia University, 1933.

256. Dudycha, G. J. and M. M. Dudycha: Adolescents' memories of preschool experiences. J. Genet. Psychol. *42:* 468–480, 1933.

257. Dudycha, G. J. and M. M. Dudycha: Childhood memories: A review of the literature. Psychol. Bull. *38:* 668–682, 1941.

258. Dunbar, H. F.: A Survey of the Literature on Psychosomatic Interrelationships, 1910–1953. New York, Columbia University Press, 1954.

259. Duncan, G. G.: Diseases of Metabolism. Philadelphia, W. B. Saunders Co., 1952.

260. Dunham, E. C.: Premature Infant: a manual for physicians. Children's Bureau Publ. No. 325. Washington, D. C., Federal Security Agency, 1948.

261. Dunham, E. C., and H. Thoms: Effects of severe rickets in early childhood on skeletal development in adolescence. Am. J. Dis. Child. *69:* 339–345, 1945.

262. Dunham, F.: Effects of television on school achievement of children. School Life *34:* 88–89, 514, 1952.

263. Dupertuis, C. W., and N. B. Michael: Comparison of growth in height and weight between ectomorphic and mesomorphic boys. Child Development *24:* 203–214, 1953.

264. Durost, W. N.: The development of a battery of objective group tests of manual laterality. Genet. Psychol. Monogr. *16:* 225–335, 1934.

265. Durrell, D. D.: Improvement of Basic Reading Abilities. Yonkers-on-Hudson, N. Y., World Book Co., 1940.

266. Edelston, H.: The Earliest Stages of Delinquency. Edinburgh, E. S. Livingstone, Ltd., 1952.

267. Edwards, N. E., and W. J. Tamblyn: The fatigue syndrome in school children. Canad. Pub. Health J. *32:* 518–523, 1941.

268. Effect of added thiamine on growth, vision and learning ability of children. Nutrition Rev. *6:* 174–175, 1948.

269. Effect of glutamic acid on intelligence. Nutrition Rev. *11:* 201–204, 1953.

270. Ehpron, B. K.: Emotional Difficulties in Reading. New York, Julian Press, 1953.

271. Eisenberg, A. L.: Children and Radio Programs: A Study of More Than 3000 Children in the New York Metropolitan Area. New York, Columbia University Press, 1936.

272. Eissler, R. S., et al.: The Psychoanalytic Study of the Child. Vol. VI. New York, International Universities Press, 1951.

273. Eliot, M. M., and E. B. Jackson: Bone development of infants and young children in Puerto Rico. Am. J. Dis. Child. *46:* 1237–1262, 1933.

274. Elliott, G. L.: Understanding the Adolescent Girl. New York, Henry Holt & Co., 1930.

275. Elliott, G. L., and H. Bone: Sex Side of Youth. New York, Association Press, 1929.

276. Elliott, H. S. and G. L. Elliott: Solving Personal Problems. New York, Henry Holt & Co., 1936.

277. Ellis, R. W. B.: Age of puberty in the tropics. Brit. Med. J. *1:* 85–89, 1950.

278. Ellis, R. W. B.: Growth and health of Belgian children during and after the German occupation 1940–1944. Arch. Dis. Childhood *20:* 97–109, 1945.

279. Engle, E. T., and M. C. Shelesnyak: First menstruation and subsequent menstrual cycles of pubertal girls. Human Biol. *6:* 431–453, 1934.

280. Eppright, E. S.: Factors influencing food acceptance. J. Am. Dietet. A. *23:* 579–587, 1947.

281. Eppright, E. S., et al.: Nutritional status of Iowa children. Federation Proc. *11:* 442, 1952.

282. Erikson, H. E.: Childhood and Society. New York, W. W. Norton & Co., 1950.

283. Espenschade, A.: Motor Performance in Adolescence including the Study of Relationships with Measures of Physical Growth and Maturity. Monogr. V(1). Washington, D. C., Society for Research in Child Development, National Research Council, 1940.

284. Evans, M. E.: Illness history and physical growth. II: A comparative study of the rate of growth of preschool children of five health classes. Am. J. Dis. Child. *68:* 390–394, 1944.

285. Exner, W.: The Sexual Side of Marriage. 6th ed. New York, W. W. Norton & Co., 1932.

286. Fahs, S. L.: The beginnings of mysticism in children's growth. Relig. Educ. *45:* 139–147, 1950.

287. Federal Security Agency: Good Posture in the Little Child. Children's Bureau Publ. No. 219. Washington, D. C., Federal Security Agency, Social Security Administration, 1949.

288. Felder, J. G.: Some factors determining the nature and frequency of anger and fear outbreaks in preschool children. J. Juvenile Research *16:* 278–290, 1932.

289. Fiedler, M. F.: Deaf Children in a Hearing World: Their Education and Adjustment. New York, Ronald Press, 1952.

290. Fiedler, M. F.: A study of the socio-economic status of a group of public school children with hearing defects. Child Development *22:* 193–198, 1951.

291. Finn, S. B.: Prevalance of Dental Caries in a Survey of the Literature of Dental Caries. Food and Nutrition Board, National Research Council Publ. No. 225. Washington, D. C., National Academy of Sciences, National Research Council, 1952.

292. Fitzgerald, D. C.: Success-failure and T A T reactions of orthopedically handicapped and physically normal adolescents. Personality *1:* 67–83, 1951.
293. Fitzgerald, D. C.: The Psychodynamic Implications of the Levy Blor Responses of Orthopedically Handicapped Adolescents. Paper presented at the Regional Meeting, Committee on Research, American Psychiatric Association, Denver, 1951. Typescript.
294. Fitzgerald, J. A.: Situations in which children write letters in life outside the school. Educ. Meth. *12:* 223–231, 1933.
295. Fleming, L., and W. U. Snyder: Social and personal changes following non-directive group play therapy. Am. J. Orthophsychiat. *17:* 101–116, 1947.
296. Flory, C. D.: Osseous Development in the Hand as an Index of Skeletal Development. Monogr. I (3). Washington, D. C., Society for Research in Child Development, National Research Council, 1936.
297. Folger, S.: Prometheus or Frankenstein? J. Educ. Sociol. *24:* 154–166, 1950.
298. Folks, H.: Changes and Trends in Child Labor and Its Control. National Child Labor Commission Publ. 375. New York, June 1938.
299. Folsom, J. K.: The Family: Its Sociology and Social Psychiatry. Rev. ed. New York, John Wiley & Sons, 1942.
300. Folsom, J. K., et al.: Plan for Marriage. New York, Harper & Bros., 1938.
301. Food and Agricultural Organization, Committee on Calorie Requirements: Calorie Requirements. Food and Agricultural Organization Nutritional Studies No. 5, June 1950.
302. Forbush, W. B.: The Character Training of Children, I, II. New York, Funk & Wagnalls Co., 1919.
303. Ford, C. S., and F. A. Beach: Patterns of Sexual Behavior. New York, Paul B. Hoeber, Inc., 1951.
304. Ford, F. R.: Diseases of the Nervous System in Infancy, Childhood and Adolescence. Springfield, Ill., Charles C Thomas, 1937.
305. Ford, M.: The Application of the Rorschach Test to Young Children. Institute for Child Welfare Monogr. Ser. No. 23. Minneapolis, University of Minnesota Press, 1946.
306. Forest, Isle: Child Development. New York, McGraw-Hill Book Co., 1954.
307. Forlano, G., and H. C. Axelrod: The effect of repeated praise or blame on the performance of introverts and extroverts. J. Educ. Psychol. *28:* 92–100, 1937.
308. Fosdick, L. S.: The reduction of the incidence of dental caries. I. Immediate brushing with a neutral dentifrice. J. Am. Dent. A. *40:* 133–143, 1950.
309. Foster, J. C., and J. Anderson: Unpleasant dreams in childhood. Child Development *7:*77–84, 1936.
310. Foster, R., A. W. Brown, and I. P. Bronstein: The Mental Development of a Group of Dwarfish Children. Part I, Proc. Am. A. Ment. Deficiency (J. Psycho-Asthenics, *44,* June 1938-June 1939); Elwyn, Pa., The Association (E. A. Whitney, editor), 1939, pp. 143–153.
311. Foster, R. G.: Marriage and Family Relationships. 2nd ed. New York, The Macmillan Co., 1950.
312. Foster, R. G., and P. P. Wilson: Women after College. New York, Columbia University Press, 1942.
313. Francis, C. C.: The Human Pelvis. St. Louis, C. V. Mosby Co., 1952.
314. Francis, C. C.: Physical therapy and the growing child. Physiotherapy Rev. *17:* 133–135, 1937.
315. Frank, J.: The people in the comics. Prog. Educ. *19:* 28–31, 1942.
316. Frank, J. D.: Individual differences in certain aspects of the level of aspiration. Am. J. Psychol. *47:* 119–128, 1935.
317. Frank, L. K.: Adolescence and public health. Am. J. Pub. Health *31:* 1143–1150, 1941.
318. Frank, L. K.: Projective methods for the study of personality. J. Psychol. *8:* 389–413, 1939.
319. Frank, L. K.: The Rorschach method: forward. J. Consulting Psychol. vii: 1943.
320. Freed, E. X., and W. M. Cruickshank: The relation of cardiac disease to feelings of fear. J. Pediat. *43:* 483–488, 1953.
321. Freeman, F.: An evaluation of manuscript writing. Elem. School J. *36:* 446–455, 1936.
322. Freeman, F. N., and C. D. Flory: Growth in Intellectual Ability. In Barker, et al.: Child Behavior and Development. New York, McGraw-Hill Book Co., 1943.
323. Freud, A.: The Ego and the Mechanisms of Defense. New York, International Universities Press, 1946.
324. Freud, A.: The Role of Bodily Illness in the Mental Life of Children. In Vol. VII The Psychoanalytic Study of the Child. New York, International Universities Press, 1952.
325. Freud, A., and D. Burlingham: Infants without Families. New York, International Universities Press, 1944.
326. Freud, A., and D. Burlingham: War and Children. New York, Med. War Books, 1943.
327. Fried, R., and M. F. Mayer: Socio-emotional factors accounting for growth failure in children living in an institution. J. Pediat. *33:* 444–456, 1948.
328. Fuerst, J. S., and R. Kaplan: Chicago's Public Housing Program helps to save babies' lives. Child *15:* 178–181, 1951.
329. Furfey, P. H.: Case studies in developmental age. Am. J. Orthopsychiat. *1:* 292–297, 1931.
330. Furfey, P. H.: A note on the relative development and age scores of urban and rural boys. Child Development, *6:* 88–90, 1935.
331. Furfey, P. H.: A scale for measuring developmental age. Ment. Hyg. *14:* 129–136, 1930.

332. Furfey, P. H.: Social and Physical Factors in Developmental Age. Chicago, National Researcn Council, University of Chicago, 1933.
333. Gallagher, J. R.: Understanding Your Son's Adolescence. Boston, Little, Brown & Co., 1951.
334. Gamble, R. C.: Disease of the Eye. In I. McQuarrie (editor): Brennemann's Practice of Pediatrics. Hagerstown, Md., W. F. Prior Co., Inc., 1948.
335. Garn, S. M.: Individual and group deviations from "channel wise" grid progression in girls. Child Development 23: 193–206, 1952.
336. Garn, S. M., and C. F. A. Moorees: Stature, body-build and tooth emergence in Aleutian Aleut children. Child Development 22: 261–270, 1951.
337. Garrison, K. C.: Growth and Development. New York, Longmans, Green & Co., 1952.
338. Garrison, K. C.: Psychology of Adolescence. 4th ed. New York, Prentice-Hall, Inc., 1951.
339. Garvey, C. R.: The Activity of Young Children During Sleep. Minneapolis, University of Minnesota Press, 1939.
340. Gates, R. R.: Genetics and Normal Mental Differences. In The Biology of Mental Health and Disease: The Twenty-Seventh Annual Conference of the Milbank Memorial Fund. New York, Paul B. Hoeber, Inc., 1952.
341. Gerard, D. L., and L. Phillips: Relation of social attainment to psychological and adrenocortical reactions to stress. Arch. Neurol. & Psychiat. 69: 352–354, 1953.
342. Gerard, R. W. (editor): Food for Life. Chicago, University of Chicago Press, 1952.
343. Gerver, J. M., and R. Day: Intelligence quotient of children who have recovered from erythroblastosis fetalis. J. Pediat. 36: 342–345, 1950.
344. Gesell, A. L.: Infant Development: The Embryology of Early Human Behavior. New York, Harper & Bros., 1952.
345. Gesell, A. L., et al.: The First Five Years of Life. New York, Harper & Bros., 1940.
346. Gesell, A. L., and C. S. Amatruda: Developmental Diagnosis. 2nd ed. New York, Paul B. Hoeber, Inc., 1947.
347. Gesell, A. L., and F. Ilg: The Child from Five to Ten. New York, Harper & Bros., 1946.
348. Gesell, A. L., and F. Ilg: Infant and Child in the Culture of Today. New York, Harper & Bros., 1943.
349. Gesell, A. L., F. Ilg, and G. E. Bullis: Vision: Its Development in Infant and Child. New York, Paul B. Hoeber, Inc., 1949.
350. Giddings, G.: The effect of emotional disturbances on sleep. J. M. A. Georgia 25: 351–357, 1936.
351. Giddings, G.: Motility of school children during sleep. Am. J. Physiol. 127: 480–485, 1937.
352. Giddings, G.: Normal sleep pattern for children. J. A. M. A. 102: 525–529, 1934.
353. Giesecke, M.: The Genesis of Hand Preference. Monogr. 1 (5). Washington, D. C., Society for Research in Child Development, National Research Council, 1936.
354. Gilchrist, E. P.: The extent to which praise and reproof affect a pupil's work. School and Society 4:872–874, 1916.
355. Gillespie, R. D.: Psychological Effects of War on Citizen and Soldier. New York, W. W. Norton & Co., 1942.
356. Glasner, P. J., and F. D. Vermilyea: An investigation of the definition and use of the diagnosis, "Primary Stuttering." J. Speech and Hearing Disorders 18: 161–167, 1953.
357. Glover, K.: Youth: Leisure for Living. Office of Education, Department of the Interior Bull. 18, Washington, D. C.
358. Glueck, S. and E. Glueck: Delinquents in the Making: Paths to Prevention. New York, Harper & Bros., 1952.
359. Glueck, S. and E. Glueck: Unraveling Juvenile Delinquency. New York, The Commonwealth Fund, 1950.
360. Glutamic acid and mental function. Nutrition Rev. 9: 113–117, 1951.
361. Goddard, H. H.: What is intelligence? J. Social Psychol. 24: 51–69, 1946.
362. Goodenough, F. L.: Anger in Young Children. Minneapolis, University of Minnesota Press, 1931.
363. Goodenough, F. L.: Can We Influence Mental Growth? A Critique of Recent Experiment. Educ. Rec. Suppl. (Jan.) 1940.
364. Goodenough, F. L.: Children's Drawings. In C. Murchison (editor): Handbook of Child Psychology. Worcester, Mass., Clark University Press, 1931.
365. Goodenough, F. L.: The development of reactive process from early childhood to maturity. J. Exper. Psychol. 18: 431–450, 1935.
366. Goodenough, F. L., and K. M. Maurer: The Mental Growth of Children from Two to Fourteen Years: A Study of the Predictive Value of the Minnesota Preschool Scale. Minneapolis, University of Minnesota Press, 1942.
367. Gottenberg, W. L., and R. L. Neal: Radio at Home. The Phi Delta Kappan, May 1940.
368. Gould, H. N. and M. R. Gould: Age of first menstruation in mothers and daughters. J. A. M. A. 98: 1349–1352, 1932.
369. Gould, R.: An experimental analysis of "level of aspiration." Genet. Psychol. Monogr. 21: 115, 1939.
370. Grant, I. W.: Effect on eating habits of nutrition education in the 5th grade. Am. J. Dietet. A. 26: 413–416, 1950.
371. Gray, H.: Anatomy of the Human Body, edited by W. H. Lewis. Philadelphia, Lea & Febiger, 1942.

372. Gray, W.: Child Development and Reading. Growth and Development: The Basis for Educational Programs. New York, Progressive Education Association, 1936, pp. 185–188.
373. Greenberg, P. J.: Competition in children: an experimental study. Am. J. Psychol. *44:* 221–248, 1932.
374. Greene, H. A., A. N. Jorgensen, and J. R. Gerberich: Measurement and Evaluation in the Secondary School. New York, Longmans, Green & Co., 1954.
375. Gr´goire, A.: L'apprentissages du langage: Les deux premières années. Paris, Droz, 1937.
376. Greulich, W. W.: Some observations on the growth and development of adolescent children. J. Pediat. *19:* 302–314, 1941.
377. Greulich, W. W., H. G. Day, S. E. Lachman, J. B. Wolfe, and F. K. Shuttleworth: A Handbook of Methods for the Study of Adolescent Children. Monogr. III (2). Washington, D. C., Society for Research in Child Development, National Research Council, 1938.
378. Greulich, W. W., et al.: The physical growth and development of children who survived the atomic bombing of Hiroshima or Nagasaki. J. Pediat. *43:* 121–145, 1953.
379. Greulich, W. W., R. I. Dorfman, H. R. Catchpole, C. I. Solomon, and C. I. Culotta: Somatic and Endocrine Studies of Puberal and Adolescent Boys. Monogr. VII (3). Washington, D. C., Society for Research in Child Development, National Research Council, 1942.
380. Greulich, W. W., and I. Pyle: A Radiographic Atlas of Skeletal Development of Hand and Wrist. Stanford University, California, Stanford University Press, 1950.
381. Greulich, W. W., and H. Thoms: The growth and development of the pelvis of individual girls before, during and after puberty. Yale J. Biol. & Med. *17:* 91–97, 1944.
382. Gruenberg, S.: We the Parents. New York, Harper & Bros., 1939.
383. Guetzkow, H., and J. Brozek: Intellectual functions with restricted intakes of B complex vitamins. Am. J. Psychol. *59:* 358–381, 1946.
384. Gustafsson, B., cited in Relation of nutrition to dental caries. Nutrition Rev. *11:* 360, 1953.
385. Gutheim, F.: Houses for Family Living. New York, The Woman's Foundation, 1948.
386. Guthrie, E. R., and F. F. Powers: Educational Psychology. New York, Ronald Press, 1950.
387. Gutteridge, M.: A Study of Motor Achievements of Young Children. Arch. Psychol. 244, New York, 1939.
388. Habbe, S.: Personality Adjustment of Adolescent Boys with Impaired Hearing. New York, Teachers College, Columbia University, 1936.
389. Hacker, F. J., and E. A. Geleerd: Freedom and authority in adolescence. Am. J. Orthopsychiat. *15:*621–630, 1945.
390. Hadley, E. E., et al.: Military psychiatry. An ecological note. Psychiatry 7: 379–407, 1944.
391. Haefner, R. W.: The Typewriter in the Primary and Intermediate Grades. New York, The Macmillan Co., 1932.
392. Hall, F.: The protection of children from tuberculous adults. J. A. M. A. *113:* 1873–1875, 1939.
393. Hall, G. S.: Adolescence: Its Psychology and Its Relation to Physiology, Anthropology, Sociology, Sex, Crime, Religion and Education. New York, D. Appleton Co., 1904.
394. Ham, A. W.: Histology. 2nd ed. Philadelphia, J. B. Lippincott Co., 1953.
395. Hammond, W. H.: The determination of physical type in children. Human Biol. *25:* 65–80, 1953.
396. Hardy, M. C.: Frequent illness in childhood, physical growth and final size. Am. J. Phys. Anthropol. *23:* 241–260, 1938.
397. Harley, W.: A Study of Children's Drawings at the Merrill-Palmer School. Out of print.
398. Harmon, D. B.: Lighting and child development. Illuminating Engineering *40:* 199–228, 1945.
399. Harmon, D. B.: Light on growing children. Architectural Record *99:* 78–90, 1946.
400. Harmon, D. B.: Some preliminary observations on the developmental problems of 160,000 elementary school children. Woman's M. J. *49:* 75–82, 1942.
401. Harrell, R. F.: Effect of Added Thiamine on Learning. Teachers College Contrib. Educ. 877. New York, Columbia University, 1943.
402. Harrell, R. F.: Mental response to added thiamine. J. Nutrition *31:* 283–298, 1946.
403. Harris, H. S.: Bone Growth in Health and Disease. London, Oxford University Press, 1933.
404. Harris, J. A., C. M. Jackson, D. G. Patterson, and R. E. Scammon: Measurement of Man. Minneapolis, University of Minnesota Press, 1930.
405. Harrison, M. L.: Reading Readiness. Boston, Houghton Mifflin Co., 1936.
406. Harsh, C. M., and H. G. Schrickel: Personality Development and Assessment. New York, Ronald Press, 1950.
407. Hartley, R. E., L. K. Frank, and R. M. Goldenson: Understanding Children's Play. New York, Columbia University Press, 1952.
408. Hartman, C. G.: On the relative sterility of the adolescent organism. Science *74:* 226–227, 1931.
409. Hartshorne, H., M. May, and F. K. Shuttleworth: Studies in the Organization of Character. New York, The Macmillan Co., 1930.
410. Hathaway, W.: Education and Health of the Partially Seeing Child. Rev. ed. New York, Columbia University Press, 1954.
411. Hattwick, B. W.: The influence of nursery school attendance upon the behavior and personality of the preschool child. J. Exper. Educ. *5:* 180–190, 1936.
412. Havighurst, R. J.: Human Development and Education. New York, Longmans, Green & Co 1953.

413. Hayman, C. R., et al.: A conservation of hearing program for school children: Review of a 3-year experience in Hartford County, Maryland. Am. J. Pub. Health *41:* 1509–1520, 1951.

414. Healy, W., and A. Bronner: Delinquency as a Mode of Adjustment. In Kuhlen, R. G., and G. T. Thompson: Psychological Studies in Human Development. New York, Appleton-Century-Crofts, Inc., 1952.

415. Heck, A. O.: The Education of Exceptional Children. Rev. ed. New York, McGraw-Hill Book Co., 1940.

416. Heider, F. K., and G. M. Heider: A Comparison of the Sentence Structure of Deaf and Hearing Children. Psychol. Monogr. *52* (1): 42–103, 1953.

417. Hellersberg, E. F.: Food habits of adolescents in relation to family, training and present adjustment. Am. J. Orthopsychiat. *16:* 34–51, 1946.

418. Hendrickson, G.: Mental development during the preadolescent and adolescent periods. Rev. Educ. Research *20:* 351–360, 1950.

419. Herskovits, M. J.: Our Cultural and Psychological Reality. In Roher, J. H., and M. Sherif: Social Psychology at the Crossroads. New York, Harper & Bros., 1951.

420. Hertzer, H., and S. Weslitsky: Experimente über Erwartung und Erinnerung beim Kleinkind. Ztschr. f. Psychol. *118:* 128–141.

421. Herzfeld, E., and F. Prager: Verständnis für Scherz und Komik beim Kinde. Angew. Psychol. *34:* 353–417, 1931.

422. Hess, A. F.: Scurvy, Past and Present. Philadelphia, J. B. Lippincott Co., 1920.

423. Hess, J. H.: Experiences gained in a 30-year study of prematurely born infants. Pediatrics *11:* 425–434, 1953.

424. Hess, J. H., G. T. Mohr, and P. F. Bartelme: The Physical and Mental Growth of Prematurely Born Children. Chicago, University of Chicago Press, 1934.

425. Hicks, J. A.: The acquisition of motor skill in young children: A study of the effects of practice in throwing at a moving target. Child Development *1:* 90–105, 1930.

426. Hildreth, G. H.: Development and training of hand dominance: Developmental problems associated with handedness: Training of handedness. J. Genet. Psychol. *76:* 39–144, 1950.

427. Hildreth, G. H.: Educating Gifted Children at Hunter College Elementary School. New York, Harper & Bros., 1952.

428. Hirsch, N. D. M.: An experimental study upon three hundred school children over a six-year period. Genet. Psychol. Monogr. *7:* 487–549, 1930.

428a. Holland, D. F.: The disabling diseases of childhood. Pub. Health Rep. *55:* 135–155, 1940.

429. Hollingshead, A. B.: Elmtown's Youth. New York, John Wiley & Sons, 1949.

430. Hollingworth, L. S.: Gifted Children: Their Nature and Nurture. New York, The Macmillan Co., 1926.

431. Hollingworth, L. S.: Special Talents and Defects. New York, The Macmillan Co., 1925.

432. Holt, L. E. Jr.: Amino Acid Deficiencies in Man. Implications of Nutrition and Public Health in the Postwar Period. Proc. of Conference, Children's Fund of Michigan, Detroit, Michigan, 1944.

433. Holy, T. C.: A survey of the schools of Euclid, Ohio. Ohio State University Bureau of Education, Research Monogr. *22:* 137–138, 1936.

434. Honigmann, J. J.: Culture and Personality. New York, Harper & Bros., 1954.

435. Honzik, M. P., and H. E. Jones: Mental-physical relationships during the preschool period. J. Exper. Educ. *6:* 139–146, 1937.

436. Hoppes, W. C.: Considerations in the development of children's language. Elem. Eng. Rev. *11:*66–70, 1934.

437. Hoppes, W. C.: The Development of Written Expression among Children of Elementary School Grades. Doctor's thesis (Unpublished). University of Chicago, 1931.

438. Hoppes, W. C.: Some aspects of growth in written expression. Elem. Eng. Rev. *10:* 67–70, 121–123, 1933.

439. Horkheimer, M. F., and J. W. Diffor: Educators' Guide to Free Films. 6th rev. ed. Randolph, Wis., Educators' Progress Service, 1946.

440. Horney, K.: Neurosis and Human Growth. New York, W. W. Norton & Co., 1950.

441. Horney, K.: Self-Analysis. New York, W. W. Norton & Co., 1942.

442. Horrocks, J. R.: The Psychology of Adolescence: Behavior and Development. New York, Houghton Mifflin Co., 1951.

443. House, R. W.: A summary of 49 radiologists' opinions on the skeletal age limits of apparently normal 6-year-old children. Am. J. Roentgenol. *64:* 442–445, 1950.

444. Houssay, B. A., et al.: Human Physiology. New York, McGraw-Hill Book Co., 1951.

445. Howard, P. J., and C. H. Worrell: Premature infants in later life: Study of intelligence and personality of 22 premature infants at ages 8 to 19 years. Pediatrics *9:* 577–584, 1952.

446. Howells, W. W.: A factorial study of constitutional type. Am. J. Phys. Anthropol. *10*ns: 91–118, 1952.

447. Huang, L.: Abstraction of form and color in children as a function of the stimulus objects. J. Genet. Psychol. *66:* 59–62, 1945.

448. Huggett, A. J., and C. V. Millard: Growth and Learning in the Elementary School. Boston, D. C. Heath & Co., 1946.

449. Hunscher, H. A., F. C. Hummel, and I. G. Macy: Variability of metabolic response of different children to a given intake of calcium. Proc. Soc. Exper. Biol. & Med. *35:* 189–192, 1936.
450. Hurlock, E. B.: Adolescent Development. New York, McGraw-Hill Book Co., 1949.
451. Hurlock, E. B.: Child Development. 2nd ed. New York, McGraw-Hill Book Co., 1950.
452. Hurlock, E. B.: Developmental Psychology. New York, McGraw-Hill Book Co., 1953.
453. Hurme, V. O.: Standards of variation in the eruption of the first six permanent teeth. Child Development *19:* 213–231, 1948.
454. Hutchinson, R. C.: Meal habits and their effects on performance. Nutrition Abst. & Rev. *22:* 283–297, 1952.
455. Hyde, R. W., and L. V. Kingsley: Studies in medical sociology. I. The relation of mental disorders to the community socio-economic level. New England J. Med. *231:* 543–548, 1944.
456. Hymes, J. L. Jr.: Effective Home-School Relations. New York, Prentice-Hall, Inc., 1953.
457. Hymes, J. L. Jr.: A Pound of Prevention: How Teachers Can Meet the Emotional Needs of Young Children. Teachers' Service Committee on the Emotional Needs of Children, 105 E. 22nd St., New York. New York State Committee on Mental Hygiene, 1947.
458. Iliff, A., and V. A. Lee: Pulse rate, respiratory rate and body temperature of children between two months and eighteen years of age. Child Development *23:* 237–245, 1952.
459. Illingworth, R. S., et al.: Relation of birth weight to physical development in childhood. Lancet *2:* 598–602, 1949.
460. International Children's Center: Courrier. Château de Longchamp—Bois de Boulogne, Paris, Centre International De l' Enfance. Monthly magazine with annotated bibliography.
461. Institute of Child Welfare, University of California: Lists of 104 Child Development publications from this Center, Sept. 1940.
462. Irwin, O. C.: Infant responses to vertical movement. Child Development *3:* 167–169, 1932.
463. Isaacs, S.: The Nursery Years. New York, Vanguard Press, 1936.
464. Jack, L. M.: An Experimental Study of Ascendent Behavior in Preschool Children. University of Iowa Studies. Child Welfare *9* (3): 17–65, 1934.
464a. Jackson, F. W.: Manitoba Health Plan and Its Effect upon the Family. In The Family as the Unit of Health. New York, Milbank Memorial Fund, 1949.
465. Jackson, K. B.: In Spite of Illness. Survey Mid-monthly *77:* 110–112, 1941.
466. Jackson, R. L., and H. G. Kelly: Growth charts for use in pediatric practice. J. Pediat. *27:* 215–229, 1945.
467. Jackson, R. L., and H. G. Kelly: Growth of children with diabetes mellitus in relationship to level of control of the disease. J. Pediat. *29:* 316–328, 1946.
468. Jackson, R. L., et al.: Degenerative changes in young diabetic patients in relationship to level of control. Pediatrics *5:* 959–971, 1950.
469. Jacobsen, A. W., and N. T. Macklin: Hereditary sexual precocity; a report of a family with 27 affected members. Pediatrics *9:* 682–695, 1952.
470. James, W.: Principles of Psychology. New York, Henry Holt & Co., 1890.
471. Jeans, P. C., and G. Stearns: The effect of vitamin D on linear growth in infancy. II. The effect of intakes above 1800 U.S.P. units daily. J. Pediat. *13:* 730–740, 1938.
472. Jenkins, L. M.: A Comparative Study of Motor Achievements of Children at Five, Six, and Seven Years of Age. Teachers College Contrib. Educ. *414:* New York, Columbia University, 1930.
473. Jensen, C. A., and H. C. Hutchins: Youth: Community Survey. Washington, D. C., Department of the Interior, Bull. 18, pp. 80–97.
474. Jensen, K.: Differential Reactions to Taste and Temperature Stimuli in Newborn Infants. Genet. Psychol. Monogr. *12* (5 & 6): 1932.
475. Jersild, A. T.: Child Psychology. 3rd ed. New York, Prentice-Hall, Inc., 1954.
476. Jersild, A. T.: Constancy of certain behavior patterns in young children. Am. J. Psychol. *45:* 125–129, 1933.
477. Jersild, A. T.: Effects of Radio Programs on Children as Revealed by Interviews with Mothers. (Unpublished.) New York, Teachers College, Columbia University, 1938.
478. Jersild, A. T., et al.: Children's Dreams, Fears and Fancies. Child Development Monogr. 12. New York, Teachers College, Columbia University, 1933.
479. Jersild, A. T., F. V. Markey and C. L. Jersild: Children's Fears, Dreams, Wishes, Daydreams, Likes, Dislikes, Pleasant and Unpleasant Memories. Child Development Monogr. 12. New York, Teachers College, Columbia University, 1933.
480. Jersild, A. T., and F. V. Markey: Conflicts between Preschool Children. Child Development Monogr. 21. New York, Teachers College, Columbia University, 1935.
481. John, E.: A study of the effects of evacuation and air-raids on children of preschool age. Brit. J. Educ. Psychol. *11:* 173–182, 1941.
482. Johnson, H. M.: The Art of Block Building. New York, John Day Co., 1933.
483. Johnson, W. M.: The tired child. Hygeia *14:* 217–219, 1936.
484. Johnston, J. A.: Adolescence. In Nelson, W. E. (editor): Textbook of Pediatrics. 6th ed. Philadelphia, W. B. Saunders Co., 1954.
485. Johnston, J. A.: Factors influencing retention of nitrogen and calcium in period of growth. VI. The calcium and vitamin D requirements of the older child. Am. J. Dis. Child. *67:* 265–274, 1944.

486. Joint Committee on Child Development of the State of Michigan: Bibliography on Child Development. Department of Public Instruction, Lansing, Mich., 1940.
487. Joint Committee on Curriculum Aspects of Education for Home and Family Living of the Home Economics Department of the National Education Association and the Society for Curriculum Study: Family Living and Our Schools. New York, D. Appleton-Century Co., 1941.
488. Jokl, E., and E. H. Cluver: Physical fitness. J. A. M. A. *116:* 2383–2389, 1941.
489. Jokl, E., and T. W. de Jongh: Physical efficiency as a secondary sex characteristic. Manpower *1:* 17–29, 1943.
490. Jolliffe, N. et al.: Vitamin B₁₂ as a growth factor in Italian children on diets low in animal protein. In Current Research on Vitamins in Trophology, Proceedings of the Scientific Sessions of the Eighth Annual Meeting, The National Vitamin Foundation, Inc., New York, March 4, 1953.
491. Jones, H. E.: The conditioning of overt emotional responses. J. Educ. Psychol. *22:* 127–130, 1931.
492. Jones, H. E.: Development in Adolescence: Approaches to the Study of the Individual. New York, D. Appleton-Century Co., 1943.
493. Jones, H. E.: The Development of Physical Abilities. In the Forty-Third Yearbook of the National Society for Study of Education. Part I. Adolescence. Chicago, Department of Education, University of Chicago, 1944.
494. Jones, H. E.: Environmental Influence on Mental Development. In Carmichael, L. et al.: Manual of Child Psychology. New York, John Wiley & Sons, Inc., 1946.
495. Jones, H. E.: Motor Performance and Growth: A Developmental Study of Static Dynamometric Strength. University of California Publications in Child Development, Vol. I (1). Berkeley and Los Angeles, University of California Press, 1949.
496. Jones, H. E.: Physical ability as a factor in social adjustment in adolescence. J. Educ. Research *40:* 282–301, 1946.
497. Jones, H. E.: Principles and methods of the adolescent growth study. J. Consult. Psychol. *3:* 157–159, 1939.
498. Jones, H. E.: Procedures of the adolescent study. J. Consult. Psychol. *3:* 177–180, 1939.
499. Jones, H. E. and M. C. Jones: A study of fear. Childhood Educ. *5:* 136–143, 1928.
500. Jones, H. E., H. S. Conrad, and M. B. Blanchard: Environmental Handicap in Mental Test Performance. Berkeley, University of California Press, 1932.
501. Jones, M. C., and N. Bayley: Physical maturing among boys as related to behavior. J. Educ. Psychol. *41:* 129–148, 1950.
502. Jones, M. C., and B. S. Burks: Personality Development In Childhood. Monogr. I (4). Washington D. C., Society for Research in Child Development, National Research Council, 1936.
503. Jones, T. D.: The Development of Certain Motor Skills and Play Activities in Young Children. Child Development Monogr. 26. New York, Teachers College, Columbia University, 1939.
504. Jones, V.: Character Development in Children—An Objective Approach. In Carmichael, L., et al.: Manual of Child Psychology. New York, John Wiley & Sons, Inc., 1946.
505. Jonxis, J. H. P.: Nutritional status of Dutch children in war time. Nutrition Rev. *4:* 97–99, 1946.
506. Jordan, A. M.: Measurement in Education. New York, McGraw-Hill Book Co., 1953.
507. Josselyn, I. N.: Emotional implications of rheumatic heart disease in children. Am. J. Orthopsychiat. *19:* 87–100, 1949.
508. Josselyn, I. N.: Emotional Problems of Illness. Better Living Booklet. Chicago, Science Research Association, Inc., 1953.
509. Jung, M., et al.: Modern Marriage. New York, F. S. Crofts & Co., 1940.
510. Kallmann, F. J.: Genetic Aspect of Psychoses. In The Biology of Mental Health and Disease. The Twenty-Seventh Annual Conference of The Milbank Memorial Fund. New York, Paul B. Hoeber, Inc., 1952.
511. Kammerer, R. C.: An exploratory study of crippled children. Psychol. Rec. *4:* 47–100, 1940.
512. Kanner, L.: Child Psychiatry. 3rd ptg. Springfield, Ill., Charles C Thomas, 1942.
513. Kanner, L.: Play investigation and play treatment of children's behavior disorders. J. Pediat. *17:* 533–546, 1940.
514. Karger, P.: Über den Schlaf des Kindes. Abtr. a. d. Kinderk. u. Grenzgebiet, 1925, pp. 1–50.
515. Keeney, A. H.: Chronology of Ophthalmic Development: An Outline Summary of the Anatomical and Functional Development of the Visual Mechanism before and after Birth. Springfield, Ill., Charles C Thomas, 1951.
516. Keeton, R. W.: Nutrition and appetite training during illness. J. A. M. A. *151:* 253–260, 1953.
517. Keifer, F. A.: A study of the relation between mental and physical status of children in two counties in Illinois. Pub. Health Rep. *44:* 1743–1784, 1929.
518. Keliher, A. V.: Life and Growth. New York, Progressive Educ. Assoc. Pub., D. Appleton-Century Co., 1938.
519. Kempe, C. H.: The family as a reservoir of childhood infections. J. A. M. A. *151:* 1472–1474, 1953.
520. Kendall, H. O., F. P. Kendall, and D. A. Boynton: Posture and Pain. Baltimore, Williams & Wilkins Co., 1952.
521. Kenyon, J. H.: Healthy Babies Are Happy Babies. Rev. ed. Boston, Little, Brown & Co., 1949.
522. Kepler, H.: The Child and His Play: A Planning Guide to Parents and Teachers. New York, Funk & Wagnalls, 1952.

523. Kerridge, P.: Recent advances in knowledge concerning hearing and speech. Physiol. Rev. *18:* 59–85, 1938.
524. Ketcham, D.: One Hundred Thousand Days of Illness. Ann Arbor, Mich., Edwards Bros., 1939.
525. Keys, A., J. Brozek, A. Henschel, O. Mickelsen, and H. L. Taylor: The Biology of Human Starvation. Vols. I and II. Minneapolis, The University of Minnesota Press, 1950.
526. Kik, M. C. and R. R. Williams: The Nutritional Improvement of White Rice. Bulletin No. 112. Washington, D. C., National Research Council, National Academy of Sciences, 1945.
527. Kingsbury, D.: Feet for the future. Parents Magazine *21:* 34, 104–105, 1946.
528. Kingsley, H. L.: The Nature and Conditions of Learning. New York, Prentice-Hall, Inc., 1946.
529. Kinsey, A. C., et al.: Sexual Behavior in the Human Female. Philadelphia, W. B. Saunders Co., 1953.
530. Kinsey, A. C., et al.: Sexual Behavior in the Human Male. Philadelphia, W. B. Saunders Co., 1948.
531. Kirk, S. A., and G. O. Johnson: Educating the Retarded Child. Boston, Houghton Mifflin Co., 1951.
532. Klapper, Z. S., and H. Werner: Developmental deviations in brain-injured (cerebral palsied) members of pairs of identical twins. Quart. J. Child Behavior *2:* 288–313, 1950.
533. Klein, H.: Dental caries experience in relocated children exposed to water containing fluorine; incidence of new caries after two years of exposure among previously caries-free permanent teeth. Pub. Health Rep. *60:* 1462–1467, 1945.
534. Klein, H.: Dental caries (D. M. F.) experience in relocated children exposed to water containing fluorine. J. Am. Dent. A. *33:* 1136–1141, 1946.
535. Klein, H.: The family and dental disease. Dental disease (D. M. F.) experience in parents and offspring. J. Am. Dent. A. *33:* 735–743, 1946.
536. Klein, H.: The family and dental disease. Caries experience among parents and offspring exposed to drinking water containing fluoride. Pub. Health Rep. *62:* 1247–1253, 1947.
537. Klein, H., and C. E. Palmer: Medical evaluation of nutritional status. Susceptibility to dental caries and family income. Milbank Mem. Fund Quart. *20:* 169–177, 1942.
538. Kleitman, N.: Biological rhythms and cycles. Physiol. Rev. *29:* 1–30, 1949.
539. Kleitman, N.: Mental hygiene of sleep in children. Nerv. Child *8:* 63–66, 1949.
540. Kleitman, N.: Sleep and Wakefulness. Chicago, University of Chicago Press, 1939.
541. Klinkenberg, E., and B. G. Bibby: The effect of topical applications of fluoride on dental caries in young adults. J. Dent. Research *29:* 4–7, 1950.
542. Knutson, J. W.: An evaluation of the effectiveness as a caries control measure of the topical application of solutions of fluorides. J. Dent. Research *27:* 340–357, 1948.
543. Knutson, J. W., and G. C. Scholz: The effect of topically applied fluorides on dental caries experience. VII. Consolidated report of findings for four study groups, showing reduction in new decay by individual tooth and by tooth surface, and frequency distribution of newly decayed teeth in treated and untreated mouth halves. Pub. Health Rep. *64:* 1403–1410, 1949.
544. Koch, H. L.: An analysis of certain forms of so-called "nervous habits" in young children. J. Genet. Psychol. *46:* 39–170, 1935.
545. Koenig, H.: What happens to prematures. Am. J. Pub. Health *40:* 803–807, 1950.
546. Koshuk, R. P.: Social Influences Affecting the Behavior of Young Children. Monogr. VI (2). Washington, D. C., Society for Research in Child Development, National Research Council, 1941.
547. Kramer, D., and M. Karr: Teen-Age Gangs. New York, Henry Holt & Co., 1953.
548. Kraus, H., and R. P. Hirschland: Muscular fitness and orthopedic disability. New York State J. Med. *54:* 212–215, 1954.
549. Krogman, W. M.: The growth of the "whole child" in relation to dental problems. Oral Surg. *3:* 427–445, 1950.
550. Krogman, W. M.: Handbook of Measurement and Interpretation of Height and Weight in the Growing Child. Monogr. 13 (3). Evanston, Ill., Society for Research in Child Development, Inc., 1950.
551. Krogman, W. M.: The skeleton talks. Scientific American *159:* 61–64, 1938.
552. Kronfeld, R.: Dental Histology and Comparative Dental Anatomy. Philadelphia, Lea & Febiger, 1937.
553. Kronfeld, R, and I. Schour: Neonatal dental hypoplasia. J. Am. Dent. A. *26:* 18–32, 1939.
554. Kuhlen, R. G.: The Psychology of Adolescent Development. New York, Harper & Bros., 1952.
555. Laing, A.: The sense of humor in childhood and adolescence. Brit. J. Educ. Psychol. *9:* 201, 1939.
556. Laird, D. A. and W. J. Breen: Sex and age alteration in taste preference. J. Am. Dietet. A. *15:* 549–550, 1939.
557. Lander, B.: Toward an Understanding of Juvenile Delinquency. New York, Columbia University Press, 1954.
558. Landis, C., et al.: Sex in Development. New York, Paul B. Hoeber, Inc., 1940.
559. Landis, J. T., and M. G. Landis: Building a Successful Marriage. 2nd ed. New York, Prentice-Hall, Inc., 1953.
560. Landis, J. T. and M. G. Landis: Personal Adjustment: Marriage and Family Living (A high school text). New York, Prentice-Hall, Inc., 1950.

561. Landis, P. H.: Adolescence and Youth: The Process of Maturing. 2nd ed. New York, McGraw-Hill Book Co., 1952.
562. Langdon, G. and I. W. Stout: The Discipline of Well-Adjusted Children. New York, John Day Co., Inc., 1952.
563. Langford, W. S.: Physical illness and convalescence: Their meaning to the child. J. Pediat. *33:* 242–250, 1948.
564. Langford, W. S., et al.: Pilot study of childhood accidents: Preliminary report. Pediatrics *11:* 405–415, 1953.
565. Lansing, A. I. (editor): Problems of Aging. 3rd ed. Baltimore, Williams & Wilkins Co., 1952.
566. Lasker, G.: The effect of partial starvation on somatotype: An analysis of material from the Minnesota starvation experiment. Am. J. Phys. Anthropol. *5:* 322–333, 1947.
567. Lazar, M.: Reading Interests, Activities, and Opportunities of Bright, Average, and Dull Children. Teachers College Contrib. Educ. 707. New York, Columbia University, 1937.
568. Lazarsfeld, P. F. and F. N. Stanton (editors): Radio Research (1942–1943). New York, Duell, Sloan and Pearce, 1944.
569. Leamy, C. M.: The nutrition of mothers and children. J. Home Econ. *45:* 25–28, 1953.
570. Lease, E. J.: Corn meal enrichment. J. Am. Dietet. A. *29:* 866–872, 1953.
571. Lee, J. M., and D. M. Lee: The Child and His Curriculum. New York, D. Appleton-Century Co., 1940.
572. Lehman, H. C., and P. A. Witty: A study of play in relation to pubescence. J. Social Psychol. *1:* 510–513, 1930.
573. Leighton, G., and P. L. McKinlay: Milk Consumption and the Growth of School Children. London, His Majesty's Printing Office, 1930.
574. Lennox, W. G.: The heredity of epilepsy as told by relatives and twins. J. A. M. A. *146:* 529–536, 1951.
575. Lennox, W. G.: The social and emotional problems of the epileptic child and his family. J. Pediat. *44:* 591–601, 1954.
576. Lennox, W. G., E. L. Gibbs, and F. A. Gibbs: The brain wave pattern, hereditary trait; evidence from 74 normal pairs of twins. J. Hered. *36:* 233–243, 1945.
577. Lerner, E.: The Problem of Perspective in Moral Reasoning (Unpublished). Reported by Murphy, G., et al. in Experimental Social Psychology. New York, Harper & Bros., 1937, pp. 546ff.
578. Lerner, E., and L. Murphy: Methods for the Study of Personality in Young Children. Monogr. VI (4). Washington, D. C., Society for Research in Child Development, National Research Council, 1941.
579. Leuba, C. J.: An experimental study of rivalry among young children. J. Comp. Psychol. *16:* 367–378, 1933.
580. Levenson, W. B. and E. Stasheff: Teaching Through Radio and Television. New York, Rinehart & Co., 1952.
581. Leverton, R. M. and M. C. Coggs: Food choices of Nebraska children. J. Home Econ. *43:* 176–178, 1951.
582. Leverton, R. M. and M. R. Gram: Nitrogen excretion of women related to the distribution of animal protein in daily meals. J. Nutrition *39:* 57–65, 1949.
583. Leverton, R. M., M. R. Gram and M. Chaloupka: Effect of the time factor and caloric level on nitrogen utilization of young women. J. Nutrition *44:* 537–545, 1951.
584. Levine, E. S.: An Investigation into the Personality of Normal Deaf Adolescent Girls. Ph.D. thesis, New York University, University Microfilms, 1948.
585. Levy, D. M.: Maternal Overprotection. In Lewis and Pacella: Modern Trends in Child Psychiatry. New York, International Universities Press, 1945.
586. Levy, D. M.: Studies in Sibling Rivalry. Research Monogr. Am. Orthopsychiat. Assoc., No. 2, 1937.
587. Lewin, K.: A Dynamic Theory of Personality. New York, McGraw-Hill Book Co., 1935.
588. Lewin, K., et al.: Patterns of aggressive behavior in experimentally created social climates. J. Social Psychol. *10:* 271–299, 1939.
589. Lewin, K., S. K. Escalona and R. S. Lippitt: Studies in Topological and Vector Psychology. University of Iowa Studies, Child Welfare, 1940.
590. Lewis, S. J.: The proper time to start orthodontic treatment. J. Am. Dent. A. *20:* 693–707, 1933.
591. Lewis, S. J., and I. G. Lehman: Observations on growth changes of the teeth and dental arches. Dental Cosmos *71:* 5, 1929.
592. Ligon, E. M.: Their Future Is Now. New York, The Macmillan Co., 1939.
593. Linde, J. F., et al.: Causes of absenteeism in New Haven schools; follow-up after 21 years. Pub. Health Rep. *65:* 1737–1744, 1950.
594. Lippitt, R. S.: The Analysis of Individual and Group Reactions to Three Different Types of "Social Climate." Ph.D. thesis, University of Iowa, 1940.
595. Lloyd, F.: Educating the Sub-Normal Child. New York, Philosophical Library, 1953.
596. Lockwood, E. A.: Activities in Nutrition Education for Kindergarten through Sixth Grade. Department of Nutrition, Harvard School of Public Health. Distributed by The Nutrition Foundation, Inc., New York, 1948.
597. Lockwood, E. A.: Activities in Nutrition Education. A Unit for High School Classes. Depart-

ment of Nutrition, Harvard School of Public Health. Distributed by The Nutrition Foundation, Inc., New York, 1950.

598. Lombard, O. M.: Breadth of bone and muscle by age and sex in childhood. Child Development *21:* 229–239, 1950.

599. Long, L., and L. Welch: Influence of levels of abstractness on reasoning ability. J. Psychol. *13:* 41–59, 1942.

600. Long, L., and L. Welch: Reasoning ability in young children. J. Psychol. *12:* 21–44, 1941.

601. Lowenfeld, V.: Creative and Mental Growth. New York, The Macmillan Co., 1952.

602. Luckiesh, M., and F. K. Moss: Light, Vision and Seeing. In O. Glasser (editor): Medical Physics. Chicago, The Year Book Publishers, 1944, pp. 672–684.

603. Lynd, R. S., and H. M. Lynd: Middletown. New York, Harcourt, Brace & Co., 1929.

604. MacCurdy, H. L.: A Text for Measuring the Physical Capacity of Secondary School Boys. The author, Yonkers, N. Y., 1933.

605. MacFarlane, J. W.: Interpersonal relationships within the family. Marriage and Family Living, *3:* 2, 1941.

606. MacFarlane, J. W.: A review of C. Zachry: Emotions and Conduct in Adolescence. Prog. Educ. *17:* 431, 1940.

607. MacFarland, M.: Relationships between Young Sisters as Revealed in Their Overt Responses. Child Development Monogr. 23. New York, Teachers College, Columbia University, 1938.

608. McCarthy, D.: Language Development in Children. In Carmichael et al.: Manual of Child Psychology. New York, John Wiley & Sons, Inc., 1946.

609. McCarthy, D.: The Language Development of the Preschool Child with Special Reference to Sentence Formation. University of Minnesota Institute of Child Welfare Monogr. Minneapolis, University of Minnesota Press, 1929.

610. McCarthy, D.: Organismic interpretations of infant vocalizations. Child Development *23:* 273–280, 1952.

611. McCloy, C. H.: Appraising Physical Status: Methods and Norms. Iowa City, University of Iowa, 1938.

612. McCloy, C. H.: The Measurement of Athletic Power. New York, A. S. Barnes & Co., 1932.

613. McGavin, A. P., et al.: The physical growth, the degree of intelligence, and the personal adjustment of a group of diabetic children. New England J. Med. *223:* 119–127, 1940.

614. McGill, V. J.: Emotions and Reason. Springfield, Ill., Charles C Thomas, 1954.

615. McGraw, M. B.: Maturation of Behavior. In Carmichael et al.: Manual of Child Psychology. New York, John Wiley & Sons, Inc., 1946.

616. McGraw, M. B.: The Neuro-Muscular Maturation of the Human Infant. New York, Columbia University Press, 1943.

617. McHose, E.: Family Life Education in School and Community. New York, Teachers College, Columbia University, 1952.

618. McKenzie, G.: Implications for Teachers and Counselors. The Forty-Third Yearbook of the National Society for the Study of Education. Part I. Adolescence. Chicago, Department of Education, University of Chicago, 1944.

619. Maccoby, E. E.: Television: its impact upon school children. Pub. Opinion Quart. *15:* 421–441, 1951.

620. Macy, I. G.: Nutritional and Chemical Growth in Childhood. Vol. I, Evaluation. Springfield, Ill., Charles C Thomas, 1942.

621. Macy, I. G., and H. A. Hunscher: Calories . . . a limiting factor in the growth of children. J. Nutrition *45:* 189–199, 1951.

622. Magnussen, G.: The sleep function and sleep disturbances. Ment. Hyg. *27:* 89–118, 1953.

623. Mahler, M. S.: Ego Psychology Applied to Behavior Problems. In Lewis et al.: Modern Trends in Child Psychiatry. New York, International Universities Press, 1945.

624. Malm, M. and O. G. Jamison: Adolescence. New York, McGraw-Hill Book Co., 1952.

625. Mann, A. W., S. Dreizen, and T. D. Spies: The determination of status and progress in children with nutritive failure. J. Pediat. *31:* 161–171, 1947.

626. Marche, J., and H. Gounelle: The relation of protein scarcity and modification of blood protein to tuberculosis among undernourished subjects. Milbank Mem. Fund Quart. *28:* 114–126, 1950.

627. Markey, F. V.: Imaginative Behavior of Preschool Children. Child Development Monogr. 18. New York, Teachers College, Columbia University, 1935.

628. Marsh, C. J.: The worries of the college woman. J. Social Psychol. *15:* 335–339, 1942.

629. Martin, K. L.: Handedness: A review of the literature on the history, development, and research of laterality preference. J. Educ. Research *45:* 527–533, 1954.

630. Martin, W. E. and C. B. Stendler: Child Development: The Process of Growing Up in Society. New York, Harcourt, Brace & Co., 1953.

631. Martin, W. E. and C. B. Stendler: Readings in Child Development. New York, Harcourt, Brace & Co., 1954.

632. Marx, H. L. (editor): Television and Radio in American Life. New York, H. W. Wilson Co., 1953.

633. Maslow, A. H.: Motivation and Personality. New York, Harper & Bros., 1954.

634. Massler, M., and T. Suher: Calculation of "normal" weight in children (by means of nomograms based on selected anthropometric measurements). Child Development 22: 75–94, 1951.

634a. Mayer, J.: Genetic, traumatic and environmental factors in the etiology of obesity. Physiol. Rev. 33: 472–508, 1953.

635. Mead, M.: Cultural context of nutritional patterns. Centennial Collected Papers presented at the Centennial Celebration, Washington, D. C., September 13–17, 1948, for the American Association for the Advancement of Science. Washington, D. C., 1950.

636. Mead, M.: Dietary patterns and food habits. J. Am. Dietet. A. 19: 1–5, 1943.

637. Mead, M.: Sex and Temperament in Three Primitive Societies. New York, W. Morrow & Co., 1935.

638. Meagher, J. F.: A Study of Masturbation and Its Reputed Sequelae. Baltimore, Williams & Wilkins Co., 1924.

639. Mecham, M. E.: The Relationship of Affectivity to Various Measures of Growth in Children. Microfilm. Ann Arbor, University of Michigan Microfilms, 1941.

640. Meek, L. H.: Influences on emotional growth inherent in the teacher's function. III. Preparation of teachers for emotional guidance of children. Am. J. Orthopsychiat. 9: 494–503, 1939.

641. Meek, L. H., et al.: The Personal-Social Development of Boys and Girls. New York, Progressive Education Association, 1940.

642. Mellanby, Sir Edward: A Story of Nutritional Research. The Abraham Flexner Lecture Series Number Nine. Baltimore, Williams & Wilkins Co., 1950.

643. Mellanby, M. H., and H. Coumoulos: Reported in Wartime dental caries incidence. Nutrition Rev. 4: 142–143, 1946.

644. Meloan, E.: Excessive appetite in behavior problems in maladjusted children. J. Pediat. 19: 632–637, 1941.

645. Members of the Department of Experimental Medicine, Cambridge, and associated workers: Studies of Under-nutrition, Wuppertal 1946–1949. Medical Research Council Special Report Series No. 275. London, His Majesty's Stationery Office, 1951.

646. Meltzer, H.: The present status of experimental studies on the relationships of feeling to memory. Psychol. Rev. 37: 124–139, 1930.

647. Mental response to thiamine supplement. Nutrition Rev. 4: 343–345, 1946.

648. Meredith, H. V.: Body size in infancy and childhood: A comparative study of data from Okinawa, France, South Africa and North America. Child Development 19: 179–195, 1948.

649. Meredith, H. V.: Height and weight of private school children in three successive decades. School and Soc. 70: 72–73, 1949.

650. Meredith, H. V.: Human foot length from embryo to adult. Human Biol. 16: 207–282, 1944.

651. Meredith, H. V.: North American Negro infant: Size at birth and during the first post-natal year. Human Biol. 24: 290–308, 1952.

652. Meredith, H. V.: A "Physical Growth Record" for use in elementary and high schools. Am. J. Pub. Health 39: 878–885, 1949.

653. Meredith, H. V.: Relation between socio-economic status and body size in boys seven to ten years of age. Am. J. Dis. Child. 82: 702–709, 1951.

654. Meredith, H. V.: The Rhythm of Physical Growth. University of Iowa Studies in Child Welfare 11 (3): 1935.

655. Meredith, H. V.: Toward a working concept of physical growth. Am. J. Orthodontics 3: 440–458, 1945.

656. Meredith, H. V., and S. S. Culp: Body form in childhood: Ratios quantitatively describing four slender-to-stocky continua on boys four to eight years of age. Child Development 22: 4–14, 1951.

657. Meredith, H. V., and E. M. Meredith: The body size and form of present-day white elementary children residing in west-central Oregon. Child Development 24: 83–102, 1953.

658. Meredith, H. V., and P. R. Sherbina: Body form in childhood: Ratios quantitatively describing three slender-to-stocky continua on girls four to eight years of age. Child Development 22: 276–283, 1951.

659. Merrill, F. E., and H. W. Eldredge: Culture and Society. New York, Prentice-Hall, Inc., 1952.

660. Merry, F. K., and R. V. Merry: The First Two Decades of Life. New York, Harper & Bros., 1950.

661. Metheny, E.: Body Dynamics. New York, McGraw-Hill Book Co., 1952.

662. Michelson, N.: Studies in the physical development of Negroes. VII. Environmental trends among the American Negro. Human Biol. 17: 207–228, 1945.

663. Michelson, N.: Studies in the physical development of Negroes. IV. Onset of puberty. Am. J. Phys. Anthropol. 2: 151–166, 1944.

664. Midcentury White House Conference on Children and Youth: Chart Book. Raleigh, N. C., Health Publications Institute, 1951.

665. Midcentury White House Conference on Children and Youth: Fact Finding Report. Raleigh, N. C., Health Publications Institute, 1951.

666. Midcentury White House Conference on Children and Youth: Proceedings. Raleigh, N. C., Health Publications Institute, 1951.

667. Miles, C. C.: Gifted Children. In Carmichael et al.: Manual of Child Psychology. New York, John Wiley & Sons, Inc., 1946.

668. Millard, C. V.: Child Growth and Development in the Elementary School Years. Boston, D. C. Heath & Co., 1951.

669. Miller, E., and G. B. Rosenfeld: The psychologic evaluation of children with cerebral palsy and its implications in treatment. Preliminary report. J. Pediat. *41:* 613–621, 1952.

670. Mills, C. A.: Geographic and time variations in body growth and age at menarche. Human Biol. *9:* 43–56, 1937.

671. Milman, D. H.: Group therapy with parents. An approach to the rehabilitation of physically disabled children. J. Pediat. *41:* 113–116, 1952.

672. Ministry of Information (on Behalf of The Board of Education; Published by His Majesty's Stationery Office, London, 1941): The Schools in Wartime. 60 Rockefeller Plaza, New York, The British Library of Information.

673. Mitchell, H. H., and M. Edman: Nutrition and Climatic Stress with Particular Reference to Man. Springfield, Ill., Charles C Thomas, 1951.

674. Moncur, J. P.: Parental domination in stuttering. J. Speech and Hearing Disorders *17:* 155–165, 1952.

675. Montagu, M. F. A.: Constitutional and Prenatal Factors in Infant and Child Health. In Senn, M. J. E. (editor): Symposium on the Healthy Personality. New York, Josiah Macy, Jr. Foundation, 1950.

676. Moreno, J. L.: A Study of Groups of Infants in a Hospital. (Unpublished.) Reported in Murphy et al.: Experimental Social Psychology. Rev. ed. New York, Harper & Bros., 1937.

677. Moreno, J. L.: A Study of 600 Girls at the New York State Training School for Girls, Begun in 1932. (Unpublished.) Reported in Murphy et al.: Experimental Social Psychology. Rev. ed. New York, Harper & Bros., 1937, p. 309.

678. Moreno, J. L.: Who Shall Survive? A New Approach to the Problem of Human Interrelationships. New York, Nervous and Mental Disease Publishing Co., 1934.

679. Morgan, A. F., and M. M. Barry: Underweight children: Increased growth secured through the use of wheat germ. Am. J. Dis. Child., *39:* 935–947, 1930.

680. Moustakas, C. E.: Children in Play Therapy: A Key to Understanding Normal and Disturbed Emotions. New York, McGraw-Hill Book Co., 1953.

681. Mueller, H.: Enkele Waarnemingen Omtrent den Groei van het Beenderenstelsel en Omtrent de Geslachtsrijpheid van Javaansche Meisjes. Mededeel. Dienst Volksgezondheid Nederlandsch-Indie Jaargang *21:* 48–63, 1932.

682. Muesse, K.: Helping teachers to evaluate the efforts of individual children. Baltimore Bull. Educ. *16:* 124–127, 1939.

683. Munn, N. L.: Learning in Children. In Carmichael et al.: Manual of Child Psychology. New York, John Wiley & Sons, Inc., 1946.

684. Murphy, G., L. B. Murphy, and T. M. Newcomb: Experimental Social Psychology. Rev. ed., New York, Harper & Bros., 1937.

685. Murphy, L. B.: Social Behavior and Child Personality. New York, Columbia University Press, 1937.

686. Murray, H. A.: Explorations in Personality. New York, Oxford University Press, 1938.

687. Nathanson, I. T., L. E. Towne, and J. C. Aub: Normal excretions of sex hormones in childhood. Endocrinology *28:* 851–865, 1941.

688. National Academy of Sciences—National Research Council: Recommended Dietary Allowances. Rev. 1953, Publ. 302. Washington, D. C., National Academy of Sciences, National Research Council, 1953.

689. National Conferences on Family Life: Dynamics of Family Interaction. Report of Committee, edited by E. Duvall and R. Hill. Mimeographed, 1948.

690. National Research Council: Manual for the Study of Food Habits. Bull. III, Washington, D. C., National Research Council, National Academy of Science, 1945.

691. National Research Council: The Problem of Changing Food Habits. Bull. 108, Washington, D. C., National Research Council, National Academy of Science, 1943.

692. National Society for the Prevention of Blindness: Classroom Lighting. Pub. 498. 1790 Broadway, New York, National Society for Prevention of Blindness, 1950.

693. National Society for the Prevention of Blindness: An Eye Health Program for Schools. Pub. 141. 1790 Broadway, New York, National Society for Prevention of Blindness, 1951.

694. National Society for the Study of Education: The Thirty-Sixth Yearbook. Part I. Second Report on Reading. Bloomington, Ill., Public School Publishing Co., 1937.

695. National Society for the Study of Education: The Thirty-Eighth Yearbook. Child Development and the Curriculum. Bloomington, Ill., Public School Publishing Co., 1939.

695a. National Society for the Study of Education: The Thirty-Ninth Yearbook. Intelligence, Its Nature and Nurture. Part I. Comparative and Critical Exposition. Part II. Original Studies and Experiments. Bloomington, Ill., Public School Publishing Co., 1940.

696. National Society for the Study of Education. The Forty-Third Yearbook. Part I. Adolescence. Chicago, Department of Education, University of Chicago, 1944.

697. Neilson, N. P., and F. W. Cozens: Achievement Scales in Physical Education Activities. Sacramento, Calif., State Department of Education, 1934.

698. Nelson, B. (editor): Education of Exceptional Children. National Society for the Study of Education, Forty-Ninth Yearbook, Part II. Chicago, University of Chicago Press, 1950.

699. Nelson, W. E.: Diabetic children in non-diabetic camps. J. Pediat. *19:* 25–27, 1941.
700. Newman, H. H., F. Freeman, and K. Holzinger: Twins: A Study in Heredity and Environment. Chicago, University of Chicago Press, 1937.
701. Newman, R. W.: Age changes in body build. Am. J. Phys. Anthropol. *10ns:* 75–92, 1952.
702. Nicolson, A. B., and C. Hanley: Indices of physiological maturity: Derivations and interrelationships. Child Development *24:* 3–38, 1953.
703. Novack, C. R.: The Appearance of ossification centers and the fusion of bones. Am. J. Phys. Anthropol. *12ns:* 63–69, 1954.
704. Norton, J. K., and M. A. Norton: Foundations of Curriculum Building. Boston, Ginn & Co., 1936.
705. Olsen, E. C.: The use of local resources in guidance. School and Society *53:* 385–391, 1941.
706. Olson, W. C.: Child Development. Boston, D. C. Heath & Co., 1949.
707. Olson, W. C., and B. O. Hughes: Concepts of growth. . . . their significance to teachers. Childhood Education *21:* 53–63, 1944.
708. Olson, W. C., and B. O. Hughes: Tables for the Translation of Physical Measurements into Age Units. Mimeographed by the Child Development Laboratories, University Elementary School, University of Michigan, 1938.
709. Orent-Keiles, E., and L. F. Hallman: The Breakfast Meal in Relation to Blood-Sugar Values. U. S. Department of Agriculture Circular 827. Washington, D. C., U. S. Department of Agriculture, 1949.
710. Orr, J. B., and J. L. Gilks: Studies of Nutrition: The Physique and Health of Two African Tribes. Medical Research Council, Special Rep. Series 155. London, His Majesty's Stationery Office, 1931.
711. Orton, S. T.: Some studies in language function. Proc. A. Research Nerv. & Ment. Dis. *13:* 614–633, 1932.
712. Overstreet, H. A.: The Mature Mind. New York, W. W. Norton & Co., 1949.
713. Overstreet, H. A., and W. B. Overstreet: The Mind Alive. New York, W. W. Norton & Co., 1954.
714. Page, M. L.: The Modification of Ascendant Behavior in Preschool Children. University of Iowa Studies, Child Welfare *12* (3), 1936.
715. Palmer, C. E.: The relation of body build to sickness in elementary school children. Am. J. Phys. Anthropol. *21:* suppl. 7–8, 1936.
716. Partridge, E. D.: A study of friendships among adolescent boys. J. Genet. Psychol. *43:* 472–477, 1933.
717. Paulasigni, I., and F. B. Knight: The Effect of Awareness of Success or Failure. Twenty-Ninth Yearbook, National Society for the Study of Education, Part II. Bloomington, Ill., Public School Publishing Co., 1930.
718. Peatman, J. G., and R. A. Higgons: Relation of Infants' Weight and Body Build to Locomotor Development. In Dennis, W.: Readings in Child Psychology. New York, Prentice-Hall, Inc., 1951.
719. Peck, L.: Child Psychology. Boston, D. C. Heath & Co., 1953.
720. Peller, L. E.: The child's approach to reality. Am. J. Orthopsychiat. *9:* 503–513, 1939.
721. Pendry, E. R. and H. Hartshorne: Organizations for Youth. New York, McGraw-Hill Book Co., 1936.
722. Penrose, L. S.: The Biology of Mental Defect. New York, Grune & Stratton, 1949.
723. Peterman, M. G.: Behavior in epileptic children. J. Pediat. *42:* 758–769, 1953.
724. Peterson, R. C., and L. L. Thurstone: Motion Pictures and the Social Attitudes of Children. New York, The Macmillan Co., 1933.
725. Phelps, W. M., and R. J. H. Kiphuth: The Diagnosis and Treatment of Postural Defects. Springfield, Ill., Charles C Thomas, 1932.
726. Phipard, E. F., and H. K. Stiebling: Adequacy of American Diets. In Handbook of Nutrition: A Symposium Prepared under the Auspices of the Council on Foods and Nutrition of the American Medical Association. 2nd ed. Philadelphia, Blakiston Co., 1951.
727. Piaget, J.: The Child's Conception of Physical Causality. New York, Humanities Press, 1952.
728. Piaget, J.: Judgment and Reasoning in the Child. New York, Humanities Press, 1952.
729. Piaget, J.: Language and Thought of the Child. New York, Humanities Press, 1951.
730. Piaget, J.: The Moral Judgment of the Child. Glencoe, Ill., Free Press, 1948.
731. Piaget, J.: The Origins of Intelligence in Children. New York, International Universities Press, 1953.
732. Piaget, J.: Play, Dreams and Imitation in Childhood. New York, W. W. Norton & Co., 1952.
733. Pigors, P.: Leadership or Domination. Boston, Houghton Mifflin Co., 1935.
734. Pilcher, J. D., and H. Tuchewicz: Premenstrual state in young girls. Am. J. Dis. Child. *65:* 296–304, 1943.
735. Pincus, G. and H. Hoagland: Adrenal cortical responses to stress in normal men and in those with personality disorders. Am. J. Psychiat. *106:* 641–659, 1950.
736. Pintner, R., and J. Lev: Worries of school children. J. Genet. Psychol. *56:* 67–76, 1940.
737. Pistor, A. D.: How time concepts are acquired by children. Educ. Meth. *20:* 107–112, 1940.
738. Plant, J. S.: The Emotions of the Child. University of Iowa Child Welfare Pamphlet No. 58, 1938.

739. Plant, J. S.: Personality and the Cultural Pattern. New York, Commonwealth Fund, 1937.
740. Platt, V. E., and R. G. Freeman, Jr.: Seasonal variation in hemoglobin. Proc. Soc. Exper. Biol. & Med. *27:* 687, 1930.
741. Pond, M. A.: How does housing affect health? Pub. Health Rep. *61:* 665–672, 1946.
742. Potgieter, M. and V. Everitt: A study of children's eating habits. J. Home Econ. *42:* 363–366, 1950.
743. Potter, E.: Present status of the Rh factor. Am. J. Dis. Child. *68:* 32–58, 1944.
744. Pratt, K. C.: The Neonate. In Carmichael et al.: Manual of Child Psychology. New York, John Wiley & Sons, Inc., 1946.
745. Pratt, K. C., A. K. Nelson, and K. H. Sun: The Behavior of the Newborn Infant. Ohio State Univ. Stud. Contrib. to Psychol. No. 10, 1930.
746. Prescott, D. (chairman): Emotion and the Educative Process. A Report of the Committee on the Relation of Emotion to the Educative Process. Washington, D. C., American Council on Education, 1938.
747. Pritchard, E., and R. H. Ojemann: An approach to the measurement of insecurity. J. Exper. Educ. *10:* 114–118, 1941.
748. Pritchard, R., and S. Rosensweig: The effects of war stress upon childhood and youth. J. Abnorm. & Social Psychol. *37:* 329–344, 1942.
749. Progressive Education Association: Growth and Development: The Basis for Educational Programs. New York, Progressive Education Association, 1936.
750. Prugh, D. G., et al.: A study of the emotional reactions of children and families to hospitalization and illness. Am. J. Orthopsychiat. *23:* 70–106, 1953.
751. Pyle, I. and L. W. Sontag: Variability in onset of ossification in epiphyses and short bones of the extremities. Am. J. Roentgenol. *49:* 795–798, 1943.
752. Quinn, R. W., et al.: An environmental and sociological study of rheumatic heart disease. Am. J. Pub. Health *40:* 1285–1295, 1950.
753. Rabinovitch, R. D., and J. Fischhoff: Feeding children to meet their emotional needs. J. Am. Dietet. A. *28:* 614–621, 1952.
754. Radwin, L. S., et al.: End results in treatment of congenital hypothyroidism. Follow up study of physical, mental and behaviorial development. Am. J. Dis. Child. *78:* 821–843, 1949.
755. Ramsey, G. V.: Sexual growth of Negro and white boys. Human Biol. *22:* 146–149, 1950.
756. Rand, W., M. E. Sweeny, and E. L. Vincent: Growth and Development of the Young Child. 5th ed., revised by M. E. Breckenridge and M. N. Murphy. Philadelphia, W. B. Saunders Co., 1953.
757. Randall, F. E.: Age changes in young adult army males. Human Biol. *21:* 187–198, 1949.
758. Rathbone, J. L.: Relaxation. New York, Bureau of Publications, Teachers College, Columbia University, 1943.
759. Read, K. H.: The Nursery School. 2nd ed. Philadelphia, W. B. Saunders Co., 1955.
760. Reardon, H. et al.: Physiological deviations of the premature. Am. J. Dis. Child. *81:* 99–138, 1951.
761. Redl, F.: Group personality elements in discipline problems. Am. J. Orthopsychiat. *13:* 77–81, 1943.
762. Redl, F., and D. Wineman: Children Who Hate. Glencoe, Ill., Free Press, 1951.
763. Redl, F., and D. Wineman: Controls From Within. Glencoe, Ill., Free Press, 1952.
764. Reimann, M.: How children become prejudiced. Commentary *11:* 88–94, 1951.
765. Remer, L. L.: Handicaps of School Entrants: A Study of Traits Which Handicap Children Entering Kindergarten and First Grade. Researches in Parent Education, I. University of Iowa Studies in Child Welfare *6:* 197–207, 1932.
766. Remmers, H. H., E. R. Ryden, and C. L. Morgan: Introduction to Educational Psychology. New York, Harper & Bros., 1954.
767. Renner, H. D.: Origin of Food Habits. London, Faber & Faber, 1944.
768. Renshaw, S., V. L. Miller, and D. Marquis: Children's Sleep. New York, The Macmillan Co., 1933.
769. Reymert, M. L., and H. Jost: Further data concerning the normal variability of the menstrual cycle during adolescence and factors associated with age of menarche. Child Development *18:* 169–179, 1947.
770. Reymert, M. L., and M. Rotman: Auditory changes in children from ages ten to eighteen. J. Genet. Psychol. *68:* 181–187, 1946.
771. Reynolds, E. L.: The appearance of adult patterns of body hair in man. Ann. New York Acad. Sc. *53:* 576–584, 1951.
772. Reynolds, E. L.: The bony pelvis in prepuberal childhood. Am. J. Phys. Anthropol. *5ns:* 165–200, 1947.
773. Reynolds, E. L.: Degree of kinship and pattern of ossification; longitudinal X-ray study of appearance pattern of ossification centers in children of different kinship groups. Am. J. Phys. Anthropol. *1:* 405–416, 1943.
774. Reynolds, E. L.: The distribution of subcutaneous fat in childrood and adolescence. Monogr. XV (2). Evanston, Ill., Society for Research in Child Development, Inc., 1952.
775. Reynolds, E. L.: Distribution of tissue components in the female leg from birth to maturity. **Anat. Rec.** *100:* 621–630, 1948.

776. Reynolds, E. L.: Physical changes associated with adolescence in boys. Am. J. Dis. Child. *82:* 529–547, 1951.

777. Reynolds, E. L., and P. Grote: Sex differences in the distribution of tissue components in the human leg from birth to maturity. Anat. Rec. *102:* 45–53, 1948.

778. Reynolds, E. L., and L. W. Sontag: The Fels composite sheet. II. Variations in growth patterns in health and disease. J. Pediat. *26:* 336–352, 1945.

779. Reynolds, E. L., and J. V. Wines: Individual differences in physical changes associated with adolescence in girls. Am. J. Dis. Child. *75:* 329–350, 1948.

780. Reynolds, M. M.: Children from Seed to Sapling. 2nd ed. New York, McGraw-Hill Book Co., 1951.

781. Ribble, M.: Rights of Infants. New York, Columbia University Press, 1943.

782. Richards, T. W., and W. Ellington: Objectivity in the evaluation of personality. J. Exper. Educ. *10:* 228–237, 1942.

783. Richey, H. G.: The Relation of Accelerated, Normal and Retarded Puberty to the Height and Weight of School Children. Monogr. II (1). Washington, D. C., Society for Research in Child Development, National Research Council, 1937.

784. Ricketts, A. F.: A Study of the Behavior of Young Children in Anger. In Jack et al.: Behavior of the Preschool Child. University of Iowa Studies in Child Welfare 9 (3), 1934.

785. Robbins, F. G.: Educational Sociology: A Study in Child, Youth, School and Community. New York, Henry Holt & Co., 1953.

786. Roberts, D. F.: Body weight, race and climate. Am. J. Phys. Anthropol. *11ns:* 533–558, 1953.

787. Roberts, K. E., and E. V. Fleming: Persistence and Change in Personality Patterns. Monogr. VIII (3). Washington, D. C., Society for Research in Child Development, National Research Council, 1943.

788. Robertson, E. C., et al.: The effect of added thiamine on growth, vision, and learning, using identical twins. J. Nutrition *34:* 691–700, 1947.

789. Robinow, M., et al.: Feet of normal children. J. Pediat. *23:* 141–149, 1943.

790. Robinow, M., et al.: New approach to quantitative analysis of children's posture. J. Pediat. *22:* 655–663, 1943.

791. Robinson, H. M.: Why Pupils Fail in Reading. Chicago, University of Chicago Press, 1946.

792. Robinson, R.: Listening Habits of Michigan Children. In Implications of the Radio in Education. 12th Yearbook of the Department of Elementary School Principals, Michigan Education Association, 1940.

793. Rockwood, L. D., and M. E. N. Ford: Youth, Marriage and Parenthood. New York, John Wiley & Sons, Inc., 1945.

794. Rose, W. C.: Amino acid requirements of man. Federation Proc. *8:* 546–552, 1949.

795. Ross, B. M.: Some traits associated with sibling jealousy in problem children. Smith College Stud. Soc. Work *1:* 346–376, 1931.

796. Ross, J. R., and P. Summerfield: Value of increased supply of vitamin B and iron in the diet of children. Am. J. Dis. Child. *49:* 1185–1188, 1935.

797. Ross, L. J.: A summer camp for children with heart disease. J. Pediat. *43:* 67–73, 1953.

798. Rowley, F.: Motor Coordination in the Field of Handwriting. Master's Thesis, Boston University School of Education, 1938.

799. Rowntree, L. G., et al.: Health of selective service registrants. J. A. M. A., *118:* 1223–1227, 1942.

800. Rubner: Cited in Rose's Foundations of Nutrition. 4th ed., revised by G. MacLeod and C. M. Taylor. New York, The Macmillan Co., 1944.

801. Ruch, G. M.: The relative difficulty of the 100 multiplication combinations with special reference to textbook construction. Elem. Sch. J. *32:* 369–377, 1932.

802. Rudolph, M.: Living and Learning in Nursery School. New York, Harper & Bros., 1954.

803. Russell, A. L., and E. Elvove: Domestic water and dental caries. VII. A study of the fluoride-dental caries relationship in an adult population. Pub. Health Rep. *66:* 1389–1401, 1951.

804. Sanchez, G. J.: Child Development in the Rural Environment. Growth and Development: The Basis for Educational Programs. New York, Progressive Education Association, 1936, pp. 112–118.

805. Sanders, B. S.: Environment and Growth. Baltimore, Warwick & York, 1934.

806. Sandiford, P.: Foundations of Educational Psychology. New York, Longmans, Green & Co., 1940.

807. Sarason, S. B.: The Clinical Interaction with Special Reference to the Rorschach. New York, Harper & Bros., 1954.

808. Sargent, H.: Projective methods: Their origins, theory and application in personality research. Psychol. Bull. 42; *5:* 257–293, 1945.

809. Sattler, H. V.: Parents, Children and the Facts of Life. Paterson, N. J., St. Anthony Guild Press, 1952.

810. Scheinfeld, A.: Women and Men. New York, Harcourt, Brace & Co., 1943.

811. Scheinfeld, A.: The New You and Heredity. Philadelphia, J. B. Lippincott Co., 1950.

812. Schlesinger, E. R., et al.: Newburgh-Kingston caries-fluorine study. II. Pediatric aspects. Preliminary report. Am. J. Pub. Health *40:* 725–727, 1950.

813. Schoenheimer, R.: Dynamic State of Body Constituents. Monograph in Medicine and Public Health No. 3. Cambridge, Mass., Harvard University Press, 1942.

814. Schonfeld, W. A.: Deficient development of masculinity. A psychosomatic problem of adolescence. Am. J. Dis. Child. *79:* 17–29, 1950.
815. Schonfeld, W. A.: Inadequate masculine physique as a factor in personality development of adolescent boys. Psychosom. Med. *12:* 49–54, 1950.
816. Schonfeld, W. A.: Management of male pubescence. J. A. M. A. *121:* 177–182, 1943.
817. Schour, I., and M. Massler: Studies in tooth development: The growth pattern of human teeth. Part II. J. Am. Dent. A. *27:* 1918–1931, 1940.
818. Schultz, F. W., and E. M. Knott: The effect of varied vitamin B ingestion upon the appetite of children. J. Nutrition *15:* 411–427, 1938.
819. Schulz, L. R.: Infant Growth from the Point of View of the Organism as a Whole. Master's Thesis, University of Michigan, 1942.
820. Schwentker, F. F., et al.: A home play and occupational program for the bedfast child. The counterpane course. Pediatrics *7:* 44–47, 1951.
821. Scott, E. M., et al.: Self selection of diet: Appetites for calcium, magnesium, and potassium. J. Nutrition *41:* 187–201, 1950.
822. Scott, R. B., et al.: Growth and development of Negro infants. I. Analysis of birth weight of 11,818 newly born infants. Pediatrics *6:* 425–431, 1950.
823. Scott, R. B., et al.: Growth and development of Negro infants: Growth during the first year of life as observed in private pediatric practice. J. Pediat. *37:* 885–893, 1950.
824. Scrimshaw, N. S., and M. A. Guzmán: The effect of dietary supplementation and the administration of vitamin B_{12} and aureomycin on the growth of school children. In Current Research on Vitamins in Trophology: Proceedings of the Scientific Sessions of the Eighth Annual Meeting, The National Vitamin Foundation, Inc. New York City, March 4, 1953.
825. Seagoe, M. V.: Children's television habits and preferences. Quarterly of Film, Radio, Television *6:* 143–152, 1952.
826. Sears, P. S.: Levels of aspiration in academically successful and unsuccessful children. J. Abnorm. & Social Psychol. *35:* 498–536, 1940.
827. Sears, R. R.: Survey of Objective Studies of Psychoanalytic Concepts. Bull. 51. New York, Social Science Research Council, 1943.
828. Sebrell, W. H.: Enrichment: A Public Health approach to better nutrition. Pub. Health Rep. *68:* 741–746, 1953.
829. Sebrell, W. H.: Nutrition—Past and future. Nutrition Rev. *11:* 65–68, 1953.
830. Seidenfeld, M. A.: Psychologic aspects of poliomyelitis. Pediatrics *4:* 309–318, 1949.
831. Seils, L. G.: The relationship between measures of physical growth and gross motor performance of primary-grade school children. Research Quart. *22:* 244–260, 1951.
832. Self selection of diet by rats. Nutrition Rev. *9:* 26–28, 1951.
833. Selye, H.: The Story of the Adaptation Syndrome. Montreal, Acta, Ine., 1952.
834. Selye, H.: Stress—The Physiology and Pathology of Exposure to Stress. Montreal, Acta, Inc., 1950.
835. Sewall, M.: Two Studies in Sibling Rivalry. I. Some causes of jealousy in young children. Smith College Stud. Soc. Work *1:* 6–22, 1930.
836. Seward, G. H.: Sex and the Social Order. New York, McGraw-Hill Book Co., 1946.
837. Sharpe, E. F.: Planning for Stability. In Rickman, J.: On the Bringing up of Children. By Five Psychoanalysts. London, Kegan Paul, Trench, Trubner & Co., Ltd., 1938.
838. Shaw, J. H.: Nutrition and Dental Caries. In A Survey of the Literature of Dental Caries. Food and Nutrition Board, National Research Council Publ. 225. Washington, D. C., National Academy of Science, National Research Council, 1952.
839. Shaw, R. F.: Out of the mouth of babes: A new way to teach the very young. Atlantic Monthly *154:* 66–73, 1934.
840. Sheldon, W. H., S. S. Stevens, and W. B. Tucker: The Varieties of Human Physique. New York, Harper & Bros., 1942.
841. Sheldon, W. H. (with collaboration of S. S. Stevens): The Varieties of Temperament: A Psychology of Constitutional Differences. New York, Harper & Bros., 1942.
842. Sherman, M.: Intelligence and Its Deviations. New York, Ronald Press, 1945.
843. Sherman, M. and T. R. Henry: Hollow Folk. New York, Thomas Y. Crowell Co., 1933.
844. Sherman, M. C., I. C. Sherman, and C. D. Flory: Infant Behavior. Comp. Psychol. Monogr . No. 4, 1936.
845. Sheviokov, G. R.: War and Adolescents. J. Psychol. *14:* 161–179, 1942.
846. Shock, N. W.: Physiological aspects of development. Rev. Educ. Research *14:* 413–426, 1944.
847. Shock, N. W.: Physiological Changes in Adolescence. In Forty-Third Yearbook, National Society for the Study of Education. Part I. Adolescence. Chicago, Department of Education University of Chicago, 1944.
848. Shock, N. W., and H. E. Jones: Mental development and performance as related to physical and physiological factors. Rev. Educ. Research *11:* 531–552, 1941.
849. Shuttleworth, F. K.: The Adolescent Period: A Graphic Atlas. Monogr. XIV (1). Evanston Ill., Society for Research in Child Development, Inc., 1951.
850. Shuttleworth, F. K.: The Adolescent Period: A Pictorial Atlas. Monogr. XIV (2). Evanston, Ill., Society for Research in Child Development, Inc., 1951.
851. Shuttleworth, F. K.: The Physical and Mental Growth of Girls and Boys Aged Six to Nineteen

in Relation to Age at Maximum Growth. Monogr. IV (3). Washington, D. C., Society for Research in Child Development, National Research Council, 1939.

852. Shuttleworth, F. K.: Sexual Maturation and the Physical Growth of Girls Aged Six to Nineteen. Monogr. II (5). Washington, D. C., Society for Research in Child Development, National Research Council, 1937.

853. Sidwell, V. D., and E. S. Eppright: Food habits of Iowa children—breakfast. J. Home Econ. *45:* 401–405, 1953.

854. Sillman, J. H.: Serial study of good occlusion to 12 years of age. Am. J. Orthodontics *37:* 481–507, 1951.

855. Sillman, J. H.: Serial study of occlusion (birth to ten years of age). Am. J. Orthodontics *34:* 969–979, 1948.

856. Sillman, J. H.: Thumbsucking and the oral structures. J. Pediat. *39:* 424–430, 1951.

857. Silverberg, W. V.: Childhood Experience and Personal Destiny. New York, Springer Publishing Co., 1952.

858. Simmons, K.: The Brush Foundation Study of Child Growth and Development. II. Physical Growth and Development. Monogr. IX (1). Washington, D. C., Society for Research in Child Development, National Research Council, 1944.

859. Simmons, K., and W. W. Greulich: Menarcheal age and the height, weight and skeletal age of girls aged 7 to 17 years. J. Pediat. *22:* 518–548, 1943.

860. Simpson, M.: Parental Preferences of Young Children. Teachers College Contrib. Educ. No. 652. New York, Columbia University, 1935.

861. Skeels, H. M., R. Updegraff, B. L. Wellman and H. M. Williams: A Study of Environmental Stimulation: An Orphanage Preschool Project. University of Iowa Studies in Child Welfare *15* (4), 1938.

862. Skinner, C. E., and P. L. Harriman: Child Psychology, Child Development and Modern Education. New York, The Macmillan Co., 1941.

863. Skodak, M., and H. M. Skeels: Follow-up study of children in adoptive homes. J. Genet. Psychol. *66:* 21–58, 1945.

864. Slavson, S. R.: Child Psychotherapy. New York, Columbia University Press, 1952.

865. Slyker, F., et al.: Relationship between vitamin D intake and linear growth in infants. Proc. Soc. Exper. Biol. & Med. *37:* 499–502, 1937.

866. Smalley, R.: The influence of differences in age, sex, and intelligence in determining attitudes of siblings toward each other. Smith College Stud. Soc. Work *1:* 23–40, 1930.

867. Smart, R., and M. Smart: An Introduction to Family Relationships. Philadelphia, W. B. Saunders Co., 1953.

868. Smith, C. A.: Effects of maternal undernutrition upon the newborn infant in Holland (1944–1945). J. Pediat. *30:* 229–243, 1947.

869. Smith, D. A., and M. F. A. Woodruff: Deficiency Diseases in Japanese Prison Camps. Medical Research Council Special Report Series No. 274. London, His Majesty's Stationery Office, 1951.

870. Smith, M. E.: An Investigation of the Development of the Sentence and the Extent of Vocabulary in Young Children. University of Iowa Studies in Child Welfare *3* (5), 1926.

871. Smith, M. F., and A. J. Burks: Teaching the Slow Learning Child. New York, Harper & Bros., 1954.

872. Smythe, D. W.: Television and its educational implications. Elem. Eng. *27:* 41–52, 1950.

873. Snyder, L. H.: The Principles of Heredity. 4th ed. Boston, D. C. Heath & Co., 1951.

874. Snyderman, S. E., et al.: Pyridoxine deficiency in the human infant. J. Clin. Nutrition *1:* 200–207, 1953.

875. Sognnaes, R. F.: Analyses of wartime reduction of dental caries in European children with special regard to observations in Norway. Am. J. Dis. Child. *75:* 792–821, 1948.

876. Sontag, L. W., and E. L. Reynolds: The Fels composite sheet. I. A practical method for analyzing growth progress. J. Pediat. *26:* 327–335, 1945.

877. Spier, L.: Growth of Japanese Children Born in America and Japan. Seattle, University of Washington Press, 1929.

878. Spies, T. D., and S. Dreizen: The effect of milk supplements on the growth of children with nutritive failure: Wetzel grid findings. J. Pediat. *34:* 393–413, 1949.

879. Spies, T. D., et al.: Detection and treatment of nutritive failure in children. J. A. M. A. *148:* 1376–1382, 1952.

880. Spies, T. D., et al.: Ch. XI—Emotional Disturbances in Persons with Pellagra, Beri-Beri and Associated Deficiency States. In The Role of Nutritional Deficiencies in Nervous and Mental Disease. Research Publ., A. Nerv. & Ment. Dis. Baltimore, Williams & Wilkins Co., 1943.

881. Spies, T. D., et al.: Endemic riboflavin deficiency in infants and children. Am. J. M. Sc. *200:* 697–701, 1940.

882. Spies, T. D., et al.: Pellagra in infancy and childhood. J. A. M.A. *113:*1481–1483, 1939.

883. Spies, T. D., et al.: Skeletal maturational progress of children with chronic nutritive failure. Am. J. Dis. Child. *85:* 1–12, 1953.

884. Spitz, R. A.: Anxiety in infancy: A study of its manifestations in the first year of life. Internat. J. Psycho-Analysis *31:* 138–143, 1950.

885. Spock, B.: Avoiding behavior problems. J. Pediat. *27:* 363–382, 1945.

886. Spock, B.: The Common Sense Book of Baby and Child Care. New York, Duell, Sloan & Pearce, 1946.
887. Springer, N. N.: A comparative study of behavior traits of deaf and hearing children in New York City. Am. Ann. Deaf *83:* 255–273, 1938.
888. Springer, N. N.: A comparative study of psychoneurotic responses of deaf and hearing children. J. Educ. Psychol. *29:* 459–466, 1938.
889. Stanger, R., and N. Drought: Measuring children's attitudes toward their parents. J. Educ. Psychol. *26:* 169–176, 1935.
890. Stavél, J.: Hlad: Přéspěvek k analyse pudů (Hunger: a contribution to the analysis of instincts). Publ. Philos. Faculty Comenius Univ. No. 26, Bratislava, 1936. Cited in Keys, A., et al.: The Biology of Human Starvation. Minneapolis, University of Minnesota Press, 1950.
891. Stearns, G., et al.: The effect of vitamin D on linear growth in infancy. J. Pediat. *9:* 1–10, 1936.
892. Steele, B. F., et al.: Role of breakfast and between-meal foods in adolescent's nutrient intake. J. Am. Dietet. A. *28:* 1054–1057, 1952.
893. Stefko, W. H.: Cited in White House Conference, Growth and Development of the Child, Part I. General Considerations. New York, D. Appleton-Century Co., 1932.
894. Stephens, J. W., and A. Marble: Place and value of summer camps in management of juvenile diabetes. Observations and a report of activities at a camp for diabetic boys in 1950. Am. J. Dis. Child. *82:* 259–267, 1951.
895. Stern, C.: Principles of Human Genetics. San Francisco, W. H. Freeman & Co., 1950.
896. Stiebling, H. K.: Trends in family food consumption. J. Am. Dietet. A. *26:* 596–598, 1950.
897. Stieglitz, E. J.: Geriatric Medicine: Medical Care of Later Maturity. 3rd ed. Philadelphia, J. B. Lippincott Co., 1954.
898. Stolz, H. R., et al.: The junior high school age. Univ. High School J. *15:* 63–72, 1937.
899. Stolz, H. R., and L. M. Stolz: Somatic Development of Adolescent Boys. New York, The Macmillan Co., 1951.
900. Stone, H. M., and A. S. Stone: A Marriage Manual. New York, Simon & Schuster, 1935.
901. Storvick, C. A., et al.: Nutritional status of selected population groups in Oregon. I. Food habits of the native born and reared school children in two regions. Milbank Mem. Fund Quart. *29:* 165–185, 1951.
902. Stott, D. H.: Saving Children From Delinquency. New York, Philosophical Library, 1953.
903. Stott, L. H.: Research in family life in Nebraska. J. Home Econ. *37:* 80–83, 1945.
904. Strain, F. B.: Sex Guidance in Family Life Education. Rev. ed. New York, The Macmillan Co., 1942.
905. Strang, R.: Introduction to Child Study. 3rd ed. New York, The Macmillan Co., 1951.
906. Strang, R.: Mental Hygiene of Gifted Children. In American Association for Gifted Children: The Gifted Child. Boston, D. C. Heath & Co., 1951.
907. Strang, R., and D. F. Smiley: The Role of the Teacher in Health Education. New York, The Macmillan Co., 1941.
908. Stratton, G. M.: Emotion and the incidence of disease: with information as to the number of diseases and of the age at which they occur. Psychol. Rev. *36:* 242–253, 1929.
909. Strickland, R. G.: The Language Arts in the Elementary School. Boston, D. C. Heath & Co., 1951.
910. Strietz, R.: When Should Reading Experience Begin? In Growth and Development: The Basis for Educational Programs. New York, Progressive Education Association, 1936.
911. Strother, C. R.: Developing personality. Crippled Child *25:* 18–19, 29, 1947.
912. Stuart, H. C.: Review of the evidence as to the nutritional state of children in France. Am. J. Pub. Health *35:* 299–307, 1945.
913. Stuart, H. C.: Studies of the nutritional state of children in unoccupied France in the fall of 1942. J. Pediat. *25:* 257–264, 1944.
914. Stuart, H. C., and E. H. Sobel: The thickness of the skin and subcutaneous tissue by age and sex in childhood. J. Pediat. *28:* 637–647, 1946.
915. Stuart, H. C., and S. S. Stevenson: Physical Growth and Development. In W. E. Nelson (editor): Textbook of Pediatrics. 6th ed. Philadelphia, W. B. Saunders Co., 1954.
916. Stutsman, R.: Mental Measurement of Preschool Children. Yonkers-on-Hudson, N. Y., World Book Co., 1931.
917. Subcommittee on Medical Nutrition, Division of Medical Sciences and the National Research Council: Recognition of early nutritional failure in infants, children, adolescents and adults. J. A. M. A. *118:* 615–616, 1942.
918. Summerfield, P.: The value of an increased supply of vitamin B and iron in the diet of children. Am. J. Dis. Child. *43:* 284–290, 1932.
919. Supplement to present knowledge in nutrition. Nutrition Rev. *11:* 353–361, 1953.
920. Sweet, C.: The teaching of body mechanics in pediatric practice. J. A. M. A. *110:* 419–426, 1938.
921. Swift, E. H.: Step by Step in Sex Education. New York, The Macmillan Co., 1938.
922. Symonds, P. M.: The Dynamics of Parent-Child Relationships. New York, Columbia University Press, 1949.
923. Symonds, P. M., and D. H. Chase: Practice vs. motivation. J. Educ. Psychol. *20:* 19–35, 1929.
924. Symonds, P. M., and H. F. Daringer: Studies in the learning of English expression. IV. Sentence structure. Teachers College Record *32:* 50–64, 1930.

925. Symonds, P. M., and M. Krugman: Projective methods in the study of personality. Rev. Educ. Research *14:* 81–98, 1944.
926. Talbot, N. B., E. H. Sobel, J. W. McArthur, and J. D. Crawford: Functional Endocrinology from Birth through Adolescence. Cambridge, Mass., Harvard University Press, 1952.
927. Taylor, C. M., et al.: The energy expenditure for quiet play and cycling of boys 7 to 14 years of age. J. Nutrition *35:* 511–521, 1948.
928. Taylor, C. M., et al.: The energy expenditure of 9 to 11 year old boys and girls (1) standing drawing and (2) dressing and undressing. J. Nutrition *36:* 123–131, 1948.
929. Taylor, C. M., et al.: The energy expenditure of boys and girls 9 to 11 years of age (1) sitting listening to the radio (phonograph) (2) sitting singing, and (3) standing singing. J. Nutrition *38:* 1–10, 1949.
930. Taylor, K. W.: Do Adolescents Need Parents? New York, D. Appleton-Century Co., 1938.
931. Teagarden, F. M.: Child Psychology for Professional Workers. Rev. ed. New York, Prentice-Hall, Inc., 1946.
932. Templin, M. C.: The Development of Reasoning in Children with Normal and Defective Hearing. Minneapolis, University of Minnesota Press, 1950.
933. Terman, L. M.: Genetic Studies of Genius. Vol. 1: Mental and Physical Traits of a Thousand Gifted Children. Stanford, Calif., Stanford University Press, 1925.
934. Terman, L. M.: Psychological Factors in Marital Happiness. New York, McGraw-Hill Book Co., 1938.
935. Terman, L. M., and M. A. Merrill: Measuring Intelligence. Boston, Houghton Mifflin Co., 1937.
936. Terman, L. M. and M. H. Oden: Genetic Studies of Genius. Vol. IV. The Gifted Child Grows Up. Stanford, Calif., Stanford University Press, 1947.
937. Terman, L. M., et al.: Psychological Sex Differences. In Carmichael, L., et al.: Manual of Child Psychology. New York, John Wiley & Sons, Inc., 1946.
938. Thayer, V. T., C. B. Zachry, and R. Kotinsky: Reorganizing Secondary Education: A Report of School Curriculum. New York, D. Appleton-Century Co., 1939.
939. Thiamine supplementation and learning capacity. Nutrition Rev. *7:* 220–222, 1949.
940. Thomas, D. S., et al.: Observational Studies of Social Behavior. New Haven, Yale University Press, 1933.
941. Thompson, G. C.: Child Psychology: Growth Trends and Adjustments. Boston, Houghton Mifflin Co., 1952.
942. Thompson, H.: Physical Growth. In Carmichael et al.: Manual of Child Psychology. New York, John Wiley & Sons, Inc., 1946.
943. Thomson, M. M.: Talk It Out With Your Child. New York, McGraw-Hill Book Co., 1953.
944. Thorndike, R. L.: Words and the comics. J. Exper. Educ. *10:* 110–113, 1941.
945. Thorpe, L. P.: Child Psychology and Development. New York, Ronald Press, 1946.
946. Thrasher, F. M.: The Gang. Rev. ed. Chicago, University of Chicago Press, 1937.
947. Timberlake, J. B.: Terminology. Deaf-hard of hearing. Volta Rev. *44:* 140–142, 1942.
948. Todd, T. W.: Anthropology and growth. Science *81:* 259–263, 1935.
949. Todd, T. W.: Atlas of Skeletal Maturation (Hand). St. Louis, C. V. Mosby Co., 1937.
950. Todd, T. W.: Objective ratings of the constitution of the growing child, based on examination of physical development and mental expansion. Am. J. Dis. Child. *55:* 149–159, 1938.
951. Topper, A.: Mental achievement of congenitally hypothyroid children. A follow-up study of 20 cases. Am. J. Dis. Child. *81:* 233–249, 1951.
952. Toverud, G.: Dental caries in Norwegian children during and after the second World War. J. Am. Dietet. A. *26:* 673–680, 1950.
953. Toverud, G.: Introductory Review. In A Survey of the Literature of Dental Caries. Food and Nutrition Board, National Research Council Publ. 225. Washington, D. C., National Academy of Science, National Research Council, 1952.
954. Toverud, K. U., G. Stearns, and I. G. Macy: Maternal Nutrition and Child Health; Interpretative Review. Bull. No. 123. Washington, D. C., National Academy of Science, National Research Council, 1950.
955. Trager, H. G., and M. R. Yarrow: They Learn What They Live: Prejudice in Young Children. New York, Harper & Bros., 1952.
956. Trémolières, J., et al.: Contribution à l'étude du phénomène de croissance et de stature en France de 1940 à 1948. Rec. trav. inst. nat. d'hyg. 4 (1), 1950.
957. Trulson, M. et al.: New York State nutrition survey. A nutrition survey of public school children. J. Am. Dietet. A. *25:* 595–605, 1949.
958. Tryon, C. McC.: Evaluations of Adolescent Personality by Other Adolescents. Monogr. IV (4). Washington, D. C., Society for Research in Child Development, National Research Council, 1939.
959. Tuttle, W. W., et al.: Effect of omitting breakfast on the physiologic response of men. J. Am. Dietet. A. *26:* 332–335, 1950.
960. Tuttle, W. W., et al.: Influence of various levels of thiamine intake on physiologic response. III. Reaction time. J. Am. Dietet. A. *25:* 21–27, 1949.
961. Tuttle, W. W., et al.: Influence of various levels of thiamine intake on physiologic response. VI. Oxygen consumption. J. Am. Dietet. A. *25:* 322–329, 1949.
962. United States Department of Labor: A study of educational achievement of a group of children

. . . working in agriculture during school hours. October–December, 1951. Child Labor Bull. No. 202. Washington, D. C., U. S. Department of Labor, 1952.

963. United States Department of Labor: If You Employ Youth. Bureau of Labor Standards Bull. 151. Washington, D. C., U. S. Department of Labor, 1952.

964. Updegraff, R., and M. E. Keister: A Study of Children's Reactions to Failure and an Experimental Attempt to Modify Them. University of Iowa Studies in Child Welfare 13 (4), 1937.

965. Valaoras, V. G.: Some effects of famine on the population of Greece. Milbank Mem. Fund Quart. *24:* 215–234, 1946.

966. Van De Velde, H. V.: Fertility and Sterility in Marriage: Their Voluntary Promotion and Limitation. New York, Covici-Friede, Inc., 1931.

967. Van Dyne, E. V.: Personality traits and friendship formation in adolescent girls. J. Social Psychol. *12:* 291–303, 1940.

968. Van Riper, C. (editor): Speech Therapy: A Book of Readings. New York, Prentice-Hall, Inc., 1954.

969. Vitamin B_{12} and growth in children. Nutrition Rev. *11:* 42–44, 1953.

970. Wagner, M. A.: Day and night sleep in a group of young orphanage children. J. Genet. Psychol. *42:* 442–459, 1933.

971. Wagner, R., et al.: Diabetic dwarfism. Am. J. Dis. Child. *63:* 667–727, 1942.

972. Walker, S. H.: Constitutional true sexual precocity. J. Pediat. *41:* 251–257, 1952.

973. Waller, J. B.: Cooperation and Competition: An Experimental Study in Motivation. Teachers College Contrib. Educ. New York, Columbia University Press, 1939.

974. Warden, C. J., and A. Cohen: A study of certain incentives applied under schoolroom conditions. Pedagog. Semin. & J. Genet. Psychol. *39:* 320–327, 1931.

975. Walters, S. A., and S. K. O'Hara: Persons and Personality: An Introduction to Psychology. New York, Appleton-Century-Crofts, Inc., 1953.

976. Washburn, A. H.: Functional disorders versus organic heart disease in childhood. California & West. Med. *34:* 179, 1931.

977. Washburne, C. W.: The Work of the Committee of Seven on Grade-Placement in Arithmetic. In Thirty-Eighth Yearbook, National Society for the Study of Education. Bloomington, Ill., Public School Publishing Co., 1939.

978. Weiner, J. S., and V. Thambipillai: Skeletal maturation of W. African Negroes. Am. J. Phys. Anthropol. *10ns:* 407–418, 1952.

979. Wellman, B.: Physical Growth and Motor Development in Their Relation to Mental Development in Children. In Murchison, C. (editor): A Handbook of Child Psychology. Worcester, Mass., Clark University Press, 1931, pp. 242–277.

980. Wetzel, N. C.: Assessing the physical condition of children. III. The components of physical status and physical progress and their evaluation. J. Pediat. *22:* 329–361, 1943.

981. Wetzel, N. C.: The baby grid. J. Pediat. *29:* 439–454, 1946.

982. Wetzel, N. C.: Growth. In O. Glasser (editor): Medical Physics. Chicago, The Year Book Publishers, Inc., 1944.

983. Wetzel, N. C.: Physical fitness in terms of physique, development and basal metabolism. J. A. M. A. *116:* 1187–1195, 1941.

984. Wetzel, N. C.: The Treatment of Growth Failure in Children. Cleveland, NEA Service, Inc., 1948.

985. Wetzel, N. C., et al.: Growth failure in school children as associated with vitamin B_{12} deficiency— response to oral therapy. Science *110:* 651–653, 1949.

986. Wetzel, N. C., et al.: Growth failure in school children. Further studies of vitamin B_{12} dietary supplements. J. Clin. Nutrition *1:* 17–31, 1952.

987. Whitehead, F. E.: Dietary studies of school age children in Ascension Parish, La. Am. J. Pub. Health *42:* 1547–1551, 1952.

988. Whitehead, F. E.: Studies in nutrition education. J. Am. Dietet. A. *28:* 622–627, 1952.

989. Whiting, J. W. M., and I. L. Child: Child Training and Personality: A Cross-Cultural Study. New Haven, Yale University Press, 1953.

990. Widdowson, E. M.: Mental contentment and physical growth. Lancet *1:* 1316–1318, 1951.

991. Wilder, R. M., and R. R. Williams: Enrichment of Flour and Bread. A History of the Movement. Bull. No. 110. Washington, D. C., National Academy of Science, National Research Council, 1944.

992. Wiles, K.: Teaching For Better Schools. New York, Prentice-Hall, Inc., 1952.

993. Wilkins, L.: The Diagnosis and Treatment of Endocrine Disorders in Childhood and Adolescence. Springfield, Ill., Charles C Thomas, 1950.

994. Williams, R. J.: The Human Frontier. New York, Harcourt, Brace & Co., 1946.

995. Williams, R. J., et al.: The concept of genetotrophic disease. Lancet *1:* 287–289, 1950.

996. Williamson, M. and M. S. Lyle: Homemaking Education in the High School. New York, Appleton-Century-Crofts, Inc., 1954.

997. Willoughby, R. R.: Sexuality in the Second Decade. Monogr. II (3). Washington, D. C., Society for Research in Child Development, National Research Council, 1937.

998. Wilson, C. A., et al.: The Merrill-Palmer Standards of Physical and Mental Growth. Detroit, The Merrill-Palmer School, 1930.

999. Wilson, G. M.: New standards in arithmetic. J. Educ. Research *22:* 351–360, 1930.

1000. Wilson, M., et al.: Influence of various levels of thiamine intake on physiologic response. V. Maximum work output. J. Am. Dietet. A. *25:* 221–225, 1949.

1001. Witmer, H., and R. Kotinsky (editors): Personality in The Making: Fact Finding Report of Midcentury White House Conference on Children and Youth. New York, Harper & Bros., 1953.

1002. Witty, P. A.: Children's interest in radio, motion pictures and television. Educ. Admin. and Supervision *38:* 138–147, 1952.

1003. Witty, P. A.: Educational provision for gifted children. School and Society *76:* 177–181, 1952.

1004. Witty, P. A.: Reading the comics—a comparative study. J. Exper. Educ. *10:* 105–109, 1941.

1005. Witty, P. A.: A Study of Deviates in Versatility and Sociability of Play Interests. Teachers College Publication. New York, Columbia University Press, 1931.

1006. Witty, P. A., and C. Skinner: Mental Hygiene in Modern Education. New York, Farrar & Rinehart, 1939.

1007. Witty, P. A., et al.: Reading the comics in grades VII and VIII. J. Educ. Psychol. *33:* 173–182, 1942.

1008. Wolf, K. M.: The Controversial Problem of Discipline. New York, The Child Study Association of America, 1953.

1009. Wolff, W.: The Expression of Personality. New York, Harper & Bros., 1943.

1010. Wolff, W.: The Personality of the Preschool Child: The Child's Search For Self. New York, Grune & Stratton, 1946.

1011. Woody, C.: The arithmetical backgrounds of young children. J. Educ. Research *30:* 188–201, 1937.

1012. Wright, H. F., et al.: Children at home in the Middlewest. Progressive Educ. *28:* 137–143, 1951.

1013. Yeager, W.: Home-School-Community Relations. Pittsburgh, University of Pittsburgh Press, 1939.

1013a. Yerkes, R. M.: A second-generation captive-born chimpanzee. Science *81:* 542–543, 1935.

1014. Young, C. B., and C. A. Storvick: Food habits of freshmen at Oregon State College. J. Am. Dietet. A. *25:* 318–321, 1949.

1015. Young, P. J.: Appetite, palatability and feeding habit: a critical review. Psychol. Bull. *45:* 289–320, 1948.

1016. Zachry, C. B.: Emotion and Conduct in Adolescence. New York, D. Appleton-Century Co., 1940.

1017. Zeligs, R.: Children's worries. Sociol. and Soc. Research *24:* 22–32, 1939.

1018. Zimaud, G. F.: The right start: Early foundations for job satisfaction. The Child *13:* 166–169; 173, 1949.

1019. Zimmerman, F. T., et al.: Intellectual and emotional make up of epileptic. Arch. Neurol. & Psychiat. *65:* 545–556, 1951.

1020. Zubek, J. P., and P. A. Solberg: Human Development. New York, McGraw-Hill Book Co., 1954.

1021. Zubin, J.: Some Effects of Incentives. A Study of Individual Differences in Rivalry. Teachers College Contrib. Educ. 532. New York, Columbia University Press, 1932.

INDEX

NOTE: Bibliographic references appear in *italics*. Superscript numbers in the text indicate the location of such entries in the Bibliography.